J.T. Saunders
Christ's Coll. Camb.

Nov 1934

RABELAIS

LONDON
Cambridge University Press
FETTER LANE

NEW YORK · TORONTO
BOMBAY · CALCUTTA · MADRAS
Macmillan

TOKYO
Maruzen Company Ltd

RABELAIS

THE FIVE BOOKS AND MINOR WRITINGS
TOGETHER WITH LETTERS AND DOCUMENTS
ILLUSTRATING HIS LIFE

A Translation by

W. F. SMITH

*Sometime Fellow of St John's College, Cambridge
and Member of the Rabelais Club*

SECOND EDITION

With a New Introduction
and the Notes Revised and Enlarged by
the late W. F. SMITH

Prepared for Press by

D. H. BEVES
*Fellow of King's College
Cambridge*

VOLUME I
GARGANTUA

CAMBRIDGE
AT THE UNIVERSITY PRESS
1934

PRINTED IN GREAT BRITAIN

CONTENTS

Preface to the First Edition   *page* xi

Preface to the Second Edition   xvii

The English Translators of Rabelais   xix

RABELAIS IN HIS WRITINGS   xxvii

  Les grandes cronicques   xli

  Pantagruel   xlv

  Gargantua   lv

  The Third Book   lxx

  Rabelais at Metz   lxxix

  Fourth Book, ed. 1548 (A)   lxxix

  Sciomachia   lxxxii

  Fourth Book, 2nd ed. 1552 (B)   lxxxiv

  The Fifth Book   xciv

  Rabelais' Language and Style   ciii

  Rabelais on Religion   cviii

  His Attitude towards Biblical Studies   cxiii

  Rabelais as Legist   cxiv

  On Scenic Representations, etc.   cxvii

  Rabelais' Medical Knowledge   cxx

  Rabelais as Botanist   cxxx

  Plants mentioned by Rabelais   cxxxi

  Rabelais as a Humanist   cxxxvi

  Historical Allusions   cxliii

  Rabelais on Church Government   cxlix

  Rabelais' Love of Geography and Travels   cliii

  The Prologues in Rabelais   clv

  Prologue to the *Fifth Book*   clxii

  Lists, Blazons and Litanies   clxiii

  Rabelais on Art   clxx

  Chronological List   clxxii

  Editions of *Gargantua* authorised by Rabelais   clxxiv

  Explanation of References   clxxiv

FIRST BOOK. GARGANTUA *page* 1

Chapters

I. Of the Genealogy and Antiquity of Gargantua 15

II. The Antidoted Conundrums found in an ancient Monument 19

III. How Gargantua was carried eleven Months in his Mother's Belly 25

IV. How Gargamelle, being big with Gargantua, did eat a huge deal of Tripes 29

V. The Chit-chat of the Drinkers 32

VI. How Gargantua was born in a mighty strange Fashion 39

VII. How Gargantua had his Name given him, and how he took his Liquor down 43

VIII. How they apparelled Gargantua 46

IX. The Colours and Livery of Gargantua 53

X. Of that which is signified by the Colours White and Blue 58

XI. Of the youthful Age of Gargantua 64

XII. Of Gargantua's Hobby-horses 71

XIII. How Grandgousier discovered Gargantua's marvellous Understanding by his Invention of a Breech-wipe (*Torchecul*) 75

XIV. How Gargantua was instructed in Latin by a Sophist 81

XV. How Gargantua was put under other Schoolmasters 87

XVI. How Gargantua was sent to Paris, and of the huge Mare that he rode on, and how she destroyed the Ox-flies of la Beauce 90

XVII. How Gargantua paid his Welcome to the Parisians, and how he took away the great Bells of the Church of Our Lady 93

XVIII. How Janotus de Bragmardo was sent to recover the great Bells from Gargantua 98

XIX. The Harangue of Master Janotus de Bragmardo made to Gargantua for the Recovery of the Bells 100

XX. How the Sophist carried off his Cloth, and how he had a Suit at Law against the other Masters 104

XXI. The Study and Manner of Life of Gargantua according to the Discipline of his Sophistical Preceptors 108

XXII. The Games of Gargantua 112

XXIII. How Gargantua was trained by Ponocrates in a Discipline such that he lost one Hour of the Day 129

XXIV. How Gargantua spent his Time in rainy Weather 140

Chapters *page*

XXV. How was stirred between the Cake-bakers of Lerné and those of Gargantua's Country the Great Strife, whereby were waged great Wars   144

XXVI. How the Inhabitants of Lerné, by the Command of Picrochole their King, unexpectedly assaulted the Shepherds of Grandgousier   148

XXVII. How a Monk of Seuillé saved the Close of the Abbey from being sacked by the Enemy   151

XXVIII. How Picrochole took by Assault La Roche-Clermaud, and the Reluctance and Difficulty which Grandgousier made in undertaking War   159

XXIX. The Tenour of the Letter Grandgousier wrote to Gargantua   162

XXX. How Ulrich Gallet was sent unto Picrochole   164

XXXI. The Harangue made by Gallet to Picrochole   165

XXXII. How Grandgousier, to buy Peace, caused the Cakes to be restored   169

XXXIII. How certain Ministers of Picrochole, by headstrong Counsel, put him in extreme Peril   173

XXXIV. How Gargantua left the City of Paris to succour his Country, and how Gymnast encountered the Enemy   180

XXXV. How Gymnast nimbly killed Captain Tripet and others of Picrochole's Men   183

XXXVI. How Gargantua demolished the Castle at the Ford of Vede, and how they passed the Ford   187

XXXVII. How Gargantua, in combing his Head, caused Cannon-balls to fall out of his Hair   190

XXXVIII. How Gargantua ate six Pilgrims in a Salad   193

XXXIX. How the Monk was feasted by Gargantua, and of the jovial Discourse he held at Supper   197

XL. Why Monks are shunned by the World, and why some have bigger Noses than others   203

XLI. How the Monk made Gargantua sleep, and of his Hours and Breviary   207

XLII. How the Monk encouraged his Companions, and how he hanged upon a Tree   211

XLIII. How the Scouts of Picrochole were met by Gargantua, and how the Monk slew Captain Rushforth, and then was made Prisoner by the Enemy   215

Chapters   *page*

XLIV. How the Monk rid himself of his Guards, and how
Picrochole's Scouts were defeated   219

XLV. How the Monk brought in the Pilgrims, and the good
Words which Gargantua gave them   223

XLVI. How Grandgousier humanely entreated Toucque-
dillon his Prisoner   228

XLVII. How Grandgousier sent for his Legions, and how
Toucquedillon slew Rashcalf and was afterwards slain by
Order of Picrochole   232

XLVIII. How Gargantua attacked Picrochole within La
Roche-Clermaud and defeated the Army of the said Picro-
chole   235

XLIX. How Picrochole in his Flight was overtaken by Ill-
fortune, and what Gargantua did after the Battle   238

L. The Harangue which Gargantua made to the Van-
quished   240

LI. How the victorious Gargantuists were recompensed
after the Battle   246

LII. How Gargantua caused to be built for the Monk the
Abbey of Thelema   248

LIII. How the Abbey of the Thelemites was built and
endowed   251

LIV. Inscription put over the Great Gate of Thelema   254

LV. How the Habitation of the Thelemites was ordered   259

LVI. How the Brethren and Sisters of Thelema were ap-
parelled   262

LVII. How the Thelemites were governed in their Manner
of Living   266

LVIII. A Prophecy in Riddles   269

Appendix

Almanack of 1533   275

Wages of Rabelais at the Hospital at Lyons   277

Election of Pierre du Castel as Physician of the Great
Hospital of the Rhone-Bridge in the Place of Rabelais   278

Epistle of Dedication to the Topography of Ancient Rome,
by John Bartholomew Marliani   280

PREFACE

TO THE FIRST EDITION

THE present translation has been made from the text of MM. de
Montaiglon and Lacour. Their text is a careful reprint of the edition of the two first Books, as revised by Rabelais for the Lyons
printer F. Juste in 1542, and of the Third and Fourth Books for the
Paris printer Michael Fezandat in 1552. In the Fifth Book these
editors print the interesting sixteenth-century MS. which was discovered about 1840 by the late Bibliophile Jacob (Paul Lacroix)
in the Bibliothèque Nationale. The list of variants from the earliest
editions has been employed for the purpose of indicating the important changes introduced by Rabelais to disarm the suscepti-
bilities of the Sorbonne.

Excellent work in the emendation of the text has been achieved
during the last fifty years in France. Besides his discovery of the
MS., much was done by Lacroix, whose handy little edition with
short notes in one volume has deservedly commanded an immense
sale in France. It is a pity the type is not better and more legible.
M. Burgaud des Marets, whose researches have done much to
establish a correct text from the oldest editions, and also for the
elucidation and explanation of his author's meaning, deserves great
praise, and it is a pleasing task to record most grateful thanks to
him for invaluable assistance, as well as to his coadjutor M. E.-J.
Rathery, for the careful and exhaustive life of Rabelais prefixed to
their joint edition. The contribution of M. Louis Moland in the
unpretentious volume published by Garnier Frères, giving a
corrected text, a lucid and judicious life of Rabelais, interesting
documents and useful bibliographical notes, has been found very
serviceable.

By a strange fatality, which I much regret, the edition of M.
Marty-Laveaux did not fall into my hands till my first volume was
printed off and the second volume nearly all in type. This edition
gives the most conscientiously exact text, and exceedingly useful

notes. Fortunately, I find myself in considerable agreement with M. Marty-Laveaux in matters bibliographical, as well as in the use made of previous commentaries. The notes on the two first Books in his edition are much fuller than those on the later Books, and I have placed in the *addenda* at the end of the first volume a few extracts from this commentary, besides one or two illustrations which subsequent reading has supplied to me.

To the learned labours of Duchat every reader of an annotated Rabelais must be deeply indebted. He was a French Huguenot refugee living in Berlin, who devoted himself with great zeal to writing commentaries on the French literature of the fifteenth and sixteenth centuries. His great work was his Rabelais, of which the last and most complete edition was published at Amsterdam in 1741. It is a very handsome book in three volumes 4°, containing the text with elaborate notes, the letters with the commentary of the brothers Sainte-Marthe, the translation of Motteux' notes by De Missy, and other matter of a less important nature. Although Urquhart and Motteux had written notes more or less continuous in explanation of their translation, no attempt at a detailed commentary seems to have been made before Duchat's edition. He was admirably fitted for his task by his wide erudition, knowledge of the French language and literature and of the manners and customs of the various parts of France, as well as by the zeal which he brought to bear on his subject. His first edition was published in 1711.

It would be ungrateful not to record considerable obligation to the *variorum* edition of Esmangart and Johanneau (Paris 1823). This edition incorporates the notes of Duchat, some from Motteux, De Marsy and others, besides giving original notes on antiquarian, linguistic and other subjects, as well as a voluminous historical commentary, the value of which, however, is marred by a kind of hallucination which seems to beset these writers that the characters in Rabelais' romance are intended for almost exact counterparts of historical personages throughout.

Very great help has been obtained from the German translation and commentary of Gottlob Regis (Leipsic 1832–41). The notes are in a great measure judiciously chosen extracts from those of the *variorum* edition, to which are added excellent notes by Regis him-

self, besides apt illustrations from the English dramatists, from
Burton, Swift and Sterne, as well as from Cervantes, Goethe and
other writers. The introduction to this commentary is very valuable,
giving, besides a life of the Author, an account of the editions up to
1836, of the translations into various languages, and a chronological
summary of the historical events, etc., during Rabelais' life. A
large number of passages from Greek and Latin authors which are
translated, adapted or alluded to in the text are given *in extenso* in
this laborious commentary, which thus extends to 960 pages in
addition to the 230 pages of introduction. While I acknowledge
great indebtedness to this conscientious work, it must reluctantly
be confessed that the bulky volume has served somewhat as a
negative example.

As to the translation itself, although it has been made inde-
pendently, it has been made with Urquhart lying open and compared paragraph by paragraph. Without hesitation a happy turn
or rare word has been adopted from the old rendering. Often it
was curious to note how the translations of a paragraph would
prove almost identical word for word, till a closer examination of
the text shewed that there could hardly be any variation in a faithful version. The excellence of Urquhart and Motteux' translation
is generally acknowledged, and a new one would have been unnecessary had the rendering been even. Urquhart's work in the
first two Books is much the better, and occasionally Motteux in the
later Books reaches that level, but not unfrequently these translators betray an inclination to amplify unnecessarily, and that in
those parts of the book which modern readers would scarcely wish
to see enlarged. Speaking generally, Motteux is much more diffuse
than Urquhart, and seems to shew a pride in parading his knowledge of the strong proverbial English expressions of which he had
so wonderful a mastery.

With regard to a plan which has been adopted in this translation,
of leaving some five chapters in the original French, exception may
be taken. In a book which *must* contain the whole in some form,
it is a question whether a very small portion may not well be left
untranslated when the matter is too offensive, especially when the
romance is in no wise helped forward by these chapters. An obvious objection is that, by leaving them in the French, special atten-

tion is drawn to what is desirable should pass without notice, in the same way as the coarse parts of Plautus, for instance, are relegated to the end of the book by themselves in the Delphin edition. This objection would be of weight if the present translation were likely to fall into the hands of schoolboys. As it is intended for readers who would neither be scandalised nor allured by such a quasi-omission, it may well be that the notes appended to these chapters will be all they will care to see of them. Certain it is, that this translation of Rabelais, at first a pleasing pastime, when only selected chapters were translated for the purpose of getting a thorough knowledge of the book, became anything but agreeable when a compliance with the suggestions of too partial friends induced the completion of the work. As it is, much had to be written from which one's feelings and pen recoiled, and it is hoped that a repugnance to put into English certain most undesirable matter may not be judged hardly.

It is a pleasing duty to record thanks to many friends who have kindly encouraged and helped me in the progress of my work, particularly to Mr Walter Besant, without whose suggestion and help this book would not have seen the light; to Mr J. Bass Mullinger, Lecturer in History in St John's College, who has greatly assisted me in a variety of ways; to Mr R. Pendlebury, Fellow of St John's, to whom I am indebted for help in matters of astronomy and musical history; to Professor Macalister in some points in anatomy; to Mr A. A. Tilley, Fellow of King's College, for suggestions and assistance in matters biographical and bibliographical; to Mr E. H. Acton, Fellow of St John's College, for some careful notes on botanical questions. For the carefully drawn map of Chinonais prefixed to this volume I have to thank the skill and sympathy of Mr A. G. Dew-Smith of Trinity College.

In common, I suspect, with many others, I have much reason to be grateful to the vigilance and care of Messrs Clark's reader, who has shewn great interest in my translation, and has been suggestive in several points, which I have greatly appreciated. If, as I fear may be the case, some inaccuracies are detected in the many cross-references in the book, the blame must be laid on the weakness of my eyesight, which has been unequal to the long-continued strain involved in correcting proofs.

The references to Greek and Latin authors given by Duchat and others have been for the most part placed in the margin.[1] They have been made more exact and accurate, and considerably increased in number. The chapters, paragraphs, sections, etc., are those in common use. Teubner's texts have generally been employed. In Pliny's *Natural History* the books, chapters, and paragraphs have been cited, and in the case of a long paragraph the place has been indicated more closely by the sections of Sillig's edition.

In the investigation of historical and archaeological matters I have found of great service Mullinger's *History of the University of Cambridge*, in points connected with the Schoolmen, Erasmus, etc.; Altmeyer's *Les Précurseurs de la Réforme aux Pays Bas* (Brussels 1886); Chancellor Christie's charming book *Étienne Dolet*, which throws a clear light on many places; Fleury's *Rabelais et ses œuvres*; Dubouchet's *F. Rabelais à Montpellier*; Heulhard's *Rabelais, ses voyages en Italie, son exil à Metz*; J. C. Brunet's *Recherches sur les éditions de Rabelais*, and other books which it is unnecessary to specify more nearly.

For the history generally I have consulted Ranke's *History of the Popes*, Robertson's *Charles V*, Roscoe's *Life of Leo X*, and Brantôme (ed. Lalanne, published by the Société de l'Histoire de France).

It may be useful to indicate the editions of some of the earlier, contemporary and later writers used in illustrating or explaining the author's language.

Le Roman de la Rose	Francisque-Michel	Paris 1864
La Farce de Maistre Pathelin	(Lacroix), Bibliophile Jacob, 1876	
François Villon	,, ,,	1877
Cretin	the second edition	Paris 1723
Sainct-Gelais	Blanchemain	Ed. Elzev. 1873
Coquillart	d'Héricault	Ed. Elzev. 1857
Charles d'Orléans	d'Héricault	Paris 1874
Poésies inédites du XVème et XVIème Siècles		Ed. Elzev.
Des Periers	Lacour	Paris 1874

---

[1] [These have now been incorporated in the notes. D.H.B.]

Clément Marot	Garnier Frères	Paris
Contes d'Eutrapel	Hippeau	Paris 1875
Merlin Coccai	Portioli	Mantua 1882
Le Disciple de Pantagruel	Lacroix	Paris 1875
L'Heptaméron	{ Le Roux de Lincy et de Montaiglon }	Paris 1880
Apologie pour Hérodote	Liseux	Paris 1879
Epistola Passavantii	,,	Paris 1875
Agrippa, *de vanitate Scientiarum*		Cologne 1531
,, *de occulta philosophia*		Cologne 1551
Regnier	Garnier Frères	Paris
Le Moyen de Parvenir	,,	Paris
Proverbes Français	Le Roux de Lincy	Paris, 2d ed. 1859
Ambroise Paré	Malgaigne	Paris 1840–1

In the notes the letters (D), (R) and (M) are used for Duchat, Regis and Burgaud des Marets respectively.

PREFACE

TO THE SECOND EDITION

A<small>FTER</small> the publication of his translation in 1892, Mr Smith continued to annotate and expand his work: and at the time of his death he was preparing the materials for a second edition. These materials, the monument of a lifetime's devotion to an author he loved, are now through the generosity of his widow and of St John's College set before the public; and admirers of Rabelais can enjoy the great stores of Mr Smith's learning, a learning as encyclopedic and as humanistic as Rabelais' own. My work has been merely to put the material in order and to see it through the press: and that has been amply repaid by the opportunity it has offered me of intimate acquaintance with two great Pantagruelists.

I have included in an appendix to the first volume certain documents relating to the period between the publication of the *Pantagruel*, 1532, and that of the *Gargantua* in 1534. They are: the Preface to the Almanack of 1533; the record of Rabelais' wages as physician at Lyons and its pendant, the notice of Pierre du Castel's election as Rabelais' successor; and Rabelais' Dedicatory Letter to Jean du Bellay, prefixed to the edition of Marliani's *Topographia*. Similar documents relating to the period before the publication of the *Pantagruel* will be placed at the end of the second volume: and those relating to the period after the publication of the *Gargantua* will be distributed according to their chronology among the later volumes.

K<small>ING</small>'s C<small>OLLEGE</small>
C<small>AMBRIDGE</small>
July, 1934

PREFACE

TO THE SECOND EDITION

THE ENGLISH TRANSLATORS
OF RABELAIS

Rabelais was known in England either in the original or in partial translations very early, as may be seen in allusions in the dramatists and in Bacon, who refers to him in two of his *Apophthegms* (1624) as well as in his *De Augmentis Scientiarum*, vi. 1 (1623), where he alludes to the *Formicarium artium* in the Library of St Victor (ii. 7). Burton also alludes to and quotes him in his *Anatomy of Melancholy*.

The well-known expression in *As You Like It*, iii. 2. 238 (1600), "You must borrow me Gargantua's mouth", seems to point to the fact that Rabelais was known to Shakespeare. Steevens' note on this passage deserves consideration: "On the register of the Stationers' Company are two items, showing that in 1592 [April 6] was entered 'Gargantua his prophesie', and in 1594 [Dec. 4] 'A booke entituled the historie of Gargantua, etc.'" Shakespeare, however, may have known only of the great Giant by hearsay, and have seen neither of these books. A passage in *Twelfth Night* (ii. 3. 22) seems to me possibly borrowed from the speech of Kissbreech before Pantagruel (ii. 11, *ad init.*): "When thou spokest of Pigrogromitus, of the Vapians passing the equinoctial of Queubus". In John Cook's *Green's Tu Quoque* (prob. 1600) occurs: "Here's a bit indeed! What's this to a Gargantua stomach?" (Dodsley, vii. 73). Ben Jonson has in *Every Man in his Humour*, ii. 1 (1596): "Your Gargantua breech cannot carry it away so"; and in *Every Man out of his Humour*, i. 1 (1599): "Debt? Why, that's more to your credit, sir...than if you gave them a new year's gift". (Cf. *Pant.* iii. 3.) South in his *Sermon on Ingratitude*, preached before the University of Oxford 1675, on the text of Judges viii. 34, 35, seems indebted for a fine passage to this same chapter on lending and borrowing. In the Second Book of Bishop Hall's *Satires* (ii. 1. 57) the translator of "Gargantua" in Laneham's *Narrative of Q. Elizabeth's Entertainment at Kenilworth Castle in 1575* is censured thus:

> But who conjured us, etc....
> Or wicked Rablais' dronken revellings
> To grace the misrule of our tavernings?

The catalogue of the Bodleian Library (1738) has the following entries:

FRANCIS RABELAIS, M.D.
First Book of his works into English. Lond. 1653.
The three first Books into English out of French, by Sir Tho. Urchard and others.
The Fourth and Fifth Books translated into English by Pet. Motteux. Lond. 1694.

The first complete translation of the whole was published in 1708 in two volumes; containing, besides, the sixteen letters of Rabelais from Rome. The following was the title:

The whole works of F. Rabelais M.D. in two volumes, Or the Lives Heroic Deeds and Sayings of Gargantua and Pantagruel. Done out of French, by Sir Thomas Urchard Knight, M. Motteux and Others. With a large Account of the Life and Works of the Author: Particularly an Explanation of the most difficult passages in them; never before publish'd in any Language. London: printed for James Woodward in Threadneedle Street near St Christopher's Church MDCCVIII.

In the first volume, containing the first three Books, smaller type is used from p. 306 to p. 532, the end. The second volume, containing the Fourth and Fifth Books, etc., is put down as translated by M. Motteux.

The commentary of Urquhart to the three first Books is in a continuous form, whereas Motteux gives notes chapter for chapter. This translation was published in a corrected form by Ozell in 1727, four times in the eighteenth century and afterwards in 1807.

The translation, as Regis remarks, is somewhat raw, but at the same time spirited, and done into idiomatic English. It is, however, to be remarked that Rabelais' style, when translated quite literally, lends itself readily to a translation of that kind, something in the nature of the English adopted by the translators of our Bible; and at times, when Rabelais is anatomical or "Hellenistic", to that of Sir Thomas Browne, whose learning is encyclopaedic, like his own, and whose manner is quaint and pedantic, although I do not think those charges can well be laid at Rabelais' door, seeing that he was then like Teiresias in the lower world, according to the *Odyssey* (x. 495), the wise one among the flitting shades, whereas a century later the case was to some extent altered, and moreover

Browne was writing almost exclusively for the learned, Rabelais for the Court, the Universities and the people.

Very sound though unobtrusive work was done in the elucidation of our author by Randle Cotgrave in his French Dictionary, published first in 1611, and dedicated to William Cecil, Lord Burleigh, Elizabeth's Prime Minister. In this is embodied a Glossary of a very large number of Rabelaisian words, often marked "Rab." Cotgrave was a good French scholar and an excellent lexicographer, and had the great advantage of living much nearer the times of the writer. He is often quoted as an authority both by French and English writers. M. des Marets defers to him considerably in his notes, and he is constantly referred to by modern English lexicographers.

Urquhart made great use of Cotgrave, but, after the manner of his time, in translating a single word of the French he often empties all the synonyms given by Cotgrave into his version, and so is guilty of needless expansion. Following upon, or rather going beyond, this example, Motteux not only gives many words as a rendering of one, but foists in a lot of his own varied English vocabulary, which may perhaps be dubbed as spirited and racy, but is not Rabelais.

Sir Thomas Urquhart[1] (or Urchard, or Urwhart, as it is sometimes spelled) was a most fantastic and original Scotchman, the representative of a very old family who "enjoyed not only the office of hereditary Sheriff-Principal of the Shire of Cromarty, but the far greater part if not the whole of the said shire did belong to them, either in property or superiority, and they possessed a considerable estate besides in the Shire of Aberdeen" (*System of Heraldry*, vol. ii. p. 274). These great possessions and privileges descended unimpaired through a long line of ancestors to Urquhart's father, Thomas Urquhart of Cromarty, who was born in 1582. He succeeded his father, Henry Urquhart, April 13, 1603, and his grandfather, Walter Urquhart, May 11, 1607, and it is recorded that he received the estate from his guardian "without any burden of debt, how little soever, or provision of brother, sister, or any other of his kindred or allyance wherewith to affect it".

A short time before his majority, T. Urquhart married Christian, daughter of Alexander, fourth Lord Elphinston, who at that time was High Treasurer of Scotland; and as he held that office only from June 24,

---

[1] Derived mainly from the preface to *The Works of Sir Thomas Urquhart of Cromarty*, published for the Maitland Society 1834.

1599, till September 5, 1601, the alliance must have taken place during the intermediate period—probably in 1600. Lord Elphinston required his son-in-law to leave his estate to the heir of the marriage "in the same freedom and entirenesse every way that it was left unto himself, which before many noble men and others he solemnly promised to doe to the utmost of his power" (*Logopandecteision*, ed. 1652, p. 42 (T.W.)).

Notwithstanding this, Thomas Urquhart, who was knighted at Edinburgh in 1617 by James VI, was unable to carry out the injunction, and from this time till his death in 1642 he got into great pecuniary embarrassment, and moreover was troubled by family dissensions.

Sir T. Urquhart was the eldest son of the family, and was born in the fifth year of the marriage of his parents. This would make his birth to fall in or about 1605. His youth was devoted to study of various kinds rather than field sports, which were the amusements of the other members of his family. At the same time he shews that he was not wanting in personal activity or spirit for manly exercises.

Like his father, he was an Episcopalian and a Royalist, but more than all an ardent Scotchman. When abroad he was led by this patriotism "thrice to enter the lists against men of three several nations to vindicate his native country from the calumnies wherewith they had aspersed it, wherein it pleased God so to conduct his fortune" that he succeeded in disarming his adversaries. He does not say where this took place, but he writes that in his travels he visited France, Spain, Italy, and Sicily.

On returning from his travels he was present on the side of the Barons, who were then in arms against the Covenanters, at the *Trott of Turreff* in 1639. A few weeks later he embarked at Aberdeen for England, and entered the service of Charles I, by whom he was knighted April 7, 1641. At this time he published his epigrams, and remained in England till 1642, when he returned at his father's death. Finding the family in a most disordered condition, he set apart the whole rents of his estate, with the exception of his mother's jointure, for the payment of the debts, and leaving the management of his affairs in the hands of friends as trustees, he repaired to the continent, hoping at his return to find his estates unencumbered.

In this he was doomed to bitter disappointment, and on his return to Scotland in 1645 he took up his abode in the ancient family mansion of Cromarty.

Much of Urquhart's writings is taken up with accounts and complaints of the difficulties and hardships which he encountered in endeavouring to clear his father's estates. He appears, moreover, to have been cruelly oppressed by an ancient enemy of their house, Leslie of Findrassie, who seems to have left nothing undone to distress him. He went so far as to get Urquhart arrested as prisoner of war "till he were contented in all his demands" (*Log.* v. p. 16). It is not known how long he was imprisoned, but it is generally stated that he made his escape from the Tower to the continent, where he died suddenly in a fit of excessive laughter on hearing of the restoration of Charles II in 1660. [This looks something like an imitation of Rabelais in his account of the death of Philemon.]

He took part in the battle of Worcester in 1651, where he lost his papers, particularly the MS. of *The Exquisite Jewel* and *Logopandecteision*, which were restored to him subsequently, and published in the years 1652 and 1653 respectively.

His epigrams were published in 1641; the *Trissotetras* in 1645. The latter is a would-be scientific book, but appears to be a wonderful jumble of Trigonometry and Memoria Technica, more confusing and unintelligible than the most abstruse speculation would be.

After the battle of Worcester he published the Παντοχρονόχανον; *or, Promptuary of Time*, the MS. of which was found among the spoil and restored to him by Captain Goodwin. This work proposes to deduce the genealogy of the Urquharts from the "red earth" in the hands of the Creator, from which Adam was made, to the year 1652, when the book was printed.

In the same year was printed in London 'Εσκυβάλαυρον; *or, The Discovery of a most Exquisite Jewel*. The book is described on the title-page as "more precious than diamonds enchassed in gold, the like whereof was never seen in any age", and it is said to have been "found in the Kennel of Worcester-streets the day after the fight". This is the most interesting of Urquhart's works. It is professedly a vindication of the honour of Scotland against the slanders of the Presbyterians, but it abounds in curious notices of various Scotchmen, especially his favourite hero the Admirable Crichton. This part is written in a euphuistic rhapsodical vein, and affords an indication of the saturation of Urquhart's mind with the style of Rabelais. It might almost be pieced together from the meeting of Pantagruel with the Limosin Scholar, the discomfiture of Thaumast by Panurge, and the meeting of Pantagruel and his party with Queen Entelechia.

In 1653 Urquhart published his *Logopandecteision; or, An Introduction to the Universal Language*. The author describes it as "now lately contrived and published, both for his own utilitie and that of all pregnant and ingenious spirits". The plan for an universal language is rather indicated than fully developed in the first Book of his work, entitled *Neaudethaumata; or, Wonders of the New Speech*, the remaining Books being chiefly occupied with domestic details descriptive of his own hardships and difficulties. Their subjects are—

Chrestasebeia; or, The Impious Dealing of Creditors.
Cleronomaporia; or, The Intricacy of a Distressed Successor or an Apparent Heir.
Chryseomystes; or, The Covetous Preacher.
Neleodicastes; or, The Pitiless Judge.
Philoponauxesis; or, Furtherance of Industry.

These topics are illustrated by a great variety of personal anecdotes and local notices, and the work concludes with a fanciful summary of the author's demands or "proquiritations" from the State.

Sir Thomas Urquhart is more widely known as the translator of Rabelais. He translated the first three Books, of which the first was published in his lifetime, and the first three together after his death.

Motteux, who finished the translation, represents Urquhart as a complete master of the French language, and as possessing both learning and fancy equal to the task he undertook. Tytler remarks in his *Life of the Admirable Crichton* that "his extravagance, his drollery, his imagination, his burlesque and endless epithets are in the task of translating Rabelais transplanted into their true field of action, and revel through his pages with a license and buoyancy which is quite unbridled yet quite allowable".

Pierre Antoine Motteux,[1] born at Rouen in Normandy, February 18, 1660, was probably the son of a merchant, Antoine le Motteux. On the revocation of the Edict of Nantes in 1685, he came over to England and lived first with his godfather and relative Paul Dominique, a merchant of considerable standing in the City. Afterwards Motteux himself became an East India merchant in Leadenhall Street, and also occupied a place in the foreign department of the Post Office, though it appears that at one time he had to eke out his income by his literary work, if we may judge by the cringing tone of some of the dedications of his writings. He must have been a remarkable linguist, for in 1691, six years only after his coming to England, he was Editor of a Monthly Miscellany called *The Gentleman's Journal*, in which were contributions by Nahum Tate, Prior, Chs. Dryden, Sir Charles Sedley, Thomas Browne, and others, as well as a considerable number by the Editor himself. In 1698 he published in French a parody on Boileau's "Ode on the taking of Namur by Louis XIV in 1692", in which he ridicules the French King and lauds William of Orange, as he does on every possible occasion.

In 1694 he edited Sir Thomas Urquhart's translation of the *Gargantua* and the first two Books of *Pantagruel*, dedicating it to Admiral Russell, afterwards Earl of Orford, and also published his own translation of the Fourth and Fifth Books.

He continued from this time to bring out plays and skits and musical pieces that were performed at the Theatre in Lincoln's Inn Fields and elsewhere, borrowing, as he admits, from foreign sources, mostly Italian, seeing that the French playwrights had been so ransacked that there was but little left to glean. He also wrote prologues and epilogues to various plays, such as Vanbrugh's *Mistake*.

His best-known theatrical pieces are *Acis and Galatea*, a masque acted at Drury Lane in 1701; *Arsinoë, Queen of Cyprus*, in 1705; *Thomyris, Queen of Scythia*, in 1707. Altogether he wrote as many as eight original pieces.

In 1708 he republished Urquhart's translation of the first three Books of Rabelais, and with it published his own translation of the last two Books, or *Pantagruel's Voyage to the Oracle of the Bottle*. To this he added a

---

[1] From the notice of the *Life and Works of Motteux*, by H. de Laun, and the note in De Missy's French translation of Motteux' notes to Rabelais.

translation of the *Pantagrueline Prognostication*, other minor pieces, and the historical letters. The preface to this edition is written in nervous manly English, with a sensible account of the original and a half-apology for the style of his own translation. It concludes with a well-turned expression of gratitude to the King and country that had found him a refuge. The explanatory remarks to this edition have been translated into French, and were made use of by Duchat in his editions.

In 1701 Motteux published a translation of *Don Quixote*, said on the title-page to have been "translated from the original by several hands, and published by Peter Motteux". It is most probable that Motteux did by far the greatest part of this translation. J. Ozell, who was a friend of Motteux, brought out in 1719, a year after Motteux' death, a revised edition, as he did of the Rabelais in 1727.

In the *Spectator*, No. 288, January 30, 1711–12, there is an epistolary puff from Motteux advertising his wares, literary and otherwise, which, as M. van Laun points out, argues no very great prosperity. Two sales of his pictures also point in the same direction. His position in the Post Office can hardly have been very lucrative, but the records before 1787 have been destroyed, and with them the means of shewing Motteux' situation.

On February 18, 1718, he was inveigled into a house of ill-fame in the Butcher Row, behind St Clement Danes Church, and there murdered. Rewards were offered by his widow and the State, and five persons (four women and a soldier) brought to trial, but acquitted.

He was held in considerable repute and esteem by his contemporary playwrights, especially Dryden, by whom there is a commendatory epistle which ends thus—

> "It moves our wonder that a foreign guest
> Should overmatch the most and match the best.
> In underpraising thy deserts, I wrong;
> Here find the first deficience of our tongue:
> Words, once my stock, are wanting to commend
> So great a poet and so good a friend".

RABELAIS IN HIS WRITINGS

In recent times much has been achieved by careful research in determining the status and surroundings of François Rabelais and his family, as well as in fixing the date of his birth and the sources of his learning and inspiration.

The old view that he was born in 1483—the birth-year of Raphael, Luther and old Thomas Parr—at the inn *La Lamproie* in a street in Chinon, and that he was the son of the innkeeper, has been completely disproved and exploded by the careful investigations of MM. Lefranc, Grimaud and H. Clouzot, and other members of the *Société des études Rabelaisiennes*, published in their Review (*R.E.R.*). The results have been obtained by minute examinations and interpretations of the writings of Rabelais, as well as by collating and sifting external evidence in the way of local registers and deeds in various provinces of France.

First as to his birth-year, which rests on the evidence of a note of his burial at St Paul's cemetery, rue des Jardins, Paris, to the effect that at that time (April 1553) he was seventy years of age. This would make him out to be born in 1483. M. Lefranc has shewn, and careful readers readily admit, that Rabelais' statements of fact, even in the midst of his highest flights of imagination, are nearly always exact. Research has shewn that Gargantua represents Rabelais' father—we shall recur to this—and that throughout the *Pantagruel* and the *Gargantua* there are frequent references to the author's relatives and personal friends, and that the romance is very often autobiographical. M. Lefranc draws attention (*R.E.R.* vi. 266) to *G.* 4-7, where Gargantua's birth is fixed on Feb. 4 and it is recorded that Gargamelle, his mother, had eaten a quantity of tripe, most of which was to be salted on Shrove Tuesday, so as to be eaten during that lenten season. He then examines the calendars for the years 1488–96, and finds that only in the year 1494 does Shrove Tuesday fall at a time when such salting could have taken place; for Easter fell on March 30, and therefore Shrove Tuesday is fixed for Feb. 12, and cattle that were killed on Feb. 3 might supply beef which could be salted on Feb. 12. M. Lefranc then goes on to point out from Rabelais (*G.* 13) that at the end of the fifth year of Gargantua's life his father Grandgousier, returning from the conquest of the Canarians, paid a visit to his young son. This is with great reasonableness referred to the return of Louis XII from the conquest of the Milanese between August and October 1499. This would fix the birth-year at 1494. Another point is made in noting the age of Panurge when he first meets Pantagruel (*P.* 9). He is said to be thirty-five, and the date of this meeting is naturally placed in 1530, at the time "when all disciplines are restored and the teaching of the ancient tongues is renewed". In March 1530 the royally appointed lecturers began to teach, while Gargantua's letter to his son Pantagruel containing his scheme of education (*P.* 8) is dated March 17. Thus if Panurge is thirty-five when he meets Pantagruel in 1530, he must have been born about 1494 or 1495.

Another suggestion, based also on an interpretation of our author's words, is permissible. In c. 9 of the *Pantagrueline Prognostication* we read: "The stars have been there [in the heavens] *I assure you*, more than sixteen thousand and I know not how many days". 16,070 days is 44 years. This second part of the *Prognostication* was written in 1533. If this means that he was forty-four years of age then, his birth-year would be 1489.

Few writers have suffered so much as Rabelais from prejudice, caused, in part at least, by the attitude of his own writings. Fired by the recently developed Humanism, he adopted all too easily the belief, so much fostered by Horace, that no one who was a water-drinker, who was not devoted to the inspiration from Bacchic enthusiasm, could achieve the distinctive title of poet. Alcaeus, Homer and Ennius are claimed as instances of the truth of this theory, which also seems to derive considerable support from the Platonic theory of "enthusiasm" developed in the *Phaedrus*. It is approved in Erasmus' *Adagia* by articles such as *Multi Thyrsigeri pauci Bacchi*, and seems to have been accepted as a truism. Thus, then, Rabelais represented his *Pantagruel* as the hero who abolished thirst in the land of the Dipsodes (the thirsty race), the hero of jollity and contentment in spite of all the attacks of fortune. The repetition of this characteristic, little as it is borne out by the actual

conduct of the humane, kindly and highly educated prince Pantagruel, has gone very far to cause the writer to be looked upon as a
drunken buffoon. Added to this, the subsequent transference of
the hostelry known as *La Lamproie* to a house that had belonged to
the Rabelais family has confirmed and stereotyped assertions to
this effect, till the belief has become inveterate and all but in-
eradicable. A house in the street *La Lamproie*, No. 15, belonged to
Rabelais' father, and in 1590 was turned into an inn; later, in the
beginning of the eighteenth century, this hostelry was transferred
to its present site, No. 2, where it still exists as an inn.

Another assertion, that his father was an apothecary, is de-
monstrably false. The son of an apothecary was received into the
medical profession without fees, whereas the record of the fees paid
by François Rabelais is extant at Montpellier.

In fact the father of Rabelais, M. Antoine Rabelais, *licencié ès lois*,
was a considerable person in Chinonais and the possessor of various
properties in the neighbourhood. (i) La Devinière, the farm and
vineyard where François Rabelais was born, belonged to Antoine
Rabelais I (1505–34); it devolved to Antoine II, our author's
brother, till 1559, when it descended to *his* son Thomas, who
was an *apothécaire*. (ii) Chavigny-en-Vallée, in the commune of
Varennes-sur-Loire. This came to the family through Andrée
Pavin, grandmother of F. Rabelais. (iii) Gravot, in the commune
of Bourgueil. (iv) La Pommardière, in the commune of Seuilly.
Smaller properties also belonged to the family: (1) Les Quinquenais, a small country house; (2) Le clos Rabelais, in the commune of Seuilly; (3) Le grand clos Rabelais; (4) Half an acre of
land near the Mill bridge (*moulin du pont*); (5) Le pré Rabelais, in
the commune of Sinais, near Pontillé, where the cows fed that provided milk for the child Gargantua. All these places are mentioned
in the course of the story, some of them several times.

François Rabelais was born then about 1494 at La Devinière, a
small hamlet close to Seuilly and three or four miles from Chinon,
and it is of this neighbourhood and the countryside that he delights to speak in his "books", especially in the *Gargantua*. He had
two brothers, Antoine and Jamet, and a sister Françoise, all older
than himself, and being the youngest he was destined for a life in
the Cloister. Of this he seems to speak with some bitterness in the

The origin and relationships of Rabelais may best be seen by the following scheme, compiled from the investigations given in the *R.E.R.*:

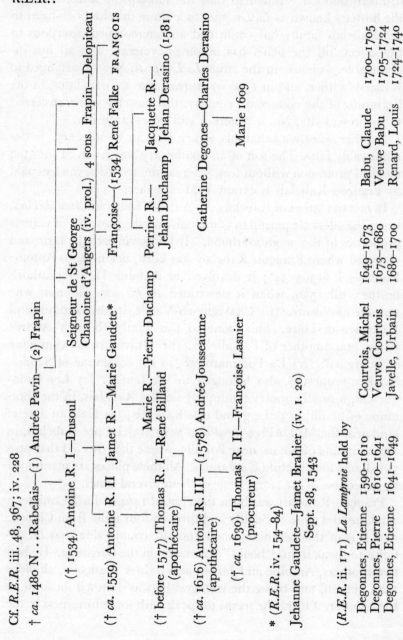

Fifth Book, c. 4, employing, as he so often does, an illustrative story which he found in Athenaeus or Erasmus (*Apophthegmata*) and adapts thus: "I do marvel whether the mothers in the other world can bear their children nine months in their womb, seeing that they cannot bear them nor brook them in their houses nine years, nay most often not seven; but by putting only a shirt over their robe and cutting a few hairs on the top of their heads, together with certain expiatory words, they...transform them into birds (*i.e.* monks) such as you see before you".

This makes it extremely probable that the youthful François was given the tonsure at the age of seven. He was sent to school at the neighbouring Cluniac or Benedictine monastery at Seuilly. As a boy we may fancy him roaming about the country in obedience to his inquisitive nature and making acquaintance with all the villages within a radius of fifteen miles or so. The numerous properties of his father in the neighbourhood would enable him to wander considerably in visiting them, and he would naturally visit the paternal house in Chinon and learn all about the streets and the castle which dominates the town. All this appears in the pages of the *Gargantua* and in various allusions in other books.

Besides the documentary evidence that has been got together by the local antiquaries, it is to the *Gargantua* that we must specially look for indications of the circumstances of Rabelais' early life, just as we find in the *Pantagruel* autobiographical touches concerning his early manhood in Poitou and Paris.

In the 14th chapter of *Gargantua* we find a list of books which formed his early studies. Some allowance must be made for exaggeration, but undoubtedly the books there recited formed the stable education of the boys of that time. This is confirmed by similar allusions in Erasmus, Maturin Cordier the grammarian, and others.

His first preceptor was Thubal Holofernes. The name is derived from a *Pronostication nouvelle*, one of the many broad-sheets hawked about by pedlars at that time, which formed so much of the reading among such of the people as could read. It is one of the eight *Pronostications* which have been collected and published by A. de Montaiglon and James de Rothschild in the thirteen volumes of their *Anciennes poésies françaises inédites du XVème et XVIème siècles.*

They date its appearance about 1525. Curiously, Holofernes is the name of the pedagogue in Shakespeare's *Love's Labour's Lost*. How Shakespeare, who does not appear to have had a first-hand acquaintance with Rabelais, came to adopt this name is difficult to say. No doubt numerous parallel expressions are to be found common to both writers, but they are generally proverbial phrases common both in England and in France; these may be due to the frequent presence in France of English soldiers during the Hundred Years' War; many such parallels may be found in the *Anciennes poésies françaises*. Very few resemblances of a striking kind appear to be common to Rabelais and Shakespeare. It is also curious to note that several coincidences may be discovered in Chaucer and Rabelais, due of course to their deriving from a common source. Shakespeare also may have learnt something from the more learned Ben Jonson, who certainly possessed a copy of Rabelais.

After Thubal Holofernes had taught him the alphabet forwards and backwards, Rabelais learnt Donatus, or his Latin grammar, and Facetus, Theodolet and Alanus *in Parabolis*. These three books were comprised in the *Auctores octo morales*, a school-book much in vogue then, though now not easily found. They contained precepts in conduct and morals, mostly in leonine or rhyming Latin hexameters, with occasional pentameters. Other tracts of this series were the *Moral Distichs* of Dionysius Cato, consisting of sentences in terse Latin, followed by a number of maxims in pairs of Latin hexameters. They form a contrast to the other tracts by being written in good, not monkish, Latin, having been composed probably in the fifth or sixth century. Then follow a selection of Aesop's Fables in elegiacs and a paraphrase of the book of Tobias (Tobit) in the same metre. In the margins of these tracts were printed maxims derived from Latin poets. It seems probable that this book (*Auctores octo morales*) formed part of the educational system on which the youthful Rabelais was brought up; some of these maxims are to be found in his writings.

These books are followed in the list by others of a more advanced stage, dictionaries and grammar books mixed with ecclesiastical manuals such as the *Computus*, a book of calculations for finding Easter, and even a book of sermons in four volumes under the name of *Dormi securè*. This title means that *the preacher* may sleep soundly by the aid of this book, which will provide him with matter for many sermons.

All this instruction rendered Gargantua an utter booby, and when he was brought in contact with another young French gentleman who had been brought up under another system—probably intended for that of Erasmus—and who makes an address after the model given by Erasmus in his *monita paedagogica*, or hints on education, in the *Colloquia*, the contrast was too striking for his father Grandgousier. He at once placed the boy under another tutor, who took him to Paris and put him under a rational system, which Rabelais now describes in contrast to the discarded method.

This new plan is probably one which Rabelais had carefully elaborated by the aid of Erasmus' *Institutio Principis Christiani*, drawn up for the benefit of the youthful Charles V, and also of the system of the great Mantuan educationalist Vittorino da Feltre. Hints may also have been taken from Guillaume Budé (*Budaeus*), the learned French scholar who befriended Rabelais and Pierre Amy, his brother student in the cloister, and with whom a correspondence had passed, which fortunately is preserved.

It must not be taken for granted that this was the education that Rabelais enjoyed, excepting perhaps the first part of it, at the seminary at Seuilly. He probably learned but little there, and subsequently as little at the clerical institution of La Baumette, near Angers, whither, according to tradition, he was sent to complete his education before entering the cloister.

Of his life at La Baumette we know but little. It was a Franciscan convent and seminary for priests founded by René d'Anjou on the model of Sainte Baume in Provence. Rabelais is said to have formed a friendship there with a fellow-student, Geoffroi d'Estissac, afterwards Bishop of Maillezais in Poitou, and with Jean, the second son of the great du Bellay family, which possessed large estates in Maine as well as at La Sarthe near Angers. This, however, is only tradition. Du Bellay was afterwards Bishop of Paris and Cardinal, and both these prelates exercised later a considerable influence on the fortunes of Rabelais.

If he learnt but little in the way of books at La Baumette, traces of his residence at Angers, on the borders of Brittany, are to be

found in his romance. He mentions La Baumette in *G.* 12, shewing some acquaintance with its topography. Angers was visited
by the youthful Pantagruel in *P.* 5. There lived Canon Frapin,
Seigneur de St George, son of Rabelais' grandmother *en secondes
noces*; in iv. *A.P.* he is styled "an old uncle". It is mentioned in
iv. 13 as celebrated for its miracle plays. Rennes in Brittany is
noted for its bells (*P.* 26). The Channel Islands are visited (iv. 66)
and St Malo is the harbour from which Pantagruel's fleet sets out
(iv. 1). In iii. 30, Judge Bridlegoose is styled deputy-governor of
Fonsbeton. As Myrelingues, the province in which this place is
situated, is almost certainly intended for Brittany, it seems permissible to conjecture that Fonsbeton is intended for Beton or
Betton, a small place a few miles north of Rennes—*du fin fons Betton*,
just as Thaumast in *P.* 20 said that he had come *du fin fond d'Angleterre.* In the *Grandes Cronicques de l'enorme geant Gargantua*, known to
Rabelais but probably not written by him, some of the scenes are
laid in Brittany. All this exhibits Rabelais in the light in which we
constantly see him throughout his books, eagerly acquainting himself
with the features of the country in which he happens to reside.

About 1511 tradition tells us that he was transferred to the Franciscan convent at Fontenay-le-Comte near Niort in Poitou, and
here it was that he laid the foundation of his extraordinary erudition. He would be about seventeen at this time, supposing him to
have been born in 1494, and we learn from his "Petition on account of Apostasy" addressed to Paul III that he was admitted as
a Brother Minor of the Observance, the strictest sect of the Franciscans, and that he proceeded to all the orders up to the Priesthood.
Our information on this important period of his life is derived
almost entirely from this petition, from correspondence of his
friends and contemporaries, as well as his own correspondence
(three letters) with Guillaume Budé. It may be gathered with a
fair amount of certainty that he had formed a close friendship with
Pierre Amy, one of the brothers, and that the two had worked
together to good purpose in acquiring a knowledge of classical
writers and especially of Greek. Amy had been known to Budé,
and no doubt the two studious brethren had been prompted and
assisted by the great scholar to become humanists and follow his
own example. For after wasting his early years of instruction in

Paris and at Orléans, where he was supposed to study law, Budé took up classical learning with such unremitting ardour that he became the first scholar in France. Among his correspondence are two letters to Amy in Latin and two in Greek, also one in Latin to Rabelais and one almost entirely in Greek. The genuineness of the letter of Rabelais to Budaeus can hardly now be questioned, for it has been published in the *R.E.R.* in photogravure and is manifestly in the beautiful handwriting of Rabelais.

The glimpses we get of his life in the convent at Fontenay, derived mostly from letters and writings of his friends, reveal to us a man such as we should expect from his book, kindly, sociable, witty, studious, and after he had been prompted by the companionship of Amy and the favour of Budé, keenly anxious to master the newly discovered Hellenic literature. He was visited occasionally by learned friends, André Tiraqueau, a distinguished jurist of Poitou, afterwards member of the *Parlement* of Paris, the advocate Jean Bouchet, Amaury Bouchard, a King's Counsel and Master of the Requests, and Geoffroi d'Estissac, Bishop of Maillezais, his old acquaintance at La Baumette, when the friends had discussions on various points of learning under "the arbour of laurels" in the convent garden. The harmony of this *coterie* was curiously disturbed by the publication of a book by Bouchard in defence of the female sex against a treatise of Tiraqueau, *de legibus connubialibus et jure maritali*, in which women had been treated with scant respect. This had been published in 1513, while Bouchard's book appeared from the house of Badius Ascensius in Paris (Almarici Bouchardi *foeminei sexus apologia* adversus Andream Tiraquellium. Paris, Josse Badius Ascensius, 1522). In this book is to be found the following reference to Amy: "quae si alio animo impositae videantur judicet ille sodalis Francisci: qui quod est, id vere et amicus nuncupatur; quem veluti testem incorruptum industriis et ignaviis his affuturum spero". A letter from Pierre Amy to Tiraqueau also is extant, in which he seems to refer to a breach in the friendship of Bouchard and Tiraqueau: it contains the following passage: "Angor enim vehementer cum prospicio sicuti, Almarici causa, a te atque a nostro Rabeleso eruditissimo sodalium Franciscanorum, quorum desiderio maceror, diu abductus fui: ita ad vos ...redire non posse nisi ab Almarici delitiis vicissim divellar".

In 1524 Tiraqueau published at the press of Galiot Du Prè, the Paris printer, a second edition of his book *Commentarii in Pictonum consuetudines: Sectio de legibus connubialibus*, and in the preface he complains bitterly of his friend Bouchard for attacking and inveighing against the first edition, which he declares had been purloined and printed without his leave or knowledge, being only the first part, while he was busy preparing the rest. There is a tradition arising from this that Rabelais and Amy were called in to arbitrate on this point between the two friends. In a later passage, fo. 117, 2, Tiraqueau recurs to this action of Bouchard, in which he repeats the charge of attacking a book written by a very young man, and a book that had been printed without the author's knowledge. He speaks of Bouchard *ut qui semper feminis placere quam viris potius studuit*, and two pages later writes thus addressing Bouchard: "Sed temperare non possum quin dicam id quod et noster ille Franciscus Rabelesus, sodalis Franciscanus, vir utraque lingua doctissimus pronuntiavit simul ac librum tuum perlegit, 'Invidia scilicet maxima apud mulieres me flagraturum esse si librum tuum γυναικοκρατούμενός τις, id est tui similis, in vernaculum verterit'".

In a letter of dedication prefixed to an edition of the *Epistolae medicinales* of Manardi, a distinguished Ferrarese physician, Rabelais speaks with great commendation of the treatise of Tiraqueau, which he styles ὑπομνήματα in *Pictonum leges municipales*. The *Sectio de legibus connubialibus* was a part of this, and Rabelais earnestly begs for the completion of it. It was completed in 1545, and the *Sectio* was still further developed, with large additions and some suppressions, prepared for the press by his kinsman Michel Tiraqueau. Rabelais must have seen this either in manuscript or while it was passing through the press, because the bulk of the 31st, 32nd and 37th chapters of the *Third Book* published early in 1546, as well as much matter in other parts of the same book, are obviously derived from Tiraqueau, whose book, as well as Rabelais' *Third Book*, was published by Fezandat. These chapters are given as the discourse of Rondibilis the physician, and deal minutely with the sexual conditions and relations of women, and it seems fairly probable that offence was thus given to Tiraqueau, who was now member of the *Parlement* of Paris; for there is no trace of any further relations between the two men; and moreover Tiraqueau was one of the twelve members of the *Conseil du Parlement* when Rabelais' *Fourth Book* was brought up for discussion in the beginning of 1552. The printer was censured (*R.E.R.* iv. 388), and Tiraqueau uttered no word of defence on behalf of his former friend.

This controversy between Bouchard and Tiraqueau is important as forming an episode in the *Querelle des Femmes*, dating in France perhaps from *Le Roman de la Rose* of the thirteenth century. The second writer of this book, Jean de Meung, who continues the poem of Guillaume de Lorris from line 4668 to the end (line 22,818), shews himself a most strenuous vilifier of the female sex. Writers on both sides appeared from time to time in the succeeding centuries, one of the best defenders of women being the elegant writer Christine de Pisan. Rabelais by the plan of his *Third Book* was bound to be adverse to women, but from the extract of Tiraqueau given above, he was already claimed as a partisan.

But the turning-point in Rabelais' life was to come about this time. The Lutheran revolt had culminated, and going on *pari passu* with it was the Renaissance movement of Humanism, with its Greek and Hebrew studies and the translation of Aristotle and the Bible. Erasmus' edition of the New Testament and his Paraphrases had caused alarm in many of the monasteries, where the monks were sluggish and ignorant by choice, and could barely read their Breviary and Vulgate, to say nothing of understanding them. The Franciscans of Fontenay now took fright and visited the two studious brothers, Amy and Rabelais, with their displeasure, confiscated their books and treated the brothers rigorously. This is established by Budé's second letter to Rabelais dated Paris, Jan. 27, 1524 (a date established by Mr Tilley in *R.E.R.* vi. 47) and by another to Amy of Feb. 26, beginning: "O by the God of Friendship and the Founder of your Brotherhood, what is this that we have just heard? I learn that you, my valued friend, and your Theseus, Rabelais, have been invaded and harassed by these culture-hating brethren of yours on account of your excessive zeal in Greek studies, and are vilely and shamefully ill-treated. O the unconquerable perversity of these men!" The letter concludes: "Farewell, and give a fourfold greeting from me to the wise and gifted Rabelais, either by word of mouth or by letter when you write". An earlier letter to Amy ends thus: "Please greet from me Rabelais, who is associated with you and the sharer of your studies".

The brothers were restored to their studies by powerful influence, but they naturally could not feel themselves secure. Amy made his escape from the convent by some means or other, taking the hint, as Rabelais tells us (iii. 10), from the line "Heu fuge crudeles terras, fuge litus avarum!" which turned up when he consulted the *Sortes Vergilianae*. Of his subsequent fate we are not informed, excepting that Erasmus tells us in a letter to Jacobus Tussanius (xxvi. ep. 4 *fin.*), dated Freiburg, March 12, 1531, that the Petrus Amicus, to whom Budaeus had addressed letters, had been brought to Bâle by Joannes Lascanus Polonus, that he had taken a chill and died, and that he had been buried *as a layman* among the Franciscans.

Rabelais escaped in another way. He obtained an indult from Pope Clement VII permitting his transference from the Order of Brothers Minors to that of St Benedict in the Church of Maillezais, in the diocese of which Geoffroi d'Estissac was Bishop. This was a relief to him and an agreeable change; the Bishop was learned himself and a patron of learned men, whom he delighted to gather round him. This we know from a rhyming letter of Rabelais to Jean Bouchet inviting him to the Bishop's seat at Ligugé and from Bouchet's answer. It seems that the Bishop, who was a learned canonist, delighted to get round him the legal luminaries who had formed part of the *coterie* at Fontenay, and to enjoy their conversation and discussions on literary and legal questions. To all these worthies Rabelais, when established at Lyons in 1532, dedicated some of his work, and fortunately the letters of dedication have been preserved, giving us some idea of their gifts and of the kindly relations subsisting between them and our author. The transference to the Benedictines took place probably towards the end of 1524, or even later, for it would take some time to get an indult from Rome, even with the help of the Bishop's influence.

And now we come to a period in which Rabelais' movements are not definitely known. In the second petition which he made to Paul III he says that he remained at Maillezais several years (*in eoque per plures annos mansit*).

In *P.* 5 the youthful Pantagruel, starting from Poitiers, visits the other Universities of France, Bordeaux, Toulouse, Montpellier, Avignon, Valence, Angers, Bourges, Orléans, Paris. Antoine Leroy, who was *curé* of Meudon (about third in succession after Rabelais) and who collected stories from the old inhabitants concerning his predecessor, wrote in his *Elogia Rabelaisiana*: "Rabelaesus Gallicas omnes scientiarum bonarumque artium academias sub Pantagruelis nomine peragravit". Evidently a reference is intended to this chapter, and it is to be taken as true that Rabelais did at some time in his life visit these places. Angers, we have seen, he knew before; in the other places he passed a short time, and studied law at Bourges, which he mentions again in *P*. 29, whereas it has been established by Mr Tilley (*Modern Quarterly of Language and Literature*, No. 3, p. 207) that he must have studied medicine in Paris during the years 1528–30 in order to take his degree of Bachelor of Medicine at Montpellier in December 1532, of which the attestation in the records of that University is in Rabelais' own handwriting. M. Lefranc comes to the same conclusion (*R.E.R.* vi. 40) on other grounds, and both writers appeal to the extraordinarily exact acquaintance with Paris shewn in the 16th and other chapters of the *Pantagruel*. M. Lefranc also points out that in all probability Rabelais resided at the *Hostel St Denis* (Pantagruel's lodging in *P*. 18), which from being originally a royal residence had become towards the end of the fifteenth century a college for Benedictine students, St Denis being closely connected with the Benedictines of Maillezais. He suggests also that it was not till he left Paris for Montpellier, in 1530, that Rabelais abandoned the monkish habit. Rabelais' own account is: "absque licentia sui superioris a dicta Ecclesia discedens, regulari dimisso et Praesbyteri secularis habitu assumpto, per seculum diu vagatus fuit, eoque tempore durante Facultati Medicinae diligenter operam dedit et in ea gradus ad hoc requisitos suscepit et publice professus est". In a later *supplicatio* (dated probably 1536) he says: "Postmodum sine Religionis habitu profectus est in Montem-pessulanum ibidemque in facultate Medicinae studuit, publice legit per plures annos et gradus omnes, etiam Doctoratus, ibidem in praedicta facultate Medicinae suscepit et praxim ibidem et alibi in multis locis per annos multos exercuit". There is every reason for believing in a two-year residence in Paris, and this confirmation is very welcome.

His matriculation and baccalaureat in Medicine are attested in his own handwriting in the registers of the University of Montpellier dated respectively Sept. 17 and Dec. 1[1], 1530. As a bachelor he gave *courses* of lectures on the *Aphorisms* of Hippocrates and the *Ars Medica* of Galen to crowded audiences with great success. Besides this and his mention of Scurronus (= Jean Schyron), the Chancellor of Montpellier, in iv. 43, there is but little to record of his residence in Montpellier.

In the beginning of 1532 Rabelais migrated from Montpellier to Lyons, with the object of getting his lectures published by Sebastian Gryphius, the celebrated printer, who was to Lyons almost what Aldus Manutius was to Venice. Whereas Aldus printed many Greek books, Gryphius printed a few Greek and many Latin books, nearly all ancient classics, or commentaries and translations from the Greek by the humanists, and he is recorded to have published only two books in French. But at Lyons, which was at this time an intellectual centre hardly second to Paris, there were many printers and among them Claude Nourry and his successor François Juste, who printed the *Pantagruel* and the *Gargantua*. It is probable that Rabelais was soon employed by Gryphius as corrector for his press; but his reputation in Humanism as well as in Medicine had preceded him and he was doubtless welcomed by the learned printers of Lyons. This enabled him to amuse his leisure time in reading the chivalric romances, which presented in vigorous prose the subjects of the *chansons de geste*. These were eagerly read at the time, notwithstanding their almost interminable length; their influence may easily be seen not only in the *Grandes Cronicques*, which is formed on the Arthurian Merlin and Lancelot du Lac, but in the *Pantagruel*, which is founded on the Carolingian romances such as Fierabras, Galien Rethoré and others. After the publication by Gryphius of the Medical Letters of Manardi (June 3, 1532), the *Aphorisms* of Hippocrates (July 15), the Will of Cuspidius, etc. (Sept. 4), Rabelais was appointed physician to the hospital at Lyons at the rate of 40 *livres* a year, an advance of 10 *livres* on the salary of his predecessor.

Inspired by the reading of the chivalric romances, Rabelais may

---

[1] By a slip Rabelais has written Nov. 1 instead of Dec. 1.

either have composed or edited a crude giant-story, entitled *Les grandes et inestimables Cronicques du grant et enorme geant Gargantua*, founded, as has been said, on the Arthurian romances of Merlin and Lancelot du Lac. King Arthur himself furnishes the title for a Breton and British romance, while the giant Gargantua and his feats, with traces of his presence, are to be found in many places in France, especially in Brittany. The slight framework of the story is simply the creation of Grand Gosier and Galemelle by Merlin, the birth and apparelling of their son Gargantua, his transport over the sea to England on a cloud raised by Merlin, his taking service with King Arthur in England and his conquest of the Irish and the Hollanders for the King. Several of the episodes of this *fabliau* are adopted later in Rabelais' *Gargantua*, and it is this book that is so warmly commended in the Prologue to the *Pantagruel*, whether it was written by Rabelais or not.

LES GRANDES CRONICQUES

The authorship of *Les grandes et inestimables Cronicques du grant et enorme geant Gargantua* has been much disputed. It has been maintained that Rabelais was the author, principally on the ground that the Prologue to *Pantagruel* is occupied almost entirely by a panegyric on its transcendent merits, and in promising *Pantagruel* as another book of the same kind, but still better credit. There is also the fact that in the *Gargantua* Rabelais employs several of the episodes recorded in this *fabliau*. This has led to the belief that the *Gargantua* was intended to be a much improved edition of the *Grandes Cronicques*. An objection has been raised that the style is almost puerile and too crude to allow the composition of it by the gifted author of the *Gargantua*. Against this it has been urged that the style as well as the matter of the *fabliau* has been imitated in this piece; also that the style of the *Gargantua* is very much superior to that of the *Pantagruel*, and that Rabelais progresses in power as he gains experience.

On the other side M. Lefranc urges that nowhere in this Prologue does Rabelais declare himself the author of the little book, notwithstanding his strong commendations of it; that the crudeness of it is too great to allow of its composition by the great Tourangeau. The publication of it was not entrusted to Nourry or Juste, who were the printers of the Lyons editions of *Pantagruel* and *Gargantua*. M. Seymour de Ricci, who gives a facsimile reprint from the unique copy in the Munich Library (*R.E.R.* viii. 57–92), inclines to ascribe it to the press of Jacques Moderne de Pinguente, who published a number of literary pieces in French in the years 1529–56. This was published in 1532, and there is a copy of the *Grandes Cronicques* containing some additions dated 1533, bound up with the *Pantagruel* of 1533 and the *Pantagrueline Prognostication* of the same date, in the Royal Library at Dresden.

A point of considerable interest is to be found in the possible origin of the name "Gargantua" in a way indicated by an episode in the *Grandes Cronicques* (c. 8). In this story Grand Gosier and Galemelle, the father and mother of Gargantua, are represented each carrying a rock out into the sea from St Malo and setting them down at a distance ($1\frac{1}{2}$ miles) from each other. One of these rocks is St Michel and the other Tombelaine. The latter actually contains Druidic remains, while the word has been explained as *tombe d'Helène* or *tumba Belenis*. It has occurred to me that the word may be derived from τύμβος λάϊνος, *i.e.* the rock that has been the tomb of many mariners.

In the *Legenda Aurea*, c. 145, and in the Breviary, *die viii Maii, In apparitione S. Michaëlis Archangeli*, is given the legend of an appearance of St Michael. Some herdsmen on Mons Garganus in Apulia (mentioned in Horace, *Odes*, ii. 9. 7), following a bull that had strayed, found him in the mouth of a cavern, and when one of them shot an arrow at him the arrow turned back and struck the bowman. In the *Legenda Aurea* the cavern is called *Tumba*, and some notion of a tomb seems to be involved. In consequence of this miracle and of an appearance of St Michael to Pope Gelasius in 493, the Bishop of Sipontum was commanded to build a sanctuary in honour of St Michael on Mons Garganus, afterwards called Monte St Angelo. Similarly about the year 710, in consequence of a vision of St Michael to Aubert, Bishop of Avranches, a sanctuary was built on the height called *Tumba* near the sea, about six miles from Avranches. St Michael's Church is built on a tremendous summit, and is only accessible at ebb tide. It was much visited by pilgrims, who are called "Michelets" or "Micquelots" in

Rabelais.[1] In the ninth and tenth centuries the relations between Mont St Michel and Monte Gargano were well maintained. Courageous pilgrims in their itinerary of Italy and the Gauls almost always included Rome, Monte Gargano, St Martin of Tours and Mont St Michel.

On Cape Malea (C. Matapan), the most southerly point of the Peloponnese, except Taenarum, was formerly placed a statue of Apollo, and subsequently a church was dedicated in honour of the specially Greek St Michael, whose aid was invoked by mariners in the dangerous strait between Cape Malea and the island Cythera (*Cerigo*).

The militant figure of St Michael, with his uplifted sword, trampling the dragon underfoot appealed strongly to the imagination of the chivalrous Normans, and this saint was adopted by them for their special cult from their first initiation to Christianity, to take the place of the ancient warrior gods whom they gave up on being converted and baptised. St Michael's Mount in Cornwall is another instance of a Norman church dedicated on a height to this saint.

Mont St Michel in Normandy was formerly called Mont Gargan, a name probably derived from Monte Gargano in Apulia, on which the former St Michael's Church had been built. The same appellation was bestowed on various mountain heights in Normandy and Brittany. From the sixth century it got the name of *Mont Tombe*; in the eighth it was called after St Michael, to whom were almost always dedicated churches on the summit of hills and by the sea coasts, so as to serve for beacons. Hence he obtained the title of St Michel *au peril de mer* and St Michel d'Aure (iv. 19) and perhaps St Adauras (*P.* 17). It seems therefore a tenable proposition that the beneficent French giant Gargantua, traces of whom may be found in all parts of France from Brittany to Provence, may have derived his name from Mons Garganus in Apulia.

Apart from *Les Grandes Cronicques* Rabelais published about this time (1532–3) a *Pantagrueline Prognostication* consisting of a prologue and six (afterwards ten) chapters. This was adapted freely from two similar ones in Latin in the Appendix to the *Facetiae* of Heinrich

---

[1] *G.C.; P.P.* 5; *G.* 38; v. 25.

Bebel and a Prognostication of Heinrichman of Sindelfingen. It is a burlesque on the numerous prognostications, which were eagerly read and perhaps believed in at this time. They were of the same kind as *Old Moore's Almanack* and *The Limping Messenger* (*Der hinkende Bote*), both of which are still current after more than a century's existence. In this we find Rabelais running riot in his copious vocabulary as he does later in the "litanies", lists of arms, viands, fish, serpents, etc.

Rabelais also brought out at this time an Almanack for 1533. We are fortunate in having the preface to this as well as that to his Almanack for 1535 still extant. They shew his real attitude towards the quack prophetic publications, and exhibit him in the light of a genuine believer in the gracious providence of an inscrutable and beneficent Creator. He denounces in the strongest terms the attempts to pry into the designs of the Deity and insists on patient submission to his decrees. This attitude may be exemplified from other parts of his writings.

M. Lefranc has shewn the probable dates of these early publications: (1) *Les Grandes Cronicques*, Aug. 3, 1532; (2) *Pantagruel*, Nov. 3, 1532; (3) *Pantagrueline Prognostication*, the Monday after Epiphany, 1533. He bases his calculations on the dates of the book fairs of Lyons, which had been fixed by Louis XII in July 1498 and confirmed by Francis I in February 1536 and April 1543.[1]

Other Almanacks were published for the years 1541, 1546, 1548, 1550; we have only the title-pages preserved, but they are useful in helping to determine the dates of Rabelais' presence at Lyons or Paris at certain periods.

Rabelais probably met Clément Marot, the French poet, in Paris in 1528–30, but it does not seem likely that Marot was resident at Lyons in 1532, except occasionally, for he preferred Paris, and his books were printed there till Dolet (who came to Lyons in 1534) printed the completed edition of his poems in 1538. The *Adolescence Clementine*, containing Marot's earlier poems, was published in 1529 and 1532; from this Rabelais borrowed phrases. Besides Marot's own poems, his editions of *Le Roman de la Rose* (Galiot du Pré, Paris 1527) and of Villon's poems (1532) were em-

---

[1] *R.E.R.* ix. 152.

ployed in the *Pantagruel* and *Gargantua*, as was also an edition by Blanchet of *La Farce de Maistre Pierre Pathelin restitué à son naturel* (Galiot du Pré, 1532). Rabelais also employed editions of Gringore, Coquillart and Le Maire de Belges.

PANTAGRUEL

It was towards the close of 1532 that Rabelais finished the *Pantagruel*, the first instalment of the romance that was to confer immortality on his name. The plan of the story is the same as that of the *Grandes Cronicques* and the chivalric romances, viz. the origin, birth, apparelling, youth, education of the giant prince, and later a tremendous battle between Pantagruel and Loupgarou with his three hundred giants; all imitated from and following the lines of the romances; interposed between these accounts are various events of Pantagruel's life at Orléans and Paris (cc. 6–23), whither he had proceeded after visiting other French Universities. This is a burlesque on Rabelais' own life, and it is in this that it differs from the *Grandes Cronicques* in being to a considerable extent autobiographical.

After the episode at Orléans of the Limousin scholar, who affected Latinised speech (c. 6), Pantagruel proceeds to Paris, where he stays till c. 23. He was then recalled by the news of the death of his father Gargantua and the invasion of his country Utopia by the Dipsodes. In the meantime the chapters relating to his stay in Paris are instructive as to the life of the students there and of the studies at the University. In the 7th chapter is given a list of books in the Library of St Victor, originally a burlesque on the goody-goody text-books on religious subjects interspersed with a few book-titles containing reflexions on some prominent members of the University and others. In the two latest editions authorised by Rabelais a list of books is inserted quite as long as the original catalogue, bearing in several instances on the quarrel of the Cologne doctors with the great hebraist Reuchlin, which is the special subject of the *Epistolae Obscurorum Virorum* (1517), as well as on some points of the Lutheran revolt.

The 8th chapter is very important, as giving a scheme of education in a letter from Gargantua to his son Pantagruel, reprobating the previous neglect of learning in the times of the Goths (*i.e.* the Schoolmen) and full of enthusiasm for the restoration of letters by the humanists of the Renaissance. This is followed by a list of studies to be recommended, Latin, Greek, Hebrew, Arabic, the *Trivium* and *Quadrivium*, Civil Law, Natural Science and the Greek, Latin and Arabic physicians, as well as the Old Testament in Hebrew and the New Testament in Greek. This is a list that might have been inspired by Budaeus himself, whom Rabelais closely followed in the ardour with which he prosecuted Greek and Latin reading. These studies are intended as a contrast to the books of instruction in the Library of St Victor.

The next chapter (the 9th) furnishes an episode full of importance for the rest of the romance—the introduction of Panurge to Pantagruel. As Panurge is almost the hero of the *Third, Fourth* and *Fifth Books*, it may be well here to give some account of his characteristics and Rabelais' manner of dealing with them. He is derived from the *Cingar* of Merlin Coccai, the pseudonym of Hieronimo (in the cloister Teofilo) Folengo (1492–1544), who was at one time a Dominican, but who unfrocked himself and led a roving life. If not the originator, he was one of the earliest writers of macaronic verse, that is, a mixture of Latin hexameters and burlesque Italian. His poem *Baldus* is written in twenty-five books, the three last of which are a fantastic description of the lower world. This poem is employed considerably in the account of the tricks of Panurge in *P.* 14–17 and iv. 5–8, 18–24, and the author is mentioned three times (*P.* 1, 7 and iii. 11). Panurge's prototype Cingar is himself formed to some extent on the Margutte of Pulci's *Morgante Maggiore* (Venice 1488), as Folengo points out. There is a portrait of the author in the Uffizi Gallery at Florence.

But it is not only Cingar (or Panurge) who is borrowed from Merlin Coccai, for a representative of Pantagruel may be found in Baldus, the hero of the poem. But though Pantagruel takes the place of Baldus, his actual home and attributes (especially that of causing thirst) are derived from the *Mystère des Actes des Apostres* of Simon Greban, in which *Pantagruel* is a small devil who represents water, or rather sea-water, as distinguished from the others who represent air, fire and earth (*R.E.R.* x. 482).

Again Carpalim, the swift runner (perhaps a Basque lackey of

Rabelais' acquaintance who furnished him with the Basque speech in this chapter), is derived from Falchettus, and Eusthenes, the strong man, from Fracassus in Folengo's poem; he is also put down in *P.* 1 as one of the giant progenitors of Pantagruel. Thus, four of the five standing characters in the *Pantagruel* represent to a great extent persons in the *Baldus* of Folengo.

The fifth, a most important personage, Epistemon, the tutor of Pantagruel, was most likely a fellow-student with Rabelais at Montpellier, as was also Ponocrates, the tutor of Gargantua (cf. iii. 34). The two are differentiated in Rabelais, in that the first is described as weakly, and Ponocrates as sturdy and able. Some day perhaps they may be identified on the Montpellier registers. Epistemon is also represented as present at the death of Guillaume du Bellay (iv. 27). Thus we may see how Rabelais combines his reading and his personal experiences in the composition of his story. A curious slip is made in the last edition (D). In c. 9 Eudemon is introduced as making a comment on Panurge's Basque speech. Eudemon is the accomplished page introduced in c. 15 of the *Gargantua* by Don Philippe des Marays (who proves to be Don Felipe of Castile, father of Charles V), and thus Eudemon may be intended as the youthful Emperor, to whom was dedicated Erasmus' treatise *Institutio Principis Christiani* in 1516. At all events he ought not to appear in the *Pantagruel*, as being a Gargantuine character.

Cingar (akin to the Italian *Zingari* and the German *Zigeuner*), the wanderer or vagabond, is adapted from Folengo's crude robber of hen-roosts and player of heartless pranks—of which a number are instanced in the early part of *Pantagruel*—and is skilfully developed into a courtier with the self-same moral proclivities, kept in due restraint by his new surroundings. His Greek name Panurge is taken from a speech of Cicero (*Panurgus Roscii servus*) through Budaeus (*de Asse*, lib. ii. p. 239), and the word in its full, unamiable meaning is richly deserved. Thus we find that the Grecised names attached to the several personages sufficiently indicate their character.

The construction of the chapter in its component parts deserves consideration. At the beginning Pantagruel sees through the woe-begone appearance of Panurge traces of a man of mark and ability. This is from the seventh book of the *Odyssey*, as given in Erasmus,

Ad. iii. 10. 51. Pasquier (*Recherches de la France*, viii. 59) is probably right in attributing the polyglot speeches of Panurge to the suggestion from the speeches in different *patois* uttered by Patelin of the Farce in his pretended delirium, while the general plan and bearing of the chapter are modelled on the visit of Ulysses to the Phaeacians in *Od.* vii. 203 *sqq.*, and the actual speech of Panurge at the end is that of Ulysses, *Od.* vii. 267 *sqq.*

The claim of Panurge to be one of the thirty-two French prisoners who were taken by the Turks at the siege of Mytilene in 1502 is very fantastic, but is used as the substructure of the 14th chapter, where Panurge records a fanciful account of his escape.

Panurge, Carpalim and Eusthenes all make their first appearance in c. 9, Epistemon in c. 5. This name is perhaps derived from the *Panepistemon* of Politian, the great Florentine scholar.

The 10th chapter is devoted to an account of a controversy between two great lords, which was too obscure for the Paris lawyers to unravel. They appeal for help to Pantagruel, who had made a great name for himself by public disputations; this enables him to denounce the study and practice of law then existing, viz. a blind deference to the glosses of practitioners that had grown round the *Corpus Juris*; these were followed more scrupulously than the text itself. In reality this is the attitude of Budaeus in his Annotations on the first twenty-four and the last four books (47–50) of Justinian's *Pandects*, while Budaeus is to some extent indebted to the work of Lorenzo Valla and Poliziano, who had made a study of the original *litera Pisana*, the copy of the Pandects now in the Medicean Library. But at the same time Rabelais pleads for a broader study of law on a philosophical basis of jurisprudence, and inveighs against the narrowing practice of case-law in the spirit of Plato (*Theaet.* 172 D–173 B) and of Bishop Thirlwall, when explaining why he gave up forensic for ecclesiastical studies (*Letters*, p. 63), and of Sir H. Maine in advocating the study of Roman Law in *Cambridge Essays*, 1856.

The 11th, 12th and 13th chapters give the unintelligible pleadings of the plaintiff and defendant and the equally unintelligible judgment of Pantagruel. Two or three historical allusions scattered up and down may be intended to mislead, but hardly to enlighten the reader.

The 14th chapter describes Panurge's escape from the Turks in a very burlesque fashion, the 15th an absurd and undesirable theory for building the walls of Paris, the 16th and 17th all kinds of mischievous student tricks of which he was guilty; they are derived for the most part from Merlin Coccai. The 18th, 19th and 20th chapters introduce us to Sir Thomas More, under the name of Thaumast, arguing with Panurge (who takes Pantagruel's place) *by signs*, without speaking. In this book Rabelais is indebted to More's *Utopia*, of which an early edition had been published in Paris by Gilles de Gourmont, 1517–18. Utopia is placed near Cathay in Upper India or China, and twice it is made the goal of a Pantagrueline voyage; the first time in this book, by following the route of the Portuguese round the Cape of Good Hope to India by Ceylon, and secondly in the *Fourth Book* by the North-West passage above Canada, which was not achieved till 1850–4 by M'Clure.

It is interesting to note that Pantagruel (*i.e.* Rabelais) lodged at the Hôtel St Denis (*P.* 18) and Thaumast at the Hôtel de Cluny. (In *G.* 39 Brother John declares that he kept open house in Paris more than six months, which seems to point in the same direction.) At the same time the Hôtel de Cluny was the residence of distinguished Englishmen who might be staying in Paris, while the contiguous *Palais des Thermes* was occupied by taverns frequented by students, especially by *les maistres de la nation d'Angleterre*.

The significance of signs and symbols seems greatly to have taken Rabelais' fancy. He recurs to it in iii. 19, where he praises the counsel of the dumb, and in iv. 37, where he instances the omens and significance of names, a science which he calls Onomatomancy (iii. 25). In the 20th chapter and in iii. 19, where the dumb Goatsnose gives his advice by gesticulation, the intention may have been to ridicule the minute directions given by Quintilian (xi. 3. 92 *sqq.*) to the orator concerning the use of fingers and arms in rhetorical argument; but from this Rabelais proceeds to argue as to the imposition of names, whether it is by nature or arbitrarily. He probably derives his ideas from Plato's *Cratylus*, to which he refers in iv. 37, but he may also have had in view the question of the imposition of names by Adam in Genesis ii. 19, which was much debated by the Schoolmen and is referred to by Cornelius Agrippa, *de occulta philosophia*, i. 70. Hippocrates also, *de arte medendi*, § 2, puts it that forms are natural but that words are made by custom.

Again, this dispute is intended as a caricature of keeping an act in the Paris University. "The process", says Mr Tilley, "is hardly more absurd, the result not a whit more barren, than many of the disputations which took place in the Paris schools" (*François Rabelais*, p. 108). In reference to a disputation he had at Oxford in 1554 Bishop Ridley said: "That when he studied at Paris he remembered what clamours were used in the Sorbon, where Popery chiefly reigned: but that was quite a modesty in comparison with this present thrasonical ostentation. Whence he concluded very truly that they sought not for the sincere truth in the conference, and for nothing but vain glory" (Strype's *Memorials of Cranmer*, iii. 115).

After a disgraceful adventure of Panurge (cc. 21, 22) Pantagruel gets news of his father's translation by the fairies (*i.e.* his death) and learns that the Dipsodes have invaded his territory of Utopia. He at once starts for Rouen and from there to Honfleur, whence he and his four companions set sail. And now we have an indication of the interest Rabelais found in geography. In the preliminary chapter (23) we find an allusion to Canaria, which had been discovered for France and partly annexed by Jean de Béthencourt. It is mentioned also in *G.* 13, 31, 50; *P.* 11, 24, though in one or two instances with the purpose of disguising some other place. But Rabelais had also read about the Canary Islands in Pliny (6. 203) and was concerned about geography historically as well as patriotically. It was his wont to keep before him two or even three points of view, and he delighted in finding modern parallels with classical incidents.

But now he conducts his hero to Utopia from Honfleur, following the route of the Portuguese round the Cape. In his itinerary he simply copies a passage from the preface of Simon Grynaeus to a book of travels of various explorers collected by Jo. Hervagius (Basel 1532). There was also a map or cosmography by Seb. Münster made for his edition of Ptolemy in 1545. The list of explorers in this volume coincides to a great extent with one given in v. 31 (MS.), thus affording a slight confirmation of the belief in the authenticity of the *Fifth Book*.

After rounding the Cape they come to Melinda, which had been reached by Vasco da Gama in 1498. He passed over from there to Calicut in India, whereas Pantagruel passes by Meden, Uti, Uden, Gelasim, the Isles of the Fairies and the Kingdom of Achoria, to Utopia. It is a question whether these are merely fanciful names derived from the Greek μηδέν, οὐδέν, etc., or whether, as M. Lefranc suggests, Meden and Uden are intended for Medina and Aden, while Gelasim stands for Ceylon. Shortly after they had arrived in the harbour of Utopia they were approached by 660 knights in hostile fashion, but these were all discomfited and burnt up by a scheme of the ever-ready Panurge. The travellers set up a burlesque trophy; when the one prisoner whom they had taken alive informs them that Anarchus, King of the Dipsodes, accompanied by Loup-garou and 300 giants and an immense army, is coming to attack them. Pantagruel sends the knight to his master to inform him that he has a tremendous force at sea and also to take him a box full of condiments to make him drink. The ruse was successful and the King and his whole camp drank so furiously that they were soon all fast asleep. Carpalim (*the Swift one*), one of Pantagruel's attendants, stole into their camp by night and fired it; in the end the enemy were all slain. The next chapter (29) is devoted to a combat between Pantagruel and the giant Loupgarou in the style of the chivalric romances. The prayer of the weaker combatant, his dexterity in avoiding the crushing blows of his huge adversary and his ultimate victory are successfully imitated and told with great spirit. The next chapter (30) is perhaps the most important of all; it narrates the resuscitation of Epistemon, whose head had been struck off in the struggle, his return to life and the account he gives of the other world. The original of this is of course the νέκυια, the 11th book of the *Odyssey*, but there is also an imitation of the similar case of Er the Armenian in the 10th book of Plato's *Republic*, who comes to life after twelve days. In the account of the inversion of lives in the other world where kings are beggars and the rich are poor, Rabelais employs Lucian's *Menippus* with good effect. But I think he also has in mind an incident which happened in Paris in September 1528 soon after his arrival. It is recorded in the *Journal d'un Bourgeois de Paris*. A young man had been hanged at the Place Maubert and after half an hour was taken away, but as he shewed some signs of life he was set down before a statue of the Blessed Virgin Mary in the Carmelite Church and subsequently placed in a room before a fire, bled and physicked. Afterwards his throat and neck were rubbed and anointed with oil, and he remained without speaking or drinking till the next day; at last he drank and ate a little, and ultimately recovered and remembered everything. A similar story is also to be found in the *Morte d'Arthur*, vii. 22. The names of persons whom Epistemon saw in the other world are derived from Herodotus, Plutarch, the chivalric romances and Homer. There are also half a dozen popes. The usurers, against whom Rabelais shews special rancour, are assigned a pitiful life. Anarchus, King of the Dipsodes, is given over by Pantagruel to Panurge, who makes him a crier of green sauce. The 32nd chapter is derived mostly from Lucian's *Vera Historia* and describes how Rabelais himself entered into Pantagruel's mouth and saw wonderful sights. In the next chapter Pantagruel is ill and cured by sixteen enormous pills containing pioneers, who emerge from their pills, clear away obstructions and restore him to health. The last chapter ends with a violent tirade against the Mendicants, and also the promise of a voyage of Pantagruel, which is carried out in the *Fourth* and *Fifth Books*.

The sources of the *Pantagruel*, heterogeneous as they are, have a great bearing and throw much light on the author's methods. He says very justly (*G.* 45) that the good workman puts all pieces of timber to use. To a certain extent his books are a record of his reading, and, as with Lucilius in Horace (*Sat.* ii. 1. 30), his faithful books reflect his life and occupation at the time. In the composition of the 1st chapter of *Pantagruel* the genealogy is founded first on that in St Matthew and St Luke and also on the *Généalogies des Roys de France*, composed by his friend Jean Bouchet (Pictavii, 1531). These contained the list of fifty-seven kings from Pharamond to Louis XII. Rabelais gives fifty-nine giants, making the two last to be Gargantua and Pantagruel, thus for a long time inducing the belief that these two represented Francis I and Henry II throughout, and causing numberless "keys" to all the characters to be prepared and advocated by their authors. The list of giants is formed first by some distorted biblical Hebrew names, perhaps changed from the names of some of the early French kings. These are followed by a string of names from classical sources; they prove to have been taken bodily from a strange book, the *Officina* of Ravisius Textor, a sort of dictionary of Antiquities, containing lists of gods, heroes, giants, dwarfs, serpents, etc., etc., followed by explanations as to who and what they were. After this come a number of giants from various chivalric romances and other names, perhaps fanciful and invented by Rabelais himself. Grandgousier occupies the place which would be that of Louis XII in Bouchet's list, and Gargantua and Pantagruel close the list of fifty-nine.

The list in the 30th chapter contains also a number of names from chivalry, and it may be useful here to append a list of such books and the places where Rabelais inserts them, as an indication of his reading at this time:

Pantagruel, c. 1:

Fierabras	Lyon, B. Chaussard, 1496.
Ferragus	in Turpini, *Chronicon*, c. 17.
Galehaut	in Lancelot du Lac.
Galaffre	in Huon de Bordeaux, c. 9.
Robsastre	in Guerin de Montglaive.
Sortibrant	killed by Regnier in Fierabras, c. 39.
Bruyer	in Ogier le Dannois, c. 16.
Mabrian	in Les IV filz Aymon.

Pantagruel, c. 30:

Lancelot du Lac	Paris, Phil. le Noir, 1533.
Charlemagne et les douze pairs de France	Lyon, B. Chaussard, 1561.
Valentin et Orson	Lyon, J. Arnouillet, 1495.
Giglain and Gawaine	Ariosto, *Or. Fur.* xix. 38.
Geoffroi à la grant dent	Lyon, O. Arnouillet, 1525.
Godefroi de Bouillon	Paris, Jean Petit, 1504.
Morgante Maggiore	Venetiis, 1488.
Huon de Bordeaux	Lyon, O. Arnouillet, 1516?
Jean de Paris	? Lyon, Pierre Sale.
Artus de Bretaigne	Lyon, 1496.
Perceforest	Pari, Galiot du Pré, 1528.
Ogier le Dannois	Lyon, Cl. Nourry, 1525.
Galien réthoré	Lyon, Cl. Nourry, 1525.
IV filz Haymon	Lyon, J. de Vingle, 1495.
Melusine	Lyon, Mathieu Husz, n.d.
Matabrune	in Godefroi de Bouillon.

After the publication of the *Pantagruel* at the end of 1532,

Rabelais continued his practice at the hospital and his labours as corrector of the press for Gryphius. It appears pretty certain that besides making alterations in the *Pantagruel*, which appeared again under his direction in 1535, 1537 and 1542, he was writing his *Gargantua* in 1533, though the date of the first edition is somewhat uncertain. The first edition (A), of which only one copy survives in the Bibliothèque Nationale, was published before 1535, but unfortunately the first leaf containing the title-page is lost and it can only be put down as of the date 1534 by conjecture. Rabelais accompanied Bishop du Bellay to Rome January–March 1534; thus it is possible that he had finished his *Gargantua* and that he published it that year. Juste published a second edition (B) in 1535 and another (C) in 1537, while he published the definitive edition both of *Gargantua* and *Pantagruel* (D) in 1542.

M. Lefranc has shewn it to be very probable (*R.E.R.* ix. 151) that Rabelais was inspired to compose his *Gargantua* by a visit to his native Touraine in September 1532 (cf. *P.* prol.) and by the law-suit between his father and Gaucher de Sainte Marthe, and that he finished it in 1533, but that it did not appear till October (or possibly August) 1534, before the affair of "the Placards", when heretical Protestant placards were introduced into the Palace and even into the King's private apartments. This led to furious reprisals and persecutions, and would have made the publication of such a book extremely dangerous.

M. Bourrilly also has pointed out in the Introduction to his edition of the *Letters of Rabelais from Rome* (p. 8) that the amusing episode of the kitchen-loving monk in Florence (iv. 11) must have taken place on the return of Bishop du Bellay from his *first* mission to Rome (January–March 1534), when he and his suite were travelling in a leisurely fashion. This has hitherto been accepted as occurring during their *second* journey *to* Rome in August 1535 or on their return in 1536. The reason for this belief is that Rabelais in the first edition of the *Fourth Book* (A, 1548) says that the episode took place "about twelve years ago" and in the second edition (B, 1552) "about twenty years ago"—neither of the dates being quite exact. Du Bellay left Rome on April 1, 1534 and did not reach Paris till May 18, thus allowing plenty of time for a stay in Florence, whereas in 1535 every step of their journey *to* Rome is accounted for; they came by Ferrara straight through the Romagna, while Florence, then under the domination of Duke Alexander de' Medici, the destined son-in-law of Charles V, was hardly a place to receive the French envoy. In his hurried return, when the Emperor was expected in Rome, the Cardinal left on Feb. 29, 1536, and his retinue on April 11, when the Pope signed a safe-conduct for them. The Emperor was daily expected in Rome, and after his violent speech in the Consistory his attack on Provence was looked for. It actually was begun in July.

GARGANTUA

The *Gargantua* is on the same lines as the *Pantagruel*, but longer and more elaborate in its details. There is the birth, childhood and apparelling of the giant prince, his education under the old and the new systems, his journey to Paris on the great mare and the episode of the bells of Notre Dame. Several points of the feeding and apparelling, the great mare that carried him to Paris and the removal of the bells are derived from the *Grandes Cronicques*. Instead of the account of the law-courts and keeping acts at the University we have the elaboration of the educational system. But while Gargantua is busy studying at Paris a war has broken out between the cake-bakers of Lerné and the shepherds of Grandgousier, Gargantua's father, and he is recalled to conduct his father's army. (This has been shewn in *R.E.R.* iii. 241–52 to be an allegorical account of the law-suit between Rabelais' father and Gaucher de Sainte Marthe, on the rights of navigation and fishing on the river Vienne.) An elaborate account of the war and its episodes occupies cc. 24–51, while the remainder of the book is devoted to the foundation, endowment and regulation of the Abbey of Thelema.

The Prologue is specially important as putting forward the claim of the author to an inner meaning intended by his drolleries, more than is apparent in a cursory perusal; he therefore requests his readers to examine his writings carefully, like the philosophical dog which breaks a bone to get the marrow, and he declares that thus will be revealed "high Mysteries as much in that which concerns our Religion as also the public Polity and private Life". This declaration is very similar to one made by Galen (*de usu partium*, vii. 14), where he claims the discovery of many points of anatomy, and begs attention to his exposition not less than is given by persons on initiation to the Eleusinian or Samothracian mysteries.

At the very outset Rabelais takes three whole paragraphs from the *Adagia* of Erasmus, thus inaugurating a system of compiling his book from various sources. It is possible that he intended the early chapters of his *Third Book* to some extent as an apology for this style of writing. Certainly Erasmus is laid under contribution much more in the *Gargantua* than in the *Pantagruel*.

The extracts—often lines or merely tags—which Rabelais borrows from various authors, especially the French poets of that time, are often deftly interwoven in the narrative and descriptive passages, so as almost to defy detection. But in this we should remember that he is only following the example of the humanist writers Budaeus and Erasmus, who were so steeped in the writings of Cicero, Virgil, Terence and other classical authors that their letters and essays are almost made up of phrases and expressions adapted from the older writers to suit the matter which they were expressing. This was carried to excess by the *Ciceroniani*. Rabelais, as he was entitled to do, goes beyond this and adapts short sentences and passages not only from the classical authors, but from the humanists themselves, as well as from the French poets Gringore, Le Maire, Cretin, Coquillart, Clément Marot, Saint Gelais, *La Farce de Patelin*, Villon, and from the broad-sheets and fugitive pieces that were hawked about by pedlars. If in addition to these we examine attentively the *Journal d'un Bourgeois de Paris*, 1513–36, comprising the greater part of the reign of Francis I, we are enabled to form a tolerable idea of the world in which Rabelais lived.

It appears to have been especially delightful to him to take a book of a contemporary and play with it, as it were, for a chapter, or sometimes for two or three chapters, constructing an episode out of a single book: thus, Geoffroy Tory's book serves for the display of the vagaries of the Limousin scholar in the *Pantagruel*. Cornelius Agrippa's *de occulta philosophia*, aided by Pliny and other sources, furnishes the bulk of the chapter on Her Trippa (iii. 25) and the principal contributions on divination proper. In Pantagruel's journey by the North-West Passage the *Odyssey* and Lucian's *Vera Historia* are never lost sight of, while the fantastic voyage is used to satirise various points in European and papal history and surroundings. These examples are taken almost at random, but it may be seen at once that this is one of Rabelais' favourite methods.

In the *Gargantua*, especially to be noticed is the change of place from that of the *Pantagruel*. In the latter the scene is laid in Poitiers, which is made the headquarters of Pantagruel's excursion to the country round about, and from which he starts for his visits to the Universities of France, finally settling in Paris to prosecute his medical studies. There we have an account of his student life till he starts on his interesting geographical tour round the Cape of Good Hope to Utopia, or Cathay. Then come the warlike adventures following the lines of the chivalric romances; and the promise of further adventurous voyages, to be ultimately realised in the *Fourth* and *Fifth Books*.

In *Gargantua* the venue is changed. The action of the piece is laid in Touraine, or rather Chinonais, with La Devinière (the birthplace of Rabelais) as the centre. The whole countryside is made the scene of the tremendous campaign carried on in this book between Gargantua and Picrochole. This episode, and indeed the whole construction of Rabelais' romance, has been made of greatly increased interest by the recent investigations of MM. Lefranc and Clouzot in the *R.E.R.* vol. iii. These scholars have turned into historical certainty the assertions of MM. Sainte Marthe in the seventeenth century, viz. that Gargantua represents Rabelais' own father and that Picrochole is intended for Gaucher, or Scévole, Sainte Marthe, their great-grandfather, a physician to the Abbess of Fontevrault. MM. Sainte Marthe had published (in Paris in 1651) an edition of three letters which Rabelais had sent from Rome to the Bishop of Maillezais in 1535–6: a second edition appeared in Brussels in 1710. In the *Menagiana* (vol. ii. p. 226) Ménage (1613–92) asserts that the great-uncle of these gentlemen, Jacques Sainte Marthe, was the original of Picrochole. A note insists that it could not have been Jacques, who was essentially a man of peace, but that it was probably his father Gaucher, who was choleric and a physician. Picrochole gets the addition *tiers de ce nom* because he succeeded his father and grandfather as physician to the Abbess of Fontevrault.

Moreover, there survive in the Collection Dupuy in the Bibliothèque Nationale at Paris some curious notes on the subject of Rabelais' characters in the *Gargantua*, which have considerable bearing on this subject. They are by a certain Sieur de Bouchereau, who was certainly of Touraine and possibly a magistrate of Loudun or Chinon. These notes have been transcribed carefully by M. H. Clouzot and are given in *R.E.R.* iii. 405 *sqq*. They confirm to a great extent the assertion of MM. Sainte Marthe, and add identifications of several of the characters in *Gargantua* with persons living in the neighbourhood of Chinon. According to Bouchereau there was a law-suit between Picrochole, or Gaucher Sainte Marthe, and the monks of Seuilly, and Frère Jean des Entommeures was their *procureur*. This in Rabelais' hands becomes the defence of the Abbey close. Marquet (c. 25) was father-in-law of Sainte Marthe, and Gallet an inhabitant of Lerné. Other identifications less important and less exact are given. These notes are set forth by Marty-Laveaux in his edition of Rabelais (1881), vol. iv. p. 22, but he records them tentatively and does not insist strongly on the correspondences. The investigations of MM. Clouzot and Lefranc however have brought such strong confirmation that the explanation may be looked upon as certain. The former "keys" of Rabelais, although full of discrepancies, had gained so strong a hold that they could be displaced only by the proof afforded by the patient and careful examination of local archives and registers.

Such proof has been furnished by the researches of these scholars, and we now know that Rabelais' work is throughout autobiographical: while the account of military preparations and achievements which shew our author in the light of a well-read military tactician are based on learning derived from old writers, such as Herodotus and others, as well as observation of more recent campaigns. This feature is well brought out in a paper by M. Gigon in *R.E.R.* v. 3–23 ("L'art militaire dans Rabelais"). But it is made more interesting by the review of the whole subject in the light of recent investigations. We learn from the diligent enquiries of MM. Lefranc and Clouzot that the father of our satirist, Antoine Rabelais, *licencié ès lois, avocat au siège de Chinon*, was seigneur of Chavigny-en-Vallée and thus lord of a whole number of lands and rights (especially fishing rights) on the right bank of the Loire to within ten kilometres of Saumur, and also within the same distance of Le Chapeau, which was on the same bank, separated from Chavigny only by the village Villebernier. Thus the Rabelais estate was contiguous with that of Gaucher Sainte Marthe, lord of Le Chapeau, just as their estate of La Devinière adjoined that of Sainte Marthe at Lerné. Antoine Rabelais possessed fishing rights on the Loire contiguous with those of Sainte Marthe, and they were damaged by the unlawful encroachments of the physician of Fontevrault. He had constructed a mill and made enclosures by piles and dams and otherwise, to the prejudice of the riparian owners higher up the Loire and the Vienne, which rivers are united at Candè about nine miles above Saumur. This came before the *Parlement* in 1529 and there were constantly orders in council made on the subject. There was a respite till Sept. 7, 1532, when matters were more vigorously prosecuted and various influences were brought to bear, till ultimately at the end of 1536 Sainte Marthe had to give way to superior right.

Moreover, the agent who conducted these negotiations was Jehan Gallet of Chinon, *avocat du roi*, a near relation of Antoine Rabelais; in the *Gargantua* Ulrich Gallet is *maistre des requestes* of Grandgousier, "a wise and discreet man, whose worth and good counsel he had proved in difficult and contentious affairs", and he is the envoy to Picrochole.

Antoine Rabelais in 1506 had become possessor through his mother, Andrée Pavin, of the "chastel et noble maison" of Chavigny, in the parish of Varennes [sur Loire], with all its appurtenances, meadows, woods, waters and *fisheries*, etc. Thus we see how he became the champion of the rights of the smaller riparian owners, and we learn in *G.* 47 how a great number of adjacent places, on account of their "ancient confederation", offered him help in every way possible in men, money and other munitions of war. In examining the names of the thirty-one places named here it is found that nine are on or near the Loire and the others on or near the Vienne; thus their interests were endangered by the unlawful usurpations of Sainte Marthe.

The allegorical representations of these acrimonious disputes under the guise of a war stirred up by the cake-bakers of Lerné (Picrochole's men) and the shepherds of Grandgousier is very entertaining. The first apparent object of this is to shew the frivolous causes which may be the origin of cruel and devastating wars, and the foolish ambitions that may promote them. Rabelais draws on his reading in Greek, Latin and later writers to illustrate this, and evidently wishes to enforce the moral insisted on by Erasmus that a prince should never enter upon war until it is absolutely necessary, but when once he has been forced to take it up he should prosecute it with all his vigour and thus bring it to a close as quickly as possible. Unless it had been made clear by documentary evidence, it would hardly be believed that it is a prolonged law-suit that is the basis of this campaign, narrated with circumstantial minuteness and enlivened by anecdotes of several actions in the field.

It has been pointed out, however, by M. Lefranc that in September 1532 Rabelais had come from Lyons to visit his "cow-country", *i.e.* his native place, "to see if any of his kindred were still living", that he had his *Pantagruel* nearly completed, and that the finishing touches and the Prologue were written then. While he was in Chinonais (Sept.–Oct. 1532) the law-suit between his father and Sainte Marthe was proceeding vigorously and the strife culminated in a brawl between certain cake-bakers of the village of Lerné, where was some of Sainte Marthe's property, and the peasants of Seuilly, where lay the contiguous property of Antoine Rabelais. This was the inspiration which impelled him to compose the *Gargantua*. The *Pantagruel* was published on his return to Lyons at the time of the next book-fair, Nov. 3, 1532, and his hospital practice, his journey to Rome in 1534, and the publication of Marliani's *Topographia Romae* occupied his time, so that his *Gargantua* was not ready for publication till the middle of 1534. It must have been published either just before the affair of "the Placards", or if afterwards, only then because it could not be withdrawn.

Another important point in this book which has come into prominence within the last twenty years is the influence in the *Gargantua* and in the *Fifth Book*—and almost only in these two books —of that strange compilation the *Hypnerotomachia Poliphili*, or "the Strife of Love in a Dream". It is the work of a Dominican, Francesco Colonna, who was widely read and a skilful architect, like many of his Order, among them the celebrated Fra Giocondo. The book was composed about 1460 and published by Aldus Manutius in 1499, and again by the same house in 1546. It has become known among bibliophiles mostly on account of some illustrations in line-engraving, which have been attributed by connoisseurs to various distinguished artists. The text is an extravagant jumble in thirty-eight chapters, the first letters of which many years afterwards revealed the name of the writers in the sentence: *Poliam Frater Franciscus Columna peramavit.* The hero Poliphilus is taken through many strange scenes, a wood infested by savage beasts, through the stomach of a giant in which all the organs, etc. are labelled, a desert in which are pyramids and obelisks, the palaces of two queens, with every kind of detail discussed, a fountain and a temple, etc. The architect's fancy runs riot in all these details and a most fantastically tedious book is the result. It is written in Lombardese Italian plentifully interspersed with words formed from Latin and Greek.

Rabelais seems to have had a fancy for weird books. In the *Pantagruel* he had pressed into his service *Baldus*, the macaronic poem of Folengo—as strange a medley as ever was penned—and in the *Gargantua* we find the *Hypnerotomachia* supplying the basis of a good deal in the construction of his anti-monastery of Thelema, besides isolated passages in other chapters; attention should be paid particularly to the strange feats of Gymnast in the 35th chapter, which surely owe much to a passage in the Living Chess game which is described in the *Fifth Book.* As I have not seen this correspondence pointed out, it may be well to put it down here in the original setting, so much abridged in the old English translation: "Per la quale cosa immediate se uide, una pugna, uno torniamento, tanto delectabile cum tanto praesto and subitanea uehementia cum inclinarse fina in terra, fasciendo poscia uno repente e torculario salto e quale Mymphurio tornatoris, cum due revolutione nel aere, una opposita ad laltra. E poi sencia mora posto il pede dextro ad terra tre fiate rotauase. E poi subito laltro pede al contrario intorniana, Tutta questa actione ad uno tempo consumauano, Tanto accomodamente and cum tanta agilitate che niente sopra, Cum le sue profunde inclinatione and composite uertigine and facile saltatione cum uenusti gesti quanto mai di tale e simigliante cosa se uedesse ne unque spectare potesse, ne mai tentata" (*Hyp.* c. 10. h. ii). The apparelling of the ladies of Thelema seems to owe something to this book, as well as the caskets

containing scents, and other small but curious matters. At the end
of the *Fifth Book* whole chapters are bodily transferred or pieced
together from various chapters of the *Hypnerotomachia*.

After the publication of the *Gargantua*, 1534–5, we read of a meeting of the governors of the hospital discussing Rabelais' super-
session, on the ground "that he had twice absented himself from
his duties without leave". The first case was probably to be attributed to his journey to Rome in January 1534 with du Bellay; the
second one is open to some doubt. In the discussion of the governors, one of them suggests that Rabelais is said to be at Grenoble,
and proposes that they should wait for his return; at a later
meeting he was actually superseded in favour of Pierre du Castel,
who was appointed at a salary of 30 *livres* annually instead of the
40 *livres* received by Rabelais. It seems probable that Rabelais
was in hiding on account of religious persecutions that were rife
and on account of his *Gargantua*. It has been plausibly suggested
that he was at this time under the protection of the Bishop of
Maillezais, before going to Rome in the company of Bishop du
Bellay. This suggestion is supported by the three letters which he
despatched to Bishop d'Estissac from Rome, and the record that
two other similar ones had been sent previously; these are now lost.
This points to an arrangement made with the Bishop before the
journey, which could hardly have been made otherwise than by
personal communication.

Jean du Bellay was in Paris July 3, 1535; at Lyons July 15, in-
valided for a few days; at Carmagnola on the 18th. He declined
an invitation of the Duke of Savoy for political reasons and hastened
on to Ferrara (July 22) to make peace between Duke Hercules and
his wife Renée de France, sister of Claude, the wife of Francis I (we
hear of this in one of Rabelais' letters), and at the very end of July
he was in Rome. He was admitted to a consistory on Aug. 2 in the
company of Charles Hemart de Denonville, Bishop of Mâcon. The
object of this mission was to gain over the new Pope, Paul III, to
the interests of France, and to detach him as far as possible from
Charles V, especially in view of the Emperor's approaching visit
to Rome. In order to harass Charles on the Hungarian side
Francis had been making overtures to Soliman, the Sultan, at
Constantinople and thus had laid himself open to the charge of

trafficking with the Infidels. This had been rendered worse by the activity of the corsair Barbarossa on the Italian coasts. Again (and this was the principal matter), the conduct of the King of England in throwing off the papal supremacy had to be palliated in some way. The negotiations were most delicate, and it cannot be doubted that du Bellay acquitted himself with great tact. Much of this is recorded in the confidential letters of Rabelais, but the influence of Charles, when he arrived (April 5) after the departure of du Bellay, proved too strong. The King of England was excommunicated and Charles prepared for his expedition into Provence.

At this time we learn from the third letter to d'Estissac that there was much talk of a Church Council. Paul III did not want it, but he was obliged to listen to suggestions. It was first convoked in Mantua in 1536 and again at Trent in 1542, but no resolutions were passed till 1547, and very little but adjournments took place till much later (1563).

Du Bellay left Rome Feb. 29, 1536, secretly, but with the connivance, if not by the advice, of the Pope. He left his suite to return later. A safe-conduct dated April 11 was granted by Paul, while the baggage was to go by sea. And here arises an interesting question, whether Rabelais did not accompany the baggage on a coasting voyage to Marseilles at this time and perhaps encounter a storm at sea, which enabled him to describe so graphically the celebrated storm of the *Fourth Book*. The reasons for this conjecture are that he mentions in iv. 25 Monte Argentario and Piombino as very subject to storms; the former bears an extraordinary likeness to the two-peaked rock described on the Isle of Ganabin (iv. 66). He also describes the grasping nature of the Genoese at the end of the Prologue to the *Fourth Book*. The large number of Italian nautical terms in the description of the storm in iv. 18 may thus be accounted for. Moreover, in v. 34 the wine of Taggia, in the Genoese territory close to San Remo, is mentioned, and also the orange trees of San Remo itself. These identifications form a cumulative presumption that Rabelais had seen these places, and it is not easy to find a period in his life so suitable as this to give him the opportunity.

The Cardinal's personal object had been gained—that of

receiving the red hat—but his diplomatic mission can hardly be characterised as successful. Rabelais had been quite successful in obtaining relief from his "apostasy" of quitting the clerical habit, and in gaining permission to practise medicine to the full extent that was allowed to an ecclesiastic, a permission couched in flattering terms.

On his return from Rome Cardinal du Bellay was at Lyons for some time, sending at once a full account of the Emperor's violent speech before the Pope (in Spanish) against the French King. Diplomacy and warlike preparations went on apace and on July 21, 1536, Jean du Bellay was appointed lieutenant-general in the Government of Paris and the Île de France.

After his return to Lyons Rabelais soon came to Paris to resume his duties with the Cardinal; at this time he probably gained some knowledge of fortifications, etc., which he utilised afterwards in the Prologue to his *Third Book*. On June 7 hostilities began, and in July 1536 Charles V carried out his threat and the Imperialist troops invaded Provence. The Constable, Anne de Montmorency, prudently retreated before them, devastating the country as he went. Probably the title of one of the books in the Library of St Victor, *P.* 7 (added in D, 1542), refers to this incident—*Entrée d'Anthoine de Leive ès terres du Brésil.* It is a parody of a romance-title such as *Entrée de Charlemagne en Espagne,* and refers to Brésil as "the burnt up land". A matter affecting Rabelais, begun in Rome in 1535–6, seems to belong to this time. There survives a petition of Rabelais to Paul III, asking for an indult to regularise his position as canon of the Abbey of St Maur des Fossés near Paris, of which Jean du Bellay, the Abbot, had appointed him as one of the canons. The irregularity lay in this, that the monastery had been secularised and the monks made canons of the Priory, but that Rabelais had been made a canon before the bull that secularised the monastery had been fulminated.

This petition was probably due to the appointment of Rabelais as a ninth canon in addition to the eight previously existing and the protest made by the canons in possession. No answer of the Pope is known to this "supplication", and, as Rabelais never gave himself the title of canon of St Maur, we may fairly conclude that this appointment was never confirmed. The date of the petition would therefore fall in 1536 rather than at any other time. Our author's residence at St Maur, of which he speaks in such eulogistic terms, especially as to its salubrity, should probably be fixed in 1544–5, but at the *château* of du Bellay, which had been built for him by Philibert de l'Orme, the first among contemporary architects to attach importance to the situation of his buildings in the matter of the salubrity of aspect, etc. Consequently, this *château* was placed on a hill of moderate elevation, and due regard was given to the laying of the foundations at a sufficient depth. It was probably at this "paradise of salubrity" that Rabelais wrote the greater part of his *Third Book*, which he had begun at St Ayl near Orléans after the funeral of Guillaume du Bellay at Le Mans in March 1543.

After the failure of the Emperor's attack Rabelais remained in Paris till about April 1537. His presence is attested by a Latin poem of Étienne Dolet (*Doleti carmina*, 1538), descriptive of a banquet given in the printer's honour by his literary friends, while he was seeking a remission of a penalty for an involuntary homicide. Rabelais is spoken of as present, together with the best of the French literary world, Budaeus, Danès, Toussain and others.

Franciscus R.

> Franciscus Rabelaesus, honos et gloria certa
> Artis Paeoniae, qui vel de limine Ditis
> Extinctos revocare potest et reddere luci.
> Hos inter multus sermo tum nascitur orae
> Externae quid docti habeant scriptoris; Erasmus,
> Melanchthon, Bembus, Sadoletus, Vida, Jacobus,
> Sannazarus plena laudantur voce vicissim.
>
> Dolet, *Carmina*, p. 59, ed. 1538.

He now proceeded to Montpellier, to obtain his licentiate and doctorate. In the transactions recorded in the *Registre des Matricules*, 1502–61, is an entry: *A Licentiandis; Magistro Francisco Rabelesio libr. 4 vij. den.* Although the fee was paid April 3, 1537, the licentiate was not conferred till somewhat later, and the Doctor's degree was taken on May 22 of the same year. A small question has been raised as to the fact that Rabelais in his *petitio pro apostasia* records that he has practised medicine and taken the degrees required for that purpose, while the Pope in his reply (dated Jan. 17,

1536) credits him with the degrees of Bachelor, Licentiate and Doctor. Again, in the second petition to the Pope touching his appointment to a canonry of St Maur des Fossés, Rabelais claims that he has taken the degree of Doctor. This document is of uncertain date and might perhaps be used to shew that Rabelais did not attempt to take up his position as canon of St Maur till at least the middle of 1537. It is made very probable, however, that the title of Doctor of Medicine was sometimes assumed by competent persons before the degree had been conferred, while no importance is attached to the assumption of M.D. by Rabelais in the preface to his Almanacks of 1533 and 1535 (cf. *R.E.R.* ii. 115; iv. 270).

It was about this time that he had a painful experience of being a suspect of the Roman Church. He was in Lyons at the end of May, after taking his degrees at Montpellier, and had sent a letter to some Reformer in Rome (probably Gaucher, brother of the great Reformer Guillaume Farel), and the letter had been intercepted by Cardinal Tournon, one of the strictest and most uncompromising maintainers of the Roman tenets. Rabelais was put under strict surveillance, from which he was not released till the arrival of Guillaume du Bellay coming from Court (Aug. 28)[1] (M. Bourrilly in *R.E.R.* iv. 105–14). This may well afford the substratum for the threadbare story of the *mauvais quart d'heure de Rabelais*.

Two years later he had a similar experience, which perhaps it will be better to mention here, especially as it is a somewhat obscure affair, and only recently cleared up by M. Bourrilly (*R.E.R.* iv. 115–26). Jean de Boysonné, a great friend of Rabelais (cf. iii. 29), wrote from Chambéry to Guillaume Bigot, a secretary of Jean du Bellay, a postscript to a letter dated Dec. 12, 1540 in the following terms: "Coteraeus rem omnem mihi in Aula narravit de Fossano et Rabelaeso, et de litteris e Roma in Aulam perlatis, et est quod uterque reprehendi possit: hic quod de tam magnis, non

---

[1] Cf. the following extracts from a letter of Cardinal Tournon to the Chancelier du Bourg: "...Il est passée par cette ville ung frère de Farellus le plus grand mutin et le plus mauvays paillard qu'il est possible, lutherien et zvynglien jusques aux dents, et est de Gap en Dauphiné...je vous envoye une lettre que Rabelezus escryvoyt à Rome, par ou vous verrez de quelles nouvelles il advertissoit ung des plus maulvays paillards qui soit à Rome. Je luy ay faict commandement que il n'eust à bouger de ceste ville jusques à ce que j'en sceusse vostre voulenté".

habito delectu ad quos scribat et de quibus scribat; ille quod amici litteras passim omnibus ostendat". M. Bourrilly shews clearly that Fossanus is intended for the Sieur de la Fosse, Barnabé de Voré, who was a relative of the du Bellay-Langey. He had been employed by Guillaume du Bellay on confidential political missions to Germany from 1532 to 1538, and from that time to 1540 he is lost to sight. From this it may be seen that he was a trusted envoy of the du Bellay, who were for treating the Reformers in Germany with moderation; on the other side the Chancellor Poyet and Cardinal de Tournon advocated most vigorous measures against them. Francis I, under the stress of both these influences, as usual vacillated. The influence of the du Bellay was waning. At this time Fossanus changed sides and went over to the Tournon party and helped them in a machiavellian plot. He proposed to join an embassy despatched by Francis and conducted by Guillaume de Fürstenburg to the German protestants, and to induce the French protestant refugees to return to France under promise of pardon, so that the Tournon party should get hold of them and persecute them. Cardinal du Bellay had been able to write to Bucer Oct. 28, warning them of their danger, but Rabelais, in ignorance of this *volte-face*, had written to Fossanus in full confidence on most important and intimate concerns. Fossanus had no scruples in shewing these revelations to his new allies, and he thus rendered Rabelais open to censure for incautious dealings with traitors.

To resume our biography from May 1537. The letter of the Cardinal de Tournon was dated Aug. 10, 1537, so that Rabelais must have gone to Lyons soon after his doctorate. He was probably engaged in correcting the press for Gryphius. Among other books an edition of Politian's writings in three volumes was published by Gryphius in 1537-9, so that Rabelais may have made near acquaintance at this time with the Italian writer, whom he alludes to in his *Gargantua* and from whom he undoubtedly borrowed in the *Third* and *Fourth Books*.

After this he returned to Montpellier to deliver his lectures for the *grand ordinaire*, which commenced on St Luke's day (Oct. 18). The *Liber Lectionum* contains the following entry, dated Sept. 27, 1537:

Anno Domini millesimo quingentesimo trigesimo septimo, facta fuit congregatio per fidem 27ª septembris, in qua comparuerunt.... Custodes clavium, D. Cancellarius, D. Johannes Falco, decanus, D. primus procurator, et D. junior doctor *Franciscus Rabelaesus*.
D. Franciscus Rabelaesus, pro suo ordinario, elegit librum Prognosticorum Hippocratis, quem graece interpretatus est (cf. *R.E.R.* iii. 309–10).

The parts of this notice which are in italics are thought to be in Rabelais' handwriting, and it seems most probable from the perfect tense *interpretatus est* used here, that he made the entry himself after he had given the lectures, so that he was not present at the meeting of Sept. 27, but was at Lyons during the stay of Francis I and his Court (Oct. 1–11), including probably the Seigneur de Langey. M. Bourrilly, to whom this suggestion is due (*R.E.R.* iv. 112–14), carefully guards us against taking it as more than a conjecture, but it certainly appears to be most probable. He goes on to point out how Rabelais resorted to Lyons almost every year from his first acquaintance with it in 1532. He was there in 1532, 1533, 1534, 1535, 1536, 1538, 1539, 1540 and 1541–2.

Thus we see that in 1537 at Montpellier during the *grand ordinaire* from Oct. 18 till Easter 1538 he occupied the chair corresponding to that of pathology. *Graece interpretatus est* must be taken to mean, not that he lectured in Greek, but that he expounded the text linguistically as well as physiologically.

A letter from Boysonné to Maurice Scève, dated 1537, speaks of him lecturing at Montpellier on the *Prognostic* of Hippocrates to a crowded audience.

Hubert Susanneau in one of his *Ludi*, dated 1537, highly commends the doctor, whom he finds busy with his lectures, for the great personal charm of his presence, enough of itself, he says, to banish sickness from a patient.

Étienne Dolet also, the impetuous humanist and printer, who had established himself at Lyons in 1534, speaks in a humorous poem published in 1538 of the great reputation as a physician and anatomist enjoyed by Rabelais. In an epitaph on a criminal who had been hanged and afterwards used as an object-lesson for anatomy, he congratulates the "subject" on having ended a worse than useless life in so serviceable a fashion as that of illustrating the prelection of the learned doctor.

Salmo Macrinus, one of the guests at the banquet in honour of Dolet, celebrates in two odes the medical skill and learning of his great compatriot in Chinonais, acknowledged, he declares, in Paris, Narbonne, on the banks of the Aude as well as at Lyons.

The following year (1538) his name is again to be found on the medical register as the recipient of a sun crown in gold for a lecture on anatomy, paid through Jean Schyron, the dean.

From the middle of 1538—except for a short visit to Aigues-Mortes (*fossa Marina*, v. 36), where he was present at the meeting of Charles V and Francis I, July 14–16 (*R.E.R.* iii. 335)—when he left Montpellier, till 1540 we have but little trace of the whereabouts of Rabelais. It is not improbable that he visited Narbonne, Castres and other towns in the South of France and, among other places, Hyères and its islands (*Stoechades insulae*, iii. 50), thus qualifying for the title "Calloier des isles Hières (ἱεραί)", which he gives himself on the title-page of the first edition of the *Third Book* (1546).

About the middle of 1540 Rabelais took service with Guillaume du Bellay, Seigneur de Langey, at Turin, where he received letters from Bishop Pellicier, ambassador of France at Venice, on literary matters. The letters are dated July 25, Oct. 17, 1540, and March 20, 1541. The first is on a question of the legitimacy of a child which was said to be a seven-months' child. He mentions Pliny (7. 5) and Hippocrates. This may well have been suggested by the 3rd chapter of *Gargantua*, in which the birth of the giant prince is discussed and in which these same references are given, with others in addition. The second letter requests Rabelais to use his influence and learning to obtain Hebrew and Syriac MSS. and Greek books for the King's library. The third letter (March 20, 1541) begs the good offices of Rabelais to ask the Seigneur de Langey to accept the dedication of an edition of some orations of Cicero by Paulus Manutius, the Venetian printer. He also speaks of some plants—*amomon* and *origanum heracleoticum* of Candia—which he had already mentioned. In July Langey lost his wife, who is duly deplored by Boysonné in some Latin elegiacs addressed to Rabelais.

In November 1541 Langey took Rabelais with him to Paris, whence they returned in May 1542. Benvenuto Cellini was at Fontainebleau in the employ of Francis I from 1540 to 1545, so that it is possible that these two geniuses may have foregathered.

The story of Friar John ripping up the old woman's feather-bed (v. 15) closely resembles one in Cellini's *Vita* (i. 79), which was not published till 1728; it may therefore have been told orally. The date of the occurrence is given in Cellini as 1535.

M. Heulhard quotes a poem of Claude Chappuis which seems to indicate that Rabelais was now made *maistre des requestes* to the King. If the chapter of the *Apedeftes* (v. 16) is authentic, this would be the time to obtain the information requisite for its composition; perhaps a slight argument for the authenticity of the chapter may be derived from this visit. The journey to and from Paris at this time also allowed an opportunity to publish a revised edition of *Gargantua* and *Pantagruel* (D), which appeared from the press of F. Juste in 1542. This is the authoritative edition from which all trustworthy reprints ultimately derive.

Before Langey left Turin the French ambassadors Rincon and Fregoso had been assassinated on the way to Venice, July 3, 1541, by order of the Spanish commander, Marquis del Vasto (cf. Martin du Bellay's memoirs, lib. ix). Their despatches, however, which Langey had induced them to leave behind, were saved. On his return to Turin (May 11) the Viceroy found increasing cause for vigilance. He had suffered much from gout, and now found himself terribly ailing. Notwithstanding this he set out for Paris in January 1543 to consult the King on state affairs. He was seized by a final access of his malady and obliged to halt at St Symphorien between Lyons and Roanne, where he died on Jan. 9th, not the 10th as Rabelais puts it. There are touching allusions to this in iii. 21 and iv. 27. Du Bellay left his *protégé* an annuity of 150 *livres Tournois* till he should have 300 *livres* from benefices, an engagement carried out probably by the Cardinal in appointing Rabelais *curé* of Meudon and St Christopher in Jambet in 1551.

THE THIRD BOOK

After the death of the Seigneur de Langey, Rabelais and Gabriel Taphenon of Savigliano embalmed the body, and the former accompanied Étienne Lorens in the funeral cortège to St Ayl on Jan. 30 and to Le Mans March 5, where the great statesman and patriot was laid to rest in the Cathedral. After this there is a blank in the account of our author's life, but one which may be filled with considerable probability. Most likely he paid a short visit to his native Touraine and then proceeded to take up his abode, for a time at least, in a retreat in the Orléanais found for him by Lorens, Seigneur of St Ayl, near his own *château*. There is a tradition still persistent, which speaks of the fountain of Rabelais and of an arbour where he worked; this is quite in harmony with what we know of his movements, so that it may be accepted, at all events provisionally.

Here then, "having lost his all by shipwreck at the Lighthouse of Misfortune", he set to work, as he says in the Prologue, "to roll his Diogenical Tub", that is, to continue his romance; and he seems to have remained in this quiet corner till after March 1544, for that is the most probable date of a jovial letter of his addressed to the bailiff Antoyne Hullot of Court Compin, north-west of Orléans, near Combleux. It is eminently characteristic of its author, being an invitation to a fish dinner in Lent, with a mocking allusion to that institution, and a request for the loan of a copy of Plato.

Probably some time in this year Rabelais was installed by Cardinal du Bellay in his *château* at St Maur des Fossés, near Paris. It had just been built for him by Philibert de l'Orme, the Lyons architect, who had achieved a distinguished position—that of chief architect to the King of France (*King Megistus*, iv. 61). This *château* had been built near the Abbey of St Maur for Jean du Bellay, who was Bishop of Paris, Abbot of this Convent, and Prior after it had been secularised. It occupied a rising ground to the south of the Abbey, and its praises are sung most enthusiastically by Rabelais in the Epistle of Dedication to the *Fourth Book*. It is described as a "Paradise of salubrity, amenity, serenity, conveniency, delights and all honest pleasures of agricultural life". The building was begun about 1541 and was dedicated in 1544. Francis I visited the *château* from July 7 to Aug. 4. Our author seems to have taken up his residence soon after, and while there to have finished his *Third Book*, for which he obtained the King's privilege dated Sept. 19, 1545.

Till recently it was believed that the *Third Book* was composed at *the Abbey* of St Maur, because of the *Supplicatio* to Paul III (without date) requesting that the position of Rabelais as one of the canons should be regularised. An informality had been committed in making him a canon of the Priory when it was secularised, whereas he had not been made a complete monk while it was still a monastery. M. Clouzot has shewn (*R.E.R.* vii. 259–84) that Rabelais was probably made a canon by du Bellay, but that great opposition was raised to his admission by the eight existing canons, that this *Supplicatio* (of which we hear no more) was presented in 1536, that Rabelais did not reside there at all as canon, or at any rate not more than six months, and that the appointment was allowed to lapse. There is no mention of him as canon in any other quarter, nor does he himself allude again to his possession of this title.

The *Third Book* therefore was written in 1543–5, probably at St Ayl and St Maur des Fossés, near Paris. The composition is more finished than that of any of the other "books", though in constructive ability it is not equal to the *Gargantua*. In fact the commencement is quite undecided. It takes up the thread from the *Pantagruel*, in which Rabelais, as Master Alcofribas, was made Governor of Salmigondin. This office is now bestowed on Panurge, who at once runs headlong into debt, and when taken to task by Pantagruel on this subject enters upon a whimsical but most eloquent defence of debtors, interpreting indebtedness as the mutual interdependence of every element in the universe, every organ and limb in the human anatomy and every person in human society, on others for support and convenience of existence. The first chapter was a kind of preface to this, being a panegyric on the able and righteous rulers of states and strenuous benefactors of the human kind, whereby they deserve divine honours. It is an expansion of one of the *Adagia* of Erasmus (i. 1. 69), *Homo homini deus*, just as the opposite attitude of the tyrant who indulges his own lust of power at the expense of his subjects, and the man who will lend nothing, that is, who will not give help and who keeps selfishly aloof from his fellows, is developed from the contrasted Adage (i. 1. 70), *Homo homini lupus*. These truly eloquent chapters are worked out with a wealth of illustration from Plato, Plutarch, Cicero, Virgil, with his commentator Servius, Macrobius and other classical writers, shewing that Rabelais, having lost his employment as physician and secretary to Guillaume du Bellay, has taken up Humanism in earnest; this book with its constant references to

Erasmus and its borrowings from the classics, as well as the writer's own experiences of daily life, thus becomes a finished treatise on many subjects, especially divination and medical botany as it was then known.

The book goes on tentatively at first. Panurge, having been freed from debt by Pantagruel, affects to be miserable and then suddenly goes into strange vagaries of dress—a brown toga and spectacles on his cap—and makes up his mind to marry. His master Pantagruel, in a most amusing chapter, laughingly chimes in with each of his arguments for and against marriage, and ultimately in the next chapter advises him to explore his future good or bad luck in marriage by means of the *Sortes Vergilianae*. This proving unsatisfactory to Panurge, dreams are tried and then, one after another, every known method of divination, till these chapters (9–28) may be looked upon as a valuable treatise on the methods of divination then known. The knowledge in support of these methods is derived from the books already mentioned, especially from the *de Divinatione* of Cicero, while the matter of the 25th chapter is to a very great extent derived from the *de occulta philosophia* of the celebrated Henricus Cornelius Agrippa. He had been appointed historiographer to Charles V, and was really a learned man, but suspected of necromancy, thanks to this book. Rabelais makes fun of him under the name of Her Trippa. Besides this, Panurge consults his friends Epistemon and Friar John, but is always confirmed in the answer he has already obtained from his various oracles, that his future wife will turn out to be an unfaithful, pilfering termagant. The 29th chapter introduces a new element into the enquiry, a *symposium* modelled on that of Macrobius, in which the question is referred to a theologian, a physician, a lawyer and a philosopher, but the result is no more encouraging than the preceding attempts, although the conversations are in the highest degree diverting. As in the *Saturnalia* of Macrobius the lawyer Postumianus is unable to appear, so in the *Third Book* the legist, Judge Bridlegoose, is absent, having been put on trial himself and summoned to appear on a charge of having given a decision by the chance of the dice. The main current of the story is agreeably diversified by the episode of the Trial of Judge Bridlegoose, at which Pantagruel determines to appear. The defence of the Judge occupies six chapters; and then, as the appeal to the judgment of the learned has not been satisfactory, the opinion of Triboulet, the court fool of Francis I, is asked on the subject. Pantagruel had already advised this consultation in a chapter which is remarkable for its intrinsic merit as a piece of learned drollery, but also for the fact that it is adapted throughout from the treatise of Rabelais' friend Tiraqueau, *On the Marriage Laws of Poitou*, to which we have already alluded. The whole of this scene, beginning with the 30th chapter (or even the 27th), is more or less indebted to Tiraqueau; but the 37th chapter, in which the advice of a fool is advocated, is taken from it throughout, with the exception of one paragraph on the attribution of the rôle of fool or jester to the most finished actor of a company. This paragraph was added in the second edition (F) of 1552. But the proverb of the fool instructing the wise man, and the assertion that kings and states have been preserved by the advice of fools, are from Tiraqueau's book, with the difference that Tiraqueau gives many historical instances of benefits to states having been attributable to the advice of Women, while Rabelais gives the merit to the advice given by Fools. How he must have chuckled as he made this change! Also from Tiraqueau comes the thought that the worldly minded, sagacious, successful man of business may be a fool in the estimation of the Celestial Intelligences; while the charming story from the gloss of Giovanni Andreae is also given by the Poitevin jurist, though it is developed by Rabelais in his own inimitable manner. Noticeable also in this connexion with Tiraqueau is a passage in the 49th chapter, when *Pantagruelion*, or hemp, is being discussed, and our author is giving a world of instruction on botany—mostly derived from Pliny; the subject of the sexes of plants is mentioned, and the plants given in illustration of this theory are clearly taken from a passage of Tiraqueau on the subject. Well may Rabelais, in dedicating his edition of the Medical Letters of Manardi to the learned jurist, have expressed an ardent expectation and hope for the appearance of the third edition of the "Poitou Laws", which as a matter of fact was published in Paris in 1546, practically synchronising with Rabelais' own *Third Book*.

The conclusion of the book is aptly given in a paean in praise of the herb *Pantagruelion*, or hemp. Panurge, dissatisfied with all the answers given him by the various oracles he has consulted, is bent on travelling to consult the Oracle of the Holy Bottle, which is in Cathay or Upper India; Pantagruel, who is all good nature, gets permission from his father Gargantua to make the voyage, and great preparations are made in the formation and equipment of a fleet of twelve ships for that purpose. Among other stores that are put on board there is a great quantity of hemp; and this leads to a disquisition on the great merits of this plant in providing for so many uses among men (including that of hanging), and especially in making sails by which ships are propelled; also on the virtues of *asbestos*, the flax that cannot be consumed by fire. The natural history required for an account of this plant and a great number of others incidentally mentioned is derived directly from Pliny, and with this loan the *Third Book* ends.

Thus we may see that though in the main current the book is greatly indebted to Erasmus, divisions of it are derived in their turn from anatomical writers, especially Galen; from Cicero and Cornelius Agrippa in divination, from Tiraqueau in moral philosophy and domestic discipline, and from Pliny in botany. But besides these main sources it must not be forgotten that there are very many other writers whom Rabelais has diligently studied; especially to be mentioned are Plutarch's *Moral treatises*—Rabelais' own copy still survives in the Bibliothèque Nationale—Catullus, and many others. With all his enthusiasm for medicine and natural science, this writer never ceased being a humanist; he carefully followed the writings of Budaeus, Erasmus, Poliziano, especially noting studies on Civil and Canon Law.

The Prologue of this book is to be noticed for the patriotic note that is struck in it. It is with a strong feeling of regret that the author takes to rolling his "Diogenical Tub", only because he is unable to take part himself in the defence of his country. The account of Diogenes at the siege of Corinth is from Lucian, but it is derived through the preface of Budaeus' *Annotations on the Pandects*, most graphically amplified in Rabelais' best vein. In its patriotism this Prologue contradicts previous utterances on war given in the *Gargantua* (c. 46) that "what was formerly called Prowess is now called Robbery and Wickedness". Now, however, the Prologue combats the view of Erasmus in his essay of *Dulce bellum inexpertis* (*Ad.* iv. 1. 1), which insists that war is anything but beautiful; it declares that "the ineffable Perfection of the Divine Wisdom" is comparable to the array of an army in the field. This is the ruling idea, now that France is resisting the attacks of Charles V, and surely such patriotic feeling is fully justified.

In composing the *Third Book* Rabelais appears to have been genuinely doing what he professes, namely, writing a patriotic book in support of his fellow-countrymen in their resistance to the enemy, and then compiling his treatise on divination, a subject which had always interested him, if we may judge by his *Pantagrueline Prognostication* and his Almanacks, and the allusion he makes to the book of Prognostications in a letter from Rome to the Bishop of Maillezais. His treatment of the various forms of divination is directed to the solution of the question of marriage and the imperfections of the female sex—for he takes part against women in the discussion of the *querelle des femmes*—but underlying this is intended the conduct of life in general, of which marriage is taken as one of the most critical steps. The line taken up by the writer is indicated two or three times over, viz. that in such near concernments a man should be his own counsellor and not consult extraneous advice, in fact that he should exercise the *liberum arbitrium*, though Rabelais would scarcely wish to draw special attention to this subject on its theological side, where it was the source of bitter controversy in opposition to predestination. A curious side-light on this subject may be seen in that strange book *Hypnerotomachia Poliphili*, in the list of contents of which Queen Eleutherillida is said to be *il libero arbitrio*. This cardinal point in life is brought out by Rabelais on every possible occasion. The cramping discipline of the cloister life had caused him to rebel sturdily and to insist that freedom from unnecessary restraint was the only rational government for rational spirits, who were not of themselves inclined to evil.

The *Third Book* (published with the Royal Privilege of Sept. 19, 1545) might have passed without opposition from the Sorbonne, but for the end of the Prologue in which the "Levitical Hypocrites" (*i.e.* the Theological Faculty of Paris) are warned off from drinking at the Rabelaisian tun, the final warning of Raminagrobis in c. 21 and the comments in the next two chapters (22, 23).

The description of the various monastic orders by Raminagrobis (derived for the most part from Cornelius Agrippa) and the pretended defence of them by Panurge in the succeeding chapters were admirably calculated to irritate the monkish fraternity in holding up their practices to ridicule, especially that of hunting out bequests for their Orders.

First, the Franciscans and Dominicans are pointed out as the guiding spirits of the Roman Church in scenting out heresy; then the Capuchins and Minims are scoffed at for their wretched and woebegone conditions of Ichthyophagy. Panurge, the *soi-disant* defender of the Orders, reviles the old poet Raminagrobis on the ground that his poem is written in sophistical disjunctives by which his statements need be true in only one part in order to gain acceptance. Next, Epistemon undertakes the defence, pointing out that Raminagrobis meant literally what he said, when he complained of fleas and other noxious insects, and did not refer to the good, holy fathers at all. This only accentuates the comparison and makes it worse. Unfortunately Rabelais was betrayed into the perpetration of what was probably a common joke in the Cloister —"son *asne* (for *âme*) s'en va à trente milles panerées de diables". This gave the Sorbonne a handle for a charge of heresy. In vain Rabelais excused it later in the *Epistre Dedicatoire* of the *Fourth Book*.

In the next chapter (c. 23) Panurge proceeds to make the case worse by his pretended advocacy. He refers pointedly and particularly to the orbits and anniversaries in honour of departed saints, as being so many excuses for gormandising, and also alludes to the notorious case of the Franciscans of Orléans (whom he styles "hobgoblins", as he does also in *P*. 7) and their pretence of the ghost of the Provost's wife, who had been buried, but who returned to scare them with her knockings. This knavery had been spoken of by Sleidan in his *de statu religionis et reipublicae* (1534), by H. Estienne in the *Apologie pour Hérodote* and by G. Buchanan in his poem *Franciscanus*. Later it is fully recorded by R. Scot in his *Discovery of Witchcraft* (1584).

It was a very sore point. Another charge is hinted at in the pseudo-defence—the presence of the monks and friars at the burial services of the wealthy and their neglect of the poor from whom they can expect nothing. This is reinforced by the story of the

Franciscan Observantin, who rather than carry money about him throws into the deep water the tax-collector whom he is carrying pick-a-back across a mill stream.

The gibe against the Cloister monks for their gormandising and putting the beef on to stew while they are mumbling through their long Matins service (c. 15) was so hackneyed that it might have gone unnoticed, but the sustained raillery of cc. 21–3 could not be allowed to pass without a retort of some kind, and the charge of heresy in the substitution of *asne* for *âme* was that retort.

Another point is dealt with in iii. 48, viz. the subject of the marriage of children without the parents' presence or consent, if a priest is there to give his consent and blessing. This priestly privilege and its abuse had grown up from Roman Imperial times, when divorce had become so scandalously frequent that the bishops of the newly established Christian Church had been able to put a ban on such laxity among their own flock and induce them to practise a greater purity and strictness of life; thus by degrees in the decadence of the Empire the Church had gained control over the celebration of marriage and later had exalted it into a sacrament. In bringing this about the clergy had weakened the bond of the *patria potestas*, to suit cases of a pagan father and a Christian son, and they went so far as to absolve a son from obedience to his father in order to submit himself to a more holy bond with the Church. In course of time this led to great irregularities, and cases occurred in which a cleric, abusing his powers in these matters, brought about great trouble and scandal in family relations. It had become flagrant, and a remedy was proposed and carried at the Council of Trent in spite of much opposition.

Rabelais writes forcibly on this subject, and undoubtedly this helped to incense the theological faculty, when it came on the top of other scandals in previous chapters. All these girds at the abuses of the Roman Church were matters of common gossip and may be found up and down in the *Colloquies* of Erasmus; indeed some of them are derived from that source, but Erasmus wrote in Latin, whereas the racy stories in the *Pantagruel* and *Gargantua* and in other books were written in colloquial French and accessible to everyone. *Hinc illae lacrimae*, and the Sorbonne was delighted to be able to seize upon the *asne* for *âme* and to found a charge of heresy upon it.

RABELAIS AT METZ

At the beginning of 1546, on the publication, or even before it, of his *Third Book*, Rabelais found it prudent to make his escape to Metz. Here he was again under the protection of M. de Sainct-Ayl (Étienne Laurens), who possessed property there and in the neighbourhood. His presence in Metz is proved by a letter to Cardinal du Bellay from Jean Sturm, director of the gymnasium at Strasburg and one of the chief leaders of the Protestant movement, to the effect that Rabelais had been driven out of France by the untoward state of affairs and that he had come to Metz. The letter is dated Saverne, March 28; the year is fixed by the mention in the same letter of the Emperor's arrival at Speyer on March 24; this we know was in 1546. At the end of March, St Ayl returned to Metz from a diplomatic visit to the German princes. Rabelais, whose *Third Book* had been censured before Easter 1546, got an appointment as physician to the hospital at 120 *livres* a year and soon afterwards received a visit from some Paris courtiers, presenting him with a silver wine-flask in the shape of a breviary and requesting him to continue his writings. This is attested by the *Ancien Prologue* to the *Fourth Book*, or rather, to the instalment of ten chapters, which he proceeded to write. A year later, St Ayl returned from another conference with his protestant friends Sturm and Sleidan, but he had not managed to see du Bellay. Upon this Rabelais wrote a letter, dated Metz, Feb. 6, to the Cardinal, asking for pecuniary assistance in a manner that seems somewhat exaggerated. The year date of this letter is in question. It is probably 1547, after the return of St Ayl, which it mentions (*R.E.R.* iii. 350–60). It seems curious that he should complain of poverty, when the payment of 120 *livres* up to Midsummer is mentioned in the records at Metz. A slight *résumé* of the rudimentary *Fourth Book* will be in place here.

FOURTH BOOK, ED. 1548 (A)

The episodes of this partial edition of the *Fourth Book* are, first, the blazoning of the twelve ships of the convoy, and then an account of their departure from the harbour of Thalassa and the purpose of their voyage. They are not to follow the route of the Portuguese round the Cape of Good Hope, as they did on their previous voyage to Cathay, but to go round by the North-West passage north of Canada, avoiding the Arctic ocean and then descending on the other side to Cathay, which was in the same latitude as Olonne (46°). After three days' sailing they meet with a ship returning from Lantern Land, their own destination before going to the Holy Bottle. On board this vessel is a sheep merchant with a number of sheep. Panurge and he get up a quarrel, which results in the purchase of a sheep from the merchant. Panurge throws it overboard and the other sheep follow and drag all the shepherds, who try to hold them back, into the sea and all are drowned. The travellers next land at the Island of Ennasin, where all the people have snub noses like the ace of clubs and are all related together. Next follows the Isle of Cheli, where the Queen and princesses all kiss the travellers. Friar John objects to this and finds his way into the kitchen. This introduces a story in Rabelais' own life on a visit to Florence (cf. p. liv). They pass by the Isle of Procuration, where Friar John accepts the invitation of one of the Catchpole inhabitants to belabour him mercilessly for money. The Islands of Tohu and Bohu succeed, where Nose-slitter devours windmills, saucepans and pots and pans, but dies by being choked by a lump of fresh butter. This leads to a disquisition on a number of strange deaths, followed by the description of a storm, which has become celebrated, recording the different conduct of Panurge and Friar John. Their escape from this storm abruptly concludes this fragmentary book.

M. Romier (*R.E.R.* x. 113–42) is of opinion that the letter to the Cardinal, mentioned above, was dated Feb. 6, 1547, and that the answer was a summons to accompany him to Rome. Accordingly, Rabelais drew his salary as physician to the hospital up to Midsummer, was in Paris by July 10, the date of the duel of Jarnac and Chataigneraye (cf. *Sciomachia init.*), and left Reims with the Cardinal, who had attended the coronation of Henry II, and reached Rome Sept. 27, 1547. Du Bellay had not been in disgrace at the accession of Henry, but had enjoyed the support of the Constable Montmorency, insomuch that he alone of all the former ministers had remained on the royal Council. It was rather a mark of distinction that he should be appointed plenipotentiary at the Roman Court during two years. He was there from Sept. 27, 1547, till Sept. 22, 1549, attended by his trusty physician at the Palazzo Sant' Apostoli.

Rabelais, as may be seen from the last part of his *Ancien Prologue* to the *Fourth Book* and the account in the Epistle of Dedication of the second edition to Cardinal Châtillon, had been disgusted at the outcry raised against him, especially at the charge of heresy, and laid down his pen, determined to write no more. On his journey from Metz to Rome in 1547 he had left with the printers his manuscript of the rudimentary *Fourth Book* as well as an Almanack for 1548, probably with the object of obtaining money. We have another record of this in the shape of a money order for thirty-two gold crowns sent by the banker Arnauld Combraglia of Paris, which he cashed in Rome July 18, 1548.

In March 1549 he was present at the *Sciomachia*, or sham fight given by Cardinal du Bellay in the Piazza Sant' Apostoli, to celebrate with suitable honours the birth of Louis d'Orléans, *second* son of Henry II and Catherine de' Medici, who, however, died in infancy. Rabelais sent an account of this in a letter to the Cardinal de Guise, which he afterwards edited with additions, published by Seb. Gryphius. One of the chief reasons for this was a desire to advocate the cause of Cardinal du Bellay and his family and to make known the services they had rendered to their country. The *Sciomachia* was held March 14, 1549, but a few days afterwards Cardinal du Bellay learned that some intrigue had been set on foot against him by his enemies the Guises, and soon afterwards he was informed that the office of "Protector of the affairs of France" had been transferred from him to Cardinal Ippolito d'Este, who arrived in Rome on June 13. Du Bellay was ordered to remain, but there was soon friction between the two ambassadors, and in reply to his request to be recalled his brother Martin, Seigneur de Langey, announced to him about Sept. 15 that leave had been granted. Accordingly, he left Rome Sept. 22 with "ten or twelve of his servants", among whom was Rabelais. He arrived at Lyons in the beginning of November, but very soon afterwards heard of the death of Paul III and received a royal command to embark at Marseilles for Rome, so as to take part in the conclave. Leaving Lyons about Nov. 20 du Bellay reached Rome on Dec. 12 accompanied by Cardinals de Guise, Châtillon and Vendôme, and they immediately joined the conclave, which lasted from Nov. 29, 1549, till Feb. 7, 1550 and resulted in the election of Cardinal del Monte, Julius III.

Rabelais had been left at Lyons in November and occupied himself in editing the letter he had sent to Cardinal de Guise on the *Sciomachia* of March 14, and in preparing an Almanack for the year 1550.

SCIOMACHIA[1]

Cardinal du Bellay in Rome determined to celebrate the birth of the royal prince in a striking manner, especially by a sham fight (*Sciomachia*) in the Piazza Sant' Apostoli, where stood the Palazzo Colonna, which was now his residence. This piazza had been the scene of extravagant festivities in 1473 given by Cardinal Riario, "nephew" of Sixtus IV, to celebrate the meeting of Ercole d'Este, Duke of Ferrara, and Leonora of Aragon. Jean du Bellay determined that his entertainment should not be inferior to this. He had intended also a *Naumachia*, or sham sea-fight, opposite the Castle of St Angelo, which had been formerly, in 1527, the scene of distinguished courage and generalship on the part of Guillaume du Bellay against the attacks of the Bourbon troops. This had to be given up on account of an abnormal rising of the Tiber, which rendered impossible any manœuvres in the river at that time. The land-fight, however, took the form of a bull-fight, a siege, and fireworks, which were carried out with great elaboration, many of the Italian nobles taking part in the various engagements. The whole was followed by a magnificent banquet, at which were present many Cardinals and the principal personages in Italy. A careful and detailed description of this was written by Rabelais in the form of a letter to the Cardinal de Guise; and even in this letter may be remarked the readiness with which Rabelais records parallels from his classical reading on every possible occasion, whether it be in instances of news of great events being announced by rumour in an impossible or incredible space of time, in a discussion of the tutelary divinities of Plato, or a description of the dish of Vitellius.

---

[1] An Italian account of the *Sciomachia* is given in *R.E.R.* ix. 321, which confirms much of the detail.

On the return of the Cardinals from Rome to Lyons Rabelais was approached by Cardinal de Châtillon and requested to finish his *Fourth Book*, but, feeling bitterly the injustice with which his *Third Book* had been treated, he declined, as he did also later in Paris. It was not till Châtillon had obtained a royal privilege, dated Aug. 5, 1550, for the continuation of the *Fourth Book* and the revision of the *Third Book*, and had assured him of the good will towards him felt by the late King Francis and the present King Henry, that he would consent to proceed. Cardinal du Bellay added his persuasions; and Rabelais was made *curé* of St Martin at Meudon in the diocese of Paris, Jan. 9, 1551 (n.s.), and of St Christopher of Jambet in the diocese of Le Mans, of which René du Bellay, the Cardinal's brother, was Bishop. This is pointed out by M. Romier as the result of a close examination of the Epistle of Dedication to the *Fourth Book*, dated Jan. 28, 1552 (n.s.), and prefixed to the book. It was therefore at St Maur des Fossés and Paris that the completed *Fourth Book* was composed.

This is supported by a statement of Antoine le Roy in his *Floretum Philosophicum*, seu ludus Meudonianus (4°, Paris 1649). He says: "in praedicto Fossatensi agro suum Pantagruelismum confecisse narratur Rabelaesus".

It is to be noted that a *crise gallicane* had arisen between the French King and the new Pope on the question of Parma and the maintenance in the duchy of Orazio Farnese, grandson of Paul III, who had married Diana, a natural daughter of Henry II. It had become acute in the middle of 1551, so much so that in August a proposition had been made in the French Council to set up a patriarch in France endowed with spiritual supremacy. Henry, however, was unwilling to become guilty of schism, and in this he was influenced by the Cardinal of Lorraine and the Jesuits, while the Pope's resentment was moderated by the Duke of Ferrara, and the crisis came to an end in the beginning of 1552. In the Prologue to the *Fourth Book* the end of the war of Parma is mentioned in passing; while the subject of the Prologue itself is that of moderation in wishes, based on Aesop's Fable of "Mercury and the Woodman" as set forth by Erasmus, *Ad.* iv. 3. 57 (*Fluvius non semper fert secures*).

It seems most likely then that, prompted by Châtillon and du

Bellay, Rabelais completed his *Fourth Book* at the *château* of St Maur des Fossés during the year 1551. The resignation of his two *cures* at Meudon and St Christopher de Jambet was made two years later, Jan. 9, 1553 (n.s.).

FOURTH BOOK, 2ND ED. 1552 (B)

As has been said, the voyage to Cathay, where is the Oracle of the Holy Bottle, is to be followed out this time by the North-West passage to the north of Canada, or *la nouvelle France*, as it was called, instead of following the route of the Portuguese round the Cape of Good Hope, by which Pantagruel and his followers had previously reached the same destination. This course was supposed to be much shorter and less perilous. In several respects this edition is more definite and detailed than A. Among other points the name of the Pilot is added, and it is interesting to find that he is called Jamet Brahier. He has been identified by M. Lefranc and M. de Grandmaison as the husband of Jehanne Gaudete, sister of Marie Gaudete, the wife of Jamet Rabelais, our author's brother. He was a merchant who trafficked on the Loire and its affluents (*R.E.R.* iv. 154, 184). This is another instance pointing to the close personal connexion between this romance and its author, such as has been proved in the *Gargantua*.

We are also told in this second edition (iv. 1) that Xenomanes, the chief director of their course, had left with Gargantua an Hydrography marking out the route they intended to take. M. Margry in his *Navigations françaises*, p. 338, had identified him with Jean Alfonse of Saintonge, who had written a *Cosmographie* for the use of Francis I, which was published later (1559) at Poitiers. It has been republished (Paris 1904) by M. Georges Musset. This suggestion was adopted by Dr Le Double and M. Lefranc, but recently (*R.E.R.* x. 1–67) it has been shewn conclusively by M. Sainéan that this *Cosmography* is a shameless piece of plagiarism from the Spanish *Suma de geografía* of Fernandez Enciso. This Spanish work was published in 1519, whereas the *Cosmographie* was unknown till 1867. The clue that Rabelais himself has given is the title of Xenomanes, *traverseur des voyes perilleuses*, and this is the title assumed by J. Bouchet in a volume published in 1526. It has been seen how Rabelais delights in using the names and titles of his friends and acquaintances in his books, and it seems possible that Bouchet is thus intended for identification with Xenomanes, notwithstanding the fact that he was no traveller. The title may suffice; but it is not improbable that he really had in view the navigations of the two great explorers.

The North-West passage is indicated in B as before, but with some slight additions. A new "Island" is now inserted, *Medamothi* (Nowhere), and this has been plausibly identified with Newfoundland, while a reference is suggested to the royal princes Francis and Henry and the marriage of the latter in 1533. This is in accordance with the present purpose of the book, to conciliate the favour and maintain the cause of the royal house.

The travellers make purchases at a fair that is being held there, each according to his taste; meantime a despatch is received from Gargantua in a specially swift sailing boat, "the Sea swallow", which is described in accordance with the natural history of the flying fish given by Pliny (9. 82) and Pierre Gilles. The Esquire who brings the despatch is fêted and Pantagruel prepares an answer, informing his father that he has procured for him a *tarand*, which by the description given is clearly a reindeer, and three "unicorns" which prove to be giraffes. Such presents were in fashion at the time. D'Albuquerque gave an elephant to Leo X and Sultan Soleiman had presented a giraffe to Lorenzo de' Medici in 1480.

At the outset of their journey, as they are beginning, after four days' sailing on a route they had traversed before, to wind about the pole (*i.e.* to steer westward) after going far enough north to be above the land, which is described as Medamothi, they fall in with a merchant vessel coming in the opposite direction from Lantern Land. This was their first objective before they reach Cathay, and it has been supposed with some probability that this vessel is one of the two sent back by the explorer Roberval to Francis I, according to the order made to bring him news. But Rabelais proceeds to adapt and elaborate an episode of Merlin Cocai (*Baldus*, bk xi) describing a trick of Cingar (the prototype of Panurge), by which he causes a number of sheep and their Ticinese shepherds to be drowned near Chioggia, by throwing one of the biggest of the sheep into the sea, whereat all the others follow and drag the shepherds with them. This story, with its dramatic incidents, occu-

pies two chapters in A and three in B. It is developed most graphically and is one of the most successful pieces of our author's art of
story-telling. They then proceed to the Island of Ennasin, or nose-
less (*i.e.* senseless) people, who are described as having red faces
and ridiculously snub noses. These characteristics have been noted
as the peculiarities of the Red-skins of North America and of the
Esquimaux and therefore lying on the way of Pantagruel's journey.
Great fun is made of their intimate relationships, which seem like
those of the community of wives and children in Plato's *Republic*,
bk v. Proceeding towards the north-east, they come to the island
of Cheli, which was subject to King Panigon, where the Court
ladies kiss the travellers all round. This has been paralleled by the
description of a similar practice among English ladies of that time
in a letter of Erasmus, though of course it is impossible from this to
say that England is intended. They then proceed to Procuration
Island, which is "scribbled all over" and inhabited by Catchpoles,
who make a living by compensation for beatings that they endure.
After an illustration from Gellius of similar conduct in a Roman
gentleman, Friar John goes ashore and asks, in a loud voice, who
wishes to be beaten for a money payment. Several men rush up
crying "Io" (the Italian for "I") to signify their readiness, and
one of them is beaten unmercifully and liberally rewarded. Next
they pass the Islands of Tohu and Bohu (Hebrew words taken
from the first chapter of Genesis, signifying "Solitude" and
"Void"), and here we have the story of the giant Bringuenarilles,
or Nose-slitter, who lives on windmills, but has had to subsist on
the frying-pans, etc., of the country, and who ultimately is choked
by a piece of fresh butter. This is abridged and altered from a
ridiculous story in the *Disciple de Pantagruel*, and illustrated from
Erasmus, Pliny, Suetonius, Baptista Fulgosius and others; the
illustrations are amplified in B. Episodes are also taken from the
same source in c. 44.

We now come to the great storm, the account of which is
founded on Merlin Cocai (*Baldus*, bks xi, xii), and the storm given
in the first book of Virgil's *Aeneid*; this is made more than probable
by citations from Virgil himself and extracts obviously taken from
Servius' commentary on the passage, *Aen.* i. 93 *sqq.* Among other
sources there is a curious one from Budaeus' translation of the

Pseudo-Aristotelian treatise *de Mundo*, where French names formed
on the model of the Greek words descriptive of "squalls", etc. are
given in the exact order which they occupy in Budaeus. In the
additions of B some lively touches are derived from a Colloquy of
Erasmus, entitled *Naufragium*. After escaping from this storm they
land at the Isle of the *Macraeons* or the Long-livers. Here the first
edition (A) ends; the story is resumed from this point in B, c. 25, for
this edition expands the ten chapters of A to twenty-five.

The identification of the Isle of the Macraeons with some place
on the North-West passage presents considerable difficulty. At the
outset the description of the island nearly resembles a passage at the
beginning of the *Hypnerotomachia Poliphili*, utilised in the *Gargantua*
and in the *Fifth Book*; indeed reference to it is pointedly made in a
note of the *briefve declaration d'aulcunes dictions plus obscures on
quatriesme livre*, a short explanation of difficulties, which is appended
to this book manifestly by Rabelais himself. An account is found
in the note of "Obelisks, Pyramids, etc., with divers inscriptions",
such as are actually to be found in the *Hypnerotomachia*. The next
chapter is composed of a long passage of Eusebius, *de praeparatione
evangelica*, v. 17. §§ 10–11. This, however, is copied from Plutarch,
de defect. orac. c. 18, a favourite treatise of Rabelais in the *Third
Book*. The passage describes the island as one of the *Sporades*, or
Scattered Islands in the Ocean, and subject to the ruler of Britain;
and it goes on to say that it is the habitation of heroes whose abiding
there brings blessing to the place, while the decease of one of them
is attended with disturbances in the Sky, the Sea and the Land. As
this passage is translated pretty closely, it is not easy to say what
place is intended; the Channel Islands, the Isle of Anglesey or the
Scilly Islands have been suggested. It may easily stand for any
unknown region.

The account of the decease of the heroes is then pointedly referred to the death of Guillaume du Bellay and illustrated by
passages from Virgil, Pliny and Josephus, ending with a longish
passage from Baptista Fulgosius (who was cited and mentioned
in A) and a passage of seven or eight lines translated almost literally from Erasmus, supported by references to Dion Cassius and
Suidas. Thus this chapter, made up as it is almost entirely of passages from classical and Renaissance writers, can hardly have more

than a general reference to one of Pantagruel's stopping places. Besides the circumstances of Langey's death, there is a mention of the names of those present, among whom are Rabelais and Epistemon (who is designated in iii. 34 as a fellow-student of Rabelais and Ponocrates at Montpellier). This parade of learning fires the emulation of Friar John, who would himself also be a scholar. The next chapter gives the story of the death of Pan and the identification with Christ, taken from Eusebius, *de praep. evan.* v. 17. §§ 5–9, though again it is derived from Plutarch. It has been pointed out by M. Reinach (*R.E.R.* iv. 100) that Plutarch's recital of the proclamation of the death of Pan is really a confused account of the Syrian lament for Adonis (Thammuz), in which a refrain was repeated three times, Θάμμους παμμέγας τεθνῆκεν. Cf. Milton, *P.L.* i. 446.

We now come to "Sneaking Island, where Lent reigned", with an anatomical account of his organs and limbs, borrowed mostly from Galen's *de usu partium*, together with a comparison of these parts in detail with various objects of common life. Two of these comparisons may be found in the great surgeon Ambroise Paré, and throughout the resemblances (which formerly were looked upon as fanciful) have been justified by a careful piece of work by Dr Le Double. Lent is thus represented as a pitiful, even a revolting, creature, and compared with *Amodunt* and *Discordance*, two misshapen beings described in an *Apologue* of Celio Calcagnini, a Ferrarese physician. Rabelais goes on to insist that Antiphysis (Anti-Nature) afterwards produced similar beings in Calvin and Gabriel de Puy-Herbaut, who had formerly assailed him with invective.

A monstrous *Physeter*, or whale, is now descried coming to attack the fleet. The description of it is borrowed from Pliny and the conduct of the Pilot in command of the fleet is taken from the similar practice of Alexander's Admiral Nearchus, reinforced by a quotation from Cicero. The incident, however, may well have been suggested by the fact that for a long time past Breton and Basque sailors had carried on whale fishery in these northern seas, so that it is natural to use this as an episode in the present voyage. Pantagruel for once resumes his gigantic proportions and powers, and slays the monster which had struck terror into the navigators, especially Panurge.

They now land at "Wild Island" and proceed to cut up and stow away certain parts of the Physeter. After a repast certain "Chitterlings" are noted spying on their movements, and they are concerned to find that huge battalions of them are marching to attack them. These are defeated however and literally "cut to pieces" by Friar John and an army of Cooks, whom he had ensconced in a military engine, called a sow (*Truye*) from its resemblance to the wooden horse of Troy (*Troye*). It can hardly be disputed that the Swiss are aimed at in this satire, indeed Rabelais hints it himself. A good deal of classical and other learning is expended on this episode and allusion is made to the Council of Trent, in which the observance of Lent had been insisted on, thus causing much heart-burning. The Queen of the Chitterlings makes peace and a treaty with Pantagruel, and the travellers go on to the Island of Ruach, or wind. This has been identified with the Island of Aeolus in the *Aeneid* and also tentatively with Avignon, which is notoriously subject to such visitations. Swift and Sterne are indebted to these chapters. A partial source is the treatise of Hippocrates, *de Flatibus*.

The wretched Island of *Popefigs*, or people who made "the fig at" (or scorned) the Pope, is next visited, and a story is told of a husbandman who got the better of the devil, in disposing of his produce; they then go on to the *Papimanes*, or the people who are madly devoted to the Pope and only live in longing for the time when they will see him among them. This leads to the panegyric of the Decretals, or book of papal government, which is extolled by Homenaz, the Bishop of the Papimanes, as the cause and source of every blessing. This exaggerated laudation is of course only satire in the thinnest disguise, and it was probably this portion of the book more than any other that led to its censure by the *Parlement* and a year later to the compulsory resignation by Rabelais of his two *cures*.

The episode of the Frozen Words, which follows, is held to refer specially to the actual voyage by the North-West passage, for it is placed at the end of June, when the Arctic ice would be melting, so that the ships which were coasting under the pole, *i.e.* about 67° N., would experience the effect of this. Pantagruel, standing up, discovers that strange noises are in the air and the travellers' own sense of hearing soon confirms this. They are then assured by the Pilot that in the preceding winter a terrible battle took place between the Arimaspians and the Cloudwalkers. This has been taken to refer to the battle of Marignano between the French and the Swiss in Sept. 1515; at all events many of the cries that are recorded here are to be found in the chorus of the celebrated song composed by the French musician Jannequin, called *Deffaicte des Suisses à Marignan.*

Chapters 57–62 are devoted to the consideration of the bad and good points of Messer Gaster, the first master of arts in the world, the text being taken from the prologue of the Latin poet Persius: *Magister artis ingenique largitor* VENTER. The considerations, which are followed out in detail, seem to be suggested by the *Plutus* of Aristophanes, in which play all works of utility and common life, not to speak of the arts and elegances, are said to be due to the compelling power of *Penia* or Poverty, whereas Plutus, or Wealth, indisposes men to exertion. After a general introduction on these lines (c. 57), Rabelais inveighs against the impostures of the *Engastrimythes* or Diviners (*i.e.* the pretenders to sanctity and power) with the gluttonous sacrifices of the *Gastrolaters*, in Lent and at other times, to Manducus, their "ventripotent God" (cc. 58–60). On the other side two chapters (61–2) are devoted to the various useful inventions that have been brought into vogue by the necessities of Messer Gaster.

The next episode is a Calm and the method of raising the wind by a good meal, and its sufficiency in answering a number of problems proposed for consideration. Into this is introduced a long list of serpents and noxious creatures, mostly derived from Pliny, Avicenna and Nicander, the poet-priest of Claros.

The last two chapters (66, 67) are taken up with the firing of the cannons of the fleet as a practical joke to scare Panurge who is in the bread-room between the decks, and with the result of his fright.

In this book are to be noticed the prevalence of Italian words and phrases, which might be expected from the author's continued residence in Rome for nearly two years (1547–9), and also the Hebrew names employed to designate many of the places visited by the fleet.

It may be fanciful to find a resemblance between the voyage of
Pantagruel and that of Ulysses, and the places visited by them, but
taking into consideration the many allusions to the *Odyssey* (and
also to the strange voyages in the *Vera Historia* of Lucian) that may
be discovered in Rabelais a parallel list of places mentioned in
both may not be without interest:

Ennasin	The Ciconians
Cheli	The Lotus Eaters
Bringuenarilles	The Cyclops
The Macraeons	Aeolus (first visit)
Sneaking Island	The Laestrygonians
Wild Island	Circe and her animals
Ruach	Aeolus (second visit)
The Frozen Words	The Sirens
The Popefigs	Scylla
The Papimanes	Charybdis
Messer Gaster	The Oxen of the Sun
Chaneph	Calypso
Ganabin	Alcinous

Of course, only the most general of resemblances can be traced,
and the Isle of Procuration has no counterpart in this list. In the
same way only a few resemblances can be made out for the peoples
along the north of Canada, and it is clear that the Isle of the
Macraeons is derived from the account in Plutarch's *de defect. orac.*,
while Bringuenarilles and the *Wild Island* are taken from the
Disciple de Pantagruel.

There is also another possible source, viz. a conjecture that in
1536 Rabelais returned from Rome with the Cardinal's baggage on
board a merchant vessel called the *Telamonia* (from Porto Tela-
mone in Tuscany) and visited an island (St Antiochia, south-west
of Sardinia, actually bearing the name *Enosis* in Pliny, 3. 84) in
order to find out what Charles V had been doing there on his visit
to the island in the previous year. Returning from there by the
south-west wind he would coast along as far as Marseilles, and
thus be able to see personally Monte Argentario, Piombino, and
other places along that coast, such as Genoa, San Remo, Taggia
and the *Fossa Mariana*, which are mentioned in the *Fourth* and the
Fifth Books. If this supposition should prove correct, a point would
be made in discovering the source of the Italian nomenclature of

the shipping-tackle and the sails, etc. which is so strikingly displayed in the description of the storm.

Noticeable also is the Italianising tendency of the language employed in the *Fourth Book*, such as the constant use of the title *Messer* as well as the repeated allusions to the *jardins secrets*, or private gardens and casinos of the Pope and of some of the nobles in Rome, while the magistrates of some of the islands where the travellers land are styled *podestà*. An interesting point also is the list of musicians in the Prologue, belonging to two periods thirty-seven years apart. (The years indicated are probably 1513 and 1550, the accessions respectively of Leo X and Julius III.) The introduction of profane airs into cathedral services by the singers of the Pope's choirs is alluded to in the Prologue, but seriously reprobated in a somewhat enigmatical passage in iv. 62, which perhaps refers to papal legislation on that subject (cf. *Extrav. Commun.* iii. 1. 1).

The object of this part of the *Fourth Book* is to support the French cause in the *crise gallicane* and to dwell on the merits of the du Bellay family, as had already been done in the *Sciomachia*. This would sufficiently account for the extremely anti-Roman attitude of the chapters on Lent, on the Popefigs, the Papimanes and Messer Gaster. These are relieved by the geographical features of the voyage and the attention drawn to the colonising policy of the French king. Other points to be noticed are a kind of excuse for Francis I in the story of the Lord of Basché and the Catchpoles (iv. 12), where Basché, maddened by the persecution of the Prior of St Louant, threatens to leave the country and to take sides with the Sultan. This may be an allusion to the odium raised by Charles V against the French king, when he entered into relations with the corsair Barbarossa and the Sultan, so as to harass the Emperor in the Mediterranean and his brother Ferdinand in Hungary. It was made a great scandal that a Christian monarch should give any countenance to the Moslems. This remark in Rabelais may be intended as a palliation of the conduct of Francis.

Again in the *Sciomachia*, published in 1549, after Cardinal du Bellay had been superseded by Ippolito d' Este, a long account is given of Diana and her nymphs, who were represented as leading personages in the sham fight, in fact as affording the subject of strife between the contending parties. This has been explained as a compliment to Diane de Poitiers, the King's mistress, who was all powerful at Court (*R.E.R.* vii. 279). There is also a complimentary allusion to "Messer Philibert de l'Orme, chief Architect of King Megistus" in iv. 61. At this time he was high in favour at Court.

The arguments that Rabelais did not return to Rome with Cardinal du Bellay in November 1549 are, that on the return journey, while passing near Florence, the Cardinal was detained by sickness at a little village named Scarperia and *not having a physician with him*, he applied to Cosimo de' Medici to send him one. Two letters of his on this subject survive. Also, there exists a list of the attendants of our Cardinal at the conclave, and Rabelais is not found among them, although physicians and surgeons are among the attendant officers. Moreover, although there was plenty of matter for satire in this conclave, there is no allusion to it in the *Fourth Book* or elsewhere, unless the additions made in F (ed. 1552) to the blazon of Triboulet (iii. 38), "Conclavist fool, bullist f., summist f., abbreviating f.", be considered as referring to this in a very slight degree.

The *Fourth Book* then, in its finished form, containing an Epistle Dedicatory to the Cardinal Odet Coligny of Châtillon, a Prologue and sixty-seven chapters, was published Jan. 28, 1552. The first twenty-five chapters consisted of the ten chapters of the old *Fourth Book* of 1548 revised and amplified, with the addition of cc. 2–4, cc. 13–15 and c. 12 very largely increased in bulk. The other chapters (25–67) are all new and contain much interesting matter.

Very soon after its publication, on March 1, 1551 (*i.e.* 1552 n.s.), the *Parlement de Paris*, through its Council of twelve members (of whom Tiraqueau was one), cited the publisher and forbade him to expose for sale any more copies till the King's good pleasure should be known. This was in consequence of the censure of the Faculty of Theology, imposed notwithstanding the Privilege of the King. The ban was removed on the return of the King in triumph from Metz, April 18. In copies sold after that date, the reading of the text in the Prologue was changed from *tant riche et triumphant royaulme de France* to *tant noble, tant antique, tant beau, tant florissant, tant riche royaulme de France*, and Tiraqueau instead of *Conseiller du roy Henri second* is styled *Conseiller du grand victorieux, triumphant roy Henri.*

It seems likely that the *Fourth Book* having served its purpose, and the *crise gallicane* having passed, the author was left to his fate to be dealt with by his enemies. At all events Rabelais resigned his two *cures* of St Martin of Meudon and St Christopher of Jambet on the same day (Jan. 9, 1553), and tradition tells us that he died in April 1553 and that he was buried in the cemetery of St Paul in the Rue des Jardins in Paris. No trace of his remains or any record has been discovered, but there seems no reason for discrediting this tradition.

It is to be observed that André Tiraqueau was one of the twelve members of the *Conseil du Parlement* and it does not appear that he raised his voice in defence of his old friend. He was more sensitive on the subject of plagiarisms from his books than many of the authors of that time, as he had suffered from the unwarranted publication of the first edition of his *de legibus connubialibus*. He had reason then to resent the wholesale borrowing from his third edition, which was published about the same time as the *Third Book* (1546), whether Rabelais gained his knowledge by seeing the book in manuscript by the kindness of the author, or whether he was corrector of the press for Fezandat the publisher, or found other means to read it before it appeared, and utilise it in his own *Third Book.*

THE FIFTH BOOK

The *Fifth Book*, which was published posthumously in 1562 and 1564, has been much suspected and questioned in the matter or authenticity. The first fifteen chapters were published under the title of *L'Isle Sonante* in 1562 as Rabelais' posthumous work; an edition containing forty-seven chapters was published in 1564 and a sixteenth-century manuscript of it containing forty-eight chapters was discovered in the Bibliothèque Nationale in 1840. In all these editions there are differences in matter included or excluded; the result of much discussion seems to be the admission generally of the book as genuine work by Rabelais, to the exclusion of certain parts as interpolated by the editor. It is also supposed that the parts were composed at different times and thrown aside by the author, or partially utilised in other portions of his work. The Prologue especially has been questioned, as containing several pieces which appear in the Prologue to the *Third Book* and that of the *Fourth Book*. It has seemed to me possible that the parts composing the *Fifth Book* may have been written, not only before the *Fourth* but before the *Third Book*, and then laid aside, discovered after the author's death and put together so as to form a continuation of the voyage in the *Fourth Book*.

The considerations that have led me to this belief are the following. The last chapter of the *Pantagruel* undoubtedly promised some such voyage as that to Cathay by some westward passage, whether taking the route of Columbus or the North-West passage. This idea was interrupted by the *Gargantua*, which represented, allegorically, the law-suit between Antoine Rabelais, the author's father, and Gaucher Sainte Marthe, the neighbouring proprietor of Lerné.

The notion of the voyage was resumed at the end of the *Third Book*, as the culminating attempt at solving *by divination* the problem of Panurge's intended marriage. There is a very large amount of matter borrowed from the *Hypnerotomachia* in the 24th and 25th chapters and in the seven or eight final chapters in the *Fifth Book*, and also an appreciable amount of passages from the same source in the *Gargantua*; but only two or three slight allusions to it in the *Fourth Book*, and nowhere else. This points to the probability that this latter portion of the *Fifth Book* was written soon after the *Gargantua*, seeing the other references to it in the *Fourth* and other portions of the *Fifth Book* seem to be reminiscences rather than direct extracts. Thus I would suggest that the episode of Queen Entelechia (cc. 18–25) was written after the last part (cc. 32–*fin.*) and before the first part (cc. 1–15). This first part seems to me to have been written soon after the second visit to Rome (1535–6), because it gives so vivid an account—allegorical no doubt—of the papal court and surroundings, and moreover because the interval of 1540–42, the period when he was physician to Langey at Turin, would otherwise be entirely unoccupied[1] with literary work, and the period between 1535 and 1543 quite barren of any production

---

[1] There is, however, account to be taken of the *Stratagemata* of G. du Bellay written by Rabelais in Latin and translated by Claude Massuau into French (Seb. Gryphius 1542).

of his pen except for the revision of the two or three editions of his *Pantagruel* and *Gargantua*, which books he published definitively in 1542.

Also the books from which extracts are taken in the *Fifth Book* are those from which he derived help in his first two books, such as Budaeus, *in Pandectas* and *de Asse*, and his translations from Plutarch (*de placitis philosophorum*), Gellius, Lucian, Athenaeus, Herodotus. From Marot, whose poems were published in 1538, there are some loans, and from *Le Disciple de Pantagruel*, which was published in the same year, and which is put to service in the *Fourth Book*.

Rabelais also mentions in the *Fifth Book* the "two little Cardinjays", who seem to suggest the two "Cardinalicules" of his third letter to the Bishop of Maillezais (1536). Panurge again is represented (cc. 11–*fin.*) wearing a doublet and hose, not the brown toga and the spectacles in his cap which he adopted in iii. 7, and which he wears thenceforth in the *Third* and *Fourth Books*.

In the *Fifth Book* are mentioned places along the French and Italian coasts, as well as places south of Montpellier, where Rabelais was Sept. 27, 1539–40. He was at Aigues-Mortes July 14–16, 1538 (*R.E.R.* iii. 335); this place is spoken of in v. 36, as are the orange trees of San Remo in v. 34, and the wine of Taggia, a little north-east of San Remo. In the *Third Book* he styles himself *Calloïer des Isles Hières*, *i.e.* Patriarch of the Sacred Islands, a punning indication of Hyères (ἱεραί), which he mentions in iii. 50 as *mes isles Hières*; thus making it almost certain that he visited these islands on a botanical excursion about 1538–9 before taking service with Guillaume du Bellay in 1540 at Turin.

The *Fifth Book* begins with a continuation of the voyage, but the account differs in the editions and the manuscript; this makes it likely that it is the work of the editor. An "Island" is then described full of the sound of bells and of singing, and the travellers land at a small rocky islet, where Aedituus (*i.e.* the Sacristan) insists on their undergoing a four days' fast before they can be received on the Ringing Island. This is clearly intended for an allegorical description of Rome, as inhabited by birds, Popejay, Cardinjays, Priestjays, etc., with their various parti-coloured dresses. These birds do nothing but live sumptuously and warble to the sound of bells. There is an allusion to the time when there were rival Pope-jays, evidently referring to one of the schisms; it seems most reasonable, by the indication of time given, to refer it to 1328, when Lewis the Bavarian set up an anti-pope. Reference is also made to the places from which these birds come; they come, we are told, mostly from Breadless-day, being generally fugitives from justice, disappointments in love or life, the *rejectanea* of society; some of them moreover are Gormander birds. This refers to the Military Orders, Templars, Hospitallers, etc. A visit is made with much difficulty to see Popejay.

The Island of Tools is next visited, where trees are laden with Tools, which fall into handles that are ready awaiting them (cf. Galen, *de usu part.* xv. 4 (iv. 226)). This is derived from *Le Disciple de Pantagruel*, but is hall-marked as written by Rabelais, by the insertion of a passage from Plutarch and another from Pliny in support of such a portent. The Island of Sharping follows, in a day's journey. Gambling and the Invocation of Devils are the occupation of the inhabitants, and loss of life and property are the consequences. It was here that a flask of San Graal was shewn, and with greater pomp and ceremony than was the case with the *liber Pandectarum* of Justinian which was shewn in Florence, as we may learn from Budaeus, *in Pandectas*, p. 47, one of the books employed by Rabelais in the *Pantagruel* and in the *Third Book*.

Another episode follows (cc. 11–15)—that of the Furred Law-cats (*Chats-Fourrés* with a pun on *chaffourés* found in *P.* 7), whose villainy and grasping propensities are described. The curious provision of *pieds poudreux*, changed in English to "pie-powder", is enlarged upon, and a contrast is pointed out between the justice of other ancient courts and the enormities of this one. Grippe-minaud, the Archduke of the Furred Cats, propounds a riddle, which is solved by Panurge, and the company escape by paying a bag of gold for the Cats to scramble for. They then escape, but still have to pay fees to apparitors, etc., till Friar John loses patience and threatens them with his cutlass. Panurge opposes a motion of Friar John to put to sack these villains and they rejoin Pantagruel, who has been left outside; he thereupon composes some elegies on the subject, recalling the practice of Gargantua under the tuition of Ponocrates (*G.* 24). Now in the 17th chapter they pass "Forth" (*nous passons outre*) as they had passed "Procuration" and "Condemnation". Here the word *outre* is made to serve for a pun between its meaning *ultra* and *outrés*, blown-out people, whose ridiculous customs are now described. By stuffing themselves and gormandising they attain an excessive bulk; this is relieved from time to time by gashing their skin and fat, like trees, till at last they die, bursting with a tremendous report. One feature in this chapter deserves special notice. The heading of the chapter is "How we passed forth, and how Panurge had like to have been killed there". There is nothing in the chapter itself to justify the second part of this heading; therefore it seems a fair inference that the writer intended to give some further matter which would have explained this, but that for some reason or other he did not; the good faith of the editor or copyist is shewn in that he did not himself add to the chapter, but allowed it to stand as he found it.

Next for consideration comes the 16th chapter, which stands practically alone, without connexion with any other part of the book. It is an account of the *Chambre des Comptes* at Paris, under the disguise of a large wine-press and certain smaller ones which squeeze taxes and fines from everyone. To me it appears to be a result of Rabelais' visit to Paris in 1541–2 in company with Guillaume du Bellay, at which time it is suggested by some commentators that he was made *maistre des requestes*. The 16th chapter is inserted in various places by different editors, some making it c. 7 and others c. 18. It is first placed as the last chapter of *L'Isle Sonante* and it does not appear in the other original versions; but it seems to be work of Rabelais for which he had found no proper place.

On this journey to Paris and the return from it he must have seen to the definitive edition of *Pantagruel* and *Gargantua* (D) published by Juste at Lyons in 1542.

Chapters 18–25 form the episode of Queen Entelechia, which might stand quite by itself, but seems almost certainly to be written by Rabelais, as it possesses distinct marks of his style and is indebted for several of its features to the *Hypnerotomachia*, quite apart from the 24th and 25th chapters which are palpably adapted from it, forming as they do the celebrated Living Chess tournament. The speeches of Queen Entelechia are quite in the vein of those of Queen Eleutherillida of the *Hypnerotomachia*, and the tremendous banquet which is elaborately described there is here alluded to and wisely omitted. Erasmus is put to considerable use in this part; indeed, throughout the entire *Fifth Book* the sources which are so much in evidence in the *Gargantua* and the *Pantagruel* are those which are employed here.

An argument that is much pressed by the critics who deny the authenticity of the *Fifth Book* is the citation of Scaliger, Bigot, Chambrier and François Fleury as disputants in the question of ἐντελέχεια. This is undoubtedly a difficulty, especially in the case of Scaliger. He had written on ἐντελέχεια in the 307th of his *Exercitationes ad Hier. Cardanum*, which was not published till 1557, while Rabelais, who died in 1553, could not have seen this. It is quite possible, however, to look upon this passage as the interpolation of an editor, without surrendering the other part, which undoubtedly derives considerable support from the fact that Argyropylus, Theodore Gaza, Cicero and Budaeus are all spoken of in the first chapter of Politian's *Miscellanea* as supporting ἐντελέχεια; they are also quoted in this chapter (with the addition of Diogenes Laertius), while the writings of Politian had been published by Seb. Gryphius (1537–9) and are often a source for Rabelais. On the other hand, many instances may be found in those times of books circulating in manuscript long before they were printed; indeed, there is the pertinent instance in the *Third Book*, where considerable use is made of the third edition of Tiraqueau's *de legibus connubialibus*.

Chapter 26 is developed from a passage in the *Hypnerotomachia* on moving roads. This idea is noted by Pascal in his *Pensées*, where he speaks of *les rivières* as *les chemins qui marchent*; and the modern moving staircase is the practical realisation of the suggestion. Rabelais proceeds to speak of frozen rivers serving as roads, and again of Greek mathematicians who had held that the truth was not stationary but revolved round the central fire or the sun. This is derived from Plutarch's *de placitis philosophorum* (translated by Budé into Latin), which was utilised in the *Pantagruel*. Another point of legal learning on the care for the embankments of the Nile and the punishment inflicted on persons who damaged them is derived from ff. xlvii. 11. 10 through Budaeus, *in Pandectas*, ii. p. 21.

The next three chapters (27–29) are very disputable, but with

the exception of c. 28—a bad imitation of a novel of Desperiers—
I am more inclined to admit their authenticity, than formerly. The
27th chapter is weak indeed for Rabelais' work, but there are
several points in it which make for his authorship. The musical
puns are feeble, but in Rabelais' vein, and there are classical
allusions from Ovid and Cicero, Martial and Horace and imitations
from *Le Disciple de Pantagruel*. Altogether it seems to be careless
work but of the right stamp. The 29th chapter on the institution of
Lent and the stimulating vegetable and fish diets ordered in its
observance and its advocacy by physicians for their own profit,
derived from Charles Étienne, *de re hortensi*, and from Erasmus,
make very strongly for its authenticity.

Chapters 30 and 31 are very interesting and scarcely admit of
doubt. The idea of c. 30, which is on the Land of Satin, *i.e.* unreal
imitation, is taken from the *Hypnerotomachia* (c. 10. h. iv. recto),
where it is presented literally. It refers to the representation of
various birds and animals, more or less fabulous, embroidered on
tapestry. Rabelais takes this up but represents it as "embroidery"
of another kind, viz. travellers' tales, exaggeration, lying and false
testimony. He brings to bear on this as illustrations a number of
strange narrations in Aristotle, Pliny's *Natural History*, Caelius
Rhodiginus' *Antiquae Lectiones*, Pierre Gilles, Erasmus and others.
The next chapter carries this notion farther, and describes a
curious being named Hearsay, who lives in the Land of Satin. This
seems to be aimed at the marvellous accounts to be found in Herodotus, who specially asserts that he "puts down by hearsay (ἀκοῇ)
what is told to him by others". A large number of other authors,
ancient and modern, are given as writing with about as good a
warrant. Some of the names of the moderns are very interesting,
as being travellers and geographers from whom Rabelais derived
instruction, and as being authors, some of whose treatises are
collected in the *Novus Orbis* of Grynaeus. These are Cadamosto,
Lodovico Romano, Pedro Alvarez, Marco Polo, Hayton the
Armenian, Paulus Jovius, Peter Martyr. To these names must be
added Thenauld the traveller, who is also quoted in the *Gargantua*.
Cadamosto had furnished geographical information in *P.* 24
descriptive of the first voyage of Pantagruel to Utopia round the
Cape of Good Hope.

Considerable resemblance is also to be remarked between these two chapters and iv. 62–4, especially in the great use of Pliny. It might be argued that all the five chapters were written at the same time but that v. 30, 31 were laid aside as superseded by the others, but in any case it is fair to consider them as work of the same pen and also as by the author who wrote the *Pantagruel* and the *Gargantua*.

We now come to the third section of this book, which is so greatly derived from the *Hypnerotomachia*. The first two chapters are introductory, bringing the mariners to Lychnopolis or Lantern Land, the harbour which is to be their stopping-place before coming to the Oracle. The description of Lychnopolis is confused between La Rochelle, where was a celebrated lighthouse, and the Lantern Land, the idea of which is derived from Lucian, who, it will be remembered, is much used in the *Pantagruel* and elsewhere.

Chapter 33 follows. It is to be found only in the manuscript and may perhaps be looked upon as Rabelais' work as to the first and the last part, but certainly not as to the middle, which consists of a number of crudely fanciful dishes made up of reminiscences of unpresentable words and phrases in divers other parts of Rabelais. The list of dances given is taken with slight alterations from *Le Disciple de Pantagruel* and so may pass muster. The plan of the chapter is simply a *menu* for Panurge's wedding breakfast made up from animals mentioned in the mythology of Ovid and Virgil, the unsavoury messes spoken of above, a feast, more or less oily, for the Lady Lanterns, the dances just spoken of, and the return from the dance.

The 34th chapter brings the travellers to the island in which is the Oracle of the Holy Bottle. There, to reach the Oracle, they have to go through a vineyard containing vines of every kind; to pass under an arch where are drinking vessels, barrels, etc. of all sizes and shapes; hams, etc. etc., provocative of thirst; cups and tankards in every form. Then they pass through an Alley of Trellis-work of Vines in every variety, colour and shape, and they are commanded to cover their heads with ivy wreaths and put vine leaves in their shoes (as directed in Plutarch), metaphorically signifying that they are not dominated by wine; whereas most women have the moon in their heads and consequently are lunatic, differently from the one whom Friar John remembers in the Revelation (xii. 1) who had the moon under her feet.

They now (c. 35) go down a staircase to the Temple decorated with frescoes, which the patriotic Pantagruel compares with those of the Painted Cellar in Chinon (or Caynon), which is proved to be the first city in the world as built by Cain, the first builder of cities. They are met by the Governor of the Holy Bottle with his guard of French Bottiglioni, and they are conducted (c. 36) down the mystic tetradic (Pythagorean) steps, as though they were going into the cavern of Trophonius. Panurge is seized with a sudden fright, but is reassured by the valiant Friar John, who makes an important geographical allusion to the stone-covered tract of *Fossa Mariana* (Aigues-Mortes). Rabelais had been present here (July 14–16, 1538) at the meeting of Francis I and Charles V, and probably derived his knowledge of this region from his own observation, as well as from the note of Pomponius Mela, which he here partly translates. At the bottom of the steps they come upon a Doric Portal of the Temple (c. 37), when the gates open of themselves. On the front of the Portal is inscribed in Greek "In Wine is Truth", and the opening of the Gates is described with much detail, all translated from the *Hypnerotomachia*. The pavement of the Temple is described in the next chapter (38) in three or four passages from the same source. The walls and vault of the Temple are in mosaic work descriptive of the battle and victory of Bacchus over the Indians, but the description of this in cc. 39, 40 is taken from the *Dionysus* of Lucian eked out by extracts from various sources, such as Ovid, Cornelius Agrippa, Pliny, Herodotus, Plutarch. Chapter 41 is taken up with a wonderful lamp derived from the *Hypnerotomachia* (c. 17), Pliny and Pausanias, while the long 42nd chapter is devoted to an account of a fantastic Fountain, the description of which is translated from the 22nd and 23rd chapters, helped out by shorter extracts from many other parts of the same book, so that the chapter itself is a veritable mosaic of architectural details, variegated marbles, precious stones and statues in different metals; Pliny, Ovid, Budaeus and Erasmus supply a few passages here and there. Goblets are now brought (c. 43), so that the travellers may drink of the pure water of this fountain, the property of which is so wonderful that it represents to each drinker the flavour of any wine that he may choose to think of, like the Manna in the wilderness which seemed to the Israelites to taste of whatsoever food they longed for (Wisdom xvi. 20, 21). Chapter 44 represents the accoutrement of Panurge in a fantastic garb, the reading of Etruscan rituals and an extraordinary number of rites and ceremonies, all derived from Colonna's book. There is also an account of a circular chapel which furnishes its own light, and is constructed in true architectural proportions. In this chapel is a heptagonal fountain of pure water, in which lies partly immersed the Holy Bottle of pure crystal in an oval wicker case. Panurge is now (c. 45) instructed to kiss the brink of the fountain, dance round it, sing a vintage song and listen. The Priestess throws something into the fountain and the word *Trinc* is then heard. This is declared to be the most perfect answer that had ever been given. Panurge has then to drink from a silver vessel, in the shape of a breviary, a gloss or commentary on the word "Drink", which is declared to be "panomphaean" or intelligible to all nations and necessary to everybody, for "in Wine is Truth". After this draught Panurge becomes inspired and spouts doggerel (c. 46), and in the next chapter is followed by Friar John and they rime in antiphone. The 48th and last chapter is taken up with fare- wells to the Priestess, who discourses philosophically on the trea- sures of wealth and wisdom which are hidden in the earth; she then furnishes them with a favourable wind, as Aeolus did to Ulysses, and they pass through a beautifully pleasant and fertile country— the description is borrowed from the *Hypnerotomachia*—and so they return home.

RABELAIS' LANGUAGE AND STYLE

The decadence of the pure Latinity, observable in the writers of the so-called Silver Age, as instanced in Juvenal, Persius, Tacitus and others, and its further decline in Ausonius, Apollinaris Si- donius, Apuleius, Marcianus Capella and others of the fourth and fifth centuries, is a matter of common knowledge. That it retained its purity as much as it did was due to the schools of rhetoric, among which those of Lyons, Bordeaux, and Madaura in Africa, as well as those of Spain were celebrated.

The policy pursued by the Romans of sending out colonies of

veterans to garrison their distant conquests had some effect in propagating the Latin language, but as the soldiers used in defence of the Imperial conquests were to a great extent recruited from the Germans and barbarians on the Rhine and in Thrace, the influence for preserving Latin from this source was not great.

Latin was also widely spread by the system of Roman Law, as administered by the praetors, especially after it had been codified by Justinian and his chancellor Tribonianus (A.D. 529–34). But the glosses used to explain the matter and make clear the ambiguities in the laws made for the corruption of the language; they were much employed later in the eleventh century and afterwards by the jurists, who wrote in a debased style and cared for nothing but a sound exposition that would be intelligible to their readers, who welcomed the explanation of the professional lawyers. In time the glosses were accepted and read in preference to the laws themselves.

Again, the Vulgate, which was used in the Roman Church services, even in St Jerome's edition, did much to debase the purity of the language. The translation of the Bible is there given in a Latin so simple as to suggest a modern schoolboy's efforts in writing Latin prose; but its baldness is due to a conscientious determination to render the Hebrew original with exactness. Many words also are used in it, which had crept into the language from barbarous sources, and others which had become distorted from their former usage. (One example of this may suffice: "A little child shall lead them", Isaiah xi. 6, "puer parvulus minabit eos". Here the active *minabit* governing the accusative *eos* has grown from the deponent *minabitur*, which governs the dative. From the word *minare* is derived the French *mener*.)

The study of Aristotle, which was introduced through the Arabic philosophers and was taken up by Albertus Magnus and Thomas Aquinas, did much to debase Latinity. For as Aristotle was known in a Latin translation which had come from the Arabic through the Syrian from the original Greek, many errors had naturally resulted. But the scrupulous examination of theological definitions by means of Aristotelian logic in Latin translations had introduced a number of philosophical terms such as *entitas, quidditas, qualitas,* etc., while Latin constructions had been simplified so as to obtain precision at the expense of elegance of expression. Good examples of this kind of Latin may be noted in the vigorous sentences and scholastic style of Dante's Latin treatises and letters. This was the Latin in use among the learned in the various European countries, while the language of the common people was made up of the native speech with a large admixture of the Latin element; and it was from Latin of this kind that the Romance languages were formed, with differences produced by varieties of climate, temperature, natural aptitudes, etc., of the different countries.

French was the eldest of these languages, and it was French of this kind that formed the language of the troubadours in their *chansons de geste*, which were translated in the fourteenth century into stories told in a more modern, but still very masculine prose; in that form the knights and ladies delighted to read the exploits of King Arthur and the Knights of his Round Table, or those of Charlemagne and his peers, derived from the Latin Chronicle of Turpin, full of all manner of fabulous exploits in various countries, often founded on the slenderest basis of historical fact. The source of the main story is the entrance of Charles into Spain and his journey to Compostella, and afterwards, on his return, the destruction by the Basques of his rear-guard under his nephew Roland, told in the famous *Chanson de Roland*. This story was amplified in the most fantastic way by accounts of other fictitious expeditions, such as a visit to King Hugh of Constantinople and others. Considerable traces of these stories and allusions to other fables may be found frequently in the earlier books of Rabelais.

The prose in which these narratives are told is often interlarded with words and phrases taken more directly from the Latin, and it is this form of expression that Rabelais delights in employing; while occasionally he himself forms words from the Latin or Greek, which diversify his writing, sometimes to the point of grotesqueness, though it diminishes nothing from its vigour. From the old romances, such as Fierabras, Huon de Bordeaux, Perceforest, Maubrian, Melusine and many others, from *Le Roman de la Rose*, *Les Cent Nouvelles nouvelles*, and also from the chroniclers Froissart and Monstrelet, he derives words such as *occir, occision, internition, tollir, ferir, felonnement, greigneur, mire, gueule bayée, ruer jus, metes, à tout* (= *avec*), etc.

The mysteries and morality plays also formed a source of amusement and instruction at this time. The language in which they were written, though often grotesque, was occasionally elevated, and therefore borrowed more from the Court language of the learned and approached nearer to the Latin. Many of the sermons, too, appealed in their quaintness to the feelings and understanding of the people to whom they were addressed, while they were occasionally interspersed with phrases from the Vulgate, as well as homely sentences in the Latin of the preacher, sometimes rendered into French for the benefit of the more unlearned. In Rabelais' time and just before it were three celebrated preachers of this type, Michel Menot, Olivier Maillard and Jean Bourgeois. He speaks of the last two in his books. In the *Gesta Romanorum* may be seen the style of stories that were woven into sermons in the Middle Ages; histories of the Roman Emperors, sometimes distorted out of all recognition, while appended to each of them is a "Moralisation", giving a religious explanation of the story. In his list of books of education of the old school Rabelais includes a book of sermons entitled *Dormi securè* (sleep soundly) composed by a Carmelite friar, named Richard de Maidstone (†1396), intended to furnish stories and moralisations to preachers, so as to enable them to sleep undisturbedly while they are in possession of such a stock of matter for their sermons. It may be noted that two of Rabelais' best stories (iii. 9, 34) are derived from sermon books.

Another element in his writings is the influence (especially in the *Fourth Book*, after two years' residence in Rome) of the Italianising spirit that prevailed in the Court of Catherine de' Medici, although it was reprobated by some French writers. His residence at Toulouse gave him a few Gascon words and phrases, while later on at Metz he picked up a German word or two.

It may be noticed, moreover, that although at this time it was almost a fashion for scholars like Erasmus, Budé, Vivès and others to compose *Institutiones Principis Christiani*, etc., following no doubt the example of Xenophon in his *Cyropaedia*, over and above these Rabelais found models in the old romances, in which the early years of a future hero played no inconsiderable part. He seems certainly to have borrowed an episode or two from *Les enfances de*

Roland, and to have been influenced by it, like Baldus, the hero of
Merlin Coccai's macaronics,

> Qui quater Orlandi *puerilia tempora* legit.

While he was in the Cloister at Fontenay-le-Comte Rabelais
seems to have formed his style, perhaps unconsciously, on the easy
flowing periods of Herodotus, full as they are of conversations, as
well as on the cynicism of Lucian, from whom he borrows freely.
From Tiraqueau[1] we learn that he translated the first book of
Herodotus, traces of whose writings may be found in the military
operations of the *Gargantua,* as well as several direct quotations in
the *Fourth Book.* Of course other classical writers influenced him;
Plato—his Aldine copy (1513) still exists—the *Odyssey,* which appealed to his love of travel and of the marvellous, and Hippocrates
and Galen, whom he often quotes and more often follows. Rabelais' folio copy of Galen (Aldus, 1525) in six volumes is now in the
University Library of Sheffield. Although his reading of Cicero
lay almost entirely in the Moral Essays (Gryphius, 1532) and the
de Divinatione in the *Third Book,* and slightly in the *de Oratore*
(Gryphius, 1533), he could scarcely help being affected to some
extent by the "Ciceronianism" of the printer Dolet and other enthu-
siasts, whose excesses Erasmus vainly tried to check by his sensible
dialogue *Ciceronianus,* 1528. This drew down upon him the angry
diatribes of J. C. Scaliger, to which Rabelais alludes in his letter
to Erasmus, so long supposed to be addressed to an unknown
Bernard Salignac. The imitation of Cicero by Rabelais may be
seen in the protest of Grandgousier and in the harangues of Gallet
and Gargantua in the *Gargantua.*

It may easily be imagined that the Comedies of Plautus would
be to the taste of Rabelais. He refers to him twice in the *Gargantua*
and in the *Third Book;* in the *Fifth Book* the citation *totidem hostes
quot servi* is wrongly assigned to him, but the strangely compounded
words in iv. 15 must surely be invented in imitation of Plautine
combinations, *Pyrgopolinices* and others, unless they are to be considered as Aristophanic compounds. Gryphius published an
edition of twenty plays of Plautus in 1535.

---

[1] *de leg. connub.* fol. 74, verso (ed. 2a, 1524); *R.E.R.* ix. 73.

In the borrowings from the scholars Budé, Erasmus, Tiraqueau and Caelius Rhodiginus it is not only the faculty of assimilation and adaptation that is remarkable, but the power of transmutation and amplification in the same strain. In the passages taken from Erasmus perhaps the changes are not so great, for instance in the first paragraphs of the *Gargantua* Prologue, adapted from the *Sileni Alcibiadis* of the *Adagia*, iii. 3. 1, as in the Prologue to the *Third Book*, where Budé's translation and adaptation of Lucian on Diogenes and his Cask is itself adapted and amplified with marvellous dramatic skill, or again in iii. 37, where Tiraqueau's bald statement of the decision of a Paris fool, in accordance with a gloss on a papal rescript in the Decretals, is transmuted into the highly graphic story of Seigny John giving his award in the dispute of the Cook and the Porter. In these cases and many more, whatever is borrowed is transformed and, if necessary, amplified in a manner that is truly wonderful; the mere matter and substratum are retained, but the presentation is so graphic and the dramatic *ethos* of the speakers so vividly maintained that the original story is almost lost and the pure Rabelais stands out.

RABELAIS ON RELIGION

That Rabelais was inspired by genuine religious feeling can hardly be doubted by anyone who reads attentively the prefaces to his Almanacks for 1533 and 1535; in the first he protests strongly against the curiosity of mortals who would pry into the hidden secrets and purposes of the Almighty; the fragment concludes with a quotation from Proverbs xxv. 27, "Whoso prieth out His Majesty shall be crushed thereby". This is curiously supported by Panurge's exclamation in iii. 30, where he resents the conditional "if it please God", as being an invitation to search out the fore-knowledge of the Deity. "You refer me to God's privy council", he cries in an expression that is comically echoed in Butler's *Hudibras*, where so much of Rabelais is repeated:

> Others still gape t'anticipate
> The cabinet designs of Fate,
> Apply to wizards to foresee
> What shall and what shall never be.
>
> *Hud.* ii. 3. 23.

In the Almanack for 1535 Rabelais adduces an argument for the immortality of the soul from the impossibility of satisfying man's desire for knowledge in this life. This desire being implanted by nature, which gives nothing in vain, must needs find satisfaction, otherwise the desire would be nugatory. As it does not find satisfaction in this life there *must* be another life: "Tunc satiabor cum apparuerit gloria tua", Ps. xvi. 15.

Again, at the end of the Prologue to the *Fourth Book*, after an amusing tirade against immoderate desires, exemplified so instructively by his version of the fable of Mercury and the Woodman, he advises his patients to restrict their desires to wishes for health, and imagining them to reply that "to the Almighty a million of gold is as little as an obol", he administers the rebuke: "By whom were you taught to discuss and talk in this way of the power and predestination of God? Hush! Humble yourselves before His sacred presence and recognise your own shortcomings".

In the *Gargantua*, c. 38, he scoffs lightly at the "application" of the 124th psalm by the pilgrims who had escaped being swallowed by Gargantua in a salad, and in the 40th chapter he inveighs seriously against the idle monks who do nothing but devour the offerings collected from the workers of the world, and "mumble through their legends and psalms without understanding them, and count Paternosters and Ave Marias without thinking of them or their meaning". This he calls "a mocking of God and not Prayer; whereas all true Christians pray to God and the Spirit prayeth and intercedeth for them and God receiveth them into favour". In this the monks are contrasted with the resolute and active Brother John, who works "and defends the oppressed, comforts the afflicted and guards the Abbey-close".

In c. 45 he represents Grandgousier venting righteous indignation against the preachers who affirm that diseases are sent by various saints to plague men for their sins, as Homer represents Apollo plaguing the Greeks at the request of the priest Chryses. Here Rabelais is probably following Hippocrates (*On Epilepsy*, c. 1), who protests strongly against the gods being made responsible for diseases. Grandgousier also warns the pilgrims against the idle and unprofitable pilgrimages which were then so much in vogue, bidding them rather follow the precepts of St Paul to care for their families and to labour each one in his vocation. Also in iv. 23 he insists that prayer ought to be accompanied by our own efforts; we ought to be fellow-workers with God (1 Cor. iii. 9).

Chapter 46 discourses against wars and invasions of neighbouring territories as opposed to the teaching of the Gospel, by which we are enjoined each to administer his own possessions and not to invade others. Men are taught not to seek their own advantage to the detriment of the public good and to avoid war by every possible means of conciliation. Later, in the Prologue to the *Third Book*, he is full of praise of the glory and beauty of war—probably in opposition to Erasmus (*Dulce bellum inexpertis, Ad.* iv. 1. 1), but in this Rabelais is speaking of the defensive war of France in 1544, when he patriotically prophesies an enlargement of her dominions.

In the chapters on the Abbey of Thelema willing obedience and mutual consideration is insisted on, as well as rational pursuits in education, mental and physical, combined with recreation; this is instead of cramping regulations, which stunt the development of cheerful compliance with reasonable discipline.

On the other side every opportunity is taken to discredit monasteries and nunneries and their inmates. They are looked upon as so many retreats for cowardly persons who shirk their duties in this world in order to live in the idleness of routine and enjoy uninterrupted gluttony and frivolity and oftentimes debauchery and immorality. The inmates are mostly *rejectanea* and offscourings, the useless or deformed scions of noble families, the failures, ne'er-do-wells and criminals of the world, who enjoy a careless life freed from necessary and reasonable labour. How opposed is this system to that of the Vestal Virgins, who were chosen from the best families in Rome and carefully scrutinised to see that they should be without the smallest spot or blemish of body or mind! (*G.* 52; iv. 46, 58; v. 4).

These were no new charges. Indeed Rabelais borrows the indictment and often its very words from Cornelius Agrippa, *de vanitate scientiarum*, c. 62. Clément Marot (*Chants divers*, ii) brings similar accusations; this system of refuges appears to have furnished commonplaces for invectives. See for instance Tacitus, *Ann.* iii. 60, Dionysius of Halicarnassus, vi. 46 (on the *Mons Sacer*), Plutarch, *de Superstitione*, 166 E. Many examples may be found in the Italian

Novelle, in the *Cent Nouvelles nouvelles* and the *Heptameron*. The "Cave of Adullam" naturally suggests itself.

But it was above all the Mendicants whom he satirised with all his weapons; against them were levelled violent terms of abuse and injurious names. He looked upon them, as he had reason to do, as the ignorant, debauched, frivolous hinderers of learning. Such indeed he had found them at Fontenay-le-Comte, and when once he was enlisted on the side of the humanists by Pierre Amy and Guillaume Budé, he could feel towards them nothing but antipathy. For the Benedictines, who had shewn themselves for ten centuries the fosterers of learning and the patrons of industry and hospitality, he entertained kindly feelings, and we cannot forget that Brother John, the resolute, helpful, ever-ready Brother John, ignorant of everything but his breviary, but handy and resourceful in every difficulty, was a Benedictine and a sturdy maintainer of the virtues of the frock and cowl.

His attitude towards the Roman Church, in which he was born and in which he had belonged to one of the strictest Orders, resembled that of Erasmus. He could not be blind to the serious charges to which that Church had been exposed by the simony and nepotism of the Popes and by the scandals of pluralism. The vicious and unclerical lives of many of the higher clergy, and of the Popes at the head of them, were a grave offence, and the building of St Peter's, which required extraordinary outlays, only to be met by special collections of pardon money and exactions, *annates*, indulgences and tithes gathered for pretended crusades, caused deep searchings of heart in many devout Romanists, even before the Lutheran revolt. In France many persons of high birth and station were well affected to what were called the new doctrines; for instance, Margaret, Queen of Navarre, sister of Francis I, and Renée, Duchess of Ferrara, his sister-in-law, extended their protection to many men of learning and culture who were suspected of heretical leanings. Renée was treated harshly by her husband on this account (*Epp. Rom.* i. § 3), and Noel Beda, the Sorbonnist doctor, had the assurance to attempt charges against Margaret, which Francis, who was tenderly attached to his sister, strongly resented, so much so that he had the accuser imprisoned.

Rabelais was naturally alive to all this and, living in Lyons, could scarcely help sympathising with the movement; for it ran to a great extent in parallel lines with the humanism which was one of the guiding principles and objects of his life; indeed these lines often were so much thought to converge that persons of humanistic tastes were suspected of the Lutheran taint. This is evidenced in Budé's second letter to Rabelais, noting that he was suspected and badly treated by the Fontenay brothers on account of the recently published Commentaries of Erasmus on St Paul's epistles; again we see in iv. 46 the junior devil attributing to the study of St Paul the difficulty experienced in providing souls of students for Lucifer's breakfast.

It seems that both Erasmus and Rabelais felt antipathy to the established religion much more on account of the persistent ignorance of the monks and the persecutions designed for the suppression of the revived learning than because of doctrinal differences, though these were not ignored by them. But men who deliberately quenched the sacred torch of literature for themselves and for others incurred the contempt and hostility of these pioneers of learning and civilisation.

In a few places a cautious protest is ventured against the merciless persecutions that were being directed against heresy or the suspicion of it, but such protests were necessarily more or less veiled. Two cases may be cited—one in iii. 29, where the "whole and sole occupation of the good Theologians" is said to be "in extirpating errors and heresies by deeds, by words, by writings and in planting deep in the hearts of men the true and lively Catholic Faith". Another very dexterous instance is in iii. 51, where "we have heard others, at the moment when Atropos was cutting the thread of their life, complaining that Pantagruel held them by the throat; but it was not Pantagruel a bit; it was Pantagruelion [hemp] serving them for a collar... I swear that the noble Pantagruel never took anyone by the throat, unless it were those who were negligent in preventing the coming thirst". And when we find that occasionally in these books *par ma soif* is substituted for *par ma foi* it is permissible to suspect covert allusions.

HIS ATTITUDE TOWARDS BIBLICAL STUDIES

As might be expected, Rabelais in the Cloister had made an intimate acquaintance with the service books, the Breviary and the Missal, which were necessary for every priest, monk and friar; but he shews that he had done more than that; for although most of his biblical quotations and allusions may be traced to the Breviary or the Missal—indeed Brother John scarcely knew anything beyond his *matière de Bréviaire*—Rabelais had characteristically gone beyond this and read his Vulgate in the light of the explanations of Nicholas De Lyra (1270–1340), the converted Jew, whose commentary was in vogue till the Reformation times, and the Pauline Epistles with the commentary of Erasmus, as we learn from the second letter from Budaeus. Indeed, he seems to have learned something of the Hebrew text and the Massoretic interpretation, as well as of the Chaldaic version or Targum, which is commended to Pantagruel by his father (*P.* 8), and referred to in the preface to his Almanack of 1533 in "Tibi *silentium* Deus in Sion" (Psalm lxiv. 1); this however may have been derived from Politian, *Miscellanea*, 83.

Notwithstanding this, M. Plattard does well to point out that Rabelais' acquaintance with the Scriptures did not extend beyond that of an ordinary well-instructed churchman. The impropriety or profanity in his quotations was less thought of than it is in our own times. It could easily be paralleled from sermons of contemporary preachers such as Menot, Maillard or Bourgeois. Two of Rabelais' best stories are derived from sermons, and the *Gesta Romanorum* were probably compiled for nothing else but to supply preachers with matter of amusement in their sermons. This appears pretty clearly from an examination of the Scriptural passages which were altered in the *Pantagruel* and the *Gargantua*, to disarm the susceptibility of the theological faculty. The propositions that were looked upon as "scandalous, heretical and offensive to pious ears" were: (1) offences against Mariolatry and worship of the saint. Rabelais changed "une liasse d'oignons liée de trois cents Ave Mariatz" into "trois cents naveaulx" (*P.* 11) in 1542. In *G.* 6 he omitted an allusion to St Margaret and in *G.* 17 he omitted a long list of adjurations of numerous saints of different nationalities.

(2) He makes no omission of the few gibes at the pardoners, etc.
(3) On the translation and interpretation of the Scriptures, on
which the theologians were very touchy, he makes one alteration.
In *P.* 34 he had written (A) "Ce sont beaux textes d'evangiles en
français"; this is changed in 1542 (D) to "ce sont belles besoignes".
(4) He had made fun of the professors of theology, and had spoken
irreverently of the Sorbonne and theologians. In every case these
words are altered into *sophiste* and *sophisticquement,* etc. He also
changes *frater de Cornibus* into *frater Lubinus,* so as not to attack, even
in fun, a well-known Franciscan preacher. Though these were the
real grievances with the Sorbonne, it was easy for the theologians
to attack the Rabelaisian books on the score of coarseness and as
being *contra bonos mores.* In point of fact his sympathies were clearly
on the side of the early Reformers, and this was the true cause of
the hostility of the Sorbonne.

RABELAIS AS LEGIST

As a legist, Rabelais shews traces of the different influences to
which he had been subjected in the very varied experiences of his
life. In the Cloister at Fontenay-le-Comte from 1511 till 1524,
when he was released by the indult of Clement VII, it was his duty
to acquaint himself with the canon law—the Decretum of Gratian
and the Decretals of Gregory IX and other Pontiffs—by which he
and his Cloister were governed, and no doubt he read diligently
Budé's *Commentary on XXIV Books of the Pandects* (or Digest) and
other parts of Roman Law, for in his second letter to Rabelais
Budé credits him with considerable knowledge of law. In his residence at Ligugé under the protection of his enlightened friend
Geoffroi d'Estissac, the Bishop of Maillezais, he was evidently in
constant communication with the distinguished lawyers and
scholars André Tiraqueau, Amaury Bouchard and Jean Bouchet,
as we may gather from his Letters prefixed to the works he dedicated to them and from his rhymed letter to Bouchet and Bouchet's
response. It may also be presumed that he studied law at Poitiers
about this time (1524–5), from the record of his travels that he
gives in *P.* 5—it is generally accepted that Pantagruel's travels
roughly describe the writer's own journeyings—and in iii. 41,
where he is represented by Judge Bridlegoose. At Bourges also he

studied law, perhaps under Alciati, and attained considerable proficiency, but his bent was undoubtedly towards medicine and natural science, as may be seen in the itinerary he attributes to Pantagruel in *P.* 5, as well as in his *Supplicatio pro Apostasia* addressed to Paul III in January 1536, where he declares: "the aforesaid Petitioner departing from the said Church [Maillezais] without leave of his Superior, having laid aside the regular habit and taken that of secular priest, long time gone abroad through the world, and during that time devoted himself diligently to the faculty of Medicine and taken in it the degrees required for that purpose".

But notwithstanding the fact that Rabelais definitely took up the study of medicine he did not lose sight of the study of law; but he was more inclined to adopt the standpoint of the humanists Valla, Politian, Budaeus, Erasmus and others, who decried the barbarous Latinity and the absurdity of the glosses of Accursius, Bartolus, Baldus, etc. in the civil law and those of Giovanni Andreae, Durand, Panormitanus, Barbatia in the canon law. Rabelais was more disposed to treat law on its scientific and philosophical side than to regard it as a mere bundle of case-law reinforced and illustrated by moral maxims from classical authors, the ethical poetry of the first four or five centuries and the leonine or rhyming hexameters of grammarians and monkish writers.

Consequently we have in the *Pantagruel*, cc. 11–13, a tissue of incoherence, with an allusion here and there to contemporary events, probably designed to set his readers guessing at the meaning of what was intentionally without meaning, and to hold up to ridicule such unintelligible pleadings.

In the *Third Book*, at the Trial of Judge Bridlegoose (cc. 39–44), we find the old judge very exact and punctilious in recounting the forms of procedure in their due order of summoning, the preparation of the papers for the plaintiff and the defendant and the examination of the testimony for both sides, the shifts and evasions of the litigants (these had been alluded to in the *Pantagruel* under the head of *cautelae*) and the judgment and its execution. Most of his knowledge on these points is derived from the *Forensia*, or Practice of the Courts, of Budaeus (cf. *R.E.R.* xi. 31–9). Bridlegoose then explains that after having several times examined these papers he gives his decision according to a throw of the dice. This is objected to by the judge presiding at the trial and defended most ingeniously by the old judge with a parade of legal learning that is quite bewildering. No statement of the most trivial kind is put forward without the support of five or six quotations from the Digest, the Code or the Decretum and Decretals to back it, generally eked out by some hexameter or pentameter, which was the form of many of the glosses, to give point to the contention. It is true that in the special case of Judge Bridlegoose, which furnishes the greatest display of legal learning in Rabelais, the sympathies of the reader are enlisted on the side of the humorous old judge and the shrewd common sense and worldly wisdom which he displays, but even then the summary of the affair in the chapter succeeding the account of the trial (iii. 44) is very severe, even on the Pandects and their compiler Tribonianus, when it is declared that cases may as well be decided by a throw of the dice as by the ordinances of laws got together in shreds and patches as were the laws of Justinian. The tenor of this agrees perfectly with what Pantagruel declares in *P.* 10 in depreciation of the legists and canonists, while in *P.* 8 he is required by his father Gargantua to acquaint himself with the admirable *texts* of the laws and to compare them with philosophy; meaning, no doubt, that law should be studied in its broad principles of equity rather than in minute technicalities, which are liable to perversion by the chicanery of case-lawyers. All this is in keeping with the breadth of view that Rabelais exhibits on every subject that he sets before us.

In the *Fourth Book*, cc. 48–53, instigated by Cardinals du Bellay and Châtillon, Rabelais ventures to attack the Roman Church on a vulnerable side, which would render it obnoxious to French policy, viz. on the exactions authorised by the Decretals in the form of *annates* and other dues payable to the Roman Church. He asserts that by the aurifluous energy of certain of the Decretals 400,000 ducats and more are drawn from France to Rome. This is the charge that would bear heavily against Rome; the extravagant laudation of the Decretals is put into the mouth of Homenaz, the Roman Bishop, in the sheerest mockery.

In the *Fifth Book*, cc. 11–14, there is only a general invective against the exactions and corruption of the law-courts; the main charge is that the laws resemble spiders' webs, through which the big malefactor wasps break their way, while the tiny gnats and moths are held fast in the meshes. It is the execution rather than the sentence of the laws that is here reprobated. An instance of the evasion and defiance of the execution is already to be found in iv. 12–15, where the Lord of Basché has the Catchpoles beaten within an inch of their lives by his servants, under pretence of celebrating a wedding, in which one of the ceremonies consisted of giving slight fisticuffs as a memorial.

ON SCENIC REPRESENTATIONS, ETC.

Rabelais seems to have resembled the *Bourgeois de Paris* who has given us in his journal so minute and detailed an account of the events that were to be witnessed during a long part of the reign of Francis I, as to remind us often of the delightful gossip of Samuel Pepys in his diary (1659–69). The allusions to mystery plays and other scenic representations, especially the songs, mountebank tricks and farces presented by Jehan de l'Espine du Pontalletz better known as Songecreux, are particularly interesting.

He is mentioned under the name of Pontalais in the dizain in honour of Rabelais prefixed to the *Pantagruel* in later editions of P. de Tours and in the edition of Four Books published in 1553. In the *Journal d'un Bourgeois de Paris* we are told that he was imprisoned in 1516 together with two other *joueurs de farce* for saying that *Mere Sotte* (*i.e.* Louise de Savoye) governed France. Rabelais speaks of him in *Pantagruel*, c. 7, as representing in a *ballade*, that is in a poem accompanied by dancing, a *Prognostication*.

The practice of presenting songs with a dancing accompaniment was very common in France; a good instance may be seen at once in the list of songs given with dancing in the *Fifth Book*, c. 33 (whether it was written by Rabelais or not), and the practice in antiquity is proved (if proof were necessary) by a line in Ovid, *Trist.* ii. 1. 519: "Et mea sunt populo saltata poemata saepe". In *Gargantua*, c. 20, Songecreux is again alluded to as provoking laughter in his audience to an extraordinary degree. There survive of this writer *Les contredictz de Songe Creux* and *Pronostication de maistre Albert Songe Creux* (*A.P.F.* xii. 168–92). Again in *Gargantua*, c. 17, the people of Paris are taunted with silliness to such an extent as to delight in the tricks of a mountebank or a fiddler more than in the preaching of the Gospel. Another kind of entertainment alluded to is the *Asnerie* (or *Asinaria*) of Plautus in iii. 38, but an oblique reference is intended to the *Feste des Asnes*, by which was represented at Beauvais and other places the flight into Egypt, when an ass with a young woman on it was led up to the altar and the priest, instead of saying *Ite missa est,* sang three times *hihan* or *inian*, imitating the braying of an ass. This exclamation is put into the mouth of Homenaz, the Bishop of the Papimanes, in iv. 52.

In iii. 38 Rabelais, in pointing out that the *Quirinalia* in ancient Rome was known as the *Stultorum festa*, practically identifies it (for his present purpose) with the *Feste des Folz* in France. The *Feste des Folz, des Diacres, des Innocents* or *de l'Asne* were of the same nature in France, according to the period or locality. They were definitely suppressed in 1547. Bishops were elected and sometimes a Pope, who, clad in pontifical vestments, was paraded through the streets, was brought into the choir of the churches with all kinds of disorderly revelry and songs, and games of cards and dice. Perhaps an allusion to this may be traced in *le maul gouvert* (the Lord of Misrule) *de Louze fougerouse*, or Loge-Fougerouse, a town near La Chataigneraye (Vendée) (cf. *R.E.R.* ii. 164). Another allusion to this may be found in the *Anciennes poésies françaises*, iii. 19: "L'abbé de Maugouverne aussi". Scott in his *Abbot*, c. 14, describes a scene of this kind and appends an instructive note (Note E) on the subject. Cf. also Frazer, *Golden Bough*, "The Scapegoat", p. 313.

Rabelais also mentions the *basauchiens* (*G.* 54), the clerks of the Bazoche (*Basilica*), the *Palais de Justice*, or law-court, in Paris. They were a very old Guild (1302) and appointed their own King, Chancellor, etc. They played at an early period *farces*, *sotties* and *moralités*, but they and the *Enfants Sans-souci* were looked upon as amateurs, as distinguished from the *Jongleurs* and the *Confrairies de la Passion*. He also mentions the Bazoche again in iii. 21 and iv. 32, but in a manner that has little or no bearing on the present subject.

He was evidently interested in representations of the Passion, for we find several allusions to such pieces. In iii. 3 *La Passion de Saulmur* is spoken of as a very grand and solemn function. It is probably the Mystery written by Jean Michel de Pierrevive and given at Angers during four days from Aug. 12, 1486; played again at Saumur in July 1534. On the other hand he twice mentions the Passion at Doué as very confused and disorderly. Twice also he speaks of the Passion played at St Maixent in Poitou (iii. 27; iv. 13), but on both occasions considerable confusion resulted from causes detailed and they may be considered as very disorderly.

The phraseology of Rabelais is full of allusions to scenic representations, most, if not all, of which have been got together in *R.E.R.* viii. 1–68 ("Rabelais et le Théâtre"). We find him speaking of political and other events as *tragicomedies*; the end of Guillaume du Bellay is spoken of as *la fin et catastrophe de la comoedie* (*Fabulae catastrophe*, Erasm. *Ad.* i. 2. 36). He gives a spirited account in iii. 34 of the moral comedy of the man who married a dumb wife, played at Montpellier by F. Rabelais and other medical students. It has been supposed by some that Rabelais himself composed it. This is quite possible, the leading ideas in it being borrowed from Terence, *Andria*, 643: "Utinam aut hic surdus aut haec muta facta sit" and Horace, *Sat.* ii. 3. 30: "Ut lethargicus hic cum fit pugil et medicum urget"; while the severing of the string of the tongue is from St Mark vii. 3: "solutum est vinculum linguae ejus et loquebatur recte", and the very word ἀγκυλόγλωσσος occurs in Manardi, *Epistolae medicinales*, vii. 3, which were edited by Rabelais. The description of the *Sciomachia* or sham fight in Rome in 1549 testifies clearly enough to his delight in all manner of theatrical display.

Allusions to the *diableries* or representations of the inhabitants of the lower world, which survived from the mystery and morality plays, abound. Lucifer, Mahoun, Proserpine, Megaera, Allecto, Ashteroth, etc. meet us as well as Demogorgon, probably derived from Ravisius Textor, who speaks of him as one of the *Di superni*, *repertus in visceribus terrae.*

A list of places where *diableries* were represented is put in Villon's mouth in iv. 13—Saumur, Doué, Montmorillon, Langès, St Espain, Angers and Poitiers, places in Touraine, Anjou and Poitou— shewing the gusto he found in such representations.

Gargantua (c. 24) "went to see the Jugglers, Conjurors and Quacksalvers and paid attention to Antics, Tricks and Somersaults, etc." This furnishes a hint of the observant character of our author, even though the idea be to a certain extent paralleled in

Athenaeus, xi. 464E, which of itself would commend the notice to
the humanistic side of his character.

The number of citations from *La farce de Maistre Pierre Patelin*
point in the same directions as do the "Morris dances, Masks,
Mummeries, Farces, Comedies and Merry Tales" played by
Rhizotomus at a wedding (iv. 52), when the use of the leaves of an
old copy of the *Sextum* in the Decretals for masks led to the miraculous disfigurement of the wearers.

In iii. 37 *les Jongleurs* are spoken of, practically corresponding to
our "Strolling Players", and among them is mentioned *le Sot* et
le Badin.

RABELAIS' MEDICAL KNOWLEDGE

Besides the lists in the "Anatomy of Lent" in iv. 30, 31, there is a
great deal of medicine and surgery to be found in Rabelais, shewing that he took up the profession of his life as earnestly as he had
done the two faculties of divinity and law, to which he had previously devoted himself. The number of citations and allusions to
passages in Scripture and his references to Church government and
canon law are sufficient proof in one case, while his many references
to Justinian's Digest and Code and the glosses thereon argue considerable familiarity with the legal studies of his time on the other
side. But his interest in medicine seems even greater than is shewn
in the other two studies.

The *Pantagrueline Prognostication*, as we might expect, refers to the
Arabic physicians and philosophers Averroes and Avicenna, as
well as Albumazar, Avenzagul, Hali Abbas and Avenzouar, but in
a Prognostication of this kind, mostly intended to raise a laugh, it
is natural to expect references to the Arabs, who have always been
looked upon as astrologers *par excellence*. But even in this burlesque
writing a reference may be found to the *Colliget*, the great medical
treatise of Averroes (c. 3), to an aphorism of Hippocrates (v. 39)
and to a dictum of Galen, *contraria contrariis curantur* (*Method.
medendi*, xi. 12). Again in the Almanack to 1533 Rabelais quotes
the celebrated first aphorism of Hippocrates, *Vita brevis, ars longa*,
and in that of 1535 Galen's frequently repeated declaration that
"Nature has made nothing without reason".

In *Pantagruel*, c. 1, there is an allusion to the *ptisane*, the celebrated diet drink of barley water, to which both Hippocrates and Galen have devoted a treatise; c. 8 speaks of "the Microcosm", which Galen ascribes to older physicists. Twice (*P.* 18 and iii. 32) he seems to derive from Galen (*de usu part.* viii. 2) an exclamation against those who dispute to maintain a thesis rather than to find out the truth.

Rabelais is learned on the subject of hot mineral springs in c. 33, but his learning is derived from Hippocrates and Pliny, and he furnishes a list of a dozen places in France and Italy where mineral waters were drunk or used in baths; after which he gives a gigantic prescription of Scammony, cassia and rhubarb for his giant prince. Besides this, two or three ordinary medical allusions may be found, as well as some mention of medicinal plants.

In the *Gargantua*, prologue, he cites Galen (*de usu part.* xi. 18), somewhat incorrectly, on the substance of the marrow, and in the 3rd chapter parades an array of learning on the possible legitimacy of a child born in the eleventh month after the death of the father. Most of his authorities (among them Hippocrates, *de alimento*) are simply taken from a passage in Gellius, while Rabelais adds two of his own, one of which is a passage in Servius' commentary on Virg. *Ecl.* iv. 61. This derives additional interest from being used again in iii. 12 and 51. Later on in 1540, Pellicier, Bishop of Maguelonne, French ambassador at Venice, consulted our author on this very point. The letter is still preserved.

In the 6th chapter the birth of Gargantua from the left ear of his mother, at first sight merely a piece of indecent profanity, proves on nearer examination to be a parade of anatomical knowledge grafted on to a singular materialistic piece of theology of the Roman Church. It is an almost literal interpretation of the text *Verbum caro factum est*, which may be found in painted windows in France and elsewhere. The speech of the angel is represented as a ray of light penetrating the ear of the Virgin, and the figure of a small child may be seen depicted in the ray. There is also a hymn of St Ephrem containing the words

> Gaude, virgo, mater Christi
> Quae *per aurem* concepisti
> Gabriele nuntio,

and still more outspokenly the pious peroration of the *Liber Thobiae*
in the *Auctores octo morales* gives

> Felix conjugium, dum se sacra verba maritant
> Auriculae, verbum fit caro patre carens.
> Angelus obstetrix; pater infans, sermo maritus,
> Auris sponsa parens nata, creatur homo.

Galen supplies anatomical passages by which such a birth might
be miraculously possible: "And so in our account we have brought
the *vena cava* to the diaphragm" (*de usu part.* vi. 1) and "conducting
upwards the *vena cava* from the diaphragm to the throat" (*id.* vi. 4).

Galen is quoted (*de simpl. med.* ix. 2. 9) on the green jasper, as
formerly worn by King Nechepsos. It was worn as an amulet
against epilepsy and divers ailments. Here Rabelais wrote probably with his tongue in his cheek (*G.* 8). In the 10th chapter he is
again cited on the subject of snow-blindness (with a quotation from
Xenophon's *Anabasis*), and in the same chapter three of his passages
are referred to on the subject of death from excessive joy when it
comes unexpectedly. Two passages in Avicenna are correctly cited
on an over-dose of saffron producing the same result, as also a
problem of Alexander of Aphrodisias in support of this experience.
The *Problems* of Aristotle and Alexander had been translated by
Theodore Gaza. Ten instances of deaths from excessive and sudden
joy are now given, apparently from Cicero, Pliny, Livy, Gellius
and others, but they are really derived from the *Officina* of Ravisius
Textor.

The treatise on education, cc. 23, 24, is supported by references
to Greek medical writings. The precepts followed are ascribed to
"Master Theodorus, a learned physician", and it is amusing to
find that in the earlier editions Seraphin Calobarsy (an anagram
on Phrancoys Rabelais) is the name given to the physician. After
bearing with the vicious system by which his pupil had been in-
doctrinated, because Nature does not well endure sudden changes
(Hippocrates), Ponocrates, the tutor, has Gargantua purged by
hellebore, so as to rid him of his perverse habit of brain, and then
puts him under his own system and, among other items of instruction, causes him to learn passages bearing on the meals that
come to table, written by Pliny, Athenaeus, Galen, Aristotle and
others; and afterwards in botanical excursions instructs him out of

Theophrastus, Pliny, Dioscorides, Nicander, Galen and others. From this we learn where to look for the information that Rabelais scatters so profusely in his "books".

The war between Grandgousier's army, conducted by Gargantua, and that of Picrochole is rich in anatomical passages and quite Homeric in the details of the wounds given. The sutures of the skull, the various parts of the neck and body, as they are gashed by Brother John, allow of the display of considerable surgical knowledge, which is pronounced to be quite correct by Dr Le Double (*Rabelais Anatomiste*). Rabelais and Galen give only two *meninges* or membranes to the brain, whereas three are known to modern anatomists; otherwise the account given is that of a skilful surgeon.

In iii. 2 is a quotation from an aphorism (i. 13) of Hippocrates that "Youth is impatient of hunger", but in c. 4 there is an elaborate account of the "Hierarchy", *i.e.* the due arrangement and subordination of the organs and limbs of the "Microcosm", *i.e.* Little World, that is Man (cf. Galen, *de usu part.* iii. 10). The whole of this eloquent and highly wrought passage is founded on a passage of Hippocrates, *de alimento*, ii. 20, a treatise previously referred to in *G.* 3, κατὰ μὲν οὐλομελίην πάντα συμπαθέα, κατὰ μέρος δὲ τὰ ἐν ἑκάστῳ μέρει μέρεα πρὸς τὸ ἔργον. This is interpreted by Galen (*de usu part.* i. 8) to mean "the parts of the body are all in sympathy with each other, that is they are in agreement for the combined performance of one task". Rabelais proceeds to describe in detail the formation of the blood, and then its conveyance by the arteries and veins to and from the various organs set apart for that purpose. Much of this is doubtless derived from the 4th and 6th books of Galen's *de usu partium*, but there is also a passage very like in matter and arrangement in Cicero, *de Nat. Deor.* ii. §§ 133–8, which is quoted by Budaeus, *de Asse*, lib. i. p. 44, so that here we may be pretty sure we have Rabelais' source. There is a considerable amount of anatomical writing in the *Timaeus* of Plato, who was well acquainted with Hippocrates' work, and our accomplished French physician had certainly read the *Timaeus* as well as several dialogues. One point is corrected by modern anatomy. The *rete mirabile* (τὸ καλούμενον δικτυοειδὲς πλέγμα μέγιστον θαῦμα τῶν ἐνταυθοῖ, Galen, *de Hippoc. et Plat.* vii. 4) is spoken of here and in iii. 31

and iv. 30. It is described as a labyrinthine system of innumerable arteries, veins and glands situated in the brain on the mucous membrane. In this are retained the vital spirits (ψυχικὸν πνεῦμα) during their elaboration into animal spirits (ζωτικὸν πνεῦμα). Dr J. P. Payne in his *Hunterian Oration*, 1896, says that "the description of the *rete mirabile* is a mistaken notion of Galen's detected by Vesalius".

Rabelais cites Galen in the 6th chapter on the danger of living in newly whitewashed houses, and in the 7th he claims his authority for the assertion that the head is made for the eyes, as lighthouses are constructed on heights near seaports. In the 13th chapter he refers to Hippocrates and Galen among others for the conditions necessary to be observed in divination from dreams, insisting that the mind must free itself from all passions, and the body must be kept clear from perturbations arising from improper or excessive food and drink; but on the other hand a long fast is not conducive to secure trustworthy visions, for that, in order to remedy hunger and the cravings of the stomach, the veins suck for themselves the substance belonging to the fleshy members (Galen, *de usu part.* iv. 19) and so draw down again the spirit which was roaming from the body towards its celestial home. In the 14th we are told from the physicians (Hippoc. *Epid.* vi. 5. 5 and Galen's Commentary on it, iv. 20) that sleep strengthens the powers of digestion and that a sudden waking from this state signifies and portends evil.

In the 22nd chapter Epistemon, who, we learn from iii. 34, was at Montpellier with Rabelais, like a true *medico* suggests from Hippocrates (*Aph.* iii. 26) that the old poet Raminagrobis may be suffering from worms in his body, or from the *filaria Medinensis* or guinea worm, a sort of subcutaneous worm which in Arabia attacks the arms and legs. This is interesting as being discussed in Galen, *de locis affectis*, vi. 3, Avicenna's *Canon*, iv. 3. 2. 21 and Ambroise Paré, vi. 23.

In c. 24 the learned Epistemon, after rallying Panurge on the vagaries of dress which he had adopted in his perplexity, is called in to give his opinion on the subject of the proposed marriage. After citing the first *Aphorism* of Hippocrates on the hazard of empirical treatment and the difficulty of judgment, he gives a learned account of various oracles in the world, but advises that, since their authority has ceased, he should not put his faith in them too readily. He also refuses to listen to Panurge's suggestion to consult Saturn, who is chained in the Ogygian islands. Most of this learning comes from Plutarch.

In c. 25 Her Trippa pronounces unfavourably on the formation of Panurge's chest. Hippocrates (*Epid.* vi. 3. 10) asserts that such persons are subject to catarrh. In c. 29 Brother John ventures on the assertion that nurses lose their milk if they desist from suckling children. This is from Galen, *de loc. affect.* vi. 6. In c. 29 Galen's *dictum* that medicine is the art of healing the sick and preserving the health of the sound (*Thrasyb.* c. 5) is propounded.

In c. 31 the physician Rondibilis, giving his advice on the subject of marriage, is naturally full of all manner of remedies in the interests of continence. He gives (1) indulgence in wine (from Plutarch); (2) the use of certain herbs (from Pliny); (3) assiduous labour (from Aristotle, Tiraqueau and Hippocrates), with a warning against idleness, with instances derived from Tiraqueau; (4) fervent study, mostly suggested from Cicero's *Tusculans*, i. §§ 74–5, and enforced from Plutarch, Lucian and Hippocrates; (5) sensual indulgence.

Chapter 32 is devoted by Rondibilis, who represents Rondelet, the Montpellier professor, to the causes of infidelity among women, and naturally the treatment of the subject is from a medical standpoint. After citing from a letter of Hippocrates to a friend, directing him to keep a watch on his wife during his absence on a visit to Democritus—not that he has reason to mistrust her, but simply because she is a woman—Rondibilis goes on to speak of the inconstancy and imperfection of women, and then proceeds to maintain a thesis of Plato in the *Timaeus*, when he asserts that the *uterus* is ζῷον ἔνον ἐπιθυμητικὸν τῆς παιδοποιίας (91 B) and that unless this animal is assuaged dire disorder results. Although a good deal of this is taken from Tiraqueau's book, it is reinforced from Avicenna and Plato with quotations insisting that the *uterus* exists as an animal apart from the control of the rest of the body. This is opposed by Galen (*de loc. affect.* vi. 5), who maintains that the loss of self-control is caused by noxious humours which arise. Galen is accused of conceit and prejudice against his elders.

At the end of this chapter is a little medical allusive banter, when Panurge offers Rondibilis some quince jelly and some white hippocras. The former he credits with a pleasing astringency (cf. Avicenna, *Canon*, v. 18: "Cydonia confita quae conveniunt ad confortandum stomachum et stringunt naturam") and assures the doctor that in the latter there is no *squinanthi* (σχοίνανθος, the scented reed, *juncus odoratus* of Pliny, 21. 120), so that he need have no fear of *esquinances* or quinzy. There is an oblique thrust at the doctor here, implying that he would call quinzy *squinantia*. Cf. Budaeus, *in Pand.* i. p. 543: "ab ignaris medicis non *synancha* (συνάγχη, cf. iv. 56) sed *squinantia* dicitur, simili errore atque...*sciatica* pro *ischiade* vel ischiaco dolore, qui et *ischiadicus* dicitur".

In c. 34 Rondibilis at the suggestion of sickness in a wife is prompt with a quotation from Hippocrates (*Aph.* ii. 35), while Panurge as a legist supplies a rubric from the Digest. At the end of the consultation and of the chapter, on the subject of a fee Rabelais develops a delicious phrase of Merlin Cocai, the macaronic poet, *medicorum more negantum*; he is himself improved on later by Molière (*Médecin malgré lui*, ii. 8). In c. 35 he speaks of a *neuter* in medicine and a *mean* in philosophy, referring probably to Galen's definition: "Medicina scientia est salubrium et insalubrium et *neutrorum*" (*Ars med.* c. 2). In c. 36 Panurge, in distress at the contradictory answers of Trouillogan, the Ephectic or Pyrrhonian philosopher, records his symptoms and fears he is bewitched. These symptoms in the *Aphorisms* (iv. 49) are put down as indicative of approaching death in the case of a continuous fever. Later he declares that his digestion is impeded and that his *phrenes, metaphrenes* and *diaphragms* are in a state of tension to understand these varying remarks. This is merely a distortion of anatomical terms.

Even Judge Bridlegoose in c. 40 parallels his delaying process with the medical practice (Hipp. *Aph.* i. 22) of waiting for the development of an ulcer before lancing it and in c. 41 cites a proverb: "Happy is the Physician who is called in at the declension of a disease".

In c. 45 physicians testify that the limbs are caused to tremble when sudden inspiration affects a small body (cf. Hippoc. *Prorrh.* i. 14). This is asserted in Shakespeare (*Hamlet*, iii. 4. 144): "Conceit in weakest bodies strongest works". Avicenna is quoted in the next chapter that the kinds of madness are infinite. The same thing is said by Galen (*de loc. affect.* iii. 7). The list of medical extracts for the *Third Book* concludes in the last chapter (52) by observations in Natural Science on the indestructibility by fire of the salamander and of larch wood. The first is from Galen (*de temper.* iii. 4) and the second from Pliny (16. 45) and Vitruvius (ii. 9. § 14).

In the *Fourth Book* the Prologue to the first (partial) edition (1548) refers to precepts given by Hippocrates and Galen to the physician to be extremely careful to avoid giving offence to the patient. He is to be scrupulously observant in every point—gestures, face, clothes, words, look, touch; he even particularises the nails. From this he turns to another passage in the *Epidemia* of Hippocrates, in which a theory is started, not as to whether the countenance of the physician, down-hearted or joyful, depresses or elates the patient—that may be taken for granted—but whether there is an actual transfusion of spirits from the physician. All this is repeated in the Epistle of Dedication of the completed *Fourth Book* to the Cardinal of Châtillon, with some additions and illustrations. The practice of medicine is compared by Hippocrates[1] (he says) to a farce played by three characters, the Physician, the Patient and the Disease. The combination of any two of them defeats the other. Bacon, *Apoph.* 152, attributes this to a Dr Johnson. Rabelais also gives three illustrations from Galen of the contrary practice in the case of some physicians, who scared and disgusted their patients by brutal answers to anxious questions. These were the Abernethys of the time.

In the Prologue to the new and completed *Fourth Book* Galen is held up as an example of a physician who was not only a successful practitioner in the case of others but also careful of his own health. For, he says, the physician will hardly be credited with care for the health of others who is neglectful of his own. The same is asserted of Asclepiades, a fashionable doctor of Pliny's time (7. 124). Galen is also said to have conversed with Christians, and three references to his writings are given to support the fact that he had some reverence for Holy writ. It is amusing to find that it is the obstinacy of the Christians in matters of faith that is most dwelt upon by Galen —"you would as easily convince Christians of their error as the

---

[1] *Epid.* i. 11. 5.

leaders of the sects of medicine and philosophy". Another passage Rabelais quotes as of doubtful authenticity, which ascribes to Christians the power of faith healing.

In the body of this book there is not much to interest us in medical matters except occasional *obiter dicta* and minor observations about teeth and unimportant points of the pharmacopoeia, and the mention of the *pericardium* as the capsule (σκληρὸς χιτών in Galen) of the heart. Attention may be drawn to one point at the termination of the celebrated storm. Epistemon the *medico* is speaking of the fright of Panurge, and insists that he felt as much fear himself but that it did not prevent him from doing his utmost to help. He goes on to say that death in this or that way lies partly in the will of God and partly in one's own discretion; therefore it is our duty to implore the help of *the Gods*, but not to make an end there; we ought to make our own endeavour to help *them*. From this it seems certain that this *dictum* is taken from Hippocrates (*de victus ratione,* lib. iv. *de insomn.* § 87) and not from the commonplace book of Plutarch (*Lac. Inst.* c. 29) copied by Erasmus. Of course the heathen "gods" are changed in the second edition and an apposite text is given on co-operation with the Deity from St Paul (1 Cor. iii. 9).

The list of the internal organs and the limbs of Lent have been spoken of (p. lxxxviii) as derived from Galen and illustrated by contemporary objects. Here perhaps the portrait of Lent as deduced by Dr Le Double from the comparisons supplied by Rabelais may be given. He was an old, lean, gawky, weak creature, tormented by repentance and physical infirmities, none too reputable. He had a round head, hollow cheeks, eyes drenched with tears, ears upstanding and ill-marked, a nose like a boot and wide nostrils, a wide mouth furnished with long yellow teeth, and no beard or hair, by reason of the tonsure. Altogether he was an unpleasant person.

Later on in the windy island (c. 43) every malady is due to Ventosity, according to Hippocrates, *de Flatibus,* and the *hypenemian* Podestà, the magistrate hatched from a wind-egg (from Galen), is spoken of. A story of Brother John's of a serpent being enticed out of a man's stomach by a bowl of milk is gravely corrected by Pantagruel out of Hippocrates. In c. 50 Rabelais recurs to a point insisted on in *Gargantua* (c. 45), that it is wicked to attribute to the Deity and to the saints the infliction of maladies. This is also the doctrine of Hippocrates. In c. 54 the sphragitid vermilion earth from Lemnos is spoken of. (A long account of it may be found in Galen.) In c. 58 a passage on "Ventriloquists", or *Engastrimythes*, is taken with references to Aristophanes, Plato, Sophocles and the *Decretum*, from Caelius Rhodiginus. Rabelais characteristically adds a passage from Hippocrates, and calls such people diviners and deceivers of the people, identifying them evidently with the pardon-pedlars and their false relics, etc.

In the *Fifth Book* not much medical lore is to be found; there is more in the episode of Queen Quintessence, cc. 18–25, but throughout the book small allusions are let fall, which go to prove that the writer was versed in anatomy and medical science. In the Prologue a *dictum* of Avicenna is quoted, *Maniae infinitae sunt species* (*Canon*, iii. 1. 4. 19), and another of Hippocrates (*Aph.* iii. 20) to the effect that madness generally shews itself in spring. In c. 9 there is a passage, probably suggested by Galen (*de usu part.* xv. 4), to the effect that under the tool-bearing trees the proper handles were growing, each suitable to its kind of tool, and that they always selected the ones fitted to them. Later the quinzy and King's evil ($\chi o\iota\rho\acute{a}\delta\epsilon s$, Hippoc. *Aph.* iii. 26) are mentioned and in c. 21 an interesting point in anatomy is brought out—that the second vertebra is called "dentiform". This is from Galen (*de usu part.* xii. 7), who asserts that by Hippocrates it was known simply as "the tooth". The three kinds of dropsy are mentioned here, and *hot* and *cold* gout. Hippocrates seems to have known only two kinds of dropsy, but Aretaeus knew of three. *Ophiasis* (falling of the hair), which is identified by Avicenna with *Alopecia* and mentioned by Galen, *Method. med.* xiv. 16 and Pliny, 28. 163–6, is spoken of in this chapter. The *pilulae aggregativae* (pills that collect and dispel all peccant humours) of Avicenna (c. 1. 9) are alluded to in c. 30, and in c. 42 occurs "the canon of Polycleitus", *i.e.* the statue of Polycleitus which was itself the rule of perfection (Galen, *de usu part.* xvii. 1) and the *vena cava* entering the heart by the right ventricle (Galen, *de Hippoc. et Plat.* vi. 3). Chapter 43 corrects "the opinion of Plato, Plutarch, Macrobius and others" that the drink descended into the lungs by the trachea and not into the stomach

by the oesophagus. This error is interesting as having been maintained by these writers and combated by Hippocrates, *de morbis*
iv. 54–6; *part. an.* iii. 3. 664 b and Galen, *de Hippoc. et Plat.* viii. 9;
de usu part. vii. 16. Sir T. Browne, *Pseud. Epid.* iv. 8 (cf. Mayor's
Juvenal, iv. 138).

As a practising physician Rabelais evidently sets before himself
the highest traditions of his predecessors, beginning with Hippocrates and Galen, whom he cites as examples. The object he assigns
for his "books" and his purpose in writing them is to beguile the
tedium of his patients in the suffering caused by their maladies,
and he cites both of the great Greek doctors and others to shew that
the physician's duty is in every way, even in the smallest particular,
to consult and indulge the well-being and the wishes of his patients.
It is unnecessary, he says, to prove that the cheerful bearing or the
reverse of the doctor is communicable to the patient—that is self-
evident—he even goes so far as to believe in the possibility of the
actual transfusion of spirits from the one to the other. That his own
cheeriness of disposition was beneficial is testified by his friends and
his patients in epigrams and poems that survive.

RABELAIS AS BOTANIST

In botany perhaps Rabelais has been credited with too great knowledge, so as to be considered almost in the light of a pioneer of
botanical science. This is carrying it too far. True it is, he had
studied the knowledge of the plants in use in ancient and modern
medicine, the *de simplicium medicamentis* of Galen, the plants mentioned by Dioscorides as well as the long lists in Pliny and some in
Theophrastus, though in almost every case it is Pliny quoting
Theophrastus rather than the Greek author himself who is the
source of his quotation or reference, as may be seen in the 49th,
50th and 51st chapters of the *Third Book.* He was also acquainted
with the pharmacopoeia of Avicenna and other Arabic physicians.
A sentence at the end of iii. 49, in which he shews acquaintance
with the sexes of plants, is hardly enough to support the claim that
is made for him, seeing that this knowledge is shared with him by
Herodotus, Theophrastus, Pliny and others, and the sentence itself
is derived from Tiraqueau. In fact, the knowledge of botany had
come to the end of a long chapter about 1530, in Rabelais' time,

and a new and more scientific phase was just beginning. It is not a little, however, to say that he knew much that was to be known in his time about botany, as well as the other numerous branches of study, and that he did himself follow up independent research in plants and their history; and it should be remembered that the plants which he mentions, long as the list is, are only those which occur to him in illustration of the subjects immediately before him; it by no means exhausts the knowledge he had acquired in botany. It would have been difficult to display a greater knowledge of this study in a book of the kind Rabelais was writing, and he certainly has succeeded in shewing that his acquaintance was considerable for the time in which he lived, and that with better opportunities he would have made himself master of a more scientific acquaintance with this subject. But the scientific study was then only beginning.

PLANTS MENTIONED BY RABELAIS

Reff. Pliny, *Hist. Nat.*; Galen, *de simpl. medicam.* ed. Kühn; Avicenna, *Canon*, ii. 2; Dioscorides, ed. Kühn.[1]

iii. 50	Achillea, 8. 24; D. iv. 36 alii sideritin; 32 aliqui Heracleam.
iii. 51; v. 36	Aconite, 8. 99, 27. 7.
iii. 50; iv. 24	Adiantum (capillus Veneris), 26. 62; G. vii. 1. 7; D. iv. 134.
iii. 51	Aegilops, 18. 155; G. vii. 1. 8; D. iv. 137.
iv. 63	Aethiopis, 26. 18; D. iv. 103.
iv. 1	Agalloch, Avicenna, ii. 2. 733; D. i. 21.
iii. 49, 52	Agaricum, 16. 33; G. 7. 1. 5; D. iii. 1.
iii. 31	Agnus Castus, 24. 59, 62; D. i. 134.
iii. 50	Agrimonia Eupatoria, 25, 65; D. iv. 41.
iii. 50	Alcibiadion, 27. 39; D. iv. 23–4.
P. 24	Alicacabus, 21. 177; D. iv. 72–5 *de strychno halicacabot*.
iii. 18	Alkermes, D. iv. 48 *de cocco tinctili*.
iii. 51; iv. 62; v. 37	Allium, Plut. *Quaest. Conv.* ii. 7. 1. 641 C; σκόροδον D. iii. 115.
iii. 50	Alopecurus, 21. 101.
iii. 50	Alyssum, 24, 95; D. iii. 95.

[1] As in nearly every case the reference is to Pliny, his nomenclature has been given, and it has not been thought necessary to prefix Pl. to the references to him. G. and D. mean respectively Galen and Dioscorides. The sections of Sillig have been employed in Pliny references rather than the old method of chapters and paragraphs, as being more exact and less cumbrous. This notation is adopted in all later editions.

P.P. 5	Amaracus (*marioletz*), 21. 61.
v. 31	Anacampseros (sedum), 24. 167.
iv. 43	Anemone (tria genera) (1) coronaria, (2) medica, (3) phrenion, 21. 164.
G. 13	Anetum (dill), 20. 196.
iii. 50	Anthyllis, *barba Jovis*, 16. 76.
iii. 51	Antranium (*ateramon*), 28. 155.
iii. 50	Apsinthium (*Santonica*), 27. 45.
P.P. 4; *G.* 9	Aquilegia (*l'ancolie*).
iii. 49, 50	Aristolochia, 25. 95; D. iii. 4.
iii. 50	Artemisia (Armoise), 25. 73; D. iii. 117.
iii. 51	Arundo, 25. 85.
iii. 50	Asarum (*sang de Mars*), 21. 29; D. i. 9, iii. 44; cf. *Bacchar.*
iii. 52	Asbestos, 19. 19.
iv. 7; v. 7	Asparagus, 19. 54, 151.
v. 7	Avena, 18. 205.
iii. 50	Bacchar, D. iii. 44; cf. *Asarum.*
iii. 50	Bechium (tussilago), 26. 22; D. iii. 116.
G. 13	Beta, 20. 69.
iii. 51	Betulla, 16. 75.
v. 18	Botrychium lunaria.
G. 13; iii. 13; iv. 7	Brassica, 20. 78–96.
iii. 49	Buglossum, 25. 86.
iii. 51	Caepe, 19. 101.
iii. 50	Callitriche, 22. 62.
iii. 49, 52	Cannabis, 19. 174, 20. 259; D. iii. 145.
iii. 51; iv. 63	Caprificus, 23. 130.
iii. 32	Cardamum seed (*graine de Paradis*).
iii. 50	Castaneae, 15. 23, 25.
iii. 51	Celtis australis (*fenabregue*, micocoulier Littré), ὀρέα, Athen. iii. 78 B.
iii. 49	Centaurea (Smyrnium olusatrum), 27. 133.
iii. 13, 50	Cerasus, 15. 102
iii. 50	Cicer, 18. 10; ἐρέβινθος, D. iii. 126.
iii. 31	Cicuta, 25. 151; *G. de temperamentis.*
iii. 50	Citron (Medica mala), 15. 47.
iii. 50	Clymenus (honeysuckle), 25. 70.
iii. 52	Colocasia, 21. 87.
G. 13	Condurdum (Fr. *consolde*, Angl. *comfrey*), 26. 26.
iii. 51	Cornus, 16. 105.
iii. 50	Coronopus, 21. 48; G. viii. 1. 44; D. ii. 157.
P. 7; iii. 51	Cotton, 12. 30, 39.
iii. 50	Crocus, 21. 137; *zafferan* in Avicenna.
G. 13	Cucurbita, 20. 13.
iii. 49	Cupressus, Theoph. *H.P.* iii. 3.
iii. 51	Cuscuta (epilenium); cf. C. Stephanus, *de re hortensi*, p. 60.

iii. 32   Cydonia (quinces), 15. 37; Avicenna, v. 1. 8.

iii. 50   Cynara Scolymus, 1a.

P. 28   Daphne cnidiorum (*coccognide*), 13. 114, 27. 70; Κόκκος Κνύδιος, G. *fac. nat.* i. 13.

iii. 50   Delphinium, *D.* iii. 77.

iv. 63   Dictamnus, 8. 97; D. iii. 34.

iii. 50   Dipsacus fullonum, labrum Veneris, 25. 171, 27. 71.

iv. 52   Echium (*personata*), 21. 87.

iii. 50   Ephemerum, 25. 170.

iii. 51   Equisetum, 18. 259, 26. 132; D. iv. 46.

Epp. Rom. 12; v. 29   Eruca, 19. 155.

iv. 62   Eryngium campestre, 22. 18; οἱ δὲ μῶλυ, D. iii. 21.

P. 33   Eryngium maritimum (panicault).

P. 28; iii. 50   Euphorbia, 25. 77; D. iii. 86.

iii. 13, 49, 50   Fabae (beans), 18. 40.

iii. 51   Fenabregue (Celtis Australis), Athen. iii. 79ᴮ ὀρέα.

G. 13   Fennel, 20. 254.

iii. 51   Ferula, 13. 22; D. iii. 81.

iii. 51   Ficus, Athen. iii. 78 ᴮ.

iii. 49, 51   Filices, 27. 80.

iii. 50   Foenum graecum, 24. 174; D. i. 57 (τῆλις).

iii. 49, 50   Gentiana, 25. 71; D. iii. 3.

v. 29   Glaucium, 20. 19. § 78; μήκων κερατῖτις, G. vii. 12. 14; D. iv. 66.

G. 24; iii. 51   Hedera, 16. 144.

G. 23; iii. 24   Helleborus, 25. 47; D. iv. 148; Theoph. *H.P.* ix. 10.

iii. 50   Helxene, 22. 41; G. vii. 5. 10.

iii. 50   Henbane (hyoscyamus), 25. 35.

iii. 50   Heliotropium (marigold), 22. 57; cf. *Solsequium.*

iii. 50   Hermadactylus (tuberosus) = colchicum autumnale, Burton's *Anat.* ii. 4. 1. 2.

iii. 50   Hieracium, 20. 60; D. iii. 65.

iii. 51   Hierobotane (peristereon), 25. 105.

iii. 50   Hippuris, 26. 132; G. vii. 9. 4.

iii. 50   Holosteum (stellaria holostea L.), 27. 91; D. iv. 11.

v. 42   Hyacinthus (orientalis L.), 21. 66.

iii. 50   Hyoscyamus 25. 35; G. viii. 20. 4; D. iv. 67.

iii. 49   Ilex (Fr. *houx*).

iii. 27   Indica herba, 26. 99; Theoph. *H.P.* ix. 18. 9.

iii. 50   Iris, 21. 44.

v. 29   Juglans, 23. 147.

iii. 32   Juncus odoratus, 12. 104, 21. 120 (σχοινάνθος, *squinanthi*).

iii. 50   Juniperus Sabina, 24. 102; D. i. 104; G. vii. 2. 15 (βράθυ).

G. 13   Lactuca, 20. 58–68.

iii. prol.; iv. 7; v. 1   Lapathium, 20. 231.

P. 32; iv. 52   Lappa (Arctium) (Fr. *bardane*), 27. 33; D. v. 106.

iii. 52	Larix, 16. 45.
iii. 49, 50	Laurus Daphne, Ovid, *Met.* i. 452.
iii. 50	Lavandula (stoechas), 27. 131; D. iii. 28.
iii. 50	Lentes, 18. 40.
iii. 50	Lepidium, 19. 166.
iii. 50	Lichen, 26. 22.
iii. 50	Ligusticum, 19. 165; D. iii. 41.
iii. 49	Linum, 19. 1; D. ii. 125.
v. 18	Lunaria.
v. 29	Lupulus (Fr. *houblon*), C. Stephanus, *de re hortensi*, p. 71.
iii. 45	Malum (blandureau).
iii. 137	Malum (curtipendium), *de court pendu.*
iii. 50	Malum granatum, Punica mala, 13. 112.
G. 13; iii. 50	Malva, 20. 222
iii. 31, 49	Mandragora, 25. 147.
G. 13; P.P. 5	Mariolaine (marjoram) amaracus, 21. 61.
iii. 51	Melitenses vites, 12. 38; Cic. *Verr. II.* ii. § 176, iv. §103.
v. 31	Mentha, 19. 159; ἡδύοσμον, D. iii. 36.
G. 13; iii. 50	Mercurialis, 25. 38.
P. 1	Mespilus (Medlar), 15. 84; D. i. 169; G. vii. 12. 11.
iii. 50	Myosota, 27. 23, 115; D. ii. 214 ἀλσίνη; G. vii. 1. 25.
iii. 25	Myrica (tamarisk), 25. 67.
iii. 50	Myrobalanus, 12. 109; Avicenna, ii. 2. 79.
iii. 50	Myrtus (Myrsine), D. 1. 155.
iii. 50	Narcissus, Ovid, *Met.* iii. 339.
iii. 50	Nardus (spica celticae), 12. 42, 14. 109.
iii. 50; v. 29	Nasturtium (cardamus), 19. 155; D. ii. 184.
v. 29	Nuces juglandes, 23. 147.
iii. 31, 51	Nuphar luteum, 25. 76.
iii. 51	Nux, Athen. iii. 78B.
iii. 31, 51	Nymphaea heraclea (nenuphar), 25. 76; D. iii. 138.
iv. 59	Oliva colymbas, 15. 16.
iii. 31	Orchis parva, 26. 95.
iii. 51	Orobanche (Lat. *ervangina*), 18. 155, 22. 162; D. ii. 171 G. vii. 15. 15.
iii. 49	Paeonia, D. iii. 149.
iii. 50	Panacea, 25. 30.
iii. 50	Pentaphyllum, 25. 109; D. iv. 42.
iii. 50	Periclymenus, 27. 120; D. iv. 14.
iii. 50	Persica, 15. 44; D. i. 164.
iv. 52	Personata (carduus), D. iv. 105; cf. *Echium.*
iii. 50	Petasites (tussilago), D. iv. 108; G. viii. 16. 15.
P. 6	Petroselinum, 20. 118; D. iii. 70.
v. 29	Phaseolus, 18. 125; D. ii. 130.
G. 13	Phlomis (verbascum), 25. 120; D. iv. 102.
iii. 50	Picea (Pitys).
v. 26	Pinaster.

iv. 54	Pirus, 23. 115 *bon christiane.*
P.P. 4	Pirus anginaria (poyre d'angoysse) of Dordogne.
iii. 13	Pirus Crustumenia, 15. 50.
iv. 60	Pistacia, 13. 51.
iii. 50	Pisum, 18. 40.
iii. 50	Polemonia, 25. 64.
G. 13	Polygonum (persicaria), 27. 113; D. iv. 4.
iii. 51	Populus, 16. 85.
iii. 13, 51	Portulaca (Fr. *pourpier*), 20. 211; ἀνδράχνη, D. ii. 150.
iii. 50	Psyllium, 25. 140.
iii. 51	Punica, 13. 112; cf. *Malum granatum.*
iii. 49	Quercus ilex.
iii. 49	Quercus robur, Athen. iii. 78 B.
iii. 50	Rha barbarum, D. iii. 2.
G. 13	Rosa, 21. 14.
iii. prol.; iv. 7; v. 1	Rumex (patientia) lapathum, 20. 231.
iv. 43	Ruta, 20. 135; D. iii. 45 πήγανον.
iii. 50	Sabina, 24. 102; cf. *Juniperus.*
iii. 31, 51	Salix (alba L.), 16. 110, 24. 58.
iii. 31	Salix Amerina, 24. 58.
G. 13	Salvia, 26. 31.
iv. 62	Sambucus (Fr. *sureau*), 16. 179; ἀκτή, D. iv. 171.
P. 17; G. 25; iv. 12	Secale.
iii. 51	Securidaca (pelacinon), 18. 155.
v. 31	Sedum anacampseros, 24. 167.
P. 15	Sedum Telephium, 25. 42.
iii. 51	Serica, 12. 17.
iii. 50	Serpyllum, 20. 245.
iii. 50	Smilax (aspera L.), 16. 153; D. iv. 175.
iii. 49	Smyrnium olus atrum, 13. 109, 27. 133; D. iii. 72; cf. *Petroselinum.*
P. 24	Solanum (physalis alkekengi L.), 21. 177; Avicenna, ii. 2. 369 *Kekengi* (= solanum halcacabot).
iii. 50	Solsequium (*Sousil*, Marigold), 2. 109, 27. 57; cf. *Heliotropium.*
iii. 50	Stoechas (lavandula), 27. 131.
iii. 51	Taxus, 16. 51.
iii. 50	Telephium, sedum, 25. 42; D. ii. 217.
iii. 49	Terebinth, 13. 54; Theoph. *H.P.* iii. 15.
v. 5	Teucrium, 21. 44; D. iii. 101; tripolium, D. iv. 133; polium, D. iii. 114.
P. 24	Tithymallus, 26. 62; D. iv. 162.
iii. 50	Trifolium, 21. 54.
iii. 51	Ulmus, 24. 48.
G. 13	Urtica, 10. 163.
G. 13	Verbascum (Mullein), 25. 120; φλόμις, D. iv. 102; Avicenna, ii. 2. 98.

iii. 51; iv. 3   Verbena (Hierobotane), 19. 5, 25. 105; περιστερεών,
                    D. iv. 60.
iii. 31   Vitex (agnus castus), 24. 59, 62.
iii. 51   Vitis, 17. 152 *sqq.*
iii. 51   Yvraye (Tares), 8. 155, 25. 85; Theoph. *H.P.* viii. 8. 3.

RABELAIS AS A HUMANIST

The account of Gargantua's reading in the 14th chapter is probably intended to represent Rabelais' own experiences. Thubal Holofernes may be the village schoolmaster, who taught the alphabet forwards and backwards, at which he was engaged "five years and three months". This would bring him to his seventh year, perhaps. Next came the *Auctores octo morales* in the Convent school at Seuilly, which occupied thirteen years, six months and two weeks. The *De modis significandi*, with its commentaries and the *Computus* or tables by which to find Easter and the holy days, and books for an intending ecclesiastic which were taught by Jobelin Bridé, completed his education.

The purpose of the chapter is to ridicule the books of instruction then in vogue and the methods of teaching, and to contrast them with the more enlightened method employed by Ponocrates. Possibly Rabelais has in view not only his own case but also the experience of Budé, who first at Paris and then at Orléans, where he studied jurisprudence, made but little progress, but spent his time at tennis and other games and in hawking, of which he has left a long account in his commentary on the Pandects. Much use is made of the *de Asse* and *Annotationes in Pandectas* in the *Pantagruel* and the *Third* and *Fifth Books*. No doubt it was Budé's example that first caused Rabelais to follow the teaching of the humanists Valla, Poliziano, and above all Erasmus, whom he has laid so much under contribution.

The course of reading marked out for Charles V by Erasmus in the *Institutio Principis Christiani* (1516) is eminently characteristic. A prince, he says, should read the *Proverbs* of Solomon, *Ecclesiasticus* and the *Liber Sapientiae*; also the Gospels; the *Apophthegmata* and *Moralia* of Plutarch; Seneca; Aristotle, *Politica*; Cicero, *de Officiis*; Plato, and Cicero, *de Legibus*. With the exception of Aristotle's *Politics* traces of all these books may be found in Rabelais.

The employment of proverbs by great writers is remarkable, but not surprising, when we find them so much employed in early Greek philosophy. In fact, the earliest form of philosophy consisted of maxims which embodied in a crystallised form the broad outlines of moral philosophy, as it was then known. The *dicta* of the Seven Wise Men and the *Symbola* of Pythagoras are of this nature, and throughout the ages this kind of portable wisdom was much in use. Such again are the glosses to the laws, civil and canon, so often in the mouths of lawyers and magistrates, to clinch their judgments. Shakespeare's justice is "full of wise saws and modern instances". Erasmus attached much importance to his book of *Adagia*, with its commentaries on more than 4000 proverbs, and we find Rabelais constantly borrowing from this book, but quoting also proverbs of physicians, theologians and lawyers to support the contentions of his interlocutors. In *Don Quixote* not only Sancho Panza, but the knight himself, resorts to this kind of support; in a way they may be compared with the Solomon and Marculphus of the queer medieval book to which Rabelais once refers, where the clown Marculphus is represented as capping the refined *dicta* of Solomon with the coarse, homespun witticisms from the fields or the stable.

The influence of Ovid on the medieval romances and writings was very great, and as there was an *aetas Vergiliana* in the eighth and ninth centuries, an *aetas Horatiana* in the tenth and eleventh, so there was an *aetas Ovidiana* in the twelfth and thirteenth centuries; and although the *Metamorphoses* with their mythological lore are mostly drawn upon—so much so that the work is styled *Ovidio maggiore* by Dante (*Conv.* iii. 3. l. 50)—yet the erotic poetry of the *Heroides*, the *Ars*, the *Amores* and the *Remedia* was much read and copied, to a great extent on account of its easy Latinity and the facility given by elegiac verse to detach maxims from their setting. This made these books favourites with the "glossers" of the Roman and Church laws. The old educational book known as *Maximianus* is full of citations from these parts of Ovid, and for this it is pilloried by the *Doctrinale* of Alexander de Villedieu, who proposes to substitute his own wholesome teaching "pro nugis Maximiani", though neither his book nor the *Grecismus* of Everard of Bethune, the two treatises which held the field of instruction in Latin grammar and versification from the thirteenth to the sixteenth centuries, are by any means blameless in this respect.

It is as a humanist that Rabelais first made acquaintance with literature properly so-called. After Budé, Erasmus served as a guide and a source from whom extracts are taken without stint, particularly from his *Adagia*, *Apophthegmata* and *Colloquia*. Lorenzo Valla also, the canon of St John Lateran (a post to which he was wisely promoted by Pope Nicholas V, who chose to have the great scholar as an ally rather than an enemy, after the publication of the *de ficta donatione Constantini*), influenced Rabelais considerably. In the proem to the first book of the *Elegantiarum linguae Latinae libri sex*, Valla inveighs bitterly against the corrupters of Latinity, comparing it with Rome when captured by the Gauls. "For these many centuries", he says, "not only has no one spoken Latin, but no one even has read Latin books so as to understand them."

In the proem to the second book he deals well-merited castigation to the grammarians who succeeded Donatus, Servius and Priscian, such as Isidorus, Eberardus, and Hugutio. The proem to the third book deals similarly with the barbarous Latinity of the lawyers, civil and canon alike. He declares that as the Goths and Vandals invaded and destroyed Rome, so these lawyers have invaded the Latin language with their Gothic jargon and writings. In the proem to the fourth book, St Jerome is chidden for discouraging Latin scholarship, when he said that he had been scourged before God's tribunal and accused "quod Ciceronianus esset et non Christianus".

Rabelais was also well acquainted with the writings of the great Italian scholar Angelo Poliziano, whom he mentions once or twice and from whom he borrows. An edition of the *Epistolae*, the *Miscellanea* and the *Prologues* of Politian, as well as his *Silvae* and his translation of Herodian, was published by Gryphius in 1537–9, which Rabelais may have seen through the press. He also takes something from J. Jovianus Pontanus, the head of the Neapolitan "Academy", and also from the *Dies Geniales* of Alexander ab Alexandro; from Eliseus Calentius he borrows the name Rodilardus, the great *cat*, although in the Latin translation of the Homeric *Batrachomyomachia*, Rodilardus is the king of the *mice*. The two last-mentioned scholars were members of the same Neapolitan Academy.

Next to Erasmus, Caelius Rhodiginus of contemporary scholars supplies most material in the *Fourth Book*. His real name was Lodovico Celio Riccheri of Rovigo (1450–1525), and he had been made professor of Greek and Latin at Milan by Francis I. He wrote a huge volume in sixteen books (afterwards divided into thirty) on every conceivable subject of literature and antiquities, which Rabelais found useful in his compilations. Caelius Calcagninus also, professor of *belles lettres* at Ferrara, supplies an important apologue on the children of Physis (*Nature*) and Antiphysis.

Hints and names are also derived in the *Pantagruel* from Sir T. More's *Utopia*, which first appeared in 1516, and of which an edition was published at Paris by Gilles de Gourmont in 1517 and one by Froben at Basel in 1518.

In the *Third Book*, which turns very much on methods of divination, very great use is made of the *de occulta philosophia* and the *de vanitate scientiarum* of that curiously learned scholar, Henricus Cornelius Agrippa of Nettesheim. The first of these treatises gained for the writer the reputation of a necromancer—not without some reason—while the second is practically a recantation of the speculations and the mysticism contained in the first, as being the errors and vagaries of youth.

The relations of Rabelais with the printers and their productions are of great importance in connexion with his life and writings. We cannot lose sight of the fact that the Renaissance could not have had such far-reaching influence but for the invention of printing and the wonderful activity of the presses of that time. Although Aldus Manutius and his partners and successors at Venice stand first, there were others who deserve special commendation for the diffusion of knowledge and learning, ancient and modern, such as Robert Stephen and his son Henry at Paris, the Giuntas at Florence, Froben at Basel, Quentel at Cologne, and many others. For our present purpose we are more concerned with the presses at Lyons, whither Rabelais had betaken himself at the beginning of 1532. Here—in a most intellectual centre of France—he found himself in congenial surroundings and was able to slake his thirst for knowledge from the shelves of Sebastian Gryphius, the great printer of classical books at Lyons. Gryphius printed for the most part only Latin and a few Greek books, and was a great benefactor to the reading public of that time by publishing handy editions of the Latin classics, like Teubner of the present day. These had a very wide circulation, and to this day one finds on book-stalls in Rome and other cities more old editions of Latin books such as Suetonius, Valerius Maximus, Macrobius, Gellius, etc., issued by this press than from any other. It is said that the only French books that he published were Cl. Marot's translation of the first book of Ovid's *Metamorphoses* and the *Arrêts d'Amour*, or "Judgments in the Court of Love", with a legal commentary on each, by a trained lawyer and scholar, Benoît d'à Court, supported by references to the Pandects and Code and a varied array of classical learning. From this press issued Erasmus' *Adagia* (1529 and 1530), also a Latin translation of several of Lucian's treatises by Erasmus and Sir T. More (1534) and a Latin translation of the *Odyssey* by Raphael Volaterranus (1541). Recently M. Baudrier has published in the eighth volume of the *Bibliographie lyonnaise* an almost complete list of the books that issued from this press. Sebastian Gryphius was born at Reutlingen in Suabia (? 1491) and died at Lyons Sept. 7, 1556. His publications range from 1528 to 1556, but other members of his family had presses at Lyons, in the cities of Italy and elsewhere. He has been accused, possibly with justice, of publishing pirated reprints of many of the Venetian productions; be that as it may, he did great service to education. It is more than probable that Rabelais acted as reader for the press in the case of many of his books. This would be about the years 1532–5 and 1537–9. It might account for his singular familiarity with books like Maturin Cordier's *de corrupti Latini sermonis emendatione*, which Gryphius brought out in 1532 after it had been badly treated by R. Stephen in the Paris press in 1531.

But there were many presses in Lyons before the arrival of Gryphius in 1528. First in interest for us stands François Juste, who succeeded Claude Nourry, and issued books from 1529 to 1547. Nourry published the first edition of *Pantagruel* in 1532. The only surviving copy is in the Bibliothèque Nationale, but unfortunately the title-page is lost. Of the second edition (B) one copy survives in the Royal Library of Dresden. It is described as *Aug-*

menté et corrigé fraischement and published at Lyons by F. Juste in
1533. It has been reproduced in phototype facsimile (Dec. 1903)
by MM. Léon Dorez and Pierre Paul Plan. Another edition in
1534, and a definitive one in 1542, also by Juste, complete the tale
of the editions which we can look upon as authoritative. They are
all enlarged in bulk and altered in the arrangement of the chapters.
Similarly, Juste published a *Gargantua* in 1534, 1535, 1537 and
1542. It is important also to notice in the list of Juste's publications, *La grande nef des folz* (1529), a translation of the *Navis stulti-
fera* of Sebastian Brandt, *Les Œuvres de Guillaume Coquillart* (1535),
Les Œuvres de François Villon (1537), all which books furnished
Rabelais with something in his writings.

Again, the lists of other Lyonnais printers give works of which
Rabelais had certainly seen the titles, if he had not read the books.
Such is the list of Olivier Arnouillet, Lyon, *près nostre Dame de
Confort* (1517–58). It comprises

> Galien réthauré, 1525; cf. *P.* 24, 30.
> Valentin et Orson, 1526; cf. *P.* 1, 24.
> Le Blason des Couleurs, 1528; *G.* 9.
> Menus propos de la Mere Sote, 1535; cf. *P.* 4; v. 47.
> Melusine, 1544; iv. 38.
> Geoffroy à la grant dent; *P.* 5.
> Huon de Bordeaux; *P.* 30; *G.* prol.

And that of Jehan de Vingle (1494–1511):

> Les IV filz Aymon, 1495; *G.* 27.
> Fier-à-bras, 1496; *P.* 30.
> Olivier Maillard, *Sermones*; iv. 8.
> Aeneas Sylvius Piccolomini, 1497; *P.* 7, v. 31.
> Pragmatica Sanctio Caroli VII, 1499; *P.* 12, iii. 39.

Jehan Trechsel came from Germany to Lyons and was perhaps
the first to set up a press there. For correctors of the press he had
first Janus Lascaris (cf. *G.* 24) and afterwards Josse Bade of Assche
(Josse Badius, Ascensius), who was born in 1462 and came from
Brussels to Lyons in 1491, where he stayed till 1510, after marrying
Trechsel's only daughter Thalia. He afterwards became celebrated as a printer in Paris. He printed an edition of the *Philo-
biblon* of Richard de Bury, together with Jean Petit in 1500.

Trechsel's list contained

Guillermi de Vorrilong opus, folio, 1489; *P.* 7.
Practica Valesci de Tharenta, quae alias *Philonium* dicitur, 4°,
    1490; iv. *Ep. Ded.*
Roberti Gaguini...de origine et gestis Francorum. Lugduni im-
    pensis Johann. Trechsel...et diligenti accuratione Jodoci Badii
    Ascensii, folio, 1497; cf. iv. 49.

Melchior and Gaspar Trechsel published

Symphoriani Campegii *Clysteriorum campi,* contra Arabum opinion-
    em, pro Galeni sententia; *P.* 7.

This was also published at Basle 1532.

Another printer was Jehan Du Pré, who set up presses in many
places: Paris, 1481, Salins 1484, Lyon 1487, Paris 1489. From his
press have been noted:

Terentii comoediae VI, 1488.
Liber qui *compotus* dicitur, 1488–9; *G.* 14.
Auctores octo morales cum glossa, 1491; *G.* 14.
Eberhardi *Grecismus,* 1493; *G.* 14.
Vie des anciens Peres hermites, 1494; *G.* 22.

Galiot du Pré was also a printer in Paris, and his press seems to
have supplied books to Rabelais, who used his motto *Vogue la galée*
twice, *G.* 3; iv. 23.

Very important in this connexion is the name of Barnabé
Chaussard, who printed at Lyons from 1496. From his press we
find

Le roman de Fier-à-Bras, 1496.
La conqueste du grand roy Charlemagne, 1501.

Also *sans date*:

Le caquet des bonnes chamberieres.
Les Cent Nouvelles nouvelles.
Le debat de l'homme et de l'argent.
Les faintises du Monde.
Le recueil des hystoires des repeues franches.

This printer was evidently one of those who issued ballads and
other fugitive pieces which were sold by pedlars (*bissouarts*) and
eagerly bought and read by Rabelais and many more. The thirteen
volumes of this kind of literature, collected and published in the
édition elzévirienne by de Montaiglon and James de Rothschild, are

of great value in illustrating Rabelais (*Anciennes poésies françaises inédites du XVème et XVIème siècles*). In the plays that are brought together in the *Ancien Théâtre Français* by Viollet le Duc, several are printed *à Lyon, à la maison de feu Barnabé Chaussard près Nostre Dame de Confort*; among them are

Sermon joyeux des Foux; vol. ii. pp. 223–43.
Farce des cris de Paris; vol. ii. pp. 303–25.
La Vie du Maulvais Riche; vol. iii. pp. 267–99.
Farce des Cinq Sens; vol. iii. pp. 300–24.
Moralité de Charité; vol. iii. pp. 337–424.

The value of such collections is clearly seen in the light they throw on the writings of a man of Rabelais' mould, one who saw and seized at once any piece of information or drollery that chance threw in his way. He evidently enjoyed this kind of literature and on occasions adopted its phrases, proverbs and sentiments.

The ballad-like poems in the volumes of the *Anciennes poésies françaises* run through the gamut of common life and may be paralleled in many cases with the *dramatis personae* of the Plautine plays; the braggart captain, the cheating servants, male and female, the diviners and prognosticators are common to both. In the French list are to be found also the *doctrinale*, or instruction in piety and good manners, the debates between good and evil tendencies, between wine and water for instance, and between the worldly and religious man and so on; there are also *cris*, or proclamations, as well as poems on events of national history. Naturally fugitive pieces of this kind, which then formed part of men's daily life, as they did also in Shakespeare's time (cf. 2 *Henry IV*, iv. 3. 52) and afterwards, supplied material from which a versatile writer, such as Rabelais, readily borrowed.

HISTORICAL ALLUSIONS

Rabelais was so many-sided and had experienced so many changes in his life and professions that in his writings he alludes in passing to events, policies and tendencies that are often forgotten or lost except to professed historians; hence it is sometimes difficult to catch the meaning of a reference that is so elusive. It may be a battle or a Church Council or a piece of policy of the Roman Church or an allusion to a bygone scandal, skilfully woven in the

web of his grotesque story. The allusions also are short and sometimes enigmatic, so that their point is easily missed, while at times
he seems to drop hints that are purposely misleading and susceptible
of two or more interpretations.

In the very first chapter of the *Gargantua* there is a reference to
the celebrated translation of the Roman Empire to Charlemagne,
whom Rabelais conveniently considers to be a Frenchman, notwithstanding the generally accepted belief that he was a German.[1]
Again, in the first chapter of the *Third Book* he speaks of the trans-
planting by Charlemagne of some Saxons into Flanders and of
Flemings into Saxony, which proved unsuccessful; this is also
mentioned by Shakespeare.[2]

Of the semi-fabulous history of the early Kings of France there
are hints, and gibes at the claim of the French to be descended
from Francus, second son of Hector, son of Priam, King of Troy.[3]
In the genealogy of Pantagruel in *P.* 1 the three first names Chal-
broth, Sarabroth and Fariboth seem to be Hebraised forms (on the
analogy of Nembroth = Nimrod) of Childebert, Charibert and
Farabert, 6th, 8th and 28th Kings of the old dynasty, according to
the account of Jean Bouchet in his *Généalogies des Roys de France*.

To the earlier history of France there are two or three allusions:
(1) The great *Truye* or Sow, a penthouse used at the siege of Ber-
gerac.[4] (2) The defeat of Philip van Artevelde by Charles VI of
France at Roosebeke in 1382, and the insurrection ten years later
of the *Maillotins* in Paris against the *gabelle*, and their submission
before the King would enter the city.[5] The troubles caused by the
long minority of Charles VI and probably by that of Henry VI of
England seem to be referred to.[6] The saying of the Duke of Bedford
at Orléans when he refused to raise the siege: "He would not beat
the bushes for another to take the birds", is in the list of Gargantua's
proverbs.[7] There is also in *G.* 50 a reference to the appointment
by Louis XII of Antoine de Crouy as tutor of Charles V, who
was entrusted to him by the Archduke Philip.

---

[1] *Decretal*, i. b. 34 (*Venerabilem*); Agrippa, *de van. scient.* c. 80; Gibbon, c. 49;
Bryce, *H.R.E.* cc. 7, 13.
[2] *Henry V*, i. 2. 43–53.   [3] *P.P.* 5; *P.* 1; iii. prol.; iv. prol.
[4] iv. 40.   [5] iv. 36.
[6] *G.* 50.   [7] *G.* 11.

There is a curious reference to the battle of St Aubin du Cormier in Brittany (July 28, 1488), as a result of which Brittany became part of France by the marriage of Charles VIII to Anne de Bretagne. It is given in an allegorical description of a battle between flocks of jays (who represented by their plumage the azure and argent of France) and pies (who bore the Breton ermines in their feathers). This took place, according to Poggio in his *Facetiae*, No. 234, on the confines of Brittany in April 1451. To add point to the story Rabelais represents one of the jays, who returned wounded from the war, to have belonged to an old uncle of his own living at Angers.

Naturally there are several allusions, direct and indirect, to the battle of Marignano, near Milan (Sept. 15, 1515). Francis I, who had just succeeded to the throne, took a great part in it, and the defeat of the Swiss did much to break down their arrogance and presumption, inspired by the defeat of Charles le Téméraire of Burgundy. Matthieu Schinner, Cardinal of Sion, had got together 50,000 Swiss troops to assist the Pope and Maximilian of Austria against Francis, who was coming to occupy Milan. In the absence of the Cardinal and of the military commander, terms had been made to allow Francis to enter Milan peaceably, but when the Cardinal came up he induced the Swiss to break the treaty and to attack the French. The result was one of the most obstinate battles on record, in which the Swiss are said to have lost 15,000 men. The Swiss minimised the crushing nature of the defeat by insisting that they were allowed to draw off unmolested, but a contemporary letter of Erasmus from Basel (Oct. 1515) shews that they felt the reverse deeply.[1] Their defeat was celebrated in a song, which still survives, by the French composer Jannequin.[2] It contains several cries and exclamations of the battlefield which Rabelais has helped to perpetuate; he has also preserved the chorus: *tout est frelore, la tintelore, tout est frelore bigoth*. It is employed as the despairing cry of Panurge in the height of the storm[3] and in the word *tintelorisé* (crestfallen) in one of the litanies.[4] This chorus is given by Scott in *Peveril of the Peak*, c. 47.

---

[1] Erasm. *Ep.* 360, ed. Allen.   [2] iv. prol.
[3] iii. 38.   [4] iv. 36.

The treachery of the Swiss in this matter is insisted on,[1] and they are compared with chitterlings or sausages, which are sold in double links, *doubles* having also the meaning of double-dealing. Their squat, burly figures are also a source of merriment in the chapters devoted to them;[2] among them is signalised "the great Bull of Berne",[3] named Pontiner, according to Paulus Jovius, lib. xv.

In *P.* 11 (which is throughout a tissue of incoherence with a hint dropped here and there) is an obscure allusion to the engagement at *la Bicocca*, formerly a hunting seat of the Visconti near Milan, where the French general Lautrec sustained a reverse by the Imperialists under Prospero Colonna, owing to the disaffection of 16,000 Swiss mercenaries. This was in April 27, 1522.

Francis I had tried to arrest Charles de Bourbon, constable of France, at his castle at Chantelle (1523).[4] Charles had slighted advances from Louise de Savoye, the King's mother, and was suspected of disloyalty. Bourbon withdrew from his allegiance, and joined Charles V. He did great mischief to the French in the Milanese, especially at Pavia, and ultimately led his mercenaries, Spanish and German, to Rome, where he was struck down by a cannon-shot while leading a storming party against the Castle of St Angelo, May 6, 1527.

The King, being unable to take the command in the Milanese, sent his favourite Bonnivet, with Bayard and Montmorency as lieutenants. Bonnivet mismanaged affairs; he was deserted by 5000 Swiss troops and was only saved by being wounded and having to entrust the command to Bayard, who succeeded in bringing off his troops but was himself killed.

Francis now (1524) marched to the relief of Marseilles, which had offered a stout resistance to Bourbon. The latter retired into the Milanese, followed by the King, who instead of marching into Milan, as he was advised by his lieutenants Chabannes and Montmorency, laid siege to Pavia. The King had been solicited by Pope Clement VII to undertake the conquest of Naples as well as that of Milan and had detached a part of his army under James Stewart,

---

[1] iv. 36.   [2] iv. 36–42.
[3] *P.* 1; iv. 41.   [4] *P.* 5.

Duke of Albany, for service against Naples and thus considerably weakened his own forces. Rabelais protests against this mistake.[1]

Things, however, were going on well with the French, when Bourbon with 16,000 German mercenaries suddenly arrived and joined the Imperial forces. The experienced French generals were for allowing him to pass into Pavia, where was a dearth of provisions, and entrenching themselves at the Certosa, which was exceedingly strong, so that famine might do its work with the enemy. Through the influence of Bonnivet this prudent advice was rejected and the disastrous battle of Pavia was risked, Feb. 24, 1525. The King was taken prisoner, while the duc d'Alençon, husband of Margaret, the King's sister, was one of those who fled at the beginning of the engagement.

Francis was imprisoned first at the Certosa and afterwards at Madrid, where he was treated with considerable harshness. Ultimately he was released March 10, 1526, through the good offices of his sister Margaret. Rabelais comments in bitter terms on this conduct of the Emperor, who was styled *the Catholic* by the Papal court.[2]

Bourbon had been appointed by Charles V to succeed his general Pescara, who had died during the siege of Milan. But taking offence at the non-fulfilment of the Emperor's promises to him, and finding himself at the head of a powerful army, he conceived the design of getting possession of Naples, and in order to provide his mercenaries with pay he promised them that they should be rewarded with the sack of Rome. They marched on and laid siege to the Holy City. Bourbon was struck down at the first assault, but the sack of Rome followed on May 7, 1527, and proved the most dreadful on record in barbarity and destruction of buildings and property. The Emperor reaped the advantage of it in the ransom of the Pope and many Cardinals after a seven months' siege in the Castle of St Angelo. Rabelais refers to it in *Epp. Rom.* i. § 1 and also enigmatically in *P.* 30, where in the next world Nero is represented as a fiddler and Fierabras as his serving-man, who played him mischievous tricks, starving him on bad bread and wine, while he himself lived sumptuously. Nero may well be intended to repre-

---

[1] *Epp. Rom.* i. § 1.   [2] *G.* 50.

sent Clement VII with his beard (Ahenobarbus) and his musical tastes, while Fierabras stands for the epicure Charles V, who pretended devotion to the Pope and allowed him to be maltreated and took a large ransom from him. It is also to be noted that in the romance *Fierabras* the first division of it is entitled "La Destruction de Rome".

In 1534 the divorce of Henry VIII from Catharine of Aragon brought about the rupture between England and the Roman Church after Charles, Catharine's nephew, had insisted on the excommunication of Henry, notwithstanding the efforts of Jean du Bellay, Bishop of Paris and French minister at Rome. Rabelais was present and speaks of the episode[1] and also of the death of Catharine, Jan. 6, 1536.[2]

Naturally Rabelais was *au courant* with contemporary history, especially where the Popes were concerned. He reprobates more than once the bellicose nature[3] of Julius II and alludes to his beard,[4] which is so well known to us in Raphael's representation of him, and in Michael Angelo's Moses. He alludes to the longstanding difference between the Popes and the Ferrarese and also to the quarrels between Louis XII and the Venetians, Maximilian and the Swiss, and the cat-and-dog-like attitude of the English and the Scots[5] of which he records a concrete instance—the battle of Inchkeith in 1549.[6] He even instances the fighting of the Russians and the Tartars[7] and the contemporary battles between the Sultan and the Sophy or Shah of Persia in 1535.[8]

In the Prologue to the *Fourth Book*, written in 1551, a review of European events is given in the person of Jupiter presiding over a Council of the Gods. The quarrels of the Turks and Persians and of the Russians and the Tartars are put aside as settled. The piracy of the Infidels on the Mediterranean coasts is also set aside. The tedious siege of Magdeburg had been finished and the quarrel on the subject of Parma and Mirandola had been settled. This was the most important for Rabelais, for it was the bone of contention between Henry II and Julius III, the newly elected Pope, who wished

---

[1] Ep. ded. Marliani *Topographia.*   [2] *Epp. Rom.* iii. § 16.
[3] iv. 12, 50.   [4] *P.* 30.
[5] iii. 41.   [6] iv. 67.
[7] iii. 41.   [8] *Epp. Rom.* i. § 1, ii. § 9.

to deprive Orazio Farnese of these towns, but as Orazio Farnese was married to Diana, a natural daughter of the French King, strained relations resulted between the Pope and France. It has been shewn by M. Romier[1] that this was the cause of the *crise gallicane*, when Rabelais was instigated to write in support of the French cause against Rome in his *Fourth Book*.

RABELAIS ON CHURCH GOVERNMENT

As might be expected from a man who had been a Franciscan Friar and a Benedictine Brother, he has many allusions, open or covert, to the Church services and to the Church Councils; also to the policy, enactments, and conduct of the Roman Church and the guiding spirits thereof, and especially to the abuses, which were crying for reformation.

In iv. prol. is an allusion to Me Pierre de Cugnières, who, in 1329, had maintained the authority of the King against the Church. The clergy caused stone marmosets resembling him in face to be placed at the corners of the chapels against which tapers were extinguished. There is still one in Notre Dame.

Clerical immunity from punishment in the secular courts, which had been conceded by Charlemagne and had grown into notorious abuse, is covertly alluded to in iv. 49.

The excessive power in shaping the counsels of the Roman Church which had been attained by the Mendicant Orders, and their practice of grasping at bequests from dying persons, notwithstanding their professions of poverty, is strongly reprobated in iii. 21–3 in the episode of the dying poet Raminagrobis.

The abuse of pluralities is glanced at in *P.P.* 5, where it is asserted that the dearth of Church folk will be so great that four and even more benefices will have to be conferred on one person. An allusion is also given in *G.* 52.

Two Popes—Boniface VIII and Nicholas III—are gibbeted for simony, which, however, was so common that it hardly called for special reprobation (*P.* 30).

The legatus *a latere*, punningly styled *altéré* (thirsty), and a number of officers of the papal chancery are ridiculed by their

---

[1] *R.E.R.* x. 140.

functions forming part of the blazon of Triboulet, the court fool (iii. 38).

The sham crusades got up by the Medici Popes, so that they could pocket the results of the taxes (*decimae*) levied for the Crusades, are pointed out in *Epp. Rom.* i. § 1; *P.* 17; iii. 7.

The shameful tax (*cullagium*) levied to allow Church dignitaries to maintain concubines is obliquely alluded to in *P.* 7.

The Council of Constance was convoked by the Emperor Sigismund in 1414, to put an end to the schism caused by the three claimants to the Papacy, Gregory XII, Benedict XIII, and John XXIII. This event is girded at by a *quaestio* of Rabelais inserted in the list of books in the St Victor Library.[1] It is put in the usual scholastic form: Quaestio subtilissima, *Utrum Chimaera in vacuo bombinans possit comedere secundas intentiones; et fuit debatuta per decem hebdomades in Concilio Constantiensi*. Whether the Chimaera, the Homeric monster consisting of a lion, a goat and a serpent (*i.e.* the triple Pope) buzzing in a vacuum (*i.e.* without a see), can devour second intentions (*i.e.* can swallow its promises to surrender the Papacy when requested by the Council).

The Council of Basel, convoked in 1431 under Martin V and concluded under Eugenius IV in 1439, was celebrated for the endeavours of the Popes to maintain their supremacy and the struggles of the Council against this contention.[2] One of the principal results affecting the French Church was the re-affirmation of the Pragmatic Sanction.[3] This enactment had been agreed to by Clement IV and Louis IX in 1268, and renewed in 1438 at Bourges by Charles VII, but with considerable differences. This new Pragmatic Sanction adopted many of the decrees of the Council of Basel, which had been passed against the will of the Pope and in his absence. Among other things *annates* were abolished, by which the Popes received payments for the appointments, confirmations or collations to benefices. Also many of the appeals to the Roman chancery courts were declared unnecessary; they might be decided in the courts of the country concerned. University nominees to benefices and graduates had previously been expected to get confirmation of their appointments by a

---

[1] *P.* 7.   [2] iv. 56.   [3] *P.* 11; iii. 41.

personal visit to Rome. A curious allusion to this is found in *La ramagne des nommez et graduez*[1] (The Alpine sledging of the nominees and graduates), alluding to the difficulties of crossing the Alps to get to Rome.

The enactments of the Pragmatic Sanction were hateful to Rome and the Popes continually tried to evade them. An amusing reference is found to the tricks of Pius II, who as Aeneas Sylvius, when secretary to the Council of Basel, had strenuously maintained its rights against Eugenius IV. When he became Pope he issued bulls (about 1460) against the claim of the Council, setting aside his former declarations as youthful indiscretions. This is put in the form of a volume in the Library of St Victor: *Pronosticatio quae incipit "Sylvii triquebille" balata per M. N. Songecrusion*[2] (The Prognostication which begins: "The Volte-face of Sylvius" danced by "Our Master" Songecreux). *Pronosticatio quae incipit* is intended as a parody of a formal papal edict such as *Constitutio quae incipit*, etc., while Songecreux, the mountebank Pontalais, is given the title *Magister noster*, so much affected by University graduates.

The Pragmatic Sanction was abolished by Francis I at the instance of Leo X at the fifth Lateran Council (1517). Both Pope and King obtained advantages by the substitution of the Concordat for the Pragmatic Sanction. The Pope regained many of his perquisites, such as *annates*, etc., while the King obtained the power of appointment to benefices, etc. The Concordat was enacted in spite of the *Parlement*, who, however, insisted on putting on record their opposition. Rabelais speaks of the Council of Lateran as wearing a Cardinal's hat and as being the husband of Pragmatic Sanction.[3] In another passage[4] the Concordat is styled a bailiff. Very little is to be made of these allusions, but the transactions were recent in 1546 and the mere mention of them was intelligible, while plainer speech might be dangerous.

The *Lateran* Councils, of which there were at least five, are alluded to mockingly as "Lantern" Councils; *Lanterns* and "lanternise" are several times applied to the members and their proceedings. Thomas Becon, Cranmer's outspoken secretary, is still

---

[1] *P.* 7.   [2] *P.* 7.
[3] iii. 41.   [4] iii. 28.

more uncomplimentary when he speaks of *Concilium Latronense* (a Council of Robbers).

The Council of *Trent* is foreshadowed[1] as being pressed by the laity on an unwilling Pope. It was first convoked at Mantua in 1536, but adjourned to Vicenza and afterwards to Trent by a bull of Paul III for May 22, 1545; but it transacted no actual business till March 1547, when seven sessions were held and some decisions were taken. Nothing was passed that concerned Rabelais till April 28, 1552, after his *Fourth Book* had been published. He only hints that some measures were expected, and he styles it the Council of *Chesil*, a Hebrew word which means "mad" or "stormy". There were hopes that the rigours of Lenten observance would be softened, but these seem to have been disappointed, judging by a remark that Lent was strictly forbidden to enter into any covenant with the Chitterlings.[2] The fish diet of Lent is glanced at more than once;[3] Lent is held up to contempt as the banner-bearer of the Ichthyophagi,[4] and Lenten fare is declared on medical authority to be the fosterer of diseases and therefore advocated by physicians.[5] This is following the lead of Erasmus in his *Colloquy* of Ἰχθυοφαγία.

A very serious chapter[6] decries the enactment in the Roman Church that a marriage was lawful and valid without the consent or presence of the parents, if only a priest were there to solemnise it. The point and some of the language is derived from Erasmus' *Colloquium* (Virgo Μισόγαμος). The phrase of the Church was *matrimonium de praesenti* (*Decretal*, iv. 1. 9 and 31). It had arisen in early Christian times when the scandalous frequency of divorce had impelled Christian pastors to enjoin the greater sanctity and permanency of the marriage bond; thus they had gradually got into their hand the celebration of the rite, which the Roman Church afterwards exalted to be one of the seven sacraments. A Christian son was exhorted to disobey a pagan father in this matter and thus the old Roman *patria potestas* was impaired. The Council of Trent did in fact remedy this to some extent in 1563 by an enactment *de clandestinis*.

---

[1] *Epp. Rom.* iii. § 16.   [2] iv. 35.   [3] Ep. Hullot.
[4] iv. 29.   [5] v. 29.   [6] iii. 48.

RABELAIS' LOVE OF GEOGRAPHY AND TRAVELS

That Rabelais delighted in topography, travel and adventure is
shewn not only in the accounts he gives of the environs of Chinon
and of the places he records in Brittany, Poitou and Languedoc
and even in his allusion to the forest of Ardennes to the north of
Metz, but also in the journeys and voyages by which he conducts
his hero round about Poitiers and Ligugé and after that to the
various University towns in France. His allusions to the Canary
Islands shew that he had found an interest in the conquests of Jean
de Bethencourt, while Pantagruel's first voyage to Utopia round
Africa proves that he had read not only Sir T. More but accounts
of the rounding of the Cape of Good Hope by the Portuguese and
their passage to Melinda and to India, while in the second voyage
in the *Fourth Book* he is alive to the attempts of Verazzano, Roberval, Cartier and other French travellers to explore Canada and
achieve the North-West passage to Cathay, or China, which had
been so curiously described by Marco Polo, the Venetian. It is
easy to see how he had familiarised himself with the fabulous stories
of travel in the *Odyssey* and the *Vera Historia* and other writings of
Lucian, besides reading the *Orbis Novus* of Grynaeus, which contains accounts of travel by Thenaud, Cadamosto, Peter Martyr
and others, whose names are mentioned in v. 30. Several incidents recorded of the storm suffered by Columbus are paralleled
in Pantagruel's second voyage to Cathay, such as the throwing
overboard of an account of his discoveries in a carefully fastened
cask, the cry of "Land! Land!", the account of St Elmo's fire, the
desire of Columbus to be the first ashore, and the landing at the
Azores adapted to Plutarch's account of the Macraeons. Rabelais
delighted thus to indulge his taste for illustrating his humanistic
reading by the events and incidents of his own times; though in
tracing a general resemblance we must beware of looking for too
great exactness in all points. Now, also, that the political purpose
of the second edition of the *Fourth Book* has been made out by
M. Romier,[1] the state of affairs in Europe must not be lost sight of
when we attempt to find exact geographical counterparts of
Canada to the "Islands" at which Pantagruel touches.

---

[1] *R.E.R.* x. 134–40.

In the *Gargantua*[1] allusions are to be found to the discoveries of Columbus, Isabella (*Hispaniola*) and the Perlas Islands, while mention is made of Java and Madagascar (*Phebol*), Greenland and Iceland[2] in the *Third Book*.

Although he followed the voyages of all these travellers, Rabelais did not altogether attach credence to all their marvellous accounts. In iv. 63 considerable incredulity is manifested towards the wonders of Pliny, who has already been stigmatised as a liar[3]; and the travellers, of whom a list is given in v. 30, are treated with considerable disrespect when they are said to have got together their narrations "by hearsay". This Herodotus honestly declares in certain cases, though it is only right to note that he is often confirmed by fuller knowledge; in one curious point incredulity on his part is proved by later experience to be unwarranted. He discredits the claim of the Phoenicians to have circumnavigated Africa, because they asserted that after sailing certain days the sun which had been on their left appeared on their right, thus making it certain to us that they had crossed the line at least. In the fanciful list of books in *P*. 7 the title of one is "Travellers Tales" (*Les brimbelettes des voyageurs*); in this Strabo[4] had preceded him when he remarks: "Every one is a boaster in recounting his travels". Shakespeare is kinder and perhaps juster when he says

> travellers ne'er did lie,
> Though fools at home condemn them.[5]

The same love of investigation in topography may be observed in Rabelais, when we find attributed to Panurge a special knowledge of the streets and lanes of Paris, as it is exhibited in the *Pantagruel*; also in the ardour with which Rabelais took up the description of Roman topography on his first visit to that city in 1534, and which he only abandoned when he found himself anticipated by Marliani in this task. He caused Marliani's book to be reprinted at Lyons, and himself prefixed an explanatory dedication to Bishop du Bellay.

---

[1] G. 56.   [2] iii. 51.   [3] G. 6.
[4] i. 30.   [5] *Tempest*, iii. 3. 26.

THE PROLOGUES IN RABELAIS

The Prologues in Rabelais are extremely interesting and sometimes useful in explaining the position and circumstances of the writer at the time he is composing them, or the purpose he has in publishing the "book" to which each of them forms the introduction. It is also instructive to note who and what are the writers from whom he borrows his material; for that occasionally furnishes a clue to the date and surroundings in which he was at the time of composition.

Roughly speaking, we may learn by examination of his books what writers were most laid under contribution for a particular portion; for although he made considerable use of contemporary writers and of those of the time immediately preceding his own, such as Marot, Gringore, Cretin, Coquillart, Villon, *Patelin* as well as the *Roman de la Rose* and the old French Romances—the last especially in his earlier books, *Pantagruel* and *Gargantua*—it is as a humanist that he is most at home, and his borrowings are mostly derived from Cicero's moral writings, from Pliny and Plutarch's *Moralia*, from Homer (especially the *Odyssey*), from Lucian and Virgil with the commentary of Servius, Gellius and Macrobius and several other classical authors. At the same time he delights to follow in the footsteps of the earlier humanists, especially of Budaeus and Erasmus, his earliest guides, as well as Valla and Politian; in the *Fourth Book* and in the revision of the *Third Book* he makes much use of Caelius Rhodiginus. It will be noticed also that Erasmus and Pliny are less employed in the earlier books and increasingly so in the later ones, when he becomes more practised in his art of composition and less satisfied with the cruder work of the earlier French romances. This will be observed generally, as also in the Prologues, which although introductory in manner, were written later, after the books to which they refer were completed.

The Prologue to the *Pantagruel* (which was the first "book" in date, though the second in the usual arrangement) is devoted to a panegyric on *Les grandes Cronicques du grant geant Gargantua*, which is allowed by some critics, though denied by most, to be Rabelais' work. This is followed by a recommendation of the *Pantagruel*, as a book of the same kind but a little more reasonable and worthy of credit. A personal note is also struck at the end, to the effect that the author—who is described on the title-page as "the late Master Alcofribas"—has just returned "to visit his native country and to know if any of his kindred are there alive". This has been cleverly used by M. Lefranc to fix the date of publication for this book (Oct. 1532) and also to help to settle the date of the *Gargantua* as in October 1534 (*R.E.R.* ix. 155). In this Prologue very few loans from other writers are to be noted. There is one from Cornelius Agrippa, *de vanitate scientiarum*, c. 47, on the Cabala, and a number of chivalric romances are mentioned by name; otherwise it is simple, almost burlesque, in its imitation of the old French romance writers.

In the Prologue to the *Gargantua* a great change is to be remarked. First, the crude simplicity of the *Pantagruel* is laid aside, and a serious tone replaces it. But most noticeable is the fact that the first three paragraphs are taken bodily, with a few burlesque additions, from the *Adagia* of Erasmus, on the admirable qualities of the ugly Socrates, as represented by Plato. The next passage, which resents the disparagement of comic and droll representations as containing nothing of value, is from Lucian, and the next which forbids the esteem of men by their dress is from Erasmus. Next comes an application of a passage of Plato in praise of the philosophical dog, which breaks the bone to get at the marrow[1], so highly commended by Galen. The next passage claims for the author's composition an inner meaning such as is involved in allegory, so much observed in sacred mysteries and Pythagorean symbols. This again is derived from Erasmus' *Adagia* or a passage very similar in thought and expression in Galen's *de usu partium* (vii. 14). Rabelais goes on to say that Homer never dreamed of the allegories that have been squeezed out of his writings by the critics and especially by Politian, whom (following Budaeus) he accuses unjustly of plagiarism. He next accuses a certain friar of foolishly deriving absurd moralisings from Ovid. He now declares that he himself, when writing his books, thought no more of such things than Homer did, though, like him and Ennius, he wrote them while eating and

---

[1] Plato's passage is also given in Plut. *Is. et Osir.* c. 11, and the notion is reinforced by Erasmus (*Ad.* ii. 9. 35) on a line, perhaps from Plautus, quoted by Jerome: *Qui e nuce nuculeum esse vult frangit nucem.*

drinking, as Horace (quoted by Erasmus) asserts. Again, Erasmus supplies a story that Demosthenes spent more on oil than wine; Rabelais makes a merit that *he* spent more on wine than on oil. "Therefore", concludes the jovial author, "do you, my readers, interpret my deeds and sayings in the best sense, and make merry over my humorous writings".

The Prologue to the *Third Book* begins by drawing attention to the old Cynic Philosopher Diogenes. Asking his French readers whether they have heard of him, Rabelais assumes that they have; for they are of Phrygian descent, like King Midas, being derived from Priam (if the claim of descent from Francus, second son of Hector, which they make, is just). At all events, if they have not the wealth of Midas they have his long ears. This is a scoff at the curiosity of the French, which he gibes at elsewhere (*P.P.* prol.). Erasmus is drawn upon for the account of the wealth and the asinine ears of Midas. An account is then given of the conduct of Diogenes at the siege of Corinth by King Philip, when, finding himself unemployed in helping in the defence of the city, he set himself to work to roll his Tub up and down the Craneium. All this is greatly amplified with truly Rabelaisian humour and spirit. Hints are taken from Erasmus in describing the activity used in preparing the fortifications and from Gellius in the list of the various arms. In the same way and from the same motive Rabelais explains that in the expected siege of Paris by Charles V in 1544, while the citizens are all busily employed in preparing the defence, he, having nothing to do and being unable to give active help, will employ himself as best he can and roll his Diogenical Tub, *i.e.* give all the assistance he can by his writings. This is derived from Budaeus in the preface to his *Annotationes in Pandectas*, where he translates and adapts Lucian's account of the siege of Corinth and the conduct of Diogenes. The Prologue goes on to commend war as, in the opinion of Heraclitus, the father of all good things, and in the judgment of Solomon resembling the perfection of divine wisdom. This is directly contradictory to what Rabelais said in the *Gargantua* (c. 46), but it may be explained that he is now speaking as a patriot in the defence of his country, and thus opposing the thesis of Erasmus (*Ad.* iv. 1. 1) that "war is sweet only to those who never tried it". In these circumstances, after drinking his inspiration as did Aeschylus (Erasm. *Ad.* iv. 3. 58), Ennius and Cato, according to Horace, the author determines to help on the work by casks of his writings in eulogy of his countrymen's deeds of arms. Notwithstanding, he fears lest his grotesque writings may give offence where he intends to give pleasure, but relying on the kindly nature of his readers he will set to work with his Tub, from which all may drink without paying. There is no fear of the wine running short, for he will pour in at the bung as his readers shall draw out at the tap. The wine is for drinkers of good qualities and for "gouty blades of the highest walk", who will take all in good part. But it is not intended for corrupt judges and advocates or for ill-natured critics, who only pry out errors for correction, still less for the hypocritical mendicants, who are for reading the books themselves and smelling out heresies. For them he has the cudgel of Diogenes, which he ordered to be laid beside his dead body to drive away roving curs.

The Prologue to the first (partial) edition of the *Fourth Book* (written in exile at Metz) begins with the acceptance of a silver flask made in the shape of a breviary, presented to Rabelais at Metz by some French courtiers from Paris, who requested him to continue his writings. On the outside this flask was decorated with hooks and magpies (*crocs et pies*), which served as a *rebus* on *crocquer pie*, a proverbial phrase signifying "to drink lustily". The author proceeds to explain this by giving a spirited account of a terrible battle between magpies and jays, which is said to have taken place at St Aubin du Cormier in Brittany and to have furnished an augury for the battle between Charles VIII and Louis, Duke of Orléans (afterwards Louis XII), in which the Breton *ermines*, as represented in colour by the magpies, were utterly defeated by the azure and argent of the French jays. The story is told in Poggio, *Facetiae*, No. 234, but it seems to have been common gossip on the borders of Brittany and France. A jay belonging to an old uncle of Rabelais at Angers is stated to have broken out of his cage and to have joined the forces of the jays and to have returned a few days afterwards badly wounded, but the magpie of a neighbouring barber never returned. She had been eaten (*la pie a esté crocquée*), for *croquer pie* must have been the watchword on the day of battle. After this explanation, Rabelais expresses his willingness to accept

this present and to *crocquer pie*. But the request had involved the
words *do, dico, addico*, the Roman praetor's phrase for his functions
on the days that were *fasti*. (This is from Ovid and Macrobius.)
The gift (*do*) being accepted, the saying (*dico*) is next examined.
You say, continues the author, that my writings have pleased you
and you invite me to continue them. This is practically assented to,
with a reciprocal compliment. Thirdly, you adjudge (*addico*) the
old quarters of the moon to the lunatic, calumniating monks and
friars, who in imitation of the *diabolos*, or calumniating spirit, have
decried the Pantagrueline writings, only in order to keep them for
their own reading, and thus to take them from the sick folk for
whose delectation they have been composed. According to a
passage in the *Epidemia* of Hippocrates, patients are undoubtedly
cheered and elated by a cheerful bearing of the physician, and de-
pressed by the contrary; perhaps also there is actually a transfusion
of spirits, gay or gloomy, between patient and physician. Consequently our doctor, unable to be present, writes his books to
console his patients in his absence. Nothing, therefore, is left for
his calumniating enemies but to select a tree and hang themselves.
This offer is in imitation of that which Timon made to the Athenians, of the fig-tree which he was intending to cut down.

M. Romier has established (*R.E.R.* x. 113–42) almost for certain
that Rabelais, utterly disgusted (at Metz) with the persistent
attacks on his books on the score of heresy, laid down his pen and
determined to write no more, after having written his fragmentary
Fourth Book. Being in straits for means, he wrote his appeal to
Cardinal du Bellay, dated March 6, 1547, the reply of the Cardinal
being a summons to accompany him to Rome after King Henry II's
coronation at Reims. Accordingly, we find that Rabelais, after
taking his salary as physician at Metz up to Midsummer 1547, was
in Paris on July 10, and from there joined the Cardinal at Reims,
which they left together for Rome July 22, passing Lyons, where
Rabelais (*circa* Aug. 15) left with the printers his first instalment of
the *Fourth Book* without corrections and an Almanack for 1548 (the
title-page of which has survived) to be published at the next November book fair. He stayed with du Bellay in Rome from Sept.
27, 1547 till Sept. 22, 1549, when the Cardinal, having been superseded by Cardinal Ippolito d'Este, returned to Lyons early in

November with Rabelais and some of his suite. Cardinal de Châtillon (Odet Coligny) had been told by Rabelais of his resolve not to continue his *Pantagruel*; but he had obtained for him a privilege from the King to continue his writings, and by this and his own efforts, backed by the request of du Bellay at St Maur des Fossés, he induced Rabelais to finish his *Fourth Book*. Very strained relations had occurred between the French Court and the Vatican, and M. Romier urges that this and the former slight on Cardinal du Bellay prompted the tone and the substance of this book, viz. a panegyric on G. du Bellay and his family and strong attacks on the policy of Rome.

This, M. Romier suggests, is explained by the Epistle of Dedication to Cardinal Châtillon of the second (complete) edition of the *Fourth Book*.

The Epistle of Dedication begins by saying that the author has been importuned to continue his "Pantagrueline Mythologies"; that he had written them entirely in the interest of his patients; setting forth that the duty of the physician is to cheer and please his patients in every way possible, in dress, bearing, speech, etc. He repeats from the Prologue to the incomplete *Fourth Book* the passage from Hippocrates on the necessity of a cheerful bearing on the part of a physician. He then proceeds to say that above all things a physician ought to be careful in his conversations, giving three instances from Galen of misconduct of physicians in this respect. After this he complains bitterly of the calumnies that have been raised against him by "certain Cannibals, Misanthropes and Agelasts", accusing him of heresies in his books. This he indignantly denies, but says that he has lost patience and has resolved not to write a jot more. This he had set forth to Cardinal de Châtillon himself, but the Cardinal had obtained from King Henry a privilege for the *Fourth Book*, which he had shewn to him afterwards, and again, together with Cardinal du Bellay at St Maur des Fossés, had persuaded him to continue his writings. Therefore, Rabelais says, under this protection he continues to write, but he asks his readers to attribute every success he may enjoy to his kind patron.

The Prologue to the *Fourth Book*, after a profession of good health and cheerfulness, which the writer attributes to the favour of God, cites the precept of the Gospel, which enjoins that a physician should see that he enjoys good health himself before he presumes to heal others. This is supported by an extract from Erasmus on Galen and one from Pliny on Asclepiades, another physician. But if health have escaped you, the writer goes on, see to it that you secure it like a runaway slave, as is enjoined by the learned jurist Tiraqueau in his recent treatise *Le mort saisit le vif*, *i.e.* by the death of the possessor the heir is seised of the property. Do you therefore pray for health and, as that is a moderate prayer, you may hope that God will hear and answer it. Prayers and wishes should always be moderate. Instances of moderate prayers obtaining an answer may be found in the case of Zacchaeus, who wished to see Christ, and in the son of the prophet, who wished that his hatchet which had fallen into the river might be restored to him (2 Kings vi. 1–7). On the subject of hatchets an illustration is given from Aesop the Phrygian, *i.e.* the Frenchman, cf. iii. prol. (*init.*). The fable is given in Erasmus, *Adagia* (iv. 3. 57: *Fluvius non semper fert secures*), but it is here told of a woodcutter of Gravot near Chinon. Rabelais gives rein to his fancy and pictures Jupiter holding a Council or "Consistory" of the gods and interrupted in his affairs of arranging the politics of the world by the cries of the woodman praying for his hatchet. The well-known story of the gold and silver hatchets is told with very graphic amplifications, such as a survey of European politics and the squabbles in the University of Paris, while Priapus gives advice, with precedents from mythology and illustrations of his own experiences as tutelary god of the gardens, where he heard madrigals sung by musicians in May at the times of the election of Popes Leo X and Julius III (1513 and 1550 respectively). This gives an opportunity to furnish a list of fifty-nine contemporary musicians, singers in the choir of the Popes and other princes; which list has been useful in recording the names of musicians of that time. Jupiter instructs Mercury to give the woodman his choice of the hatchets—gold, silver, and his own. He chooses his own and is enriched. His neighbours sell their possessions to buy hatchets, but by choosing the gold one instead of their own subject themselves to the penalty of losing their heads. Thus, the Prologue says, it will be, if you do not indulge your wishes in moderation. A racy illustration is given of two immoderate wishers, who paid a heavy penalty. Consequently, do you wish and pray for health, in sure faith that such a moderate wish will be granted. Do not imitate the Genoese, who after looking over their swindling transactions, go out in the morning and wish one another "Health and Gain", and consequently are often disappointed of both.

PROLOGUE TO THE FIFTH BOOK

This Prologue is also founded on the *Adagia* of Erasmus, from which are taken several allusions. It begins with *salsitudo non inest illi* (*Ad* ii. 3. 51), then expanding a text of Ecclesiastes vii. 10: "Why were the former days better than these?" and afterwards by the help of an old French proverb to the effect that fools are most in season when beans are in flower, Rabelais advises his readers to eat copiously of beans *in pod*, which he figuratively explains to be his own books. This, he says, should be done without scruple by his readers, notwithstanding the prohibition of Pythagoras *a fabis abstineto* (Erasm. *Ad.* i. 2. 17); for Pythagoras, he declares, only forbade them to others in order that there might be the more for himself. The Prologue then proceeds to say that although the author cannot pretend to rival the excellent compositions of Colin, Marot, Heroet, Saint-Gelais, Salel, Masuel and, above all, those of Margaret of Navarre, whom he must be satisfied to hear and commend, yet he hopes to be accepted as the *Rhyparagrapher*, or *genre*-painter and comic writer as compared with the writers of high rhetorical style. There are passages and expressions in this Prologue nearly identical with several in that of the *Third Book*, and some that correspond very nearly with others in that of the *Fourth Book*. This is made out by some critics to be an argument against the authenticity of the *Fifth Book*. On the other hand, it may be used to maintain the thesis that the *Fifth Book* was written earlier than the other two and laid aside by the author, possibly for further elaboration, or perhaps altogether, and therefore passages and ideas in it were employed for the other two books. This was the case, we know, with the Old Prologue of the *Fourth Book*, which was made by the writer to supply matter for the Epistle of Dedication and for the New Prologue.

LISTS, BLAZONS AND LITANIES

One of the features of the *Pantagruel* and *Gargantua* is the lists of persons, books, games, fishes, serpents, etc., and those of epithets or blazons of persons, with which Rabelais regaled his readers. He readily fell in with the fashion of his times, and perhaps was enabled to go beyond his contemporaries in having at command lists of plants, animals and all sorts of collections in Athenaeus, Pliny and other writers. He seems to have revelled in taking a long catalogue from some source or other and in adding to it anything that was suggested to him by his own experience, observation or fancy. To begin with, there is the long list of persons or characters subject to the various planets in c. 5 of the *Pantagrueline Prognostication*, in the compilation of which he was following a widespread fashion and adapting and translating some Latin ones which had been printed in Germany. This is made more interesting from the fact that many of the curious names that he has got together reappear later in various parts of his "books". In the first chapter of *Pantagruel* we find the pedigree of Pantagruel adapted from the Genealogies of the Kings of France composed by his friend Jean Bouchet, the Poitevin jurist. The *form* in which it is put is clearly an imitation of the genealogies of our Lord in St Matthew and St Luke, while the names are derived from the Old Testament, classical writers and the names of heroes in chivalric romances, such as Fierabras, Morgante Maggiore and others. This goes to shew that he had used the opportunity afforded him by the Lyons printers to read these prose romances.

In the 7th chapter of *Pantagruel* is a fanciful catalogue of books supposed to be found in the theological Library of St Victor in Paris. It consists of a number of pious books with the titles burlesqued and a few books relating to historical events; but it is important to observe that, while in the first two editions (A, 1532; B, 1535) the list is comparatively short, in the third and fourth editions (C, 1535; D, 1542) an addition is made at least as long as the original list; this allows the introduction of books suggesting comments on various political and religious events of the time, while much of the matter is derived from that strange book composed and edited by Ulrich von Hutten and his friends under the

name of *Epistolae Obscurorum Virorum*, a most powerful satire against
the ignorance and debauchery of the monks and friars. This was
quite to the taste of Maistre François, and he makes much use of
it in the later part of the chapter. Unfortunately for modern readers
this chapter can only be rendered intelligible by a commentary,
which must needs be much longer than the original, though historically the titles are very interesting. One instance may be given to
illustrate the double-edged point of much of Rabelais' satire:
L'entrée de Anthoine de Leive ès terres du Brésil. This is an imitation of
a well-known historical romance *L'entrée de Charlemagne en Espagne*,
but the reference is to the attack on Provence by Antoine de Leyva,
Charles V's general, in 1536, when the Constable Anne de Montmorency forced him to a disastrous retreat by devastating and
burning up (*Brésil* = burnt up) the country before him. Brazil had
not long been discovered by the Portuguese Pedro Alvarez Cabral.

   The 30th chapter gives a list of heroes and heroines in Hades and
their various employments (generally reversing their position and
importance), furnished by Epistemon, who has been restored to
life by Panurge after the battle with the Giants. It is imitated from
the tenth book of Plato's *Republic* and modelled on the νέκυια, or
account of the dead, as told by Ulysses in the eleventh book of the
Odyssey, aided by some amusing touches from Lucian. A long list
is provided, firstly from characters in Herodotus and Plutarch with
occupations found for each of them, sometimes on the principle of
contrariety (*i.e.* great kings are made beggars, etc.) or sometimes
to be explained by historical adaptations, as when Marcellus is a
bean-sheller (*esgousseur de febves*) because he superseded Fabius, and
Scipio Africanus cries Lye in a Sabot (*cornoit la lie*), from his gentile
name, Cornelius, and many others, the explanation of which is not
easy. Then come a number of Roman Emperors, heroes of chivalry,
Popes, etc., Homeric and historical heroes and heroines, followed
at the end by Diogenes, the cynic, and Epictetus, the needy philosopher, who are paralleled with Minos and Orion in Homer, while
Patelin, Le Maire, Villon and the braggart poltroon, the Franc-
Archier de Baignolet, occupy the places of Tityos, Tantalus,
Sisyphus and Heracles. Some of the strokes of satire are exceedingly comic, but it must be confessed that other comparisons have
lost their point, if they ever had any.

In the *Gargantua*, the 11th chapter is mostly taken up with a list of proverbs, or rather anti-proverbs, which the vicious education of the old monkish system causes the young prince to follow so as to act in immediate contradiction to accepted maxims of wise and correct conduct. The proverbs are gathered from Hesiod and old-world philosophy, and nearly a dozen are from Cordier's *de corrupti sermonis emendatione* (Gryphius, 1532), which gives a long list of phrases in the Latinity of the Paris University followed by the French equivalent and then by the proper Latin phrase. Many others are simply current proverbial philosophy of the period reversed. The object of the chapter is to burlesque the result of the monkish education in contrast with that provided by Rabelais' own system of moral, intellectual and physical training, which is described later on (cc. 23, 24).

The 22nd chapter of *Gargantua* supplies a list of games (about 120) which the youthful hero played after dinner. It begins with games at cards, dice, draughts, chess and backgammon. Interesting among the card games is the game of *cent*, or a hundred, which proves to be the well-known game of picquet, according to the judgment of "Cavendish". Other games given here are simpler parts of this rather complicated game, out of which it seems to have grown. These games are followed by others, such as shovel-board, fox-and-geese, and other social games; then come hunt-the-slipper, forfeits and the like. These are succeeded by games indoors and outdoors, in fact any kind suggested by the fertile imagination or retentive memory of the author. It is to be observed that the same games are sometimes introduced under different provincial names. The moral intended is that the youth under such training finds recreation in any and every pastime, whether useful or not, but that he merely fritters away his time, the most valuable of all things. In contrast to this the new system in c. 23 supplies cards, "not to play with, but to learn from them a thousand pretty tricks and new inventions, which were all derived from arithmetic".

The *Third Book* furnishes two litanies and a blazon, which are the best known of all these lists. Urquhart has done a great disservice to Rabelais by indefinitely increasing the number of epithets, in a spirit of bravado, as it seems. The first litany in c. 26 consists of

a number of epithets hurled by Panurge at Brother John as a
mocking compliment to his virile powers; this is retorted in c. 28
by Brother John taunting Panurge as being weak and forlorn in
respect of such qualities. Each list has very nearly the same number
of epithets. Another injury has been done in the second edition by
the printer Fezandat (F, 1552), in arranging the lists with two
epithets in a line instead of three, as was the case in the first edition
(W, 1546). A careful examination of the epithets shews that the
system of three in a line was the one Rabelais intended, and moreover it is essential to the proper setting forth of the qualities attributed to each character. For instance, "ebony, brazil-wood, box-
wood" are bracketed, and also come together in *P.* 19, where they
occur before. Then there are "Raphe-like, Guelphic, Ursine", and
three lines in a sequence "gerundive, genitive, active", "gigantal,
vital, oval", "magistral, claustral, monachal". The same feature
is to be observed in the litany in c. 28, where may be noticed
"choused, cosened, cajoled", "foundered, spavined, galled", from
veterinary surgery, and "drawn, cupped, scarified", from the
process of cupping. To break up these trios, merely to form the list
in two lines, is to destroy the sequence of ideas. Both in this *Third
Book* and in the *Fourth Book*, as printed by Fezandat, much careless-
ness is to be found and many misprints, which are corrected in a
later edition by Aleman. In iv. 59 a list of dishes, obviously intended by Rabelais for a litany, is spoiled by ignoring the proposed
bracketing of similar dishes and printing the dishes mentioned all
in one sequence, notwithstanding that there are two lists of twenty-
eight each. A few additional names are supplied in each of the
litanies of the *Third Book*, whether furnished by Rabelais or the
printer, and their insertion undoubtedly breaks the three-word
arrangement, but the spirit of each chapter is so entirely spoiled by
their introduction, that I would rather insert them at the end in a
note. In this connexion also I would note that in iii. 22, *Demogorgon*
is changed to *Demiourgon* in the second edition, and that Demiourgon
is read in iv. 47 by Fezandat. "Demogorgon" is a fiend and should
properly find place in both chapters; Demiourgos is a creator in
Plato and Galen. The change I attribute to Fezandat.

In c. 38 we have the celebrated blazoning of the fool Triboulet
by Pantagruel and Panurge in antiphone. Blazon, of course, is a

heraldic term signifying a shield, the arms represented upon it and the description of such arms by heralds, who to the cry "largesse" which followed added an enumeration of the exploits and attributes of an incoming champion. Afterwards, losing its heraldic significance, the word came into common use, and became "a perpetual praise or continued vituperation of him who is its object" (Ch. Fontaine, 1548). Thus it became a kind of rhetorical exercise. Sicile, herald at arms to Alphonso, King of Aragon, taking the word partly in its heraldic, partly in its poetical sense, composed a *Blason de toutes armes* (1495) and later a *Blason des Couleurs*, which Rabelais mercilessly ridicules in *G*. 9. Coquillart (1421–1519) wrote *Le Blason des Armes et des Dames* and in 1504 Gringore inserted *Le Blason de Practique* in his *Folles Entreprises*. These *Blasons* soon became fashionable and everything conceivable was *blasonné*. Rabelais here follows this fashion and adapts a *Cry du Prince des Sotz* of Gringore's (vol. 1, p. 201, ed. Elzevir) beginning *Sotz lunaticques, sotz étourdis, sotz saiges*, and borrowing somewhat from a *Monologue des nouveaulz sots*, of which two examples may be found in the *Anciennes poésies françaises* (vol. i. pp. 11–16; vol. iii. pp. 13–18), compiles a kind of litany descriptive of Triboulet. To him must attach the credit or discredit of giving this *Blason* in antiphone. Epithets derived from any and every source may be found in these lists, from medicine, from the kitchen, from grammatical treatises, from falconry, from astrology, etc., but I think that two sources stand out particularly—terms derived from the office-holders in the Roman Church and a longish list of epithets belonging to birds. These are reminiscent of the *Fifth Book*, cc. 2–6, in which all the orders of that Church are compared to birds, such as Pope-jay, Cardin-jay, etc.; also a quotation from Pliny is given (iv. 58) comparing the *Cuculli* or cowls of the monks and friars with the *coquilles* or shells which Nature has formed in endless variety of shapes, colours and streaks. It seems as though Rabelais had been struck by the clerical dresses, the singing and bell-ringing attached to the Roman services, and had whimsically recorded them in several places of his book.

To these, perhaps, should be added the list of verbs in the Prologue to the *Third Book* grotesquely describing the manner in which Diogenes is represented as rolling his Tub up and down the

Craneium at Corinth. It should be observed that of the sixty-one verbs descriptive of his action, the first part merely treats of him turning and twisting the Tub about, the second part consists of words relating to the direction of a carriage and horses, while the third part is applicable to the preparation and limbering of a piece of artillery; so that Rabelais is guilty of a very comic anachronism in representing Diogenes as treating his Tub as though it were a mortar or a similar piece of ordnance for the purpose of defending the city.

The anatomy of Lent, as to his organs and limbs, given in iv. 30, 31 may fairly be looked upon as a list or litany something of the same kind as the others. Till recently this anatomy of Lent and the comparison of each of the organs and members with some object to which a resemblance is traced was looked upon as a mere trick of a grotesque fancy, but in 1899 Dr Le Double, a Touraine physician, published a book in which these resemblances were carefully made out and shewn to be reasonable and real. In a few cases the comparisons may seem far-fetched, but generally the drawings of the anatomical parts contrasted with the representations of their counterparts as given by Dr Le Double from drawings of the objects to which they are compared—in most cases contemporary with Rabelais—are striking in their similarity. In anatomical books that were accessible in the sixteenth century possibly the same or similar comparisons were to be found; in two cases—the *mediastinum* compared to a leather-bottle, and the *pleura* to a crow's bill—the same resemblances may be seen traced by Ambroise Paré, the celebrated surgeon, who was a younger contemporary of Rabelais (lib. ii. c. 8; ix. c. 4, and x. c. 22), so that the source of the other comparisons may perhaps be found. What Dr Le Double does not point out is that the anatomical lists given in these two chapters are derived from the *de usu partium* of Galen with two or three items taken from Avicenna's book on Anatomy; but as Avicenna's treatise was probably derived to a great extent from Galen, who also includes these special features in his treatise, it would seem that this was only introduced by a fondness for variety, exhibited elsewhere by our author, or from a complaisance to his medical confrères, who still held to the Arabian nomenclature.

In c. 40 a list of cooks is introduced under the command of

Brother John, drawn up in eight bands for the purpose of fighting against the Chitterlings, who are attacking the Pantagruelists. This is perhaps intended as a parody of the enrolment of a force of *condottieri*, and serves to exemplify the fertility of invention required for this bestowing of nicknames. It is a trait worthy of Plautus, whose genius in many ways seems to have descended to his French disciple. Otherwise there is little to remark in this exuberant display.

In the list of foods (c. 59) sacrificed by his followers to Messer Gaster, a slight examination will, I think, shew that the printer, as I have pointed out, was careless in not arranging the dishes in a responsive litany, which was intended by the author. He has merely printed in sequence two lots of twenty-eight dishes which were intended to be in parallel columns. Thus we should read

Legs of Mutton with garlic sauce	Shoulders of Mutton with capers
Pasties with hot sauce	Pieces of Beef *à la royale*
Pork cutlets with onion sauce	Breasts of Veal
Capons roasted in their relish	Boiled Hens with blanc-manger
Woodcocks, Snipes	Hazel Hens
etc. etc.	etc. etc.

A very slight re-arrangement of these would make a double list of twenty-eight dishes very nearly corresponding in character. The intention of all this chapter is to point out the self-indulgence of Messer Gaster (*i.e.* the high dignitaries of the Roman Church) in the matter of gormandising.

The 60th chapter proceeds to set forth the dietary of Messer Gaster on the "interlarded" (for "intercalated") lean days. First we find a number of appetising dishes such as *caviar, herrings*, etc. to promote thirst, which must needs be appeased. This is followed by a list of eighty-four fishes, which may be served to the gluttonous churchman. In the composition of this list Rabelais has had recourse to the 9th and 32nd books of his faithful Pliny, in which a list and sometimes an account of a large number of fishes is put down. He also employs the book (*de Piscibus*) of his old friend the Montpellier professor, Rondelet, and that of Pierre Gilles, *De piscium Massiliensium gallicis et latinis nominibus*, which had been published by Seb. Gryphius, 1533. He may also have consulted Athenaeus. This is succeeded by more egg-dishes and salt fish and then wine, and lastly by dried fruits, etc.

The last list in the *Fourth Book* (c. 64) is devoted to serpents, reptiles, etc. It is introduced on a very slight pretext. In the previous chapter Eusthenes, during the calm, which had put the travellers out of sorts, had proposed a problem, "why a fasting man's spittle is dangerous to a fasting serpent"; Pantagruel had wisely answered this problem and dissipated their *ennui* by order-ing dinner. After this all the company one after another declare themselves satisfied, and Eusthenes declares that for the whole of this day all serpents may abide in safety from his spittle. He then proceeds to enumerate a list of ninety-seven noxious creatures which are in this category. The list is interesting to us principally for the sources from which it is derived. These are Pliny, libb. 8 and 29, Avicenna's *Canon*, libb. iv and v, Nicander's *Theriaca* and one or two more isolated instances. Interesting cases are the ser-pent *arges*, which proves to be the ὄφις ἀργής of Hippoc. *Epit.* v. § 36, a passage employed in iv. 44 in refutation of a story of Brother John taken from a *Colloquy* of Erasmus, and the serpent *Cychriodes* (Κυχρείδης ὄφις), which was nurtured by Cychreus and became the *famulus* of Demeter at Eleusis (Strabo, ix. 393). The list itself seems to be merely a parade of erudition.

In the *Fifth Book* there is only one long list and that is taken almost unaltered from the *Disciple de Pantagruel*. It is a list of dance songs and it occurs in c. 33, a chapter which is found only in the MS. of the *Fifth Book*, and of which the authenticity has been much questioned. The list, however, is interesting, as it furnishes the titles of many of the songs and ballads which were popular in the fifteenth and sixteenth centuries.

RABELAIS ON ART

In art Rabelais seems to have cared but little for painting or sculpture, notwithstanding the wonderful achievements in paint-ing in Rome just before his visits, 1534-6. He knows nothing of the Stanze of Raphael which had only just been completed; he only knows of the portrait of Alexander VI by Pinturicchio in the Borgia apartments owing to a scandalous story attached to it. He just mentions the paintings of Charles Carmoy and the pictures on each side the window of the Hôtel Jacques Cœur at Bourges; on the other hand he is keenly interested in the castles on the Loire which were built or in course of construction by the Kings or great nobles of France, and his own Abbey of Thelema is the result of his love for architecture. Although the details are incorrect, not to say impossible, the general idea is sound and several of the features are suggested by the King's castle at Blois. The Abbey was to be more magnificent than Bonnivet, Chambord or Chantilly, but the number of chambers assigned to it (9332) is enormously in excess of the space for their accommodation. The *Hypnerotomachia*, from which much is borrowed in the details of the Abbey, was the work of a Dominican, the Order which paid special attention to architecture. Rabelais also mentions the two bridges over the Seine connecting the *Ville* with the *Cité* and the *Université*, which were constructed from the designs of Fra Giocondo, another Dominican. He gives also two or three allusions to Vitruvius, and was a personal friend of Philibert de l'Orme, the distinguished architect from Lyons.

His other *penchant* was music. Several poems and songs are inserted in his books, whether from his friend Saint-Gelais, or from old French song-books; the most curious contribution that he makes is the list of fifty-nine musicians in the Prologue to the *Fourth Book*. They are mostly Flemings or Hollanders, for it was in those countries that music found most encouragement, especially at the Court of Margaret of Austria, the aunt of Charles V. In Rabelais' list they bear names of a French form, and there are also of course some French musicians. Nearly all of them were trained in the choirs of various European Courts, and had achieved distinction as singers before they attained fame as musicians. One point in the time indicated as their *floruit* is that about half of them are mentioned as preceding the other division by thirty-seven years. This seems to suggest the accession to the pontificate of Leo X (1513) for the first group, and that of Julius III (1550) for the second. Many of these musicians have been recorded in the history of music and their compositions published in Venice and elsewhere.

Another enigmatical mention of musical history is to be found in iv. 62, where flutes made from the wood of the elder tree that has grown far from human habitation are preferred to those made from ordinary elder wood which sprouts from ruinous buildings in peopled neighbourhoods. This is interpreted to mean that sacred music devoted to church services should be "celestial, divine and more abstruse" rather than common and trivial. This refers to a long-standing quarrel between composers who preferred the old Gregorian chants, which admitted only semibreves and the heavy notes, as opposed to the lighter music which allowed quavers and other quicker notes. There exists in the *Decretals* an order of John XXII, dated Avignon 1224 (*Extrav. Commun.* iii. 1. 1), setting forth a detailed prohibition of every note save those of the more solemn church music. Rabelais illustrates all this curiously by citing the proverb: *Non ex quovis ligno Mercurius, i.e.* the god Mercury is not to be represented by a statue carved from any chance wood but from the thyme wood. In this case the meaning is that teaching should be adapted in every case to the learner's capacity. The musical point here mentioned is also brought out with a number of puns in v. 27, a chapter which many critics will not allow to be Rabelais' work.

There is a note by Antoine Leroy, who was *curé* of Meudon with two or three *curés* intervening between himself and Rabelais, to the effect that he had learnt from old men in his parish who had heard from their fathers of their former pastor François Rabelais. They describe him as very expert in singing and assert that he trained chorister boys in what was called plain chaunt with wonderful kindness and gentleness, that he "arranged everything with exactness and order and that he administered everything in the church with the utmost vigilance, and that his house afforded refuge and protection to all". This is from a volume called *Floretum philosophicum*, Paris 1649.

CHRONOLOGICAL LIST

A chronological list of the extant writings and correspondence of François Rabelais and of some documents bearing on his life.

Letter of Rabelais to Budaeus	March 4, 1520
Letter of Budaeus to Rabelais	April 12, 1521
Letter of Budaeus to Rabelais	Jan. 27, 1524
Rhymed letter to Bouchet	Sept. 6, (? 1525)
Rhymed letter of Bouchet in reply	Sept. 8, (? 1525)
Matriculation of Rabelais at Montpellier	Sept. 17, 1530

Baccalaureat of Rabelais at Montpellier	Dec. 1, 1530
Epistle of Dedication (*Manardi Epistolae medicinales*) to A. Tiraqueau (Lyons)	June 3, 1532
Epistle of Dedication (*Hippocratis Aphorismi*) to Geoffroi d'Estissac	July 15, 1532
Epistle of Dedication (*Testamentum Cuspidii*) to Amaury Bouchard	Sept. 4, 1532
Letter to ERASMUS	Nov. 30, 1532
[*Grandes Cronicques*	? Aug. 3, 1532]
Appointment as physician to the hospital at Lyons	Oct. 1532
PANTAGRUEL (also 1533, 1537, 1542)	(? Nov. 3), 1532
PANTAGRUELINE PROGNOSTICATION	(? Monday after Epiphany), 1533
Almanack (Preface)	1533
Epistle of Dedication (*Marliani Topographia antiquae Romae*) to Bishop du Bellay	Aug. 31, 1534
GARGANTUA (also 1535, 1537, 1542)	? Aug. or Oct. 1534
Almanack (Preface)	1535
Supersession as physician at Lyons	March 5, 1535
Supplicatio pro Apostasia	1535
First Letter to the Bishop of Maillezais	Dec. 30, 1535
Answer to petition by Paul III	Jan. 17, 1536
Second letter to the Bishop of Maillezais	Jan. 28, 1536
Third letter to the Bishop of Maillezais	Feb. 15, 1536
Second Petition to Paul III (cf. *R.E.R.* vii. 260–9) (*Supplicatio Rabelesi*)	(?) 1536
Doctorate at Montpellier	May 22, 1537
Lectures on Hippocrates' *Prognostic*	Sept. 27, 1537
Three letters from Bishop Pellicier at Venice to Rabelais at Turin	July 23, Oct. 17, 1540 and March 20, 1541
Letter from Rabelais to Antoine Hullot	March 1, (? 1544`
Privilege of Francis I for *Third Book*	Sept. 19, 1545
THIRD BOOK (W), Ch. Wechel, Paris	Jan. 1546
Letter from Metz to Cardinal du Bellay	Feb. 6, (? 1547)
FOURTH BOOK (A), P. de Tours, Lyon	1548
Almanack (title-page)	1548
SCIOMACHIE, Seb. Gryphius, Lyon	1549
Privilege of Henry II for *Fourth Book* and revised *Third Book*	Aug. 6, 1550
Collation to St Martin of Meudon	Jan. 18, 1551
Epistle of Dedication of *Fourth Book* to Odet Coligny, Cardinal of Châtillon	Jan. 28, 1552
THIRD BOOK revised (F)	Jan. 28, 1552
FOURTH BOOK (B), Fezandat, Paris	Jan. 28, 1552
Resignation of the *cure* of Meudon	Jan. 9, 1553

Resignation of the *cure* of St Christopher of Jambet	Jan. 9, 1553
Death of François Rabelais	? April, 1553
L'ISLE SONANTE (16 chapters)	1562
FIFTH BOOK (47 chapters)	1564
Manuscript of *Fifth Book* (48 chapters) discovered	1840

EDITIONS OF GARGANTUA *AUTHORISED*
BY RABELAIS

A. The edition before 1535. There is known only one copy, incomplete in the first leaf. It was discovered by the Marquis de la Garde, and communicated by its second possessor M. Roche de la Carelle to M. Jannet, who first collated it; afterwards it belonged to M. Sollar, and was bought at his sale by the Bibliothèque Nationale.

B. The edition of François Juste, Lyon 1535: GARGANTUA | ΑΓΑΘΗ ΤΥΧΗ | La Vie | inestima|ble du grand | GARGANTUA pere de | PANTAGRUEL iadis com|posée par L'Abstra|cteur de quīte esēce | Livre plein de | pantagruelisme | M. D. XXXV. | On les uend a Lyon chés | frācoys Juste deuāt nostre | Dame de confort.

C. The edition of Juste, Lyon 1537. GARGANTUA and ἀγάθη τύχη are omitted; the rest is identically the same, with the change of date.

D. The definitive edition of François Juste, 1542.

EXPLANATION OF REFERENCES

G.C.	*Les grandes Cronicques*, 1532.
P.	*Pantagruel*, 1532–42.
P.P.	*Pantagrueline Prognostication*, 1533.
G.	*Gargantua*, 1534–42.
Epp. Rom.	Three letters from Rome to the Bishop of Maillezais (1535–6).
R.R.	*Le Roman de la Rose*, ed. Francisque-Michel.
C.N.N.	*Les Cent Nouvelles nouvelles*.
A.P.F.	*Anciennes poésies françaises du XVème et XVIème siècles*.
R.E.R.	*Revue des études rabelaisiennes*, 1903.
J.B.P.	*Journal d'un Bourgeois de Paris*, 1513–36.
Fr. ed.	*Œuvres de François Rabelais*. Edition critique publiée par Abel Lefranc, Jacques Boulenger, Henri Clouzot, Paul Dorveaux, Jean Plattard et Lazare Sainéau. Paris 1913– .

Budaeus, *in Pandectas*, i and ii. Lyon, Gryphius 1541; *de Asse*. Lyon, Gryphius 1550.

FIRST BOOK

GARGANTUA

ἀγαθῇ τύχῃ

THE VERY HORRIFIC LIFE

OF

THE GREAT GARGANTUA

FATHER OF PANTAGRUEL

FORMERLY COMPOSED BY

MASTER ALCOFRIBAS[1]

ABSTRACTOR OF QUINTESSENCE[2]

A book full of pantagruelism

M.D.XLII

SOLD AT LYONS BY FRANÇOIS JUSTE

OPPOSITE OUR LADY OF CONSOLATION

---

[1] *Alcofribas.* Nasier Alcofribas is an anagram on François Rabelais.
[2] *Quintessence.* Rabelais regards the mirth of his book as the πέμπτη οὐσία of things. In the same sense he calls Aristophanes "The Quintessential" in v. 22.

TO THE READERS

My kindly Readers, who this Book begin,
  All Prejudice, I pray you, lay aside,
And reading it, find no Offence therein;
  In it nor Hurt nor Poison doth abide.
    'Tis true that small Perfection here doth hide;
Nought will you learn save only Mirth's Delight;
No other Subject can my Heart indite,
  Seeing the Dole that wastes and makes you wan;
'Tis better far of Mirth than Tears to write,
  For Laughter is the special[1] Gift to Man.

LIVE MERRILY

---

[1] μόνον γελᾷ τῶν ζώων ἄνθρωπος (Arist. *de part. an.* iii. 10).

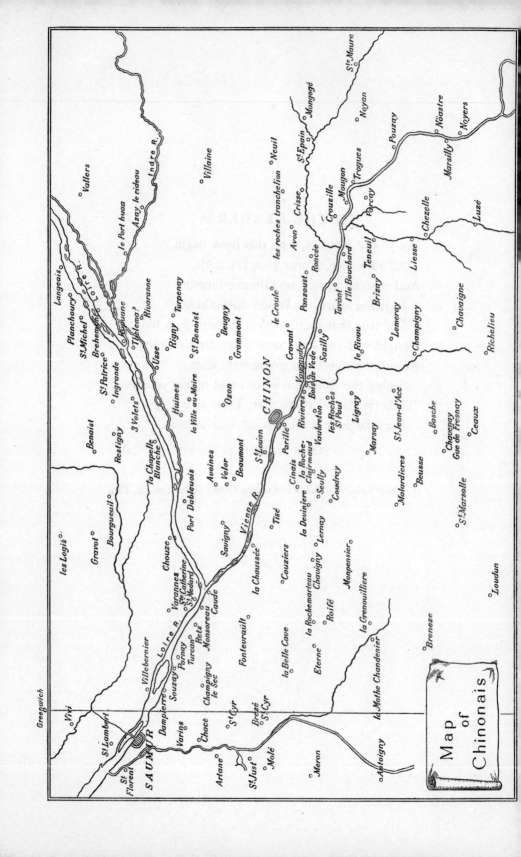

FIRST BOOK
PROLOGUE OF THE AUTHOR

DRINKERS very illustrious and you, very precious pockified Patients,—for to you and none other are dedicated my Writings—Alcibiades[1] in the Dialogue of Plato entitled *The Banquet*, praising his Preceptor Socrates, without controversy Prince of Philosophers, among other Remarks, says that he was like the Sileni.

Sileni of old were little Boxes, such as we see at present in the Shops of the Apothecaries, painted outside with wanton toyish Figures, such as Harpies, Satyrs, bridled Geese, horned Hares, saddled Ducks, flying Goats, Stags in Harness, and other such Paintings counterfeited at pleasure, to stir people to laugh, such as was Silenus, Master of the good Bacchus; but within were stored fine Drugs, such as Balsam, Ambergris,[2] Amomum,[3] Musk, Civet, Minerals,[4] and other precious Things.

---

[1] *Alcibiades....* The first three paragraphs of this Prologue are taken from Erasmus, *Adagia*, iii. 3. 1. One or two other passages are also taken from the *Adagia*. *Sileni Alcibiadis* (iii. 3. 1), *Scarabaeus aquilam quaerit* (iii. 7. 1), and *Dulce bellum inexpertis* (iv. 1. 1), long essays, which serve as prefaces for various "Centuries" of the *Adagia*, were written and published separately, *cum scholiis Joh. Frobenii, Basileae*, 1517, and it is probably from the essay rather than from the *Adagia* itself that Rabelais here borrows. "Et Alcibiades apud Platonem in Convivio [*Sympos.* 215A], Socratis encomium dicturus, eum Silenis similem fecit", Erasm. *Ad.* iii. 3. 1. Bacon (*Adv. Learning*, i. 3. § 8), in using the same comparison of Socrates, speaks of the "gallipots of apothecaries", instead of the "Sileni of statuaries", and thus shews that he borrows from Rabelais rather than from Plato or Erasmus. "Aiunt enim Silenos imagunculos fuisse sectiles et ita factas ut diduci et explicari possent, et quae clausae ridiculam et monstrosam tibicinis speciem habebant, apertae subito numen ostendebant, ut artem sculptoris gratiorem jocosus faceret error. Porro statuarum argumentum sumptum est a ridiculo illo Sileno Bacchi paedagogo", Erasm. *loc. cit.* Pico della Mirandola had employed the same comparison of the "Sileni Alcibiadis" in a letter to Hermolaus Barbarus (1485). Cf. the correspondence of Politian, lib. x. *Ep.* 4 (ed. Gryph. 1537). Cf. also Plato, *Rep.* vi. 488: "Like painters when they paint goat-stags and similar monsters".

[2] *Ambergris* (cf. *P.* 24), a kind of scented fat, formerly much used in cookery.

"In pastry built, or from the spit or boiled,
Gris amber steamed." Milton, *P.R.* ii. 344.

ἀμβρόσιος is probably not a pure Greek word at all, but borrowed from the Semitic *ambar*, ambergris, the famous perfume to which Oriental nations assign mythical miraculous properties (Leaf, *Iliad*, ii. 19n.). For the plant *ambrosia* cf. Pliny, 27. 28.

[3] *Amomum*, a perfume prepared from the leaves of the *Indica vitis labrusca* (Pliny, 12. 48); cf. Virg. *Ecl.* iii. 89; Mayor's *Juvenal*, iv. 108; Dioscorides, i. 14; Avicenna, ii. 2. 51.

[4] Fr. *pierreries* here bears the meaning of minerals used as drugs (M).

Such he declared Socrates[1] to be, because, seeing him from out-side and rating him by his exterior Appearance, you would not have given a Shred of an Onion[2] for him, so ugly was he in Figure and ridiculous in his Bearing, with a pointed Nose, his Look that of a Bull, and the Countenance of a Madman; being simple in Manners, boorish in Apparel, poor in Fortune, unfortunate in his Wives,[3] unfit for all Offices of State, always laughing, always carousing and drinking to every one, always gibing, always dis-sembling his divine Knowledge; but on opening this Box you would have found within a celestial and inestimable Drug, Understand-ing more than human, admirable Virtue, indomitable Courage, unparalleled Sobriety, imperturbable Content, unshaken Firmness, incredible Misprision of everything for which Men do so much watch, run, toil, sail and wrangle.[4]

To what Object,[5] in your Notion, does this Prelude and pre-liminary Flourish tend?

---

[1] *Socrates.* "Quem si de summa, quod dici solet, cute quis aestimasset, non emisset asse. Facies erat rusticana, taurinus aspectus [Plato, *Phaedo*, 117B], nares simae. Sannionem quempiam bardum ac stupidum dixisses. Cultus neglectus, sermo simplex ac plebeius, atque humilis....Fortuna tenuis, uxor qualem ne vilissimus quidem carbonarius ferre posset....Denique iocus ille perpetuus nonnullam habebat morionis speciem....Videbatur ineptus ad omnia reipublicae munia....Atqui si Silenum hunc tam ridiculum explicuisses, vide-licet numen invenisses potius quam hominem, animum ingentem, sublimem ac vere philosophicum, omnium rerum pro quibus caeteri mortales currunt, navi-gant, sudant, litigant, belligerantur, contemptorem, injuriis omnibus superiorem, et in quem nullum omnino jus haberet fortuna", Erasm. *Ad.* iii. 3. 1.

[2] *Shred of an Onion.* "Ecce unum calamum qui non valet unum oignonum", Cordier, *de Corr. Serm.* 47. § 10. Cf. Hom. *Od.* xix. 233 (quoted Galen, *de usu part.* x. 6):

οἷόν τε κρομύοιο λοπὸν κάτα ἰσχαλέοιο.

[3] *unfortunate in his Wives.* The scholia of Froben gives an account of his two wives, who were both quarrelsome. This seems to shew that this account was taken from Froben's separate essay and notes, rather than from the *Adagia*, but the story about his second wife Myrto is disproved in Athen. xiii. 556A. Cf. Bentley on Socrates' epistles.

[4] Cf. Sall. *Cat.* 2. § 7: "Quae homines arant, navigant, aedificant, virtuti omnia parent".

[5] ἀλλὰ τί πρὸς Διόνυσον ὁ Διόνυσος οὗτος εἴποι τις ἄν· ὅτι μοι δοκοῦσιν ὅμοιόν τι πάσχειν οἱ πολλοὶ πρὸς τοὺς καινοὺς τῶν λόγων τοῖς Ἰνδοῖς ἐκείνοις οἷον καὶ πρὸς τοὺς ἐμούς. οἰόμενοι γὰρ σατυρικά καὶ γελοῖά τινα καὶ κομιδῇ κωμικὰ παρ' ἡμῶν ἀκούσεσθαι κ.τ.λ., Lucian, *Dionys.* c. 5. Cf. also Erasm. *Ad.* ii. 4. 57 (Quid ad Bacchum?) and *Colloq.* ἀπροσδιόνυσα or *Cross-purposes.*

It is forasmuch as you, my good Disciples, and some other Fools who are at leisure, in reading the pleasant Titles of certain Books of our Invention such as *Gargantua, Pantagruel*,[1] *Fesse-pinte, The Dignity of Cod-pieces, Of Peas and Bacon*[2] *cum Commento, etc.*, judge too readily that there is nothing treated on within but Scoffing, Drolleries, and pleasant Fictions; seeing that the outward Sign (that is, the Title), without further Enquiry, is commonly received with Derision and Merriment.

But it is not fitting so lightly to esteem the Works of Men; for you yourselves say that it is not the Habit that makes the Monk,[3] and many a one is clad in monkish Dress who inwardly is anything but a Monk, and many a one wears a Spanish Cloak who in point of Courage has nothing to do with Spain. Therefore it is that you must open the Book and carefully weigh what is treated therein. Then shall you find that the Drug contained within is of far higher Value than the Box promised; that is to say, that the Matters treated on here are not such Buffoonery as the Title without shewed forth.

And, put the Case, that in the literal Sense you find Matters pleasant enough[4] and well corresponding to the Name, for all that, you should not stop there as at the Song of the Sirens, but interpret in a higher Sense what perhaps you thought was spoken only in Gaiety of Heart.

---

[1] *Gargantua* is perhaps intended to indicate *Les grandes Cronicques*, and *Pantagruel* must refer to the *previously written Pantagruel*.

[2] *Peas and Bacon* (*P.* 7 n.; v. 27). Cf. Macrob. *Sat.* i. 12. 33: "*Carna dea*... hanc deam vitalibus humanis praeesse credunt. Cui pulte fabacia et larido sacrificatur".

"Pinguia cur illis gustentur larda Kalendis
Mistaque cum calido sit faba farre rogas."

Ovid, *Fast.* vi. 169 (on June 1).

[3] *Habitus non facit monachum sed professio regularis.* Clement, iii. a. 1199; Decretal, iii. 31. 13: "De regul. et transitu ad relig. c. porrectum". Cf. Argum. in Authent. *De monachis et praesulibus* (Novell. v. praef.); St Paul, Rom. ii. 28; Plut. *Is. et Osir.* c. 2. 352 c; *R.R.* 11824; Charles d'Orléans, *Rond.* 195; Shakesp. *Meas.* v. 1. 263, *Tw. N.* i. 5. 62, *Hen. VIII*, iii. 1. 23; Erasm. *Ad.* i. 7. 6 (*Multi thyrsigeri*, etc.).

[4] *you find Matters pleasant enough*, etc. Erasm. *Ad.* ii. 8. 5: "*Siren amicum nunciat*, etc....Quoties complures eadem de re bona ominantur". The *sirens* occur in Hom. *Od.* xii. 39–54, 165–200. Victor Bérard (*Phéniciens et l'Odyssée*, ii. 335) would derive the word Σείρην from Semitic roots *sir hen*, a binding song, like the δέσμιος ὕμνος of Aesch. *Eum.* 331.

Did you ever pick open Wine-bottles? Tchuck![1] Recall to your Memory the Countenance you then wore. But did you ever see a Dog encountering some Marrow-bone? He is, as Plato says (*lib. ii. de Rep.*), the most philosophical[2] Animal in the World. If you have seen him, you may have noted with what Devotion he watches it, with what Care he guards it, how fervently he holds it, with what Prudence he gobbets it, with what Affection he breaks it,[3] and with what Diligence he sucks it. What induces him to do this? What is the Hope of his Research? What Good does he set before him? Nothing more than a little Marrow. True it is that this Little is more delicious than Quantities of all other sorts of Meat, because the Marrow is an Aliment perfectly elaborated by Nature, as Galen saith,[4] *iii. Facult. nat.* and *xi. De usu partium.*

In imitation of this Dog it becomes you to be wise, to smell, feel, and value these goodly Books stuffed with lofty Matters,[5] easy in the Pursuit and tough in the Encounter, and then by careful Reading and frequent Meditation to break the Bone and suck the substantial Marrow, that is to say, what I understand by these Pythagorean Symbols;[6] in the assured Hope[7] of becoming expert and valiant in the said Reading; for in it you will find quite another kind of Taste and more abstruse Learning, which will reveal to

---

[1] Fr. *Caisgne! = chienne* (*C.N.N.* 28). Here used as an exclamation of delight at success; perhaps it suggests the metaphor of the Dog which follows.

[2] *most philosophical*, from Plato, *Rep.* ii. 375 E, quoted by Plut. *Is. et Osir.* c. 11. 355 B.

[3] *breaks it.* "Qui e nuce nuculeum esse vult frangit nucem", Erasm. *Ad.* ii. 9. 35 (from Plaut. *Curc.* 55).

[4] *as Galen saith.* Rabelais does not quote correctly. Galen says, *fac. nat.* iii. 15, that marrow is the nutriment of the bones as the blood is of the flesh, and, *de usu part.* xi. 18, "I have shewn in my *fac. nat.* that marrow is the special nutriment of the bones".

[5] Fr. *de haulte gresse* (*P.* 7 sub *fin.*; iv. 6). *Gresse* is mostly taken = *graisse*, cf. *chapons, porcs*, etc. *de haulte gresse.* Here it may be an allusion to constant reading, "well-thumbed": cf. Juv. vii. 226: "Cum totus decolor esset Flaccus et haereret nigro fuligo Maroni"; or it may be taken from Lat. *gressus*, and mean "high-stepping", "grand".

[6] *Pythagorean Symbols* means the recondite texts of Pythagoras, such as *a fabis abstineto*, Erasm. *Ad.* i. 1. 3.

[7] *in the assured Hope*, etc. This is adapted from Lucian, *Dionys.* c. 5; it is from the passage that follows the one imitated earlier in the Prologue (n. 5, p. 7).

you very high Sacraments[1] and dread Mysteries, as much in that which concerns our Religion as also the public Polity and private Life.

Do you believe, on your Oath, that Homer, when writing the *Iliad* and *Odyssey*, ever thought of the Allegories which have been squeezed out of him by Plutarch,[2] Heraclides Ponticus,[3] Eustathius,[4] Phornutus,[5] and which Politian,[6] in his turn, has filched from them? If you do believe it, you do not either by Feet or

---

[1] *very high Sacraments*, etc. This seems to be imitated from Galen, *de usu part.* vii. 14: "Attend therefore to me more closely than you did when, on initiation to the Eleusinian or Samothracian, or any other holy rite, you were entirely taken up in the doings and sayings of the sacred ministers; and look upon my rite as in nothing inferior to theirs, nor less able to set forth the wisdom, or forethought, or power of the creator of living creatures; and attend especially because I was the first to discover this very mystery of which I now treat".

[2] There is a treatise on *The Life and Poetry of Homer*, wrongly attributed to Plutarch.

[3] *Heraclides* of Heraclea in Pontus, a pupil of Plato and afterwards of Aristotle. He was a Pythagorising and allegorising Platonist. He is mentioned by Cicero, *de Nat. Deor.* i. § 34; *Tusc.* v. § 8. An extant work, Ἀλληγορίαι Ὁμηρικαί (appended to Heyne's *Iliad*), was wrongly attributed to him. Erasmus has (*Ad.* iii. 5. 24) "Heraclides Ponticus in allegoriis Homeri". In it everything (gods, etc.) is allegorised. It is probably the work of some Alexandrine critic.

[4] *Eustathius* (iii. 18), Archbishop of Thessalonica in the twelfth century, was the author of a voluminous commentary on Homer. Born at Constantinople, died 1198.

[5] *Phornutus* (properly L. Annaeus Cornutus, but printed *Phorn.* in *Heraclides Ponticus de allegoriis Homeri, Phornutus de natura deorum*, Ald. Venet. 1505) was a Stoic of Leptis in Africa, instructor of Persius (v. 37) and Lucan, banished by Nero. His book is Ἐπιδρομὴ τῶν κατὰ τὴν Ἑλληνικὴν Θεολογίαν παραδεδομένων, a short treatise rationalising etymologically on the names and attributes of the gods. "Cornutus, aut (ut alii dicunt) Phornutus, *de natura deorum*", Tiraqueau, *de leg. conn.* iv. 26 (ed. 3a).

[6] *Angelo Poliziano* (1454–94) (*G.* 24; v. 19), the great scholar and humanist, friend of Budaeus, Lascaris and Picus Mirandula, *protégé* of Lorenzo the Magnificent. He wrote a preface to Homer, in which he was falsely accused of plagiarism by Budaeus, *Annot. in Pandectas*, i. p. 547: "Plutarchus in eo libro quem de Homero composuit, qui liber nondum ex professo factus est, licet Politianus, vir ille quidem excellentis doctrinae, sed animi non satis ingenui, ex eo libro rerum summas ad verbum transcribens quasique flores praecerpens, non erubuit id opus pro suo edere, in quo nullam praeterquam transcribendi ac vertendi operam navaverat". This remark is not fair to Politian, whose "preface to Homer" was published with his other works by Aldus Manutius in 1498 and again by Gryphius in 1528 and 1533. It is a detailed panegyric on Homer as a universal genius following the cue given by Horace (*Epp.* i. 2). The treatise by the pseudo-Plutarch is rather written to exemplify the grammatical and rhetorical figures in Homer.

Hands[1] come over to my Opinion, which decrees that they were as little dreamed of by Homer[2] as the Sacraments of the Gospel were by Ovid in his *Metamorphoses*; though a certain lickerish Friar,[3] a true Chaw-bacon, has striven to prove it, in case he should meet people as very Fools as himself and (as the Proverb says) "a Lid to match the Kettle".[4]

If you do not believe it, what Reason is there why you should not do as much for these jovial new Chronicles of mine; although while inditing them I thought no more of it than you, who possibly were drinking, as I was? For in composing this lordly Book I never lost or employed more or other Time than that which was appointed to take my bodily Refection, to wit, whilst eating and drinking.[5] Moreover, that is the proper Time to write these high Matters and profound Sciences, as Homer, the Paragon of all Philologers, knew well how to do, and Ennius too, Father of the Latin Poets, as Horace[6] witnesseth, though a certain misbegotten[7] Knave has declared that his Verses smacked more of Wine than of Oil.[8]

---

[1] *not either by Feet or Hands*, an extension of the phrase *pedibus ire in sententiam*. "Quintilianus dixit manibus pedibusque in sententiam discedere", Erasm. *Ad.* ii. 7. 12. Cf. Quint. *Declam.* xii: "In uno quodam sensu...probavimus, decrevimus, pedibus, manibus ivimus in sententiam necessitatis".

[2] Montaigne expresses the same opinion, ii. 12 *ad fin.*

[3] Fr. *Frère Lubin* (P. 7. 15). Thomas Wallis, *sive Galliensis*, an English Dominican. "Respondeo quod nuper acquisivi unum librum quem scripsit quidam magister noster Anglicus de ordine nostro, et habet nomen Thomas de Walleys, et compositus est ille liber super librum Metamorphoseos Ovidii, exponens omnes fabulas allegorice et spiritualiter", Frater Dollenkopf M. Ortuino Gratio, *Epist. Obs. Vir.* i. 28. Wallis professed theology at Paris and Oxford. He was accused of heresy before John XXII at Avignon and imprisoned, but soon afterwards released. † *ca.* 1340. The book was often published: Bruges 1484, Paris 1493, 1509 (ex officina Ascensiana), 1511, 1521, 1523. Virgil and Ovid were early translated into Italian prose; Ovid was especially subjected to "moralisations" (Comparetti, *Virg. nel med. evo*, ii. 16).

[4] *a Lid to match the Kettle.* "Dignum patella operculum", St Jerome, *Epist. ad Chromatium* (i. p. 340, Migne), quoted by Erasmus, *Ad.* i. 10. 72.

[5] *eating and drinking.* Cf. *passetemps epicenaires* (iii. prol.).

[6]   "Laudibus arguitur vini vinosus Homerus.
    Ennius ipse pater numquam nisi potus ad arma
    Prosiluit dicenda."

                    Hor. *Epp.* i. 19. 6, quoted Erasm. *Ad.* iv. 3. 58.

[7] Fr. *malautru* (P. 30; G. 37; iii. 28; v. 29), O.F. *malostru*, from Lat. *male structus* or *male instructus* (see Ducange, *s.v.*).

[8] Who it was that declared that Ennius' verses smacked of wine rather than oil has not been discovered.

A certain scurvy Fellow[1] said the same of my Books; but a Fig
for him! The Odour of Wine, oh! how much more dainty, alluring,
enticing,[2] more celestial and delicious than that of Oil! And I will
glory as much that it should be said of me that I have expended
more on Wine than on Oil, as ever Demosthenes did when they
said of him that he spent more on Oil than on Wine. To me it is
only an Honour and Glory to be called and reputed a Good fellow
and a pleasant Companion, and under this Name I am welcome in
all good Companies of Pantagruelists; it was imputed as a Reproach to Demosthenes by a Malignant[3] that his Speeches smelt
like the Sarpler or Clout that had stopped a filthy, dirty Oil-lamp.

Therefore interpret all my Deeds and Sayings in the perfectest
Sense; hold in Reverence the cheese-shaped Brain which feeds you
with all these jolly Maggots,[4] and to the utmost of your Power keep
me yourselves always merry.

So be frolic, my little Dears, and joyfully read the rest to the
Ease of your Body and Comfort of your Reins. But, hearken, Jolt-
heads, Boils and Blains be on you;[5] remember to drink to me, that
I may do you Reason,[6] and I will pledge you on the spot.[7]

---

[1] *scurvy Fellow.* Fr. *tirelupin*, *P.* 7; iv. 65.

[2] Fr. *friant, riant, priant.* From Cl. Marot, *Chans.* iii. st. 2:

"La blanche colombelle belle
Souvent je voys priant, criant;
Mais dessoubz la *cordelle* d'elle (Cretin, p. 219)
Me jecte un œil friant, riant."

[3] *Malignant.* It was Pytheas. Cf. Plut. *praec. ger. rep.* c. 6. 802 E; Aelian, *Var. Hist.* vii. 7. Cf. also v. 33 and Erasm. *Ad.* i. 7. 71 (*Olet lucernam*).

[4] *Maggots.* Fr. *billes vezées* (*P.* 13) = *bulles vezées* (Lat. *vesica*), blown-up bladders. Cf. *bullatae nugae*, Pers. v. 19, quoted Erasm. *Ad.* iii. 6. 98.

[5] Fr. *Vietz dazes que le maulubec vous trousque.* This is Gascon. *Vietdazes*, properly ass-pizzles, generally a term of abuse (*P.* 5; iii. 28; iv. N.P.; v. prol., 18). *Maulubec* (*mal au bec*), properly the disease *Lupus* which ulcerates the face (*P.* prol. *fin.*; iii. 28).

[6] *that I may do you Reason.* Fr. *pour la pareille*, Lat. *pro pari*, a favourite expression of First President Lizet.

[7] Fr. *ares metys*, a Gascon expression for "at once", perhaps derived from Low Latin *horametipsa*.

CONTENTS OF THE FIRST BOOK

THE genealogy, birth, name, clothing, youth, etc., of Gargantua, cc. i–xiii. His instruction under a sophist and other pedagogues, xiv, xv. His journey to Paris on the great Mare, xvi. He takes away the bells of Notre-dame, xvii. The sophist Janotus de Bragmardo comes and pleads for their restoration, goes away with his cloth, and enters an action against the Sorbonne, xviii–xx. The studies of Gargantua under the old system, xxi, xxii; under the new, xxiii, xxiv. The strife between the cake-bakers of Lerné and Gargantua's men, and the war that arose from it between Picrochole and Gargantua, xxv, xxvi. How a Monk of Seuillé saved the abbey close, xxvii. The course of the war—Gargantua's overtures for peace— The advice of Picrochole's councillors—Various adventures— Gargantua and his men totally defeat Picrochole—The rewards given by Gargantua to his men, and the treatment and jovial behaviour of the Monk, xxviii–li. Building of the Abbey of Thelema as a reward to the Monk—Inscription on the gate of Thelema— The dress and rules of the Order—Enigma discovered in digging the foundations, lii–lviii.

CHAPTER I

Of the Genealogy and Antiquity of Gargantua

I REFER you to the Grand Pantagrueline Chronicle[1] for the Knowledge of the Genealogy and Antiquity whence Gargantua is descended unto us. Therein you will understand more at length how the Giants were born in this World, and how from them by direct Line issued Gargantua, Father of Pantagruel, and it shall not misplease you if for the present I pass it over, although the Matter be such, that the more it should be remembered the more it would please your Lordships; for which you have the Authority of Plato *in Philebo et Gorgia*, and also of Flaccus, who says that there are certain Subjects (without doubt such as this) which are the more delectable the oftener they are repeated.[2]

Would to God that every one had as certain Knowledge of his Genealogy from Noah's Ark up to the present Age. I think there be many this day who are Emperors, Kings, Dukes, Princes and Popes on the Earth who are descended from some Carriers of Indulgences and Faggots;[3] as on the contrary many are Beggars from Door to Door, suffering poor Wretches, who are descended from the Blood and Lineage of great Kings and Emperors,[4] when

---

[1] *Pantagrueline Chronicle* must refer to the genealogy of Gargantua and Pantagruel in *P*. 1, thus affording another argument for the priority in composition of *Pantagruel*.

[2] Cf. Erasm. *Ad*. i. 2. 49 (*Bis ac ter quod pulchrum est*): "Usurpatur a Platone... in Philebo [59E]....Idem in Gorgia [498E]. Atqui pulchrum aiunt ea quae pulchra sunt iterum ac tertio tum dicere tum considerare....Ea vis est rebus egregiis ut quo saepius ac pressius inspiciantur hoc magis atque magis placeant, ut ait Horatius [*A.P.* 365]".

[3] *Carriers of...Faggots*. Cf. Petronius, c. 38: "De nihilo crevit; modo solebat collo suo ligna portare". But the reference is to the mendicants, *portatores rogationum et indulgentiarum et bullatores* (O. Maillard).

[4] Politianus, *Lamia* (Gryphius, 1537): "Nec esse regem quempiam qui non sit e servis natus, nec item servum cui non origo sit regis". This is from Seneca, *Ep*. 44. § 4 and Plato, *Theaet*. 174E–175B. Cf. also Dante, *Par*. xvii. 89:

> "Per lui fia trasmutata molta gente,
> Cambiando condizion ricchi e mendici".

we consider the wonderful Translation of Kingdoms and Empires:[1]

> From the Assyrians to the Medes,
> From the Medes to the Persians,
> From the Persians to the Macedonians,
> From the Macedonians to the Romans,
> From the Romans to the Greeks,
> From the Greeks to the French.[2]

And to give you to understand concerning myself, who am speaking, I believe that I am descended from some rich King or Prince in times of yore; for never did you see a man who had a greater Desire to be a King and to be rich than I; to the end that I may make good Cheer, do no Work, trouble myself not a whit, and plentifully enrich my Friends and all people of Worth and of Knowledge: but herein do I comfort myself that in the other World I shall be all this, nay, greater than at present I dare to wish. Do you then in such, or a better, Belief take Comfort in your Misfortunes and drink lustily, if it can be done.

To return to our Point,[3] I declare to you that by the sovereign

---

[1] *Translation of Kingdoms and Empires.* A scoffing allusion to the famous theory of the Translation of the Roman Empire, about which has been so much controversy down to the seventeenth century. Rabelais renders *Translatio a Graecis ad Francos* as above, making out Charlemagne, King of Franconia, to be a Frenchman. In this he is followed by other French writers. By "Greeks" are intended the Greeks of the Eastern Empire, whose Roman Empire passed from Constantine VI to Charlemagne. There is a detailed account of this "translation" in Agrippa, *de van. scient.* c. 80 (*de nobilitate*), in which however he writes: "imperium...translatum est ad *Germanos*". Thomas Aquinas made out that the papal jurisdiction was derived from the Donation of Constantine and the translation of the Empire to the Franks: *de regim. princ.* Cf. Innocent III in *Δ*, i. 6. 34 (*Venerabilem*); Bryce, *H.R.E.* cc. 5, 7, 13.

[2]   "Sic Medus ademit
> Assyrio, Medoque tulit moderamina Perses;
> Subjecit Persen Macedo, cessurus et ipse
> Romanis".   Claud. *Cons. Stil.* iii. 163.

[3] Fr. *retournant à nos moutons* (*G.* 11; iii. 34; Coquillart, ii. 214, 247; *A.P.F.* iii. 184). This well-known phrase is taken from the old French comedy, *La farce de Maistre Pierre Pathelin* (line 1293), which Rabelais often quotes. The actual words in the farce are *revenons à ces moutons*, used by a judge before whom a draper is suing a shepherd for maltreating his sheep. The draper forgets the case in point when he sees the rascally advocate Pathelin, who has cheated him out of some cloth, defending the shepherd. He wanders off in his speech to the robbery of the cloth and is called to order by the judge with this phrase. (*Maistre Pierre Pathelin restitué à son naturel par Pierre Blanchet*, Galiot Du Pré, Paris 1532.)

Gift of the Heavens, to us hath been reserved the Antiquity and
Genealogy of Gargantua more perfect than any other, except that
of the Messias, of which I do not speak, for to me it doth not per-
tain; moreover the Devils (that is the Calumniators and Hypocrites) are against me. And it was found by John Audeau[1] in a
Meadow which he had near the Arch Gualeau[2] below the Olive[3]
leading to Narsay.[4] As he was having the Ditches of this opened,
the Diggers with their Mattocks struck on a great Tomb of Bronze,[5]
immeasurably long, for they never found the End of it, by reason
that it entered too far into the Sluices of the Vienne.[6]

Opening this at a certain Place which was sealed at the Top with
the Sign of a Goblet, round which was written in Etruscan Letters[7]
HIC BIBITUR, they found nine Flagons, in order such as they range
their Skittles in Gascony, of which that which was placed in the
middle, covered a great, greasy, grand, grey, pretty, little, mouldy
Booklet,[8] Stronger, but not sweeter-scented than Roses.[9]

---

[1] *John Audeau.* Probably some early acquaintance of Rabelais.

[2] *L'arceau Gualeau* was situated in the meadows of St Mexme (cf. c. 27), as
may be seen in the inventory of the archives of Indre-et-Loire, G. 611 and 686
(*R.E.R.* ii. 45). It still bears the same name and is near the railway bridge
(*R.E.R.* v. 57).

[3] *L'Olive,* a hamlet in the commune of Chinon. It was once a fief of the
archbishopric of Tours: in 1505 it belonged to René de Maillé.

[4] *Narçay* (*G.* 23), an ancient fief of the de Mauléon in the sixteenth century.
It was a hamlet in the commune of Cravart (*R.E.R.* v. 58).

[5] *Tomb of Bronze.* "Bronze" is derived from Brundisium, the port at which
the Corinthian bronzes were landed (Skeat, *s.v.*).

[6] The *Vienne* is the river on which Chinon stands (v. 35) and which flows into
the Loire a little below, about half-way between Chinon and Saumur. At a
place called Civaux two leagues from Chauvigny in Lower Poitou are to be
found a number of stone tombs, nearly two leagues around, especially near the
Vienne. Tradition asserts that these are tombs of the Visigoths slain by Clovis
(Le Duchat, 1711).

[7] *Etruscan Letters.* Cf. Pliny, 16. 237: "Vetustior autem urbe in Vaticano ilex
in qua titulus aeneis litteris Etruscis religione jam tum dignam fuisse significat".

[8] In Plutarch's *Numa,* c. 22, it is recorded that Numa was buried in one stone
coffin and his books of ritual, etc. in another. He thought that such important
doctrines could not be preserved in lifeless records, but must be handed down
by oral tradition. Cf. *P.* 10. The chests with Numa's remains and his books were
said to have been discovered: Pliny, 13. 84; Livy, xl. 29; Val. Max. i. 1. 12;
St Aug. de Civ. D. vii. 34. The *Ephemeris Belli Trojani* of Dictys Cretensis, which
with the account of the Destruction of Troy by Dares Phrygius supplied the
material to Boccaccio for his *Philostratus* and Chaucer for his *Troilus and Cressida,*
was similarly said to have been discovered, written on the bark of a lime-tree, after
an earthquake at Cnossus in Crete. An edition was published by Cratander at Basel
in 1529.   [9] Regnier (*Sat.* x. 219) has borrowed this proverbial expression.

In this Book was the said Genealogy found written out at length in a Chancery Hand,[1] not on Paper, not on Parchment, not on Wax, but on Elm-bark,[2] so much, however, worn by Age that scarcely could three Letters on end be discerned.

Unworthy though I be, I was sent for thither, and with much Help from Spectacles, practising the Art by which one can read Letters that are not apparent,[3] as Aristotle teaches, translated it, as you may see in your Pantagruelising, that is to say, in drinking to your Heart's desire and reading the horrific Exploits of Pantagruel.[4]

At the End of the Book was a little Treatise, intituled "Antidoted Conundrums". The Rats[5] and Moths or (not to lie) other malignant Vermin had nibbled off the Beginning; the Remains I have hereto subjoined, from my Reverence to Antiquity.

---

[1] Fr. *lettres cancelleresques*. "Characteres quos cursivos, sive cancellarios appellant" (*i.e.* italics, used by Aldus Manutius who took as his model the handwriting of Petrarch): Brief of Leo X to Ald. Manutius, 1513 (Roscoe's *Leo X*, vol. ii. p. 488).

[2] *on Elm-bark*. "Item quidem rotulus de corticibus arboris scriptus litteris quasi illegibilibus" (Ducange, s.v. *illegibilis*). So the Troy story of Dictys Cretensis was said to be written on lime-bark.

[3] *not apparent* (cf. *P.* 24). I have found nothing in Aristotle bearing on this point.

[4] *the horrific Exploits of Pantagruel* must refer to the book *Pantagruel* which was written before this.

[5] Fr. *les Ratz*, intended for the Monks, "the shaven ones". Cf. *P.* 12; iv. 32.

CHAPTER II

The Antidoted Conundrums[1] found in an ancient Monument

||e!:!re is come the Cimbrians' mighty Victor[2]
:::hing through Air, from Terror of the Dew.
–.his Incoming all the Tubs were filled
:!..h Butter fresh, all falling in a Shower:
∽.ith which when mighty Ocean was bespattered
He cried aloud: "Sirs, pray you, fish it up;
Therewith his Beard is nearly all embossed;
Or, at the least, pray hold a Ladder for him".

Some did aver that so to lick his Slipper
Was better than the Pardons for to gain;
But there came up a crafty Graymalkin
From out the Hollow where they fish for Roach,
Who said: "For God's sake, Sirs, keep we from it,
The Eel is there, 'tis hiding in this Pond.
There will you find (if we look closely in it)
A great Blot at the Bottom of his Amice".[3]

---

[1] Fr. *fanfreluches*. Cf. *R.R.* 21,284: "Ce sont trufles et fanfelues". This chapter, the beginning of which is printed in a fragmentary fashion, in accordance with the statement in c. 1, that it had been nibbled by vermin, has been translated into rough blank verse as simply and literally as possible. What meaning (if any) it was intended to convey is difficult to discover. It seems to have been partly borrowed from the poet Mellin de Saint-Gelais, from whom was derived the poem in c. 58. Saint-Gelais' poems were not published till 1547, while the *Énigme* which is copied in c. 58 was not published till 1574. Many of Saint-Gelais' poems were circulated in MS. among his friends before 1534, so that c. 2 may have been composed by Rabelais from what he could remember of a recitation of the poem, while c. 58 was copied from a MS.; the dizain in iv. prol., which was not published till 1552, could have been taken from the edition of 1547 (Lyon, P. de Tours). The poems are to be found in Saint-Gelais' works (i. 70–73, ii. 202–5, and ii. 266, ed. Elz.). The lines in Saint-Gelais that correspond are indicated in the notes. Cf. *R.E.R.* ix. 90–108.

[2] "Le grand vainqueur des haults monts de Carthaige."
S.-G. *Énigme*, l. 1.

[3] *Amice* (Fr. *aumusse*, Lat. *almucia*), a sort of furred hood worn by canons and others of the clergy from the thirteenth century. It is worn now as a strip of

When he was at the point to read the Chapter,
Nothing was found save only a Calf's Horns.
Said he: "I feel the Bottom of my Mitre
So cold that all about my Brain is chilled".[1]
They warmed him with the Perfume of a Turnip,
And he was glad to keep at the Chimney Corner,[2]
Provided a new Man was put in Harness
Of all the Folk that so cross-grainèd are.

Their Subject was the Hole of St Patrick,[3]
Gibraltar's Strait,[4] a thousand other Holes:
If any Skill could heal them to a Scar,
By means such that they should not have a Cough;
Because it seemed impertinent to all
To see them gaping thus at every Wind.
Perhaps if they were tightly closed and stopped,
They might as Hostages be given up.

By this Decision was the Raven scotched
By Hercules, who came from Libya.
"How now?" said Minos; "why am I not summoned?
Excepting me, see! all the World is called.

---

fur attached to the arm. (Cf. J. W. Clark's *Augustinian Canons*, p. lxxviii. x[n] and
Eccl. Rome, pt iii. p. 213.)

        "De luy prester son haulmusse ou sa chappe." S.-G. *Énigme*, l. 16.

[1]   "Et feist serment que le fons de sa mitre
           Estoit si froid qu'il en avoit la toux."   S.-G. *Énigme*, ll. 59, 60.

[2] *Chimney Corner*. Fr. *atres*, Lat. *atrium*. "Ibi [in atris] et culina erat, unde et
atrium dictum est; atrium enim erat ex fumo", Serv. in *Aen*. i. 726.

[3]   "On devisa du trou de la sybille,
      De Sainct Patrice, et de mille autres troux." S.-G. *Énigme*, ll. 63, 64.
The hole of St Patrick (v. 36) in Loch Dearg in County Donegal was a great
place for pilgrimages from the twelfth century onwards. It was looked upon as
one of the entrances into the lower world and into Purgatory, and a visit to it
in one's lifetime gave full absolution from all sins. In 1497 Pope Alexander VI
ordered the destruction of the Purgatory of St Patrick on St Patrick's day. In 1632
and in the reign of Queen Anne the prohibition of the pilgrimages was renewed;
but they continued notwithstanding. An account of this Purgatory is given in
R.E.R. viii. 200, also in Matthew Paris, an. 1153. Erasmus says (*Ad.* i. 7. 77) the
cave of Trophonius and the hole of St Patrick were similar in practices.

[4] Fr. *Gilbathar*. The Straits of Gibraltar were also looked upon as a sort of
Sibyl's cave. They were near Seville and are called *l'estroict de Sibyle* in *G.* 33 (le
Duchat). Sibilia is used for Seville in Dante, *Inf.* xx. 126, xxvi. 110. "Le Deable
l'ait ou trou Sebille" (Ch. d'Orléans, *Rond*. 274).

And since they wish that my Desire should pass,
To furnish them with Oysters and with Frogs,
In case that they shew Mercy to my Life
I give their Sale of Distaffs to the Devil".[1]

Them to defeat came up Q. B. who limps
Under Safe-conduct of the mystic Starlings.[2]
The Sifter, Cousin of the great Cyclops,
Put them to massacre. Each one blows his Nose:
In this waste Field few Heretics were born
But on the Tanner's Mill were winnowed.
Run thither all, and sound the loud Alarm;
More shall you find than last year were produced.

Soon afterwards the Bird of Jupiter
Determined with the weaker Cause to side;[3]
But seeing them so mightily enraged
Feared they would hurl the Empire ruined down,
And rather chose from Empyrean Heaven
To steal the Fire to where the Herrings are sold,
Than subject to the Massoritic Gloss
The Air serene, against which men conspire.

All was concluded then "at point of Fox",
In spite of Atè[4] and her Hern-like Legs,[5]

---

[1]   "Ouy, dict l'une, on ne faict que prescher
        Du différent des rats et des grenoilles,
        Et si veut-on tout le monde empescher
        De les fournir de fuseaulx et quenoilles."   S.-G. *Énigme*, ll. 21–4.
Croutelles in Poitou (*P.* 5) produced quantities of spindles and distaffs (*R.E.R.*
xi. 22, n. 5).
[2] Fr. *mistes sansonnetz*. In O.F. *mister* = gentle, pet, etc. (Fr. ed.)
[3] Fr. *pariser* = parier. (Fr. ed.)
[4] *Atè*, etc. The allusion is to Homer, *Il.* ix. 505:
        'Η δ' "Ατη σθεναρά τε καὶ ἀρτίπος· οὕνεκα πάσας
        πολλὸν ὑπεκπροθέει, φθανέει δέ τε πᾶσαν ἐπ' αἶαν
        βλάπτουσ' ἀνθρώπους.
Cf. also *Il.* xix. 92: ἀπαλοὶ πόδες.
[5] *Hern-like Legs, i.e.* gaunt, sinewy, like those of the heron.
        "Tant affoibly m'a d'estrange manière
        Et si m'a faict la cuisse heronnière."
                        Cl. Marot, *Epist. au Roy pour avoir esté dérobé*, 29.
"*Cuisses heronnières* fort couvertes de poil": Paré, *De la licorne*, C. 4; *Perdicis crura*:
Erasm. *Ad.* ii. 2. 29.

Who sitting there Penthesilea saw
In her old Age made a cress-selling Quean;[1]
Each one cried out: Thou ugly Collier-wench,
Is it for thee to be thus in the Way?
'Twas thou didst take the Roman Banner off,
Which had been well drawn up on Parchment Bonds.

And Juno too, beneath the heavenly Bow
Who with her Duke[2] was laying Snares for Birds—
A very grievous Trick on her was played,
That at all Points she should be discomposed.
The Bargain was, that from this mighty Slice
Two Eggs from Proserpine should be her Share,
And if she ever there should nabbèd be
She should be made fast to the Whitethorn Mount.[3]

Seven Months thereafter, barring twenty-two,[4]
He that did Carthage once annihilate[5]
Did courteously come into their midst,
Requiring them to take his Heritage,

---

[1] It seems not improbable that his comparison of Penthesilea, given also in
P. 30, is derived from Quintus Smyrnaeus, i. 396 *sqq.*:

"And as within the dewy close has leapt
A heifer, longing for the sweet spring grass,
With none to hinder; this side and on that
She frisks, and wastes the freshly sprouting herbs,
And much she crops, much tramples underfoot—
So did the warlike maid the Grecian youths,
Some slaying, scaring others in the press".

[2] Fr. *Duc.* This has been taken for a large bird, a horned owl (*Bubo maximus*).
Cf. Brantôme, i. 10. 25, *Ch. de Lannoy* (*fin.*). Owls were used as decoys for other
birds.

[3] *to the Whitethorn Mount.* Fr. *On la lierait au mont de l'Albespine.* Cf. Ovid,
Fast. vi. 129 (Janus to the nymph Cardo):

"Sic fatus *spinam* qua tristes pellere posset
A foribus noxas (haec erat *alba*) dedit";

and vi. 165:

"Virgaque Ianalis de *spina* ponitur *alba*
Qua lumen thalamis parva fenestra dabat".

[4] *Seven Months thereafter, barring twenty-two.* This is a transposition (for 22 − 7)
which Rabelais sometimes affects. (Fr. ed.)

[5] Scipio Africanus the younger, 146 B.C. Saint-Gelais has, *Énigme*, l. 1: "Le
grand vainqueur de haults monts de Carthaige", and l. 13: "Mais Scipion
pensant de son retour".

Or rather that they justly should go Shares,
According to the Law of "Take from each",[1]
Distributing a Snack of Brewis to each
Of the Understrappers, who drew up the Brief.

The Year will come, marked with a Turkish Bow,[2]
With Spindles five and with three Saucepan-bottoms,
In which the Back of a discourteous King
Shall peppered be under a Hermit's Frock.
The Pity of it! For a wily Woman
So many Acres will you see engulfed?
Cease, cease! This Vizard there is none to copy.
Withdraw yourselves unto the Serpents' Brother.[3]

This Year gone past, the He that is shall reign
In Peace and Quiet with his trusty Friends;
Nor Scathe nor Scorn[4] shall lord it then at all,
And each good Wish shall its Fulfilment find.
And the Observance that of old was promised
To the Heavenly Host shall from their Belfry peal.
And then the breeding Studs, that were sore troubled,[5]
Shall ride in State on royal Palfrey borne.

This Hocus-pocus Season shall endure
So long until that Mars is put in Chains.[6]
And then shall come a Time surpassing all,
Delightful, pleasing, beyond Measure fair.
Lift up your Hearts, go forth to this Repast,
My true Friends all: for he is dead and gone

---

[1] Fr. *tirer au rivet* (cf. *tireurs de rivetz, P.P.* 5, perhaps = shoe-makers), explained by Cotgrave "to sew like a shoe-maker; also to pluck as much from one as from another".

[2] *a Turkish Bow* was bent backwards (παλίντονος). Villon, *Ballade joyeuse des Taverniers*.

[3] *the Serpents' Brother, i.e.* the Devil.

[4] *Nor Scathe nor Scorn.* Fr. *ny brusq ny smach.* Cf. *R.E.R.* vi. 290. Ital. *braxo* and *smacco*.

[5] Fr. *estommis* (c. 43), astonished, stupefied.

[6] *Mars is put in Chains, i.e.* till peace is brought about. For the fettering of Enyalios and other images see Frazer's *Pausanias*, iii. 15. 7, vol. iii. p. 136.

Who for the World would not return again;
So much shall former Times be called for then.

And lastly, he that was of Wax compact
Shall near the Hinge of a Jack o' the Clock[1] be lodged.
No more shall he be styled: "My Lord, My Lord",
The Jangler,[2] he that holds the Sacring-bell.
Alas! if one his Cutlass could but seize!
Soon should be cleared all carking Cares away,
And then we could by dint of Packthread Stitch
Sew up[3] and close the Storehouse of Deceit.

---

[1] Fr. *Jacquemart*. Cf. Shakesp. *Rich. II*. v. 5. 60.

[2] *The Jangler*. Most likely Martin of Cambrai (cf. iv. N.P.: *Les xv. ioyes de Mariage*, no. 11), a metal figure that strikes the hours on a clock-bell. At Dijon to the right of the façade of the Church of Notre-Dame is a clock with a figure which strikes the hours, presented by Philip the Bold in 1383. The name "Jacquemart" is derived from the maker, the Flemish Jacques Marc.

[3] *Sew up*. Fr. *baffouer*. Cf. *R.E.R.* vii. 337.

CHAPTER III

How Gargantua was carried eleven Months in his Mother's Belly

GRANDGOUSIER was a merry Jester in his time, loving to drink neat as much as any man then alive in the World; and he did willingly eat salt Meat.

To this end he commonly had good store of Hams of Mayence and Bayonne,[1] a quantity of smoked Neats' Tongues, plenty of Chitterlings in season and powdered Beef with Mustard, a Supply of Botargos,[2] provision of Sausages, but not of Bologna—for he feared *gli bocconi Lombardi*[3]—but of Bigorre,[4] Longuaulnay,[5] Brene[6] and Rouergue.[7]

When he came to Man's Estate he married Gargamelle, Daughter of the King of the Butterflies,[8] a fine Lass and of a good Phiz. And

---

[1] *Mayence*, referring to the Westphalia hams, which were sent to the fair at Mayence; those of Bayonne were much esteemed in Paris, next after the Westphalian (*R.E.R.* viii. 207).

[2] *Botargos* (ᾠὰ τάριχα), sausages made of the roe of gray mullet, sturgeon or tunny-fish made up with oil and vinegar (*G.* 21; iv. 18, 60; v. 34, 43). "*Oataricha* Itali caviaria vocant, Graeci nostrae aetatis corrupte *Botaricha* nominant", Pierre Gilles (cf. v. 30), *De Gall. et Lat. nominibus piscium Massiliensium*, c. 41; Rondelet, *de pisc. marin.* x. 3. Cf. Pepys, *Diary*, June 5, 1661.

[3] *bocconi Lombardi*, tid-bits of Lombardy. During the wars in the Milanese the French learned to mistrust the Italians of poisoning. Cf. *A.P.F.* iii. 196: "Par *boucons* sont plusieurs marris", and xiii. 262: "Plus dangereuse que *boucon de Lombart*".

[4] *Bigorre*. Bagnères de Bigorre in Gascony, the *Aquensis Vicus* of the Romans (Caes. *B.G.* iii. 27).

[5] *Longuaulnay*, cant. Siténiac, arr. Saint-Malo. (Fr. ed.)

[6] *La Brene* (*G.* 15), a small place in Berry.

[7] *La Rouergue*, the province of which Rodez is the capital, the *Ruteni* of Caes. *B.G.* i. 45. Modern department of L'Aveyron. (Fr. ed.)

[8] The "Kingdom of the Butterflies" (cf. *G.* 11) represents in the old romances any fanciful kingdom. Cf. *Morg. Magg.* x. 59:

"Che di' tu *re di farfalle* o di pecchie?"

Fr. *parpaillos* also has a meaning akin to *paillard*. Cf. *R.E.R.* vii. 249.

these two did often play the two-backed Beast[1] together, joyously rubbing together their Bacon, insomuch that she became big of a fine Boy and went with him right unto the eleventh Month.

So long, even longer, can Women go with Child, especially when it is some Masterpiece and Personage who is destined in his time to perform great Exploits, as Homer says that the Child which Neptune begat upon the Nymph was born after the Revolution of a Year[2]—that was the twelfth Month; for (as saith Aulus Gellius, *lib. iii.*) this long time was fitting for the Majesty of Neptune, to the end that in it the Child should be formed to Perfection. For the like reason Jupiter made the Night last forty-eight Hours in which he lay with Alcmena; for he could not in less time have forged Hercules, who purged the World of Monsters and Tyrants.

My Masters, the ancient Pantagruelists, have confirmed that which I say, and have declared not only possible, but also legitimate, a Child born of a Woman the eleventh Month after the Death of her Husband:

Hippocrates,[3] *lib. De alimento* [II. 23 K.];

Pliny, *lib. vii. cap. v.*;

Plautus in the *Cistellaria* [160];

Marcus Varro in the Satire inscribed *The Testament*, citing the authority of Aristotle on the subject;

Censorinus, *lib. De die natali* [cap. vii. § 7];

Aristotle, *lib. vii. cap.* 3, 4, *De nat. animalium*;

Gellius, *lib. iii. cap.* 16;

---

[1] *La beste à deux dos* (v. 30). This quasi-proverbial expression, possibly derived from Plato (*Symp.* 191; cf. G. 8), occurs in Shakesp. *Oth.* i. 1. 117. Delius, *ad loc.* thinks that Shakespeare borrowed it from Rabelais, "whose writings he must have known in a translation". But it may also be found in *C.N.N.* 20; Coquillart, *Mon. des Perr.* ii. 277; *A. Th. F.* ii. 221; *A.P.F.* i. 77, ii. 138, vi. 25.

[2] Pelias and Neleus were born to Poseidon of the nymph Tyro. Cf. Hom. *Od.* xi. 235–59; Aul. Gell. iii. 16. 15–16. On the subject of the duration of gestation consult *Law Quarterly Journal*, vol. xx. No. 78, p. 135.

[3] *Hippocrates*, etc. These citations, with the exception of those from Censorinus and Servius, are simply taken from Aul. Gell. iii. 16, perhaps suggested by Erasm. *Ad.* i. 10. 77. A note in the Servius collection has: "*decem menses*, quia mares in decimo nascuntur mense foeminae vero in nono". Pellicier, Bishop of Maguelonne, French ambassador at Venice, consults Rabelais in a letter on this very point, citing some of the authorities given here. But that was in 1540, so he may have known this chapter.

Servius *in* ¦*Eclog.* expounding that line of Virgil, *Matri longa decem, etc.* [*Ecl.* v. 61];

and a thousand other Fools, the number of whom has been increased by the Legists *ff.*[1] *De suis et legit. l. Intestato § fin.* and in *Autent.*[2] *De restit. et ea quae parit in xi mense.*

Moreover they have scrawled their Robidilardick[3] law *Gallus ff. De lib. et post. et l. septimo ff. De stat. homin.* and some others, which for the present I dare not mention, by means of which Laws the Widows may freely play the close-crupper Game with all their Might and all their Leisure-time,[4] two Months after the Death of their Husbands.

I pray you of your Goodness, my good Lusty Blades,[5] if of such you find any that are worth the untrussing of the Cod-piece, get on and bring them to me; for, if in the third Month they conceive, the Child shall be Heir to the deceased; and the Conception once known, thrust boldly forward and "Launch out lustily",[6] since the Hold is full.

Just so Julia, Daughter of the Emperor Octavian, never abandoned herself to her Drummers save when she found herself with

---

[1] The *Digest* of Justinian was indicated by the letters *ff*, the *Code* by the letter *C* and the *Institutes* by *I*. The laws are quoted by their initial words, called *rubrics*, because printed in red letters. Here consult ff. xxxv. 4.

[2] *Authentica.* The authorised translation of the ordinances of the earlier Greek Emperors, as excerpted by Justinian, now called *Novellae*.

[3] *Robidilardick*, coined from *rober*, to steal, and *lard*, bacon, alluding to the great Cat *Rodilardus* mentioned iv. 67, and taken from the Latin imitation of the pseudo-Homeric *Batrachomyomachia*, by Calentius Eliseus (Rome 1503), translated into French, "Les fantastiques batailles des grands roys Rodilardus et Croacus: translation de Latin en françoys" (F. Juste, 1534). Cf. *R.E.R.* vi. 201. The Greek hero πτερνοτρώκτης = Rodilardus. The word *chaffouré* (scrawled) also refers to the *Chats fourrés* (furred Law-cats) of *P.* 7 and v. 11–15.

[4] Fr. *à tous enviz et à toutes restes.* Terms from the card-game *primero* (cf. *prime*, G. 22). *Envi* is the money staked by each player, and *à toutes restes* denotes the play of declaring to win with the cards then displayed. The phrase in the old English adaptation of this is "set up all rests". A game at *primus* between Henry VIII and a courtier is thus described: "The King, eldest hand, set up all rests and discarded flush, etc."

[5] Fr. *averlans* (*R.E.R.* vii. 453).

[6] Fr. *vogue la galée* (iv. 25). The refrain of an old song of the fifteenth century. It was the motto of Galiot du Pré, the Paris printer. Cf. *Les menus propos, A.P.F.* xi. 394: "Sus gallans, vaulgue la galée".

Child, after the manner of the Ship[1] which doth not take on board her Pilot until she first be caulked and laded.

And if any blame them for being thus still burrowed after Pregnancy, seeing that the Beasts never endure[2] the covering Male after Conception, they will answer that those be Beasts, whereas they are Women, who do well understand the fine and glorious Perquisites of Superfetation,[3] as Populia formerly answered, according to the relation of Macrobius *lib. ii. Saturnal.* [cap. v. § 10].

If the Devil will not have them conceive, he must twist off the Spigot and stop the Vent.

---

[1] Cf. Macrob. ii. 5. 9.

[2] *The Beasts never endure*, etc. "Praeter mulierem pauca animalia coitum novere gravida, unum quidem omnino aut alterum superfetat", Pliny, 7. 48; Plut. *Bruta rat. uti*, c. 7. 990 D.

[3] *Superfetation*, "ut praeteream quae scribit Julianus jure consultus atque item Paulus Digestis: *si pars hereditatis petatur* [ff. v. 4. 3] ubi et superfetationem admittere videtur", Cael. Rhod. *Ant. Lect.* iv. 2. Cf. also Hippoc. *de salub. vict. rat.* [i. 653]; Arist. *de gen. an.* iv. 4. 36, 5.13; Bud. *in Pand.* i. p. 394, ed. Gryphius; Paré, xviii. 39; Sir T. Browne, *Pseud. Epid.* iii. 17.

CHAPTER IV[1]

How Gargamelle, being big with Gargantua, did eat a huge deal of Tripes

THE Occasion and Manner how Gargamelle was delivered was thus; and if you do not believe it, may your Fundament fall out!

Her Fundament did fall out one After-dinner, the 3d Day of February,[2] through having eaten too much Godebillios.[3] Godebillios are the fat Tripes of Coiros:[4] Coiros are Beeves fattened at the Stall and Guimo[5] Meadows: Guimo Meadows are those which are mowed twice in the Year. Of those fat Beasts they had killed three hundred and sixty-seven thousand and fourteen, to be salted at Shrove-Tuesday, that at Springtide they might have Abundance of Beef in season, so that at the Beginning of their Meals they might have *Commemoration*[6] of Salt meats, and better relish their Wine.

The Tripes were abundant, as you have heard, and so dainty were they that every one licked his Fingers. But the great four-

---

[1] In ABC chapters iv and v of D make one chapter (iv). D divides them and makes considerable additions to v.

[2] M. Lefranc suggests (*R.E.R.* vi. 265) that Feb. 3 was Rabelais' own birthday. He points out that Shrove-Tuesday fell on Feb. 12 in 1494, and on Feb. 27 in 1489, and suggests that the salt beef might be ready on either of those days, and that Rabelais might be born in either of those years. He inclines to 1494. In the *Prognostication*, c. 9 (written 1533), Rabelais declares that "the stars have been in the heavens more than 16,000 days, *I assure you*". 16,060 days is 44 years; if he means this to refer to himself 1533 − 44 = 1489, and that might be his birth-year.

[3] *Godebillios* (*guodiveaulx*, iii. 18 *ad fin.*) are tripes of a fattened cow (*R.E.R.* vii. 462).

[4] *Coiros* (Fr. *coiraux* = *paresseux, coyrault,* iii. 26), *i.e.* idle as being stall-fed (*R.E.R.* vii. 98).

[5] *Guimeaux* should be *gaineaulx*, a suggestion of Le Duchat endorsed in *R.E.R.* vii. 97. *Gaineaulx* = *prata restibilia*, because they bring *regain*.

[6] *Commemorations*, or *suffragia de sanctis*, are short prayers for a saint who is not the saint of the day, said at the end of Vespers and Lauds at certain seasons: *e.g.* St Thomas on the Sunday after Christmas. Here it means a kind of *hors d'œuvre*.

manned Devilry[1] was in it that they could not be kept longer, for
they were tainted, which seemed improper; whence it was determined that they should gulch them up without losing aught therein.
To this effect they brought together all the Citizens of Sainais,[2]
Suillé,[3] la Roche-Clermaud,[4] Vaugaudray,[5] not to omit le Coudray,[6] Montpensier,[7] le Gué de Vede[8] and other Neighbours, all
stiff Drinkers, good Companions, and rare Skittle-players, ha![9]

The good man Grandgousier took mighty great Pleasure therein,
and ordered that all should be without Stint; nevertheless he told
his Wife to eat the more sparingly, seeing she was near her Time,
and that this Tripe was no very commendable Meat. "Those",
said he, "would fain chew Dung, who would eat the Bag thereof".

Notwithstanding these Remonstrances she ate sixteen Quarters
two Bushels and six Pecks. A rare lot of Loblolly to swell in her!

---

[1] A *diablerie* with four devils would mean general confusion, as it was not so
easy to manage four as a small number. There was always a *diablerie* in a mystery
play.

[2] *Sainais* (*Sinays*, cc. 25, 45, *Sinay*, c. 27, *Cinays*, iii. 20), a small village south-
west of Chinon, bordering on Seuilly, in which parish was La Devinière, Rabelais' birthplace. The family of Rabelais possessed property in Seuilly. In the
church of Cinays was a statue of St Cloud which was the object of many pilgrimages (cf. St Clouaud, c. 27).

[3] *Suillé, Seuillé, Seuilly* (cc. 25, 27, 52; iv. 20, 23, 50, 52), a village close to
La Devinière. It contained an abbey belonging to the Benedictines of St Maur
of which some remains exist, and a castle of the Coudray-Montpensier family.

[4] *la Roche-Clermaud* (cc. 28, 30, 34, 46, 51), a village on an eminence a short
distance from La Devinière with the small stream, the Vede (or Veude),
running along the valley between them. The castle was replaced in the seventeenth century by a seignorial mansion; some few fortifications remain.

[5] *Vaugaudray*, a hamlet of the commune of Chinon, formerly part of the
ancient parish of Parilly.

[6] *le Coudray* (cc. 38, 43, 51; iii. 23), a castle in the commune of Seuilly, stands
out boldly on a little hill over against Seuilly and La Devinière, from which it
is separated by a narrow valley.

[7] *Montpensier* (c. 51), a castle near Seuilly, but in the department of Vienne.
Up to the sixteenth century it belonged to a family of that name. The present
castle was built in 1483.

[8] The ford and wood of *Vede* (or *Veude*) (cc. 27, 34, 36, 37, 48) is on the stream
Nègrou near the Moulin du Pont. In the sixteenth century this belonged to a
family named Dupuy, who were also lords of the lands of Basché (cf. iv. 12–15).
As a fief the Vede wood was attached to the abbey of Cormery, the abbot of
which, in 1536 to 1545, was Jean du Bellay, Bishop of Bayonne and Paris. Again
this wood was in the occupation of Gaucher Sainte Marthe, lord of Lerné and
Le Chapeau.

[9] "Et beau joueur de quilles", Cl. Marot, *Epist.* 29.

After Dinner they all went pell-mell to the Osier-bed,[1] and there on the thick Grass danced to the Sound of the jolly Flageolets and the sweet Bag-pipes, so blithely that it was a heavenly Sport to see them so frolic together.

---

[1] *La Saulsaye* (cc. 6, 32, 42) was the name of a small meadow on the bank of the Vede, east of the burgh of Seuilly, below the hill occupied by La Devinière, and therefore well known to Rabelais. These notes of places are taken from *R.E.R.* iii. 406 (in which are *les notes de Bouchereau,* who asserts that "La plus grande partie des lieux que Rabelais cite en son libvre sont de nostre ressort") and v. 82.

CHAPTER V

The Chit-chat of the Drinkers[1]

THEN they fell to Dessert[2] in the same Spot: and forthwith began Flagons to go, Gammons to trot, Goblets to fly, Glasses to rattle:

Draw, reach, fill, mix—Give it to me—without Water; so, my Friend.—Whip me off this Glass gallantly. Bring me here some Claret[3] in a Glass weeping over.—A Truce to Thirst.—Ha! false Fever, wilt thou not away?—By my Faith, Gossip, I cannot get in the drinking Humour.—You have catched a Cold, Gammer?—Yea forsooth, Sir.—By the Belly of St Quenet[4] let's talk of drinking. —I only drink at my *Hours*, like the Pope's Mule.[5]—I only drink

---

[1] A similar instance of disconnected after-dinner talk may be found in Petronius, cc. 44–6. Rabelais can hardly have seen this because it occurs in the *cena Trimalchionis*, which was not discovered till the seventeenth century. This chapter may be a sort of imitation of the *convivium profanum*, one of the early *Colloquia* of Erasmus. Discursive chatter is given also in *G*. 39–41; *P*. 14; iv. 51–2. Here gossips of various professions take part, a cleric, a lawyer and others, who indicate their occupation by their remarks. A German and a Basque are present. (Fr. ed.)

[2] Fr. *resieuner* (*ressiner*, iv. 46). Ducange would spell it *reciner* (Lat. *recenare*) and derive it from *recticinium*, which, he says, "videtur dici colloquium quod post coenam inter convivas peragitur". Montaigne has (ii. 2) "en mon enfance les desjeuners, les *ressiners* et les collations furent plus frequentes qu'à present". From Cordier, 24. § 90, we get the following list of meals and the Latin correspondents:

Le desjeuner = jentaculum.
Le disner = prandium.
Le gouster, lequel à Paris⎫
s'appelle reciner ⎭ = merenda (Plaut. *Most.* 948; Calpurn. v. 60).
Le soupper = coena.
La collation, ou banquet⎫
après souper ⎭ = comissatio.

Cotgrave has *Regoubilloner*, "to make a reare supper (cf. iv. 46), steale an after supper".

[3] Fr. *vin clairet*, *i.e.* of a light red colour (*R.E.R.* vii. 99).

[4] *St Quenet* is one of the many saints of Brittany (*P*. 26; iii. 8).

[5] The Pope's mule only drank at his hours. This was a joke very current, cf. *P*. 7; v. 8. There seems to be an intentional confusion between the Pope's mule and the Pope's slipper (Fr. *mule*), so called from the dye derived from the red mullet, Pliny, 9. 65.

32

in my Breviary,[1] like a good Father Guardian.—Which was first, Thirst or Drinking?[2]—THIRST, for who would have drunk without Thirst in the time of Innocence?[3]—DRINKING, for *privatio prae-supponit habitum*.[4] I am learned, you see:

> "Fecundi calices quem non fecere disertum?"[5]

We poor Innocents drink only too much without Thirst.—Not I, truly, as I am a Sinner, without Thirst, if not present, at least Thirst to come, preventing it, you understand. I drink for the Thirst to come. I drink for ever and ever. My Eternity is in drinking, and my Drinking in Eternity.—Let us have a Song, let us have a Toast; a Catch;[6] let us sing around. Where is my Tuning-fork?— What! I only drink by proxy.[7]

Do you wet yourselves to dry, or do you dry to wet you?

I do not understand your Theorick; by Practice I help myself some little.—Quick![8] I wet, I humect, I drink, and all for fear of dying. Drink always and you will never die.—If I drink not I am high and dry, and as good as a Dead man. My Soul will fly to some Frog-marsh. The Soul never dwells in a dry Place.[9]

---

[1] *at my Hours...in my Breviary*. The mendicant orders invented cups shaped like Breviaries for drinking on the sly. In iv. *A.P.* a silver cup of this kind is described, presented to Rabelais by some courtiers. Cf. *G.* 41; iv. 20; v. 46.

[2] *Which was first, Thirst or Drinking?* An adaptation of the query whether an egg existed first or a hen, Macrob. *Sat.* vii. 16. 1; Plut. *Quaest. Conv.* ii. 3; Sir T. Browne, *Pseud. Epid.* v. 5.

[3] *who would have drunk without Thirst in the time of Innocence?* Cf. Shakesp. 1 *Hen. IV*, iii. 3. 186: "In the state of innocency Adam fell: and what should poor Jack Falstaff do in the days of villany?"

[4] *privatio praesupponit habitum* (Dedicatory Letter to Tiraqueau), an Aristotelian maxim (*Categ.* 10. § 17) quoted in a gloss to l. decem ff. de verb. obl. (xlv. 1. 116) Joh. Nev. fo. 43. 2; l. remittit. ff. de jurejurando (xii. 2. 6) (Brocardica Juris).

[5] *Fecundi calices*, etc. (Hor. *Epp.* i. 5. 19), gloss to *Δ*, iii. 1. 14.

[6] Fr. *motet*, either a chant or a catch: so *entonner* is either to raise a psalm or pour down wine, and *entonnoir* may be either a *tuning*-fork or a *tunning*-fork, a funnel.

[7] *drink by proxy*. It is a lawyer who speaks; in v. 23 *Quintessence* took her food through a funnel.

[8] *Haste!* is the correct reading, not *Basta* which has been generally received.

[9] This is from St Augustine (*Questiones Vet. et Nov. Test.* c. 23): "Anima certe, quia spiritus est, in sicco habitare non potest"; quoted in 2 D. 32. 2. 9, and imitated in the *Nef des Fols* (1497):

> "Jamais (nostre ame) *ne se contient*,
> Ainsi que lisons, en sec lieu".

O ye Butlers, Creators of new Forms, make me of No-drinker a Drinker;[1] a Perennity of Sprinkling going through these parched and sinewy Bowels. He drinks in vain who feeleth it not. This entereth into the Veins; the p—g-tool shall have none on't.—I would willingly wash the Tripes of this Calf[2] which I—dressed this Morning.—I have well ballasted my Stomach.—If the Paper of my Bonds and Bills drank as well as I do, my Creditors would have enough to do[3] when they came to produce their Titles.—That Hand spoils your Nose.[4]—O how many others will enter there before this comes out! What! drink at so shallow a Ford?[5] It is enough to break your Girths.—This is called the Counterfeit in Flagons.—What is the Difference between a Bottle and a Flagon?[6] —A great Difference: for a Bottle is stopped with a Cork, and a Flagon with a Cock.—Excellent!

"Our Fathers drank deep and emptied their Cans."[7]

Well cackled, well cackled! Let us drink.—Will you send nothing to the River? That Fellow there is going to wash his Tripes. —I drink no more than a Sponge.—I drink like a Templar.[8]— And I *tamquam sponsus*.[9]—And I *sicut terra sine aqua*.—Give me a

---

[1] *of No-drinker a Drinker*. A laughing reference to the Heraclitean theory of Not-being passing into Being. The butlers, as supplying wine, make a man's brain full of "nimble, fiery and delectable shapes", and so are creators of Forms.

[2] *this Calf*, i.e. himself: cf. ὅδε ἀνήρ. *Habillé*, like the English word "dress", applies to a calf which is "dressed" by a butcher, as well as to a man dressing himself. Cf. "Lors les (perdrix) fit ainsi *habiller* et quand elles furent prestes et rosties, etc.", *C.N.N.* 99.

[3] Fr. *auroient leur vin*, i.e. they would have enough to do to make out their titles which would be obliterated by the wine absorbed by the paper. In *la formule de exhiber* there seems to be an allusion to the *Digest*, ff. xliii. 5. 3. § 6: *De tabulis exhibendis*.

[4] *Hand spoils your Nose*: addressed to a clumsy drinker who cannot find his mouth; or "makes your nose red" by too many draughts.

[5] *so shallow a Ford*, i.e. from a glass so nearly empty. A remonstrance against heel-taps.

[6] *Flagon*. Fr. *Flaccon*.

[7] *Nos peres beurent et viderent les potz* is from a Norman drinking-song of the sixteenth century. It is No. 27 of a collection printed as an appendix to the edition of Basselin by P. L. Jacob, in the Bibliothèque Gauloise.

[8] *like a Templar* (P. 16). The Knights Templars, who were dissolved by Clement V and Philippe le Bel (1312), had become notorious drinkers.

[9] *sponsus*, a pun on *éponge*: Ps. xix. 5; *Sicut terra sine aqua*, Ps. cxliii. 6.

Synonym (definition) for a Ham.—It is a Compeller of Draughts;[1] it is a Pully. By the Pully-rope Wine is let down into the Cellar, by the Ham into the Stomach.—Ha, there! some Drink! drink, ha!— That is not a Bumper.—*Respice personam;*[2] *pone pro duos; bus non est in usu.*

If I could only get up as well as I can tipple-topple[3] down, I had long ago been high in Air.

> Thus James Harte[4] grew rich amain;
> Thus the Brushwood grows again;
> Thus did Bacchus conquer India;
> Thus Philosophy Melinda.[5]

A little Rain allays a deal of Wind;[6] long Draughts break the Thunder.—But if my Cod voided such Liquor, would you like to suck it?—I retain it afterwards.—Here, Page, give me to drink; I will register my Nomination[7] for you when my Turn comes.

> ...Sup it, Will,
> There's yet somewhat left to swill.

---

[1] *Compulsoire* is a legal term, an order to produce papers, etc. This joke of *jambon* and *compulsoire* is given in Jean le Houx, *Vaux de Vire*, p. 69 (ed. maj.).

[2] *Respice personam*, etc., *i.e.* "see for whom you are pouring; pour enough for two" (*duos* instead of *duobus*). *Bus* (the last syllable of *duobus* and the past participle of *boire*) is not in use here. Cf. *Epist. Obs. Vir.* i. 1: "*nostro -tras -trare non est in usu*".

[3] Fr. *avaller* = to run down, and to swallow. Cf. *P.* 14.
> "L'une partie de la sale
> Va contremont et l'autre avale". R.R. 6829.

[4] *Jacques Cœur*, treasurer to Charles VII, was born at Bourges and became afterwards Master of the Mint. He worked mines in the Lyonnais, paying a royalty to the King, but his immense wealth was due to his trade as a merchant in the Levant. As an ambassador he represented France with splendour, but was disgraced in 1453 on suspicion of having debased the coinage and of poisoning Agnès Sorel. He fled to Rome and was appointed by Calixtus III to lead a force against the infidels, but died at Chios in 1456. Cf. Pasquier, *Lettres*, iii. 9; Pierre Clément, *Jacques Cœur et Charles VII*. His wealth was proverbial, cf. *Epp. Rom.* ii. § 8; *A.P.F.* ii. 69; Villon, *Grand Test.* xxxvi:
> "Se tu n'as tant qu'eust Jacques Cueur".

[5] *Melinda* (G. 8; iii. 28), a town in Africa north of Zanzibar, won by the Portuguese as much by strong drink as by persuasion; mentioned in Milton, *P.L.* xi. 399 and the *Adagia* of Joh. Aegidius. Discovered by Vasco da Gama April 5, 1498; rich in carbuncles, rubies, etc.

[6] *A little Rain*, etc. The title of iv. 44. It occurs in *Huon de Bordeaux*, c. 3. *Long Draughts* are also a kind of heavy rain, and the clinking of the glasses acts like bells to break the thunder. *Fulmina frango*, says the Bell in Schiller.

[7] Fr. *insinuer nomination* (*P.* 12; iv. 10). Certain Councillors had the privilege

I stand forth as Appellant against Thirst, as against Abuses.—
Page, sue out my Appeal in Form.—See this Heel-tap?—I used
formerly to drink all; now I leave nothing.—Let us not hurry and
let us carry all with us.—Here are Tripes fit for our Sport, excellent Godebillios of the dun Ox with the black Streak. Let us
curry him a' God's name, for the good of the House.—Drink or
I'll...[1] No, no, drink, I pray you.—Sparrows never eat unless you
bob them on the Tail; I drink not unless you speak me fair.

Lagona edatera.[2] There is not a Rabbit-burrow in all my Body
where this Wine doth not ferret out my Thirst. This whips me it
soundly; this shall banish it utterly.—Let us make a Proclamation
to the Sound of Flagons and Bottles that whosoever has lost his
Thirst has nothing to look for here. Long Clysters of Drinking have
made him void it out of Doors.—The great God made the Planets
and we make the Plates neat.—I have the Word of the Gospel in
my Mouth: *Sitio.*—The Stone called *asbestos* is not more unquench-
able than the Thirst of my Paternity.—The Appetite comes with
eating, says Angest[3] of le Mans; Thirst goes away with drinking.—
A Remedy against Thirst? It is the opposite of that which is good

---

of recording their title to the nomination for the first benefice vacant in some
diocese or abbey, in consideration of the *annates* or first-fruits that accrued to
the Pope. After being allowed to lapse for some time, the privilege was revived
in the time of Paul III (Pasquier, *Recherches*, ii. 4).

[1] *Drink or I'll....* An *aposiopesis* like *Quos ego...* in Virg. *Aen.* i. 135. Cf. v. 19.

[2] *Lagona edatera*, Basque words meaning "Drink, Comrade". In D the words
are printed *Lago- | na edatera*, so that my suggested substitution of the Latin
words *et altera* falls through. I am informed by the late distinguished Basque
scholar, the Rev. Wentworth Webster, that *Laguna edatera* is the proper Basque
form.

[3] *The Appetite comes with eating*, etc. "Tum etiam ille actus appetendi, cum
sit ens ipsum, appetit actu appetendi", Hieronymi ab Hangesto, sacr. Theol.
Prof., *Liber de causis* (Lib. i. va, *Proprietas materiae*) (Paris, Jean Petit, 1515).
Jerome de Hangest was a doctor of the Sorbonne and a bitter enemy to the
Reformation, †1538 at Le Mans. Cf. "Estne...sitienti in bibendo voluptas?
Eademne...quae restincta siti?" Cic. *de Fin.* ii. § 9.

> "As if increase of appetite had grown
> On what it feeds on."   Shakesp. *Ham.* i. 2. 144.

> "Cibus omnis in illo
> Causa cibi est, semperque locus fit inanis edendi."
>   Ovid, *Met.* viii. 841.

> "Mais quant plus prent et plus aprent
> Et plus son desirier l'esprent
> Toujours li croist son apetit."   *R.R.* 5101.

against the Bite of a Dog. Always run after the Dog and he will never bite you; always drink before the Thirst and it will never come to you.—There I catch you napping; I awake you. Eternal Butler, guard us from Sleep.[1] Argus had a hundred Eyes to see with; a Butler needs a hundred Hands, as Briareus had, to pour out indefatigably.—Let us wet, Lads, ha! it is no use being dry.— White Wine here! Pour out all, pour a' the Devil's Name! Pour it all; quite full; my Tongue is peeling. *Lans trink*;[2] to thee, Comrade, lustily, lustily! La, la, la, that was a good Drink, that! *O lacryma Christi!*[3] 'Tis from *la Devinière*;[4] 'tis from the pine-apple Grape.[5]— O the fine white Wine; and by my Soul 'tis Wine of Taffeta.—Ha! ha! 'tis of one Ear, "well wrought and of good Wool".[6] Courage, Comrade! We shall not be bested this Game, for I have made a Trick.[7]—*Ex hoc in hoc*.[8] There is no Deception; every one of you saw it. I am a Past Master in this:

Ahem! ahem! I am a Mast Pastor.[9]

---

[1] Fr. *sommelier* and *somme* (Lat. *somnus*), *P.* 28, an untranslatable pun. Cf. *C.N.N.* "Je meurs de somme".

[2] *Lans trink* = *trink Landsmann*. Cf. *P.* 2 (*fin.*), 28, and *Epist. Obs. Vir.* i. 48: "Ego habeo unum bonum fautorem qui est lansmannus meus". It is a German speaking.

[3] *Lacryma Christi* is properly a wine made from grapes grown at the foot of Vesuvius, but in *Epist. Obs. Vir.* ii. 12 it is said to be made at Montefiasco near Viterbo, and the German monk remarks: "Utinam Christus vellet etiam flere in patria nostra".

[4] *La Devinière*, a vineyard property and house, where Rabelais was born, belonging to his father, between Seuilly and La Roche-Clermand: *P.P.* 6; *P.* 9; *G.* 49; iii. 32. It is the headquarters of Gargantua in the war and the centre of action for all the doings in the Chinonais throughout. It was a fief of the Abbey of Seuilly and was occupied by the Rabelais family from 1480 to about 1630 (*R.E.R.* v. 64; iii. 55).

[5] Fr. *raisin pineau*, a small grape shaped like a pine-apple, from which was produced excellent wine of Anjou. Cf. *G.* 25, 38 and *R.E.R.* vii. 104.

[6] *well wrought*, etc. Fr. *bien drappé et de bonne laine*. Expressions borrowed from the draper in the farce of *Maistre Pierre Pathelin* (l. 193) and suggested by the word *Taffeta*. *Of one Ear* refers to the jar which, as holding the best wine, would be smaller and have but one Ear, or handle. Cf. v. 44, 45.

"Voici du gourd piot *à une aureille*."

Le retour de Bacchus, A.P.F. i. 241.

[7] Fr. *nous ne voulerons pas, car j'ai faict un levé*.

[8] *Inclinavit ex hoc in hoc*. Ps. lxxiv. 9. (He poured it) from this into that, *i.e.* from the glass into the stomach.

[9] *Mast Pastor* for *Prebstre Macé*, with an allusion to René Macé, a Benedictine, cf. *G.* 27. He is mentioned as a friend by Geoffroy Tory in the *Champ Fleury* (Toynbee's *Dante Studies*, p. 281).

O the Drinkers that are a-dry!—Page, my Friend, fill in here and crown the Cup,[1] I prithee.—In Cardinal[2] fashion. *Natura abhorret vacuum*.[3] Would you say now that a Fly had drunk therein?—In the Brittany fashion.[4] Clean off, neat, for this Brimmer.[5]—Swallow it down, it is wholesome Medicine.

---

[1] *crown the Cup.* Cf. Hom. *Il.* i. 470: κρητῆρας ἐπεστέψαντο ποτοῖο, and Virg. *Aen.* i. 724, vii. 147: "vina coronant".

[2] Fr. *à la Cardinale, i.e.* all red, full to the brim of red wine.

[3] *Natura abhorret vacuum* (iv. 62). Aristotle confutes the assumption of a vacuum by the atomists in *Physica*, iv. 6–9. Cf. Zeller's *Aristotle*, i. 432–4.

[4] In Brittany it was the fashion to drink to the last drop. Cf. *P.* 28.

[5] Fr. *net net à ce pyot.* In translating this passage Urquhart uses *supernaculum*, .e. that not more than a drop will remain that would stay on a finger-nail. Scott has it in *Peveril of the Peak*, c. 27: "Nay it shall be an overflowing bumper, an you will, and I will drink it *supernaculum*". Cf. Pliny, 28. 124: "Lac vernum probatissimum quod in ungue haeret nec defluit".

CHAPTER VI

How Gargantua was born in a mighty strange Fashion

WHILST they were on this pleasant Tattle of Drinking, Gargamelle began to be unwell in her lower Parts; whereupon Grandgousier got up from the Grass and fell to comforting her kindly, believing that she was in Travail, and telling her that she had been out to Grass in the Willow-grove[1] and that she would soon grow new Feet;[2] therefore it was fitting that she should take fresh Courage at the new Coming of her Baby, and that although the Pain was somewhat grievous to her, yet it would be short, and the Joy which would soon succeed would take from her all that Pain, so that even the Remembrance of it would not remain. "I will prove it to you",* he said; "our Saviour says in the Gospel, *Ioannis xvi.* [21]: 'A Woman when she is in Travail hath Sorrow; but when she is delivered of the Child she remembereth no more her Anguish'." "Ah," quoth she, "you say well, and I like much better to hear such Sentences of the Gospel, and I find myself much better for it than from hearing the Life of St Margaret[3] or other such Cant."

"On with a Sheep's Courage," said he, "despatch this Boy and we will soon fall to making another."

"Ah!" said she, "you speak at your ease, you Men![4] Well, a' God's Name I will do my best since you will have it so; but would to God you had cut it off."

"What?" said Grandgousier.

"Ah!" said she, "you are a good Man indeed! You know well enough."[5]

---

* "I will prove it to you...Cant."—ABC. Om. D.

[1] *in the Willow-grove.* Fr. *la Saulsaye.* Cf. *G.* 4.
[2] Alluding to the horn of the hoof growing *and* to the feet of the new child.
[3] The *Life of St Margaret* was read to women in childbirth, and sometimes even laid on the parts affected, cf. *P.* prol. The girdle of St Margaret was also bound round them. "S. Margareta devote oravit: addens ut quaecunque in partu periclitans se invocaret illaesam prolem emitteret" (*Legenda aurea,* c. 93).
[4] Cf. "O mes Seigneurs, nos maistres, vous parlez bien à vostre aise", Menot, quoted in the *Apol. pour Hérod.* ii. 164.
[5] *Vous l'entendez bien* is a chanson.

"What! my Member?" said he. "By the Blood of all the Goats,[1] have a Knife brought hither at once, if you think well."

"Ah," said she, "the Lord forbid! God forgive me, I did not say it from my Heart; don't do anything more or less to it for anything I said; but I shall have Trouble enough to-day unless God help me, and all through your Member, that you might be well pleased."

"Courage, Courage", said he. "Do you have no Care in the Matter, and let the four leading Oxen[2] do their Work. I will go and take another Draught; if meantime anything should befall you, I will keep near; whistle in your Palm and I will be with you at once."

A little time after she began to sigh, lament and cry out. Suddenly there came in swarms Midwives from all sides, who groping her below found some Peloderies of a bad Savour enough, and thought it was the Child, but it was her Fundament which was slipping out through the Mollification of the *intestinum rectum*, which you call the bum-gut, through her having eaten too much Tripe, as we have declared above.

Whereupon a filthy old Hag of the Company, who had the Reputation to be a great Physician and had come thither from Brisepaille[3] near Saint Genou threescore Years before, made her so horrible an Astringent that all her Membranes were so stopped and constricted that you could very hardly have enlarged them with your Teeth (which is a thing very horrible to think of), in the same way as the Devil at a Mass of St Martin, copying down the Tittle-tattle of two Wenches, lengthened out his Parchment by tugging with his Teeth.[4]

---

[1] *By the Blood of all the Goats* is a Gascon adjuration.

[2] *the four leading Oxen*. An expression of Poitou, where oxen were much employed for draught. Cf. the World's four Oxen, *P.* 12, 29; iv. 24. Sometimes used for the four Evangelists.

[3] *Brisepaille* is a hamlet in the commune of St Genou (Indre) (Fr. ed.). It seems possible that a midwife was summoned from here to La Devinière to attend women in childbirth.

[4] Cf.   "Notez en l'Ecclise de Dieu
Femmes ensemble caquetoyent.
Le diable y estoit en ung lieu,
Escripvant ce qu'elles disoyent.
Son rollet plein de poinct en poinct
Tire aux dents pour le faire croistre;

By this Mishap the Cotyledons[1] of the Matrix were all loosened above, and by these the Child leaped up and entered into the *vena cava*,[2] and clambering by the Diaphragm right above her Shoulders, where the said Vein parts in two, took his Way to the left and issued forth by her left Ear.[3]

As soon as he was born, he did not cry, as other Children do, *Mies*,[4] *mies, mies!* but with a sturdy Voice bawled out *Drink, drink, drink!* as though inviting all the World to drink, so loud that he was heard by all the Country of Beusse and Bibaroys.[5]

I doubt me, you do not with full Assurance believe in this strange Nativity. If you do not believe it, I care not; but an honest Man, a Man of good Sense, always believes what is told him and what he finds written.

Doth not Solomon say, *Proverbiorum xiv.* [15]: *"Innocens credit omni verbo"*, etc.; and St Paul, *prim. Corinthior. xiii.* [7]: *"Charitas omnia credit"*? Why should you not believe it? Because, say you,

---

        Sa prinse eschappe et ne tient point;
        Au pilier s'est heurté la teste."
                Grosnet, *Les Motz doréz de Cathon.*

A prose version is given in "La vie de Mgr. S. Martin", *R.E.R.* viii. 343.

[1] By *cotyledons* are meant the orifices of the menstrual veins and arteries (Hippoc. *Aph.* v. 45; Galen, *de usu part.* xv. 5; Parè, i. c. 34).

[2] *vena cava* (v. 42 *fin.*). Cf. Le Double, p. 236 n. This point of anatomy seems to be derived from Galen: ἄχρι μὲν τοῦ διαφράγματος ἠγάγομεν λόγῳ τὴν κοιλὴν φλέβα, *de usu part.* vi. 1; αὐτὴν δὲ τὴν κοιλὴν ἀναφέροντες ἀπὸ τῶν φρενῶν ἄχρι τῆς σφαγῆς, id. *ibid.* vi. 4. The anatomy of the *vena cava* is given also by Parè, i. c. 25, ii. c. 15 (vol. i. pp. 151, 194).

[3] *left Ear.* This notion, profane to us, was represented not uncommonly in painted windows and in hymns. It is strangely put in the pious peroration of the *Liber Thobiae* in the *Auctores octo morales* (cf. *G.* 14), which may well have been a source for this chapter:

    "Felix conjugium dum se sacra verba maritant
      Auriculae, verbum fit caro patre carens.
    Angelus obstetrix; pater infans, sermo maritus,
      Auris sponsa, parens nata; creatur homo.
    Intus et exterius totus quia virgine totus:
      Totus apud patrem; totus ubique Deus".

[4] *Mies.* Diez makes this an old French word from M. Lat. *mezium*, akin to Eng. *mead*, Gk. μέθυ.

[5] *Beusse* is a town and river in the department of Loudun, near Chinon. *Bibaroys* is the Gascon pronunciation of *Vivarais*, a province in Languedoc, north of Avignon, on the Rhone. They practically mean here *drinking* towns. So the Emperor Tiberius Claudius Nero was called in the camp Biberius Caldius Mero, on account of his drinking powers (Suet. iii. 42).

there is no Seeming in it. I tell you for this Reason only you ought to believe it in perfect Faith. For the Sorbonnists say that Faith is the Evidence for Things not seen.*[1]

Is it against our Law, our Faith, against Reason, against the Holy Scripture? For my part, I find nothing written in the Holy Bible, which is against it. But if the Will of God had been so, would you say that He could not have done it?

Ah! I beseech you, never cudgel and addle your Wits[2] with these idle Thoughts; for I say to you that to God nothing is impossible, and if He pleased, all Women hereafter would thus bring forth Children at their Ear.

Was not Bacchus engendered from the Thigh of Jupiter?

Was not Rocquetaillade[3] born from his Mother's Heel?

Crocquemouche[4] from the Slipper of his Nurse?

Was not Minerva[5] born of the Brain through the Ear of Jupiter?

Adonis of the[6] Bark of a Myrrh-tree?

Castor and Pollux[7] from the Shell of an Egg laid and hatched by Leda?

But you would be far more staggered and astonished if I should presently set forth to you the whole Chapter of Pliny, wherein he treateth of strange and unnatural Births. And in any case, I am not so hardy a Liar as he hath been. Read the Seventh Book of his *Natural History, cap. iii.*,[8] and do not further trouble my Head about it.

---

* "Doth not Solomon...things not seen."—ABC and Dolet. Om. D.

[1] From Heb. xi. 1: "Fides est substantia rerum sperandarum, argumentum non apparentium". Cf. Dante, *Par.* xxiv. 64, and Erasm. *Mor. Enc.* c. 53, where two of the texts here given are shewn to be subjects of controversy. This passage and the one above containing the quotation from John xvi are not in D (the present edition) but are inserted here from ABC, to exemplify the care Rabelais took to propitiate the religious scruples of the Theologians.

[2] *addle your Wits.* Fr. *emburlucoquer* (P. 13; iii. 22). This word is decried by Geoffroy Tory, cf. *P.* 6.

[3] *Rocquetaillade* castle was in Languedoc, and belonged to the Montfaucon family. There is a hamlet of this name near Carcassonne (Le Double, p. 243).

[4] *Crocquemouche.* Perhaps intended for Domitian, see *Happemousche*, P. 1.

[5] Cf. Hes. *Theog.* 924.   [6] Cf. Ovid, *Met.* x. 503–14.

[7] Cf. Serv. ad Verg. *Aen.* iii. 328.

[8] The 7th book of Pliny's *Natural History* is devoted to Anthropology and contains an account of many aberrations of nature, etc. The 3rd chapter is full of such accounts and is referred to by Aulus Gellius iii. 16. 23 and ix. 4. 7–16.

CHAPTER VII

How Gargantua had his Name given him, and how
he took his Liquor down

THE Good man Grandgousier, as he was drinking and making merry with the rest, heard the horrible Cry which his Son had made as he entered into the Light of this World, when he roared out calling for "Drink, drink, drink"; whereupon he said: "QUE GRAND TU AS", *supple* the Gullet.

Hearing this, the Company said that verily the Child ought to have the Name GARGANTUA[1] from this, seeing that such had been the first Word uttered by his Father at his Birth, in imitation and after the Example of the ancient Hebrews. Which the Father graciously permitted, and his Mother was well pleased thereat; and to quiet the Child they gave him to drink till his Throat was nigh unto bursting,[2] and he was carried to the Font and there baptized, as is the Custom of good Christians.

And there were ordered for him seventeen thousand nine hundred and thirteen Cows from Pautillé[3] and Brehemond[4] to furnish him with Milk in ordinary; for to find a Nurse sufficient

---

[1] In the *Grandes Cronicques* (c. 6) "Gargantua" is said to be a Greek word. That is the only allusion to Greek or Latin in that composition.

[2] Fr. *boire à tire larigot* (P. 28; v. 33). *Larigot* is probably connected with *larynx*, and appears to have been used as a windpipe in a bagpipe. Cf. iv. 31, where the vertebrae (or back-bone) are said to resemble a *cornemuse*, which must there mean the pipe or *larigot*, and a passage in the *Varlet à tout faire* (*A.P.F.* i. 7), a poem from which Rabelais has borrowed several points:

> "Puis je sonne la cornemuse
> Avec le petit larigot
> Afin de reveiller Margot,
> Quand elle est par trop endormie".

[3] *Pautillé* (v. 15), a hamlet in the commune of Cinais. *Pontille* was a vast prairie watered by the Vienne at the foot of the hills of Cinais and Seuilly. Flocks and herds of all kinds, especially geese, were fed there (*R.E.R.* v. 72).

[4] *Bréhémond* (*G.* 47; iii. 25), a commune of the canton of Azay-le-Rideau. It consists of meadows watered by the Loire, the Indre and the Cher, and pastured herds of kine (*R.E.R.* v. 59).

for him was not possible in the whole Country, considering the great Quantity of Milk required to nourish him; albeit certain Scotist Doctors have affirmed that his Mother suckled him, and that she could draw from her Breasts fourteen hundred and two Pipes and nine Pails of Milk each time;[1] which is not probable. And the Proposition has been declared by the Sorbonne* scandalous, and to pious[2] Ears offensive, and savouring of Heresy afar off.

In this state he lived for a Year and ten Months, at which time, by Advice of the Physicians, they began to carry him abroad, and there was made for him a fine little Cart with Oxen, of the Invention of John Denyau.[3] In this he was taken about hither and thither right joyously, and it did one good to see him; for he had a fine Countenance and nearly eighteen Chins, and cried but very little; but he bewrayed himself every Hour, for he was marvellously phlegmatic in his Haunches, as much from his natural Complexion as from the accidental Disposition which had come to him from too much Quaffing of the Septembral Juice. And he never quaffed a Drop of it without a Reason.[4] For if it happened that he

---

* "*par Sorbonne*", ABC; "*mammalement*", D.

[1] In the *Grandes Cronicques*, c. 6, it is stated that Gallemelle could carry 50 pipes of milk in each of her breasts. Hence *mammalement* in D.

[2] Fr. *pitoyables = pieuses*. In *G*. 29 *pitié = piété*, Lat. *pietas*; v. prol. *pitoyablement = pieusement*. For the phrase cf. Erasm. *Ad*. ii. 5. 98: "conclusionem scandalosam, offensivam piarum aurium, haeresim sapientem"; and Bull of Leo X against Luther, M.D.XX 17 Kal. Julii: "alios vero [errores] vel haereticos, vel falsos, vel scandalosos, vel piarum aurium offensivos". This was a stock phrase. Cf. *Epist. Obs. Vir.* i. 11; Pasq. *tomi duo*, p. 141.

[3] *Denyau*, a physician, who prescribed carriage exercise for well-to-do patients. There was a Gatien Deniaud, a landowner at Seuilly (*R.E.R.* ii. 45). For the prescription, cf. also Pliny, 26. 12: "Asclepiades...oratione blandiens omnia abdicavit totamque medicinam ad causas revocando conjecturae fecit. Professus est...*gestationes*, quae cum unusquisque semetipsum sibi praestare posse intelligeret, faventibus cunctis...universum prope humanum genus circumagit in se".

[4]   "Si bene commemini, causae sunt quinque bibendi;
          Hospitis adventus, praesens sitis atque futura,
          Et vini bonitas, et—quaelibet altera causa."
                    Attributed to Père Sirmond in *Menagiana*, ii. 352.
An adaptation has been attributed to Dean Aldrich of Christ Church, Oxford:
          "A friend, good wine, because you are dry,
          Because you may be by and bye;—
          Or any other reason why".

was vexed, angry, displeased or troubled, if he stamped with Rage, if he wept, if he cried, by bringing him Drink they restored him to good Temper and he at once remained quiet and happy.

One of his Governesses has told me, swearing by her Fecks,[1] that he was so accustomed to this that at the mere Sound of Pint-pots and Flagons he would fall into an Ecstasy, as though he were tasting the Joys of Paradise. So that they, considering this divine Complexion of his, in order to cheer him up would of a Morning make the Glasses chink[2] before him with a Knife, or the Flagons with their Stopple, or the Pint-pots with their Lid; at which Sound he would become merry, leap for Joy, and rock himself in the Cradle, noddling his Head,[3] monochordising[4] with his Fingers, and barytonising with his Tail.

---

[1] *Fecks* = faith, so in Shakesp. *Wint. T.* i. 1. 120. Fr. *Fy* = *foi*, G. 5. *Par ma Soif* (for *Foi*) is found in iii. 27, 28; iv. 37 and v. 20. Also *par ma Figue*, iii. 52; *par la Figue*, v. 7 and "juroit *Figues dioures* (son grand serment)", iv. 52.

[2] *make the Glasses chink*, etc. Cf. the account of Tony Weller and his grandson in the *Introduction* to *Master Humphrey's Clock*, vol. 1. p. 70, 1st ed.

[3] Fr. *dodelinant de la teste* (G. 22; P. 12; iii. 37). Cf. iii. 45; Hom. *Od.* xviii. 153:

αὐτὰρ ὁ βῆ διὰ δῶμα φίλον τετιημένος ἦτορ
νευστάζων κεφαλῇ;

and *Cortegiano*, ii. 37: "molti Italiani…non sanno par altro che *crollar la testa* parlando".

[4] *monochordising.* τὸ μονόχορδον (Pollux, iv. 60), a monochord (cf. iv. 63), was called by the Pythagoreans κανών (μουσικός) a tuning string, by which they measured the scale physically and arithmetically: this process was called μονοχορδίζειν (Lid. and Scott). The *monochordion* is the "trumpet-marine" mentioned in Pepys' *Diary* (Oct. 24, 1667), where see Wheatley's note, and Molière, *Bourgeois Gentilhomme*, ii. 3.

CHAPTER VIII

How they apparelled Gargantua[1]

WHEN he was of this Age his Father ordered that Clothes should
be made for him of his own Livery, which was White and Blue.[2]
So they went to work and Clothes were made, cut and sewn for
him in the Fashion that was then in vogue.

I find by the ancient Records, which are in the Chamber of
Accounts at Montsoreau,[3] that he was apparelled in manner as
followeth:

For his Shirt were taken up nine hundred Ells of Chasteleraud[4]
Linen, and two hundred for the Gussets, in the shape of Squares,
which they put under his Arm-pits. And it was not gathered; for
the Gathering of Shirts had not been invented until after that the
Seamstresses, when the Point of their Needles was broken, began
to work with their Tail-end.[5]

For his Doublet were taken up eight hundred and thirteen Ells
of white Satin, and for his Points fifteen hundred and nine Dog-
skins and a half. Then it was that men began to fasten the Hose to
the Doublet, and not the Doublet to the Hose, for it is a Thing

---

[1] Several points in this chapter are borrowed from the *Grandes Cronicques*, c. 11,
with considerable amplifications. Hints also seem to have been taken from the
Hypnerotomachia Poliphili. Cf. *G*. 9.

[2] *White and Blue* were the colours of France. Cf. iv. *A.P.* n. 19.

[3] *Montsoreau* (*G*. 47; iv. 19, 24), a little village contiguous to Cande near the
junction of the Loire and the Vienne, about 9 miles from Chinon. From here
the Loire was crossed to go to Chavigny-en-Ville, a property of Antoine
Rabelais.

[4] *Chasteleraud*, a town on the Vienne about 30 miles south-east of Chinon, very
productive of flax and consequently of linen (*R.E.R.* ii. 153; vi. 92).

[5] Cf. *La Chamberiere à tout faire* (1530), *A.P.F.* i. 100:

> "Et quand mon esguille est rompue
> Je m'ayde du cul proprement".

against Nature, as Ockham[1] hath amply declared on the *Exponibles*[2] of Messer Hautechaussade.

For his Hose were taken up eleven hundred and five and a third Ells of white Tamine; and they were pinked in form of Pillars, indented and notched behind, so as not to overheat his Reins. And from within the Pinking was puffed out with as much blue Damask as was needful. And note, that he had very fine Greaves and well proportioned to the Rest of his Stature.

For his Cod-piece were used sixteen Ells and a quarter of the same Cloth, and the Form of it was as that of a bowed Arch most gallantly fastened with two fine gold Buckles which were held by two Clasps of Enamel, in each of which was set a huge Emerald of the size of an Orange. For as Orpheus[3] says *libro de Lapidibus*, and Pliny *libro ultimo*, it hath an erective Virtue and a strengthening of the natural Member.

The Outlet of the Cod-piece was of the length of a Rod,[4] pinked like the Hose, with the blue Damask puffing it out as before.

But on looking at the fine Embroidery of the needlework Purl

---

[1] William of Occam, *Doctor Singularis* (cf. *P.* 7), 1280–1347, an English Franciscan, was a great advocate of Nominalism in the fourteenth century. He was a pupil of Duns Scotus at Merton College, Oxford, and asserted the true value of Nominalism as Deduction leading to Induction. Cf. Mullinger, *Hist. Univ. Camb.* i. 189. The refinements about the doublet and the hose appear to be intended as a gibe against the Nominalist doctrine of Universals and Particulars.

[2] *Exponibilia* is a term in the *Parva Logicalia* of Petrus Hispanus (*G.* 20), applied to the procedure of expounding a word in different ways. Cf. Petrus de Alliaco, Cardin. Cameracens. Tractatus *Exponibilium* de Anima (Paris 1494).

[3] The treatise (ascribed to Orpheus) περὶ λιθῶν was written about the time of Constantius (A.D. 351–61). It is on the magical properties of precious stones. Several editions were published in the beginning of the sixteenth century. On the Agate (᾿Αχάτης) are the following lines, which may have caught Rabelais' eye:

ἐν γὰρ οἱ δήεις ὁρόων ὑαλῶπιν ῎Ιασπιν
Σάρδιά θ᾽ αἱματόεντα καὶ αἰγλήεντα Μάραγδον.
. . . .
ἱμερτόν τε γυναικὶ δυνήσεται ἀνέρα θεῖναι.

Cf. Serv. *in Aen.* i. 174, who refers to Pliny as asserting that the wearer of the *Achates* is *gratiosior*, but I have not found this in Pliny's *Natural History*. Pliny in his 37th and last book has much to say about emeralds but not this "fact".

[4] Fr. *canne* (*G.* 37), probably a Gascon measure, = 8 pans = 1 m. 805, about 71 inches.

and the curious Inter-tissue of Gold-work set off with rich Diamonds, precious Rubies, fine Turquoises, costly Emeralds and Persian Pearls,[1] you would have compared it to a fair Horn of Abundance,[2] such as you see on ancient Monuments, and such as Rhea gave to the two Nymphs Adrastea and Ida, Nurses of Jupiter. Ever was it gallant, succulent, moist, ever verdant, ever flourishing, ever fructifying, full of Juices, full of Flowers, full of Fruits, full of all Delights. I answer for it to Heaven, if it did not do one good to see it. But I will set forth to you much more concerning it in the Book that I have made *On the Dignity of Cod-pieces*.

On one Point I advise you, that if it was right long and ample, it was also well furnished within and well victualled, and in nothing resembling the hypocritical Cod-pieces of a lot of fond Suitors, which are only full of Wind, to the great Prejudice of the female Sex.

For his Shoes were taken up four hundred and six Ells of blue crimson Velvet, and they were daintily slashed in parallel Lines joined in uniform Cylinders; for the Soling of them were employed eleven hundred Skins of brown Cows cut like the Tail of a Stockfish.[3]

For his Cloak were used eighteen hundred Ells of blue Velvet

---

[1] Fr. *unions* (G. 56; P. 21, 30; iv. 4, 49; v. 42; Bud. *de Asse*, ii. p. 218), from Lat. *uniones*, in Martial and Pliny (9. 112: *quod nulli duo reperiuntur indiscreti*), are pearls of the largest size. "And hereupon it is that our dainties and delicates here at Rome have devised this name for them and called them Vniones; as a man would say Singular and by themselves alone" (Phil. Holland's translation of Pliny).

"And in the cup an *union* shall he throw
Richer than that which four successive kings
In Denmark's crown have worn."
Shakesp. *Ham.* v. 2. 283. Cf. also Evelyn's *Diary*, Feb. 17, 1645.

For the passage cf. "Fili doro, per medio di quali erano traiectati in bacce longiuscule corruscanti balassi & terebrati & di p̄fulgentissimi saphiri & di scintillanti adamanti & di vernãti smaragdi cum gratiosa & amicale alternatione coloraria infilati, cum inextimabile & monstruose margarite, che sencia dubio tale dono Octaviano non fece a Iove Capitulino", *Hyp.* c. 17. o. iii verso. This passage is employed again in iv. 49.

[2] A *cornucopia* (derived mythologically from the horn of the goat Amalthea, cf. Ovid, *Fast.* v. 115–28) is one of the commonest emblems on statues of River-gods, Fortune, etc. The story of Rhea giving Amalthea's horn to Adrastea and Ida is from Erasm. *Ad.* i. 6. 2. Cf. also Apollodor. i. 1. 6.

[3] *like the Tail of a Stockfish.* Cf. G. 20; P. 6.

dyed in grain,[1] embroidered all round with fine Flourishes and decked in the middle with silver Pints worked in Purl, intermixed with Bands[2] of Gold with many Pearls, by this denoting that he would be a good Pint-whipper[3] in his time.

His Girdle was made of three hundred Ells and a half of silk Serge, half white and half blue, or I am much mistaken.

His Sword was not of Valentia, nor his Dagger of Saragossa; for his Father hated all those *Hidalgos Bourrachous*,[4] Infidels[5] like Devils; but he had a fair Sword of Wood, and the Dagger of boiled Leather, as well painted and gilded as any one could wish.

His Purse was made of the Cod of an Elephant, which was given him by Her Pracontal, Proconsul of Libya.[6]

For his Gown were used nine thousand six hundred Ells, wanting two-thirds, of blue Velvet, as above, all purfled with Gold in a diagonal Arrangement, from which by true Perspective resulted a nameless Colour, such as you see on the Necks of Turtle-doves,[7] which wonderfully rejoiced the Eyes of the Beholders.

---

[1] Fr. *en grene. migraine* (= *demi-graine*). Cf. *G.* 56; iii. 18; well-dyed and in durable colours. Regis quotes Shakesp. *Tw. N.* i. 5. 255: "'Tis *in grain*, Sir; 'twill endure wind and weather".

[2] Fr. *verges*. Cf. "*virgatis* lucent sagulis", Virg. *Aen.* viii. 660. Cf. also iii. 17; "Abstinentibus a vestibus devisatis seu *virgatis*", Ioh. Nev. 179. 1; "virgatas figere tigres", Claud. *Cons. Stil.* i. 66; *à la tigresque*, iv. 12.

[3] Fr. *Fesse-pinte*. Cf. *P.* prol.; *G.* prol.

[4] Fr. *Indalgos Bourrachous* for Hidalgos, *i.e.* drunken swaggering Spanish mercenaries. *Borrachos* is a Spanish term of contempt, meaning "drunken sots", from *Borracha*, a wine-skin. Shakesp. *Much Ado*, iii. 3. 111, has "BORACHIO (loq.)...and I will, like a *true drunkard*, utter all to thee". Francis I naturally hated Spaniards after Pavia. Valentia and Saragossa were celebrated for their sword cutlery at that time. Cf.

> "Lacent lur helmes mult bons sarraguseis,
> Ceignent espées de l'acier vianeis,
> Escuz unt genz, espiez valentineis".   *Chanson de Roland*, 996.

[5] Fr. *marranisés*. The descendants of the Moors in Spain and Spanish Jews were called *marranes* and *marrabais*. *Marrano* in Spanish means "accursed", originally a baptized Jew (? Hebr. *marah*); *marrana* (fem.) was used of a sow, the beast accursed to the Jews (Diez, *Wörterbuch*). (Cf. iii. 18, 25; iv. 40; *P.P.* 5; Erasm. *Epist.* 549. 12, vol. ii. p. 50, ed. Allen.)

[6] It was from Libya (Africa) that the Roman proconsuls would send wild beasts for gladiatorial shows. Humbert de Pracontal, Seigneur d'Anconne, commander of 300 men, was a corsair in 1544 and thoroughly acquainted with the African trade (*R.E.R.* vii. 477). Her is for the German *Herr*, as in *G.* 2; *P.* 12; iii. 25; v. prol.

[7] Cf.   "Pluma columbarum quo pacto in sole videtur
> Quae sita cervices circum collumque coronat". Lucr. ii. 800.

For his Cap were taken up three hundred and two Ells and a quarter of white Velvet, and the Form of it was wide and round according to the Largeness of his Head; for his Father said that these Caps of the Marrabaise[1] fashion, made like the Crust of a Pasty, would some day bring a Mischief on their close-shaven Wearers.

For his Plume he wore a fine large blue Feather taken from a Pelican (*onocrotal*)[2] of the Country of Hyrcania the wild, very daintily hanging over his right Ear.

For his Cap-brooch[3] he had, set in a Plate of Gold weighing sixty-eight Marks,[4] a fair Piece of enamelled Work, in which was represented a human Body having two Heads, one turned towards the other, four Arms, four Feet, and two Rumps, such as Plato says in his *Symposium* Man's Nature was at its mystical Beginning; and round about it was in Ionic[5] letters: Η ΑΓΑΠΗ ΟΥ ΖΗΤΕΙ ΤΑ ΕΑΥΤΗΣ.

To wear about his Neck, he had a golden Chain weighing twenty-five thousand and sixty-three Marks of Gold, made in form of great Berries, among which were worked large green Jaspers engraved[6] and cut like Dragons surrounded with Beams and

---

[1] *Marrabaise* = Moorish, from *Maure* and *Arabe*. Cf. *supra* and iii. 22. Formerly the Jews were compelled to wear such caps to distinguish them from Christians. Paul IV Caraffa (1555-9) made all the Jews in Rome reside in the Ghetto or Jews' quarter and wear yellow caps of this kind. Cf. Evelyn's *Diary*, Nov. 15, 1645. In the *Journal d'un Bourgeois de Paris*, p. 429, are mentioned (1532) certain *Marrabais italiens* who killed little children *pour en avoir le sang*. They were greatly maltreated, but it turned out to be *toute menterie*.

[2] *Onocrotalus*, the pelican, so called by the Greeks on account of its rasping cry, like the braying of an ass. It is described by Pliny in 10. 131, where he incidentally mentions a strange kind of bird whose feathers shew like fire by night (the fiery-eyed hoopoe), which he says is found *in Hercynio Germaniae saltu*. This accounts for "Hyrcania the wild". Rabelais elsewhere makes merry over this bird and its strange name, purposely confounding it with *Crotonotary* and *Protonotary* (P. prol.; iii. 26; v. 8, 30).

[3] Cap-brooch (Fr. *image*) was an ornament much in vogue at the time (Commynes, ii. 8; Coquillart, ii. 221). Benvenuto Cellini was often employed in making them. Cf. *Vita*, lib. i. c. 25; Ioh. Nev. fo. 177. 3: "et moriatur cum penna vel *imagine* super birreto".

[4] *Marks* (G. 2). "Regia libra Parisina 16 unciarum est; ejus semissem monetarii et aurifices libram sibi fecerunt, *marcam* eam vocantes", Bud. *de Asse*, ii. p. 162. Marca = 64 grossi (= drachmae). 1 dr. = 2½ sterlinos.

[5] *Ionic* (iv. 25), as the oldest form of Greek (Pliny, 7. 210).

[6] From "green Jaspers" to the end this paragraph is taken nearly literally

Sparks, as they were formerly worn by king Necepsos. And it came down to the Hollow of his Stomach, and of this all through his Life he had the Benefit, such as is known by the Greek Physicians.

For his Gloves were employed sixteen Skins of Hobgoblins, and three of Wer-wolves[1] for the Bordering of them; and they were made for him of this Material by the Order of the Cabalists of Sainlouand.[2]

For his Rings, which his Father wished that he should wear to renew the ancient Sign of Nobility,[3] he had on the Index finger of his left Hand a Carbuncle as large as an Ostrich Egg set in Seraph[4] Gold very delicately. On the Medical finger[5] of the same Hand he had a Ring made of the Four Metals together in the most wonderful Fashion that ever was seen, so that the Steel did not rub the Gold or the Silver crush the Copper. All this was made by Captain Chappuys[6] and Alcofribas[7] his good Helper. On the Medical

---

from Galen, *de simplic. medic. temp.* ix. 2. 19. Necepsos (v. 42) was a great Egyptian king and astrologer, mentioned in conjunction with Petosiris by Pliny, 2. 88, where their system is briefly described. Cf. also Ausonius, *Epist.* xix. 18:

"Quique Magos docuit mysteria vana Nechepsos".

Much interesting matter on this subject may be found in King's *Gnostics and their Remains* (p. 220, 2nd ed.).

[1] Fr. *Loup-garous.* Cf. *P.* 26; iii. 3.

[2] *the Cabalists of Sainlouand* (*G.* 47). The monks of the Priory of St Liventius or *Lupentius* on the Vienne, not far from Chinon, are intended as patrons of the *loups-garous.* It was the Prior of St Louant who persecuted the Lord of Basché with his Catchpoles in iv. 12.

[3] *ancient Sign of Nobility.* The Romans confined the wearing of gold rings to the Senators and Knights (Pliny, 33. 29; Dio. Cass. 48. 45, 7; Hor. *Sat.* ii. 7. 53: *annulo equestri*). Cf. Bud. *de Asse,* ii. p. 236; *in Pand.* i. p. 197.

[4] *Seraph* is an Egyptian gold piece (= European *ducat*, very nearly a *besant*, cf. *G.* 31 *fin.*), first coined by the Soudan Melech Seraph (*P.* 14; iii. 2) (D) (*R.E.R.* vii. 464).

[5] *Medical finger.* "Medium sequitur παράμεσος, medicis dicatus, atque ab iis nomen sortitus", Galen, *Ars medica* (tr.).

[6] *Captain Chappuys.* This is not Claude Chappuys, librarian to Francis I (cf. Ep. Ded. to Bishop du Bellay), but Michel Chappuys, the captain of some French ships, who was charged with the duty of conducting the Queen of Scots to France in June 1538. He conveyed cloth, silk and other wares. Alcofribas (Rabelais) is mentioned as his agent for the sale of such commodities (*R.E.R.* vii. 475).

[7] *Alcofribas* (Nasier) is the anagram of François Rabelais, adopted by him as the name of the writer of *Pantagruel* and *Gargantua.* Cf. the Title-pages and *P.* 32. In *G.* 23 *Seraphin Calobarsy* (Phrançois Rabelays) was read in the first edition and changed to *Theodorus* in D.

finger of his Right he had a Ring made in spiral Form, in which
were set a perfect Balas-ruby,[1] a pointed Diamond, and an Emerald of Physon[2] of inestimable Value; for Hans Carvel, grand
Jeweller to the King of Melinda, estimated the Value of them at
sixty-nine millions eight hundred and ninety-four thousand and
eighteen long-woolled Sheep;[3] and at so much did the Fourques[4]
of Augsburg prize them.

---

[1] *Balas-ruby* (Fr. *balais*, It. *balascio*), a specially fine ruby (iv. 49; v. 42). It is
often spoken of in the *Hypnerotomachia*. Cf. *R.R.* 20, 857: "Que saphirs, rubis, ne
balai". Cf. also Marco Polo, i. 33–5, Yule's notes; "*Rubi balais,* variété de
corindon, en Latin *balascus*" (Ducange); "Venant de Balaschen près Samar-
cande" (Popelin's trans. of *Hyp.* i. p. 348 note); "A delicate rose-red variety
of the spinel ruby" (*New Eng. Dict.*).

[2] *Physon* or Pishon is one of the four rivers of Eden encompassing the land of
Havilah: "There is bdellium and the onyx-stone" (Gen. ii. 12).

[3] Fr. *moutons à la grande laine* (*G.* 53; iii. 2; iv. N.P., 6), gold pieces (St Louis—
Charles VIII) bearing the *Agnus Dei* with a cross, hence called *mutones* or *moutons*.
They were worth 16 francs of modern money [before 1914—allowing 25 francs
to the pound sterling].

[4] *Fourques* (Germ. *Fugger*), of Augsburg, immensely rich merchants, jewellers
and bankers of the sixteenth century. Cf. *Epp. Rom.* i. § 1. They were established
in Rome 1495–1523, and among other bankers they were employed by the
Popes to collect the proceeds of *annates* and indulgences, especially those for the
building of St Peter's. Their portion was fifty per cent. Cf. *Camb. Mod. Hist.* i.
667. The founder of the family was a weaver of Goggingen who had burgess-
rights in Augsburg in 1370. They are mentioned in the *Contes d'Entrapel*, c. 5,
and in *Don Quixote*, ii. 23, and Montaigne in his *Voyages* (1581), *s.v.* Augsburg,
speaks of *Les Foulcres* (the Coots). They were the Rothschilds of their age, and
like them ennobled. A separate quarter of Augsburg, founded by Joh. Jacob
Fugger "the Rich" in 1519, is still called the Fuggerei. A house or bank built
by a Fugger in 1556 at Sterring in the Tyrol, on the high road from Innsbruck
to Rome (now the *Alte Post*), contains many relics. The story of Cardinal
Johann Fugger and his fatal surfeit of the Montepulciano wine, *Est, est, est,* is
well known.

CHAPTER IX

The Colours and Livery of Gargantua

T HE Colours of Gargantua were white and blue, as you may have read above; by which his Father wished it to be understood that it was to him a heavenly Joy, for the White did signify to him Gladness, Pleasure, Delights and Rejoicing, and the Blue heavenly Things.

I understand right well that in reading these Words, you scoff at the old Toper, and look upon this Exposition of the Colours as far too clumsy[1] and wide of the Mark, and tell me that White signifies Faith, and Blue Constancy. But without moving, vexing, heating or chafing you, for the Season is dangerous,[2] answer me, if it seemeth good to you. No other Constraint will I put upon you or any other, whosoever they be; only I will tell you a Word of the Bottle.[3]

Who stirreth you? Who pricks you? Who tells you that White signifieth Faith, and Blue Constancy? An old beggarly[4] Book, you say, sold by Pedlars[5] and Ballad-mongers, intituled " *The Blazon of Colours*".[6] Who made it?—Whoever it is, in this he hath shewn Wisdom that he hath not set his Name to it. But otherwise, I know not whether I ought to wonder at most, his Presumption or his Stupidity.

---

[1] Fr. *indague* (iii. 28), clownish, clumsy. Derivation unknown.

[2] *the Season is dangerous* (*P.* 3). Cf. Gen. xlii. 36: "All these things are against me".

[3] *a Word of the Bottle* = an invitation to drink; perhaps an anticipation of the journey to the Holy Bottle begun in iii. 47.

[4] Fr. *trepelu* (*G.* 26; iii. 20, 28), a word of Southern France, properly "ragged": hence "paltry", "beggarly".

[5] Fr. *bissouarts* (*P.P.* 5, Ep. against Dolet). Mountaineers from the land of the *bise* (*R.E.R.* v. 84, vii. 396, viii. 155); generally Waldenses of Dauphiné, who sold tracts, almanacks, etc. which they carried in satchels.

[6] *The Blazon of Colours*. A book published in 1528 entitled *Le Blason des couleurs en armes, livrées et devises*. The name of the author appears only on the first line of the prologue: "Sicille, herald-at-arms to the most mighty king Alphonso of Aragon, etc." There is a modern reprint by H. Cocheris, Paris, 1860. The passages here ridiculed are: "Quant aux sept sacremens de l'Eglise, *blanche couleur* represent le sacrement de *baptesme*...Azur se prend pour le sacrement de *confirmation*" (M).

His Presumption, for that without Reason, without Cause and without Probability he has dared to prescribe by his private Authority what Things should be denoted by the Colours; which is the Custom of Tyrants who wish their Will to hold the place of Reason,[1] and not the Manner of the Wise and Learned, who with the Evidence of Reason do satisfy their Readers.

His Stupidity, in thinking that, without other Proofs and sufficient Arguments, the World would rule their Devices by his doltish Impostures.

In fact as the Proverb saith: "To filthy Tale Ears never fail", he has found some Remnant of the Ninnies of the old Time when high Bonnets[2] were in fashion, who gave some Trust to his Writings, and in accordance with them have shaped their Apophthegms and Mottoes, caparisoned their Mules, clothed their Pages, quartered their Breeches, embroidered their Gloves, fringed their Bed-curtains, painted their Ensigns, composed Songs and (what is worse) have been guilty of Impostures and base Tricks clandestinely among chaste Matrons.

In the like Darkness are wrapped up these vainglorious Courtiers and Transposers of Names, who wishing to signify in their Devices *espoir*[3] have pourtrayed a *Sphere*,

> birds' *pens*[4] for *pains*,
> *l'ancholie*[5] for *melancholy*,
> the horned moon for *a crescent fortune*,
> a broken bench for *bankrupt*,[6]

---

[1] *hold the place of Reason.* In *Δ*, i. 7. 3 (*De translatione episcopi*), Innocent III writes (a. 1198): "Romanus Pontifex, qui non puri hominis sed veri Dei vicem gerit in terris,...divina potius auctoritate dissolvit". A gloss adds: "In illis quae vult stat pro ratione voluntas" from Juv. vi. 223. Cf. also Erasm. *Ad.* i. 6. 29 *sub fin.*

[2] *high Bonnets* (iv. *A.P.*). This ridiculous headgear was worn from before the time of Louis XI till about 1560, but was derided as a foolish fashion. Before this *chapperons* were in vogue. Cf. *A.P.F.* iv. 326.

[3] *Espoir* and *sphere* (written *espere*) were very like in pronunciation.

[4] birds' *pens.* Cf. Milton, *P.L.* vii. 421: "They summ'd their pens". D'Urfé gives "une penne de geay voulant signifier peine j'ay". (Fr. ed.)

[5] *l'ancholie* (*P.P.* 4) is the *aquilegia* or columbine.

[6] Fr. *banque roupte.* Cf.

> "dit qu'il est contraint
> Pour vostre train rompre banque en la ville". *A.P.F.* viii. 246.

non and a *corselet*[1] for *non dur habit* (= *non durabit*),

a *lict sans ciel*[2] for a *licentié*,

which are Equivocations so absurd, so stale, so clownish and barbarous, that a Fox's Tail[3] ought to be pinned to their Collar, and a Mask made of a Cow-pat for each of those Persons, who should henceforth offer, after the Restoration of Letters, to employ them in France.

For the same Reasons (if Reasons I ought to call them and not Ravings) I should have a *Panier* painted to denote that I am *pained*;

and a *Mustard-pot* to shew that my Heart is *much tardy*,

a *Chamber-pot*[4] for a *Chamberlain*;

the *Bottom of my Breeches* for a *wind-vexed Bottom*;[5]

my *Cod-piece* for the *Lance in Rest*,[6]

and *Estronc de Chien* for *Tronc de ceans*,

wherein lies the Love of my Lady.

Far otherwise in times long ago did the Sages of Egypt, when they wrote by means of Letters which they called Hieroglyphics,[7]

---

[1] *non* and a *corselet*, etc. Cf. Cretin, p. 220:

> "Fer ou acier est labbit et *labit*
> Mon hauberion, hoc est, *non durabit*".

"Si loricam france interpretabimur durum habitum signat, id est, ut vulgus loquitur, dur habit, quae latine accepta non durabit significant", R. Gaguini, *Epist.* 15. "And is not a buff jerkin a most sweet robe of durance?" Shakesp. 1 *Hen. IV*, i. 2. 48.

[2] *lict sans ciel*, a bed without a canopy.

> "Et tous les licts dessoubs les *cieulx*
> Fussent de parenté d'itieulx". *A.P.F.* vii. 298.

[3] *Fox's Tail*, etc. (cf. *P.* 16). "Qui te deridet caudam trahat", Hor. *Sat.* ii. 3. 53 (Fr. ed.); "I shall prove him such a noddy that all the world will deeme him worthy to wear a coxcombe in his forehead for his foolishnesse and on his back a *foxtayle* for his badge", *The Pope's Funerall* (1605), quoted by Douce, p. 511.

[4] Fr. *official*, the slang name for such a vessel: cf. *G.* 21 and iii. 17: "officialement forgerent Orion". The comparison is intended "ideo quod officiales (chambellains) praesto sint ad officium". Cf. Martial, xiv. 119.

[5] Fr. *vaisseau de petz* (*paix*).

[6] Fr. *le greffe des arretz*, the engrosser of judgments. *La greffe = graphius* or *stylus*.

[7] "Id autem symboli nihil aliud sibi velle quam illud Augusti Caesaris dictum σπεῦδε βραδέως" (Suet. ii. 25; Aul. Gell. x. 11. 5; Macrob. *Sat.* vi. 8, 9); "indicis sunt monumenta literarum hieroglyphicarum: sic enim vocantur aenigmaticae sculpturae quarum multus fuit usus potissimum apud Aegyptios vates ac theologos...qui...si quid cognitu dignum judicassent id animantium rerumque variarum expressis figuris ita repraesentabant ut non cuivis statim

which none understood who did not understand, and every one
understood who did understand the Virtue, Property and Nature
of the Things figuratively represented by them. On these Orus
Apollo[1] hath composed two Books in Greek, and Polyphilus in his
Dream of Love[2] hath further expounded. In France you have some
Instance of them in the Device of the Lord Admiral, which was
first borne by Octavian Augustus.[3]

---

esset conjicere: verum si cui singularum rerum proprietates, si peculiaris
cujusque animantis vis ac natura...perspecta fuisset...aenigma sententiae
deprehendebat", Erasm. *Ad.* ii. 1. 1 (*Festina lente*).

[1] "Homo Aegyptius cujus extant duo super hujusmodi symbolis libri, etc.",
Erasm. *Ad.* ii. 1. 1 (Orus Apollo *de Hieroglyphicis Aegyptiorum* libri duo a Berna-
dini Trebatio latine. Paris, R. Stephanus, 1530).

[2] Poliphili *Hypnerotomachia*, or the Strife of Love in a Dream, is a singular
work by a Dominican Friar named Francesco Colonna (1433–1527), written
about 1467 and published by Aldus Manutius in 1499 and 1545. It is profusely
illustrated with designs which have been attributed to Andrea or Benedetto
Mantegna, or Bellini, or even to Raphael. It describes in the form of a dream the
adventures of Poliphilus (probably from πολιή (antiquity) and φιλεῖν) as he passes
through wild woods and the interior of a huge giant, into gardens, pleasure-
grounds and palaces of the most sumptuous and quaint architecture. The name
of the author was discovered long after the publication of the book by com-
bining the first letters of its thirty-eight chapters: *Poliam frater Franciscus
Columna peramavit*. From this book are taken short passages and hints in *Gargantua* and large portions of v. 24, 25, 37, 38, 41–4, besides ideas for cc. 26 and
30, in 48 and other chapters of the *Fifth Book*. An account of the *Hypnerotomachia* is given in *Menagiana*, iv. 70. It is mentioned again in iv. 25, *briefve
declaration*.

[3] "On the other side there was ingraven a cyrcle, then an Anchor with a
Dolphin winding about the strangule thereof, which I conjectured should
signifie this, *ΑΕΙ ΣΠΕΥΔΕ ΒΡΑΔΕΩΣ, semper festina tarde*", *Hypner.
Poliph.* c. 7. d. vii recto (Eng. Transl.). Erasmus must have seen this book,
judging by a later note of his in the chapter cited above (*Ad.* ii. 1. 1): "Horus...
serpentis circumvoluti sculptura non *annum* sed *aevum* representari tradit.
Scripsit de his rebus Plutarchus in coment. de Osiride, et Chaeremon apud
Graecos, testimonio Suidae, cujus ex libris excerpta suspicor ea quae nos nuper
conspeximus ejus generis monimenta, in quibus etiam haec inerat pictura:
Primo loco Circulus, deinde ancora quam mediam, ut dixi, Delphinus obtorto
corpore circumplectitur. Circulus, ut indicabat interpretamentum adscriptum,
quoniam nullo finitur termino, sempiternum innuit tempus. Ancora, quoniam
navim remoratur et alligat sistitque, tarditatem indicat. Delphinus, quod
nullum aliud animal celerius...velocitatem exprimit; quae si scite, connecta
efficient hujusmodi sententiam ἀεὶ σπεῦδε βραδέως, id est, semper festina
lente". The emblem of the anchor and the dolphin was first adopted by Aldus
in his *Poetae Christiani veteres*, mense Ianuario M.DI. It had been adopted by
Vespasian, and, as Erasmus says: "Nunc vero in Aldum Manutium Romanum

But further my little Skiff shall not sail amongst these unpleasant Gulfs and Shoals; I return to disembark at the Port whence I set out. Yet do I hope one day to write on this more at large, and to shew both by philosophical Reasons and by Authorities received and approved by all Antiquity, what and how many Colours are in Nature, and what may be designated by each, if God save[1] the Mould of my Cap,[2] that is the Wine-pot, as my Grandam used to say.

---

ceu tertium haeredem devenit". The Lord Admiral referred to is Guillaume Gouffier, Sieur de Bonnivet (1517–25), the favourite of Francis I, who was killed at the battle of Pavia. This emblem may be seen on his tomb in the Collegial Church at Oiron (Deux-Sèvres), *R.E.R.* vi. 370. Cf. Paul. Jovius, *Hist.* Lib. 22 (epitome): "Moriente Hadriano, Gulielmus Gofferius, appellatus *Ammiras*, in Italiam descendit".

[1] Fr. *si Dieu me saulve, etc.*, D. A reads: *Si le Prince le veult et commende: cil qui en commendant donne et pouvoir et sçavoir.* Marty-Laveaux thinks that this indicates a design on the part of Rabelais to publish an official treatise on Colours, etc., of which this chapter is a specimen; but that he afterwards abandoned his purpose and substituted the sentence in the text. Cf. also the end of the next chapter, where he says that he reserves the rest for a book devoted to the subject.

[2] Fr. *moule du bonnet* (*G.* 21), the head, which is also intended in the expression *pot au vin* (*P.* 33; iii. 8) = Lat. *testa* = Fr. *teste*, tête. Cf. Monstrelet, iii. fo. 69: "le bourreau lui osta le moule de son chapperon, c'est à sçavoir la teste".

CHAPTER X

Of that which is signified by the Colours White and Blue

THE White therefore signifieth Joy, Solace and Gladness, and not wrongfully so signifieth, but by good Right and just Title; which you may verify if, putting your Prejudices aside, you will give Ear to what I will presently expound unto you.

Aristotle saith,[1] that supposing two things Contrary in Kind, as Good and Evil, Virtue and Vice, Cold and Hot, White and Black, Pleasure and Pain, Joy and Grief, and so on of the others; if you couple them together in such fashion that the Contrary of one Kind may agree in Reason with the Contrary of another, it follows that the other Contrary answers to the other remaining Contrary.

For example: Virtue and Vice are Contraries in one Kind, so are Good and Evil. If one of the Contraries of the first Kind agrees with the one of the second, as Virtue and Good (for it is known that Virtue is good), so will the two remaining ones agree, being Vice and Evil, for Vice is evil.

This logical Rule being understood, take these two Contraries, Joy and Sadness; then these two, White and Black; for they are physically contrary; so then if Black signifieth Grief, by good Right White will signify Joy.

Nor is this Significance instituted by mere human Attribution, but received by Consent of all the World, which Philosophers call *Jus Gentium*,[2] universal Right, in force in all Countries.

As you know well enough that all Peoples, all Nations and

---

[1] *Aristotle saith*, etc. (*Top.* v. 6; vii. 3): a very similar argument is also in Galen, *de temper.* i. 2.

[2] *Jus Gentium.* Cf. Justinian, *Inst.* i. 2: "quod vero naturalis ratio inter omnes homines constituit, id vocatur *jus gentium*, quasi quo jure omnes gentes utuntur". Also Cic. *de Off.* iii. § 23; Maine's *Ancient Law*, c. 3, pp. 46–50, with Pollock's notes. Cf. also Prof. Vinogradoff's lecture on Maine, *Law Quarterly Review*, vol. xx. No. 78, p. 122. Ulpian in ff. i. 1 f. 4: "Jus gentium est quo gentes humanae utuntur; quod a naturali recedere facile intellegere licet, quia illud omnibus animalibus, hoc solis hominibus inter se commune sit". Cf. also Arist. *Eth. Nic.* v. 7. 1, where *natural* and *conventional* law are distinguished.

Languages—I except the ancient Syracusans and some Argives[1]
who had cross-grained Souls—when wishing to shew their Sorrow
externally do wear a Black Garb, and all Mourning is done with
Black; which universal Consent does not take place without Nature
giving for it some Argument and Reason; which each Person can
at once understand by himself without being otherwise instructed
of any; and this we call the Law of Nature.

By the White, by the same natural Induction, all the world hath
understood Joy, Gladness, Solace, Pleasure and Delectation.

In times past the Thracians and Cretans[2] marked their Days that
were of good Fortune and joyous with white Stones, the sad and
unfortunate ones with black.

Is not the Night mournful,[3] sad and melancholy? It is black and
dark by the Privation of Light.[4] Doth not the Light rejoice[5] all
Nature throughout? It is whiter than anything that is. To prove
this I could refer you to the Book of Laurentius Valla[6] against
Bartolus;[7] but the Evangelical Testimony will content you. In

---

[1] "Quod fuit in more Syracusanis qui candido amictu relati... Timoleonem
extulere" (Plut. *Tim.* c. 39). "Argivi quoque in luctu albas vestes aqua ablutas
induunt", Alexander ab Alexandro, *Dies geniales*, iii. 7. Alexander was a
Neapolitan advocate born about 1460, who gave up his profession for polite
literature. His *Dies geniales*, which touch on many antiquarian points, were
edited by Tiraqueau.

[2] "Apud Cretenses observatum est ut albis lapillis laetos dies, lugubres nigris
calculis adnotarent. Item apud Thracas", Alex. ab Alex. iv. 20 (cf. Pliny, 7. 13;
Erasm. *Ad.* i. 5. 54).

[3] *Is not the Night mournful.* "Tristior idcirco nox est quam tempora Phoebi",
Ovid, *R.A.* 585.

[4] *dark by the Privation of Light.* δοκεῖ τὸ φῶς ἐναντίον εἶναι τῷ σκότει· ἔστι δὲ
τὸ σκότος στέρησις τῆς τοιαύτης ἕξεως ἐκ διαφανοῦς. Arist. *de anima*, ii. 7.
418b, 18. Cf. Milton, *P.R.* iv. 400: "Privation mere of light and absent day".

[5] *Light rejoice*, etc.: χαῖρε φίλον φῶς, Erasm. *Ad.* ii. 7. 30.

[6] *Laurentius Valla* (1406–57). The celebrated humanist translator of Herodotus, Thucydides and Homer for Pope Nicholas V. His chief works were *de
elegantiis Latini sermonis libri sex* and *de ficta donatione Constantini*. Cf. Villari,
N. Machiavelli, vol. i. introd. pp. 134–41. His tomb is in a chapel in the right
transept of the Lateran, where he had been made a canon by Nicholas V. Cf.
Sandys, *Haro. Lect.* pp. 136–8.

[7] The treatise of Bartolus (*P.* 10; v. 33), *de insigniis et armis* (Basil. Cratander,
1518), was assailed by Valla in a letter *ad Candidum Decembrium*: "Color aureus,
inquit Bartolus, est nobilissimus colorum, quod per eum figuratur lux....Paulo
post ait album esse nobilissimum colorum, nigrum abjectissimum, alios vero ita
quemque optimum ut est albo conjunctissimus". For an account of this, cf.
Mullinger, *Hist. Univ. Camb.* i. 419.

Matt. xvij. it is said that at the Transfiguration of our Lord, *vestimenta ejus facta sunt alba sicut lux,*[1] His Garments were made white as the Light; by which luminous Whiteness He gave His three Apostles to understand the Idea and Figure of the Joys eternal. For by the Light all men are cheered, according to the Saying which you have of an old Woman who had no Teeth in her Head, and still she said, *Bona lux.*[2] And Tobias, *cap. v.,* after he had lost his Sight, when Raphael saluted him, answered: "What Joy can I have that do not see the Light of Heaven?"[3] In such Colour did the Angels testify the Joy of the whole Universe at the Resurrection of the Saviour, *Ioan. xx.,* and at His Ascension, *Act. j.* With the like Vesture did Saint John the Evangelist, *Apocal. iiij.* and *vij.,* see the Faithful clad in the heavenly and beatified Jerusalem.[4]

Read the ancient Histories, Greek as well as Roman, and you will find that the Town of Alba, the first Pattern of Rome, was founded and so called after the Discovery of a white Sow.

You will find that, if it was decreed to any one, after he had gained a Victory over his Enemies, that he should enter Rome in triumphant State, he did so enter on a Chariot drawn by white Horses, as did also he who made an Entry in an Ovation,[5] for by no other Sign or Colour could they more surely express the Joy of their Coming than by white.

---

[1] *vestimenta...sicut lux,* Matt. xvii. 2. The Vulgate reads *nix.* Erasmus corrected it from the Greek τὸ φῶς.

[2] "Sed multo etiam suavius si quis animadvertat anus longo jam senio mortuas adeoque cadaverosas ut ab inferis rediisse videri possint (cf. Aristoph. *Eccl.* 1073) tamen illud semper in ore habere φῶς ἀγαθόν", Erasm. *Mor. Enc.* c. 31; "Graeci quoque cum lumen affertur solent dicere φῶς ἀγαθόν", Varro, *Lat. Ling.* vi. § 4. Cf. Eccles. xi. 7.

[3] *What Joy,* etc. This is not in our English translation, but in the Vulgate, verse 12: "Et ait Tobias: Quale gaudium mihi erit qui in tenebris sedeo et lumen caeli non video?" This chapter has twenty-eight verses in the Vulgate. It should be noted that the name of father and son is *Tobias,* not *Tobit. Quale gaudium,* etc. is one of the versicles on the Festival of the Archangel Raphael (Oct. 24).

[4] The four last texts may be found in the *Grand Concordance to the Bible* (Froben, 1523; Gryphius, 1535), s.v. *Albus* (*R.E.R.* viii. 279).

[5] According to Servius, *in Aen.* iv. 543, *ovatio* is a minor triumph and celebrated by a procession to the Capitol with one horse and a sacrifice of sheep. A *triumph* was with four white horses and a sacrifice of bulls.

You will find that Pericles, Duke of the Athenians,[1] ordered that Part of his Men-at-arms, unto whose Lot befell the white Beans, should pass the whole Day in Joy, Solace and Repose, while those of the other Part should fight. A thousand other Examples and Places could I set forth to this Purpose, but here is not the Place.

By means of this Intelligence you can resolve a Problem which Alexander of Aphrodisias[2] has accounted insoluble: "Why the Lion, who by his Cry and Roaring alone affrights all Animals, dreads and feareth only a white Cock?" For as Proclus[3] saith *lib. de Sacrificio et Magia* it is because the Presence of the Power of the Sun, who is the Instrument and Storehouse of all terrestrial and sidereal Light, doth more symbolise and agree with the white Cock (as well in regard of that Colour as of his Property and specific Order) than with the Lion. Further he said that Devils have often been seen in the Form of a Lion, which at the Presence of a white Cock have suddenly disappeared.

---

[1] *Pericles, Duke of the Athenians*, etc. This is recorded in Plut. *Pericl.* c. 27, but Rabelais derives it from Erasm. *Ad.* i. 5. 54 (*Creta notare*), which is devoted to matters in this chapter, and gives a translation of the passage from Plutarch. The title "Duke" is probably derived from Genesis, *e.g.* xxxvi. 5: "*duces filiorum Esau*". Theseus is styled *Duke* of Athens in Dante, *Inf.* xii. 17; Chaucer, *Knight's Tale*, l. 2 and Shakesp. *Mids. N. D.* Cf. Hodgkin, *Italy and her Invaders*, vi. 539–43, 573.

[2] *Alexander of Aphrodisias* in Caria, head of the Peripatetic School at Athens under Septimius Severus (A.D. 198–211), a distinguished follower and commentator of Aristotle. His surviving writings include *de fato, de anima, quaest. naturales* and others. The present problem appears in his *problemata medica et naturalia* (praef.): "Quaestiones quae inexplicabiles dixi hujuscemodi...unde fit ut leo gallum tantummodo extimescat" (trans. Theod. Gaza).

[3] *Proclus Diadochus* (A.D. 412–85), one of the most distinguished of the Neo-Platonists. Astronomical treatises and commentaries on Plato (*Tim., Rep.* and *Parm.*) by him are still extant. The passage here alluded to is as follows in the version of Ficinus: "Deinde et animalia sunt solaria multa, velut leones et galli, numinis cujusdam solaris pro sua natura participes; unde mirum est quantum inferiora in eodem ordine cedant superioribus, quamvis magnitudine potentiaque non cedant; hinc ferunt gallum timeri a leone quam plurimum et coli.... Nonnumquam etiam daemones visi sunt solares leonina fronte; quibus cum gallus objiceretur, repente disparuerunt", *lib. de sacrificio et magia.* Proclus says nothing about the cock being white; that is supplied by Agrippa, *de occulta philos.* iii. 33: "Hinc illud Procli: sicut leo timet gallum *praecipue album,* sic spiritus apparens in forma leonis objecto gallo subito disparuit". Rabelais recurs to this in iv. 62, and it is mentioned by Lucretius, iv. 710–17; Pliny, 8. 52, 10. 47; Plut. *de Inv. et Odio,* 537 C, *de Soll. An.* 981 E. Cf. also Shakesp. *Ham.* i. 1. 150–60; Sir T. Browne, *Pseud. Epid.* iii. 27. § 7.

That is the Reason why the Galli (that is, the French, who are so called, because they are naturally white as Milk,[1] which the Greeks call *Gala*) do willingly wear in their Caps white Feathers; for by Nature they are merry, candid, gracious and well disposed, and for their Symbol and Ensign they have the Flower that is whiter than any other, the Flower de luce.

If you ask how it is that by the Colour White Nature leads us to understand Joy and Gladness, I answer you that the Analogy and Conformity is thus. For, as White doth outwardly disperse and scatter the View, manifestly dissolving the Spirits visual, according to the Opinion of Aristotle in his Problems and in his Perspectives[2] —and you perceive it by Experience when you pass over Mountains covered with Snow, so that you complain that you cannot steadily look at them, as Xenophon records to have happened to his Men, and as Galen amply expoundeth *lib. x. De usu partium*[3]—just so the Heart by exceeding Joy is inwardly dilated, and suffereth manifest Resolution of the vital Spirits; which can be heightened to such a

---

[1] *Galli...white as Milk.* "Lactantii nostri verba ponamus: Galli antiquitus a candore corporis Galatae nuncupabantur...Quod significare voluit poeta cum ait: *Tum lactea colla Auro innectuntur*" (*Aen.* viii. 660) "cum posset dicere *candida*", Jerome, *in Galat. comment.* lib. ii *init.* Similarly Dante in *Conv.* iv. 22 says: "*Galilea è tanto a dire quanto bianchezza*". Thus he connects the word with γάλα, borrowing perhaps from Isidore (xiv. 3. § 23): "Galilaea regio Palaestinae vocata quod gignat candidiores homines quam Palaestina". Isidore also indicates the same source for Gallia (c. 4. § 25). Cf. Toynbee, *Dante Studies*, p. 285.

[2] *in his Problems and in his Perspectives* (*Probl.* xxxi. 20). Cf. Vincent de Beauvais, *Spec. Hist.* iii. 84: "Extat enim liber qui dicitur *Perspectiva* Aristotelis".

> "Il li convendroit prendre cure
> D'estre desciples Aristote
> Qui trop miex mist Nature en note
> Que nus hons puis le tens Caym.
> Alhacen li niés Hucaym,
> Qui ne refu ne fox ne gars,
> Cis fis le livre *des Regars*".   R.R. 18,965–71.

"They speken of Alocen and Vitulon
And Aristotle, that writen in hir lives
Of queynte mirours and *prospectives*".

Chaucer, *The Squire's Tale*, F. 232 and Skeat's note, vol. v. p. 494.

[3] "Bear in mind how much we are injured in our sight by resplendent and excessive brightness; for perhaps you do not know how much Xenophon's soldiers suffered as they marched through the deep snow", Galen, *de usu part.* x. 3.

Degree, that the Heart remains deprived of its Nourishment, and consequently Life is extinguished by this perichareia,[1] as Galen saith, *lib. xij. Method., lib. v. De locis affectis* and *lib. ij. De symptomaton causis*; and as is testified to have happened in former Times,[2] by Marcus Tullius *lib. i. Quaest. Tusc.*, Verrius, Aristotle, Titus Livius, after the Battle of Cannae, Pliny *lib. vij. c. xxxij.* and *liij.*, A. Gellius *lib. iij.* 15 and others to Diagoras of Rhodes, Chilo, Sophocles, Dionysius, Tyrant of Sicily, Philippides, Philemon, Polycrita, Philistion, M. Juventius and others who died of Joy. And as Avicenna saith *in ij. canone et lib. De viribus cordis*, of Saffron,[3] that it doth so rejoice the Heart that it robs it of Life, if it be taken in an excessive Dose, by superfluous Resolution and Dilatation. Here see Alexander Aphrodisiensis *lib. primo Problematum cap. xix.*,[4] and that for a Cause.

But what? I am going farther in this Matter than I proposed at the Beginning. Here then I will furl my Sails, referring the rest to the Book entirely devoted to this. Meanwhile I will say in a Word that Blue doth certainly signify Heaven and Things celestial, by the same Tokens that White signifieth Joy and Pleasure.

---

[1] *perichareia.* αἱ δ'ἐναντίαι τοῖς φόβοις ἡδοναὶ μέγισται, καλοῦσι δὲ ταύτας περιχαρείας. ἴσμεν δ' ἐξ ἀμφοῖν ἀποθανόντας τινας, Galen, *method. medendi*, xii. 5.

[2] *happened in former Times.* The ten instances given here are taken from the *Officina* of Ravisius Textor, who derives them from Pliny, 7. 180, Cic. *Tusc.* i. § 3, Aul. Gell. iii. 15, Lucian, Macrobius and Suidas. Cf. also Politian, *Sylvae* (*Nutricia*, l. 700):

> "Implicitusque sophron risuque Philistio tandem
> Perditus".

[3] *of Saffron.* "*De croco*...Confortat cor et est laetificationis causa...Dicitur quod tres aurei de ipso interficiunt laetificando", Avicenna, *Canon*, II. tract. ii. c. 126; "*Crocus*...inest ei proprietas vehemens in confortando cor et substantiam spiritus et laetificando....Multitudo vero comestionis ejus superfluae dilatat spiritum et movet ad extra ut...et sequatur mors", id. *de viribus cordis*, ii. 3.

[4] *Alexander Aphrodisiensis* (Theod. Gaza interpret.), *Problem.* i. 19: "Quamobrem qui laetitia exultant vehementer resolvuntur? Quoniam vitalis vis et insitus calor foras ad rem laetabilem immodice profluens dispalatur ac interit. Unde fit ut sudent et rubeant sanguinis adventu. Calorem etiam nativum ignemque ipsum ut per loci sui appetitionem sursum effecti, sic per alimenti desiderium ima petere necesse est. Igitur utralibet movendi ratione perempta, calor insitus interit et vis omnis vitalis evanescit".

CHAPTER XI

Of the youthful Age of Gargantua[1]

FROM three Years upwards unto five Gargantua was brought up and instructed in all convenient Discipline, by the Command of his Father; and he spent that Time like the other little Children of the Country; that is to wit, in drinking, eating and sleeping;[2] in eating, sleeping and drinking; in sleeping, drinking and eating.

He was ever wallowing in the Mire, slobbering his Nose, blurring his Face, treading his Shoes down at Heel, he did often gape after Flies and willingly ran after the Butterflies, over whom his Father held Sway.

He p—d in his Shoes and s—t in his Shirt, he wiped his Nose on his Sleeve and snivelled in his soup. And he paddled about everywhere and drank out of his Slipper,[3] and did ordinarily rub his Belly with a Basket.

v. 21 He would pick his Teeth with a wooden Shoe,
       wash his Hands in his Broth,
       comb his Head with a Bowl,
v. 45 sit down betwixt two Stools,[4] Rump on the Ground,
iv. 50 cover himself with a wet Sack,[5]

---

[1] The list of proverbs given here is derived from old sources such as Cordier, Coquillart, Cretin, Erasmi *Adagia*, etc., but was not included in this chapter till the edition of 1542 (D). They seem intended to exemplify the waywardness of a headstrong and spoilt child and to set forth a list or *blason*, such as was the delight of those times. Cf. iii. 26, 28, 38, etc. Other places in Rabelais where the proverbs are employed are indicated in the margin.

[2] *drinking, eating and sleeping.* Donatus on Terence quotes from Varro: "initiari pueros Eduliae et Poticae et Cubae, divis edendi et potandi et cubandi, ubi primum a lacte et cunis transferuntur". Politian, *Misc.* 89.

[3] *and drank*, etc. From here to "flayed the Fox" (p. 69) the proverbs quoted are not in A.

[4] *sit down betwixt two Stools*, etc. From here to "flayed the Fox" (p. 69) is an addition of D. Cf. Erasm. *Ad.* i. 7. 2: "duabus sedere sellis"; Cordier, 58, § 130; Seneca, *Controv.* vii. 3. § 9.

[5] "On dit proverb. et fig. *Se couvrir d'un sac moüillé*, pour dire *Apporter une meschante excuse*" (Dict. Acad. 1ère éd.); Joh. Aegid. *Ad.* Cf.

"Ceulx qui veulent narrer ce compte
Se couvrent bien d'un sac moillé".

Le songe doré de la Pucelle, A.P.F. iii. 225.

P. 12	drink while eating his Soup,
	eat his Cake without Bread,
iv. 32	bite laughing, and laugh biting,
P. 12; iv. *A.P.*	often spit in the Dish,[1]
v. 17	f—t with Fat,
	p— against the Sun,[2]
iv. 32	hide himself in the Water against the Rain,[3]
(*P.* 31)	strike the Iron when it was cold,[4]
	dream crooked,[5]
	give himself Airs and Graces,[6]
G. 22; iv. 44	flay the Fox,[7]
	say the Ape's *Paternoster*,[8]
	come back to his Sheep,
	turn the Sows out to Hay,[9]

---

[1] *spit in the Dish.* Cf.

> "A tels peu entendus qui portent chapperons
> Sans cracher au bassin à peine eschapperons".
>
> *Les Omonimes, A.P.F.* iii. 111.

> "Toutefois, si ilz ont *craché*
> Depuis peu de temps *au bassin*".
>
> Roger de Collerye (p. 9, ed. Elz.).

The meaning is to give through fear of public opinion. A gloss is given to 2 D. 23. 6. § ex his omnibus:

> "Da facie laeta: sine laetitia faciei
> Si dederis perdis rem meritumque rei".

[2] μηδ' ἀντ' ἠελίου τετραμμένος ὀρθὸς ὀμιχεῖν, Hes. *O.D.* 727. Cf. Pliny, 28. 69 and Erasm. *Ad.* i. 1. 20.

[3] "Cucurrit quispiam ne pluvia madesceret et in fovea suffocatus est", Erasm. *Ad.* iii. 3. 89.

[4] Cf. Cordier, 58. § 244 and Joh. Aegid.: "Il faut battre le fer pendant qu'il est chault".

[5] Cf. *Maistre Songecreux, P.* 7; *G.* 20; iii. 13. "*Hic somniat,* cest homme songe creux", Cordier, 11. § 27.

[6] *give himself Airs.* Fr. *faisoyt le succré.* Cf. Coquillart, *Mon. du puits,* ii. 255: "Ne faictes point tant la succrée". (Fr. ed.)

[7] "*Il a escorché le renart,* evomuit crapulam", Cordier, 58. § 266.

[8] *say the Ape's* Paternoster, *i.e.* mutter and mumble to himself as Apes do.

[9] "*Il tourne la truye au foin,* quand je luy parle d'ung, il me repond de l'aultre", Cordier, 51. § 12.

beat the Dog before the Lion,[1]
put the Cart before the Oxen,[2]
P.P. 5   scratch himself where he did not itch,[3]
iv. 63; v. 27   draw the Worms from men's Noses,[4]
G. 46   grasp at too much and hold fast little,[5]
eat his white bread first,[6]
P. 11   shoe the Grasshoppers,[7]
iv. 63   tickle himself to make himself laugh,
iv. 10   revel thoroughly in the Kitchen,[8]
offer Straw to the Gods for Corn,[9]

---

[1] *beat the Dog before* (= *in the presence of*) *the Lion*, *i.e.* flog the whipping-boy. "Sir Mungo Malagrowther had been whipping-boy to James VI", Scott, *Fortunes of Nigel*, c. 6.

> "Aucune foiz est que le hon
> Bat le chien devant le lyon;
> Bel doctrine met en luy
> Qui se chastoye par autruy".

Prov. ruraux, saec. xiii. *Prov. Franç.* ii. p. 243.

"As by the whelp chasted is the leoun."
Chaucer, *The Squire's Tale*, F. 491 (cf. Skeat, vol. v. p. 354).

> "Va, Lyon, que Dieu te gouverne.
> Assez longtemps s'est esbatu
> Le petit chien en ta caverne
> Que devant toi on a batu."

Cl. Marot, *Epist.* 49 (*Adieu à la ville de Lyon*).
"Even so one would beat his offenceless dog to affright an imperious lion."
Shakesp. *Oth.* ii. 3. 292.

[2] Erasm. *Ad.* i. 7. 28: "Currus bovem trahit"; Lucian, *Mort. dial.* c. 6: ἡ ἅμαξα τὸν βοῦν; Cordier, 58. § 137: "La charette va devant les bœufs. Tout va à rebours"; Joh. Aegid. *Ad.*: "Fol est de mettre la charrue devant les bœufs".

[3] Dante, *Par.* xvii. 129: "E lascia pur grattar dov' è la rogna".

[4] "Josephe recite qu'il *tira le ver du nez* à un certain ambassadeur, que les ennemis luy avaient envoyé, l'ayant faict *boire d'autant*", Montaigne, ii. 2 *sub init.* Cf. Hor. *A.P.* 434. Cf. also iii. 51 on Bonosus and iv. 63.

[5] "Tant embrasse-t-on que chet la prise", Villon, *Ballade des Prov.*; "Qui trop embrasse mal estraint", Coquillart, i. 196; Joh. Aegid. and often elsewhere. "In proverbio dicitur: Qui nimis capit, parum stringit", Albertanus Brixiensis, *lib. cons.* c. 27.

[6] "Car j'ay mangé mon pain blanc le premier", Cretin, p. 194.

[7] *I.e.* to spend one's time unprofitably.

[8] "Et n'estoit bruit de ruer en cuisine", Cl. Marot, *Rond.* 63 (Vict. Brodeau).

[9] "Faisant souvent à Dieu barbe de paille", *La Boutique des Usuriers* (*A.P.F.* ii. 178); "Il ne fault poinct faire barbe de foärre à Dieu comme on dict",

	have *Magnificat* sung at Matins and find it in season,[1]
(iv. 7)	eat Cabbages and s— Beet,
P. 12; iii. 22	know Flies in Milk,[2]
	pull the Legs off Flies,
G. 5	scratch out a Writ on Paper,
G. 44; iv. 32	blot the Parchment,
	get off by his Heels,[3]
P. 20, 28	pull at the Kid's Leather,[4]
P. 26	reckon without his Host,[5]
	beat the Bushes without taking the Birds,[6]
v. 22	believe that Clouds were brass Frying-pans and that Bladders were Lanterns,[7]

Montaigne, ii. 12 *ad init.* Pasquier (*Recherches*, viii. 62) explains in this way that hypocrites instead of offering a *gerbe* or *garbe* (a sheaf of corn) offered a *barbe de paille*, or a truss of straw from which the corn had been threshed.

[1] "Tantum ad propositum sicut Magnificat in matutinis", Cordier, 58. § 70.

[2] "Je congnois bien mousches en laict", Villon, *Ballade des menus propos*.

[3] "Il a *gaigné au pied*, dedit se in pedes quantum potuit", Cordier, 25. § 24; "Volam pedis ostendere", Erasm. *Ad.* iv. 10. 56.

[4] " *Tirez au chevrotin* (trahe ad chevrotinum), tirez à la bourse", Cordier, 58. § 73. (Here = drink to excess. Cf. *R.E.R.* vii. 198.)

[5] "Qui sans son hoste compte deux fois compte", Joh. Aegid.; "Absque tabernario ratio disponitur ergo?" Merl. Coc. *Baldus*, iv. 81.

> "Found in few minutes to his cost
> He did but count without his host."   *Hudibras*, i. 3. 21.

[6]

> "Que le simple batte le buisson
> Et ung aultre en ayt les oiseaux."
>
>   Coquillart, *Plaidoyer*, ii. 25.

> "A batre buissons je m'amuse."
>
>   *Le Varlet à louer*, *A.P.F.* i. 87.

> "Vous battez les buissons
> Dont ung aultre a les oisillons."   Joh. Aegid. *Ad.*

The Duke of Bedford at the siege of Orléans (1428–9) refused to accept the surrender on terms, with the expression: "We will not beat the bush and not take the birds".

[7]   "*Laterna ex vesica.*

> Cornea si non sum num quid sum fuscior? Aut me
> Vesicam contra qui venit esse putet?"
>
>   Martial, xiv. 62.

> "Me voulez-vous faire entendant
> De vessies que sont lanternes?"   Patelin, l. 802.

"Me veulx tu faire croire de vescies que ce sont lanternes?" Joh. Aegid. *Ad.*

> "Et rend *vessies pour lanternes,*
> Du ciel une poisle d'airain."   Villon, *Test.* 57–8.

take two Grists from one Sack[1]
play the Ass to get Bran,[2]

iv. 32   use his Fist for a Mallet,[3]

iii. 31   take the Cranes at the first Start,[4]

iii. 42   have Coats of Mail made Link by Link,[5]
always look a gift Horse in the Mouth,[6]
leap from the Cock to the Ass,[7]
put one ripe between two green,[8]

(iii. 3)   make a Ditch of his Land,[9]

---

[1] "En avoir d'ung sac moulture double", Cretin, p. 266; "To take multure twice from the same meal-sack", Scott, *Monastery*, c. ult. *sub fin.*

[2]   "Fay du badin, du fol ou bien de l'yvre
            Qui ne sçait comme en ce monde fault vivre,
            Contrefaisant un peu l'asne qui raille."
                              La Boutique des Usuriers, A.P.F. ii. 178.

[3] "Fol est qui de son poing fait coing", *Proverbe*. Glaucus, a Carystian boxer, is said as a boy to have *used his fist instead of a hammer* in fixing a ploughshare (Paus. vi. 10. 1; Philostr. *Gymn.* 20).

[4]   "Et cuide (Jonesce) prendre au ciel la grue
            Quand il se met ilec en mue."   *R.R.* 5168.

Cf. "supra volat ardea nubem", Virg. *G.* i. 364.

[5]   "Plusieurs raisins procedent d'un bourjon
            Et maille à maille faict-on le hauberjeon." Cretin, p. 232.

[6]   "A cheval donné
            On ne doibt pas la gueulle ouvrir."
                              Coquillart, 1. 80; Joh. Aegid. *Ad.*

Cf. also "Quadrupedis dentes donati cernere noli", gloss to Clem. iii. 12. 2; "Equi dentes inspicere donati", Erasm. *Ad.* iv. 5. 24, from St Jerome's *pref. in Ephes.*; also *Hudibras*, i. 1. 490.

[7] "Tu saultes du coq à l'asne, *de calcaria in carbonariam*", Cordier, 58. § 103; Politian, *Praefatio "Miscellaneorum"*.

            "From grave to gay, from lively to severe."
                              Pope, *Essay on Man*, iv. 380.

[8] "Entre deux vertes une meure." Coquillart, *Plaidoyer*, ii. 21; Joh. Aegid.

            "Duro con duro
            Non fai mai buon muro."
                              Prov. ap. Dennis C. of Etr. ix. 135.

            "D'entre deux meures une verte
            Vous fault servir."   Ch. d'Orléans, *Rond.* 91.

            "Et se, pour verte on vous rend une meure." *A.P.F.* iv. 163.

"Durum et durum non faciunt murum", Burton, *Anat.* ii. 3. 7.

[9] "Il a destoupé ung trou pour boucher l'aultre, *Versuram facit*", Cordier, 58. § 34.

P.P. 7; v. 22   keep the Moon from the Wolves.[1]

iv. 17   If the Skies fell he would hope to take Larks,[2]

v. 20   make a Virtue of Necessity,[3]

          have Soup to match his Bread,[4]

iv. 32   care as little for the Shaven as the Shorn.

Every morning he flayed the Fox; his Father's little Dogs ate out of his Dish, and he likewise ate with them. He bit their Ears, they scratched his Nose; he would blow on their Rump and they would lick his Chaps.

And what think ye, my Honies? Listen, or may the Cask-fever spin ye giddy![5] This little Lecher was always groping his Governesses topsy-turvy, backwards and forwards, "Gee up, Neddy" (*harri bourriquet*);[6] and he already began to use his Cod-piece. This his Governesses[7] did every day deck with fair Nosegays, fine Ribbons, sweet Flowers and pretty silken Tufts, and would pass their Time

---

[1] "Luna tuta a lupis." This proverb must refer to the baying of wolves and dogs at the moon. Cf. "And the wolf behowls the moon", Shakesp. *Mids. N. Dr.* v. 1. 379; "I had rather be a dog and bay the moon", *J. Caesar*, iv. 3. 27.

[2] "Si caelum rueret multae caperentur alaudae."

[3] *make a Virtue of Necessity* (v. 20). "Force est que tu faces de necessité vertu", *C.N.N.* 36; *R.R.* 14,960. The proverb seems to be derived from Herodotus, vi. 140: ʽΕρμώνιος χάρις. Hermon, King of Hephaestia in Lemnos, finding that the Athenians under Miltiades had reduced the other town Myrina, gave himself up "from good-will to the Athenians". Cf. Rawlinson's note and Erasm. *Ad.* ii. 6. 50: "Hermonium officium".

[4] "On vous fera de tel pain soupe, *ab alio expectes alteri quod feceris*", Cordier, 58. § 197; Cretin, p. 201; Joh. Aegid.

> "Puisque vous m'avez faite coupe
> Je vous ferai d'autel pain soupe."   *R.R.* 15,163.

[5] This is written in Gascon (cf. *G.* prol. *fin.*; iii. 42): "Et sabez quey, hillotz? Que mau de pipe bous byre".

[6] *harri bourriquet.* A cry in Languedoc and elsewhere to make asses mend their pace. A *noel* is preserved in *A.P.F.* vii. 46, of which the refrain is "Hari, hari l'asne! Harri bourriquet!" Cf. Merl. Coc. *Baldus*, vii. 138: "Non qui substigans asinos pronuntiat: arri!"

> "*O utinam* gliscit, sed *io* festinat et *arri*."
>   Eberhard, *Graec.* 24. 46.

[7] Cf.   "Sovent voi veis norrices,
> Dont maintes sont baudes et nices,
> Quant lor enfant lavent et baignent,
> Qu'elles les desbaisent et aplaignent,
> Si les nomment-el autrement."   *R.R.* 7680–4.

in making it thrive in their Hands like a Cylinder of Salve.[1] Then they would burst out laughing when it lifted its Ears, as if the Sport had pleased them.

One called it my Pillicock, another my Nine-pin, another my Branch of Coral, another my Stopple, my Cork, my Nimble-wimble, my Ram-rod, my Auger, my Dingle-dangle, my Steady go stiff-and-low, my Crimping iron, my little ruddy Sausage, my little dainty Cod.

"It belongs to me," said one.

"'Tis mine," said another.

"What," quoth a third, "shall I have no Share in it? By my Faith then, I will cut it off."

"What!" said another, "cut it off! You would do it hurt, Madam; is it your way to cut off Children's Things? Why, he would be Master Bob."

And that he might disport himself like the little Children of the Country, they made him a pretty Whirligig[2] of the Wings of a Myrebalais Windmill.

---

[1] Fr. *magdaleon d'entraict*. Cf. Gk. ἀπομαγδαλία. Paré, xxv. c. 27; Sir T. Browne, *Pseud. Epid.* ii. 5. § 5.

[2] *Whirligig*. Fr. *virolet*. This plaything was made by piercing a walnut shell on both sides to allow a stick to pass through, and also by piercing another hole horizontally to allow a piece of string to wind round the stick, at the bottom of which were fastened two small flat pieces of wood cross-wise, to represent the sails of a windmill. These were made to revolve fast by pulling out the string, which was wound up again by the whirling of the sails. Cf. iv. 63 (*R.E.R.* ii. 228).

CHAPTER XII

Of Gargantua's Hobby-horses[1]

AFTERWARDS, to the end that all his Life he should be a good Rider, there was made for him a fine great wooden Horse, which he made to prance, leap, curvet, fling out and rear all at a time; to pace, trot, rack, gallop, amble, go the Pace of a Hobby, a Hackney, a Camel, or a wild Ass. And he had the Colour of its Hair changed as the Monks do their Dalmatics[2] according to the Festivals; bay, sorrel, dapple-grey, mouse-dun, deer-colour, roan, cow-colour, zebra, skew-bald, piebald, white.

He himself with a huge Post made a Hunting-nag, and another for every-day Use out of a Beam of a Wine-press; and out of a great Oak he made a Mule with its Housings for his Chamber. Moreover, he had ten or twelve for a Relay, and seven Horses for the Post. And he put them all up in their Stall close by himself.

One day the Lord of Bread-in-bag[3] came to visit Gargantua's Father with a great Retinue and Pomp; on which Day likewise were come to see him the Duke of Freemeal and the Earl of Wet-gullet. In truth the House was somewhat small for so many People,

---

[1] This chapter is perhaps intended as a parody of the episode of the entertainment of the ambassadors of the King of Persia by Alexander when Philip was away (Plut. *Alex.* c. 5, 666E–F). In the same chapter Plutarch proceeds to speak of the preceptors of Alexander and in the next chapter (c. 6) recounts his cleverness in taming the wild horse, which Rabelais quotes in *G.* 14.

[2] Fr. *courtibaux* (Lat. *curtum tibiale*), a sort of tunic or dalmatic coming just below the knees. "*Curcinbaldus, cortiballus*, aut *cortibandus*. Tunica brevior est, seu Dalmatica, quam gestebant Diaconi caeterique ministri inferiores" (Ducange). Cf. *courtepy*, Chaucer, *C.T.* (A. 290). *Dalmaticatus* occurs in Lamprid. *Commodus*, 8, *Heliog.* 26. The Dalmatic was a long frock of white Dalmatian wool reaching as low as the feet, with purple stripes down the front and loose sleeves. It was not worn till the late Empire, and was adopted by the Roman Church under the early popes (Rich. *Dict. Ant.*).

[3] *Bread-in-bag* (Fr. *Painensac*), probably from the pseudo-Villon's *Penessac*, in the third of the *Repeues Franches*, or "Free meals", which are probably represented here by *Franc repas*. The seven *Repeues franches*, attributed to Villon, are humorous poems describing methods of cheating innkeepers and others of meals, pursued by poor scholars.

and especially the Stables; whereupon the Steward and Harbinger[1] of the said Lord of Bread-in-bag, in order to know if elsewhere in the House there were empty Stables, applied to Gargantua then a young Lad, asking him secretly where were the Stables of the great Horses,[2] with the notion that Children[3] readily discover everything.

Upon this he led them by the great Staircase of the Castle, passing through the second Hall into a large Gallery, by which they entered into a great Tower; and as they were going up by another pair of Stairs, the Harbinger said to the Steward:

"This Child is deceiving us, for the Stables are never at the Top of the House."

"That is a Mistake on your Part," says the Steward; "for I know Places at Lyons,[4] la Basmette,[5] at Chaisnon[6] and elsewhere, in which the Stables are at the very Tops of the Houses; so it may be that behind the House there is an Outlet to the Mounting-stone. But I will ask him more exactly."

Then he asked Gargantua: "My pretty little Boy, whither are you leading us?"

---

[1] *Harbinger* (Fr. *fourrier*, *C.N.N.* 87), the officer who preceded a great personage to look out for his accommodation. Properly *herbergeour*, from Fr. *herberge*.

[2] *the great Horses* mean the heavy chargers of the knights. Cf. v. 7; Burton's *Anat.* ii. 2. 4.

[3] Cf. *C.N.N.* 23 *fin.*: "Car il se souvint que folz, yvres et enfans ont de coustume de vray dire".

> "And make the infant stars confess,
> Like fools and children, what they please."
>
> *Hudibras*, ii. 3. 931.

[4] *Lyons*. The reference is to houses built on the side of the hill of Fourvières on the right bank of the Saône. From the street Saint-George are alleys in flights of steps which serve two or three houses placed above (*R.E.R.* vi. 214).

[5] *la Basmette*, a Franciscan convent just south of Angers built by René d'Anjou, King of Sicily, on the model of Sainte-Baume in Provence. It was here that Rabelais, Geoffroi d'Estissac and Jean du Bellay, afterwards Bishop of Paris and Cardinal, foregathered. Rabelais left la Basmette for Fontenay-le-Comte. Cf. *R.E.R.* iii. 62.

[6] *Chaisnon* (*P.* 9; iv. N.P. 20; v. 19, 35). This form of the name *Chinon* is taken from *Caïno* of Gregory of Tours, lib. v. 17. In v. 35 Rabelais recurs to this, suggesting that the town was founded by Cain, "the first builder of cities" (Gen. iv. 17). "In the Rue du Puy-des Bancs (at Chinon), the chief approach to the Château, are several caverns in the rock, still used as dwellings" (Bädeker's *Northern France*, p. 259, ed. 1889). Cf. *R.E.R.* iii. 57; v. 60.

"To the Stable", said he, "of my great Horses. We shall be there directly; only let us climb these Stairs."

Then taking them through another large Hall, he led them to his Chamber, and opening the Door: "See here", said he, "are the Stables which you are asking for; there is my Gennet, there is my Gelding, my Courser,[1] my Hackney"; and loading them with a great Lever, he said, "I make you a Present of this Friesland Horse; I had him from Frankfort, but he shall be yours; he is a pretty little Nag with great staying Power: with a tassel Goshawk, half-a-dozen Spaniels and a brace of Greyhounds, there you are King of the Partridges and Hares for all this Winter".

"By Saint John," said they, "we are rarely taken in; this time we have the Monk."[2]

"I say nay to you for that", said he. "He has not been here the last three Days." Now judge which they had most Cause to do, to hide themselves for Shame or to laugh at the Pastime.

As they were thus coming down again quite confused, he asked them, "Would you like a Whim-wham?"[3]

"What is that?" said they.

"It is", answered he, "five T—ds to make you a Muzzle."

"For this Day present", said the Steward, "if we are roasted, we shall never burn at the Fire, for we have been larded to a Turn, to my way of thinking. O my little Dapper one, thou hast given us 'Hay on the Horn';[4] I shall see thee Pope some day."

"So I understand it," said he; "but then you shall be a Puppy (butterfly), and this gentle Popinjay shall be a Popeling[5] ready made."

---

[1] *Courser* (Fr. *Lavedan*, v. 30). Lavedan is a district somewhat south of Pau in the Pyrenees, not very far from Cauterets, celebrated for its breed of riding-horses. Cf. *Heptaméron* (preface): "L'Abbé les fournit des meilleurs chevaux qui fussent en Lavedan".

[2] *avoir (donner) le moine* (G. 43, 45; iv. 16) are proverbial expressions, indicating something to one's heart, either inflicted or suffered; to be explained by the schoolboy trick of "toe-ing" a comrade. Possibly *moine* in this case = *cordelier*.

[3] Fr. *aubeliere*. Cf. *R.E.R.* vii. 232: from *aubelier* = *aubier*, white poplar.

[4] Horace's "faenum habet in cornu", *Sat.* i. 4. 34. According to Plutarch, *Quaest. Rom.* c. 71. 280F, first used of M. Crassus Dives, from whom Julius Caesar was said to have removed the hay. Cf. also Erasm. *Ad.* i. 1. 81. Perhaps it means "furnished with wisps of hay" like cattle that are for sale. (Fr. ed.)

[5] *Popeling.* Fr. *papelard* (P. 29), translated by Chaucer, *Romaunt of the Rose*, l. 415, etc., "pope-holy" = hypocritical.

"Verily, verily", said the Harbinger.

"But", said Gargantua, "guess how many Stitches there are in my Mother's Smock."

"Sixteen", quoth the Harbinger.

"You do not speak Gospel," saith Gargantua; "there are *centum* before and *centum* behind, and you counted them quite wrong."

"When?" said the Harbinger.

"Even then," quoth he, "when they made of your Nose a Tap[1] to draw off a Measure of Dung, and a Funnel of your Throat to put it into another Vessel because the Bottom of the old one was out."

"Copsbody," said the Steward, "we have found a Prater. Farewell, master Tatler, God keep you from Harm, who have your Mouth so ready."

So, as they were going down in great Haste, under the Arch of the Stairs they let fall the great Lever which Gargantua had laden them with, whereupon he said: "What devilish bad Horsemen ye are! Your Cob fails you at Need. If you had to go from here to Cahusac,[2] whether had you rather ride on a Gosling or lead a Sow in a Leash?"

"I would like rather to drink", said the Harbinger.

Saying this they entered into the lower Hall where all the Company was, and relating to them this new Story they made them laugh like a Swarm of Flies.[3]

---

[1] *your Nose a Tap.* Cf. Erasm. *Colloq.* (*de sacerd. captand.*): *Cocl.* "Deinde si quid hauriendum erit e cavo profundiore, fuerit [nasus] loco promuscidis" (p. 25, ed. Elz.).

[2] *Cahusac.* The Cahusac in Guyenne about 40 miles north-west of Toulouse, where was the estate of Louis d'Estissac, kinsman of Rabelais' patron, the Bishop of Maillezais. It is mentioned in this connexion in iv. 52. Cf. also *Ep. de Bouchet* and *Epp. Rom.* iii. § 12. (Cf. *R.E.R.* vii. 387, 400.)

[3] *a Swarm of Flies* seems to refer to the passage in Homer (*Il.* i. 599) where the gods laugh at Vulcan limping. Cf. iv. N.P. It has been explained as a proverbial Picard expression:

"Pi ches mouques su le palissate
Qu'i se teurdraient de rire".   *R.E.R.* v. 153.

CHAPTER XIII

How Grandgousier discovered Gargantua's marvellous Under-standing by his Invention of a Breech-wipe (Torchecul)[1]

ABOUT the End of the fifth Year, Grandgousier returning from the Conquest of the Canarians[2] paid a visit to his Son Gargantua. There he was rejoiced as such a Father might well be at the Sight of such a Son. And as he kissed and embraced him he asked him a number of little childish Questions on diverse Matters. And he drank Toasts with him and with his Governesses, of whom he asked

---

[1] This objectionable chapter was no doubt eagerly read by personages of distinction both in Church and State at the time it was written. Plain speaking is vigorously defended by Raison in *Le Roman de la Rose*, 7688 *sqq.* and by Milton, *Apol. for Smect.* § 1 on biblical grounds. Montaigne puts in a defence in a similar case: "Il fault laisser aux femmes cette vaine superstition des paroles". Cf. also Quintilian, viii. 3, 38. On the other side cf. Cope's Arist. *Rhet.* iii. 2. § 13; *Pol.* iv. 17. 1336 b. By buffooneries and obscenities of this kind Rabelais attracted readers and perhaps gained protection.

> "Covering discretion with a coat of folly;
> As gardeners do with ordure hide those roots
> Which first shall spring and be most delicate."
> Shakesp. *Hen. V*, ii. 4. 38.

They afforded, however, a handle for the theologians who wished to persecute him. He more than hints (iii. prol.) that these portions of his writings were most to the taste of his enemies. The third *Repeue franche* among the poems attributed to Villon is headed *Des torcheculz*. The rhymed parts of the chapter are borrowed or parodied from Marot. Shakespeare strikes the right note on this subject:

> "'Tis needful that the most immodest word
> Be look'd upon and learn'd; which once attain'd
> Your highness knows comes to no further use
> But to be known and hated". 2 *Hen. IV*, iv. 4. 70.

[2] *Canarians* (cf. *P.* 23), one of several allusions to the conquest of the Canaries by Jean de Béthencourt. They were the *Fortunatae Insulae* of Pliny (6. 204–5) and the geographers he quotes. They were west of Mauretania, and consisted of Ombrion, which was uninhabited, Junonia, Capraria, Ninguaria, with perpetual snow (*Teneriffe*), and Canaria, so called from its breed of large dogs. They all abound in fruit and birds of all kinds, and Canaria has abundance of pineapples. M. Lefranc (*R.E.R.* vi. 269) suggests that *retournant de la defaicte des Canariens* refers to the return of Charles VIII from Italy in 1495 or of Louis XII in 1509. (Cf. also *R.E.R.* vii. 249.)

with great Solicitude among other matters whether they had kept him clean and neat. To this Gargantua made answer that he had given such order to it that in all the Country there was not a Boy cleanlier than he was.

"How is that?" said Grandgousier.

"I have", answered Gargantua, "by long and curious Experience invented a Means to wipe my Breech, the most lordly, the most excellent, the most convenient that ever was seen."

"What Means?" said Grandgousier.

"It is as I will relate to you at once", said Gargantua.

"One time I wiped myself with a Gentlewoman's velvet Mask[1] and found it good; for the Softness of the Silk caused an exceeding great Pleasure to my Fundament;

"Another time with one of their Hoods and it was with the same result.

"Another time with a Neck-kerchief, another time with Ear-pieces[2] of crimson Satin; but a lot of mucky golden Spangles that were there flayed my Behind all over; may St Anthony's Fire burn up the Bum-gut of the Goldsmith who made them and of the Lady who wore them.

"This Hurt I cured by wiping myself with a Page's Cap well be-feathered in the Swiss fashion.

"Afterwards, as I was dunging behind a Bush, I found a March-cat[3] and with this I wiped me, but his claws ulcerated all my Perinaeum.

"Of this I healed myself next day by wiping myself with my Mother's Gloves which were well-scented with Benzoin.[4]

"Then I used Sage, Fennel, Dill, Marjoram, Roses, Gourd-leaves,

---

[1] Fr. *cachelet* (v. 27): cachelaid, a sort of mask willingly worn by ugly women.

[2] Fr. *aureillettes*. Cf. Pierre Grosnet, *Les mots dorés de Caton*:

> "Vos *aureillettes* de velours,
> Vos grands manches, aultres atours,
> Et grands queues trainant par terre
> En enfer vous feront grand guerre".

They were pendants to the *chaperon*, worn by ladies in France in the sixteenth century, sometimes with, sometimes without gold spangles.

[3] *March-cat* (iv. 32), *i.e.* one kittened in March, which was supposed to be the most vigorous.

[4] Fr. *maujoin* (P. 30; iii. 36, 46), used as a pun on *benjoin*.

Cabbages, Beet-root leaves, Vine-leaves, Mallows, Mullein[1] (which is Tail-scarlet), Lettuces and Spinach-leaves. (All this did great Good to my Leg.) Then with Dog's Mercury,[2] Persicaria,[3] Nettles, Comfrey.[4] But from this I got the Dysentery of Lombardy. Then I was cured by wiping myself with my Cod-piece.

"Then I wiped myself in my Sheets, in my Coverlit, in the Curtains, with a Cushion, with Hangings, with green Baize,[5] with a Napkin, with a Hand-kerchief, with a Combing-Cloth (Dressinggown). In all this I found pleasure more than do mangy Horses when they are curry-combed."

"Yea, but", said Grandgousier, "which Wipe didst thou find the best?"

"I was coming to that," said Gargantua, "and you shall soon know the *tu autem*[6] of it. I wiped myself with Hay, with Straw, with Litter, with Cow-hair, with Wool, with Paper; but

> He that with Paper his foul Tail doth wipe
> Leaves ever on his Cods a dirty stripe".

"What!" said Grandgousier, "my little Codkin, hast thou burnt to[7] that thou dost rime already?"

"Yea verily, my Lord the King," answered Gargantua, "I rime to any amount; and in riming often enrheum myself.[8] Listen to what our 'Retreat' says to the Dungers:

---

[1] Fr. *verbasce*, mullein, *Verbascum Thapsus* L., the great mullein which has leaves 6 or 8 inches long. Pliny, 25. 120; Galen, *de simpl. med.* viii. 20. 5.

[2] Fr. *mercuriale*, a plant of the family Euphorbiaceae.

[3] Fr. *persiguiere* (*Polygonum Orientale, Polygonum persicaria*).

[4] Fr. *consolde*. ? Lat. *condurdum*. Pliny, 26. 26.

[5] Fr. *verd*. Lat. *viride* (Ducange).

[6] *tu autem* (P. 11; P.P. prol.) = the whole from beginning to end. When the prior in a convent wished to indicate to the reader that the lesson during a meal was to stop, he rapped the table and uttered the words: "*Tu autem* Domine miserere nobis". Cf. *Le Moyen de Parvenir*, c. 60. The same form of words is used at the end of each of the short lessons at Prime. "Nous en dit tout le tu autem", Coquillart, *Enquête*, ii. 136.

[7] Fr. *prins au pot*. In Saintonge and Languedoc the word *rimer* is used to express "burn to" (*prendre au pot*), of milk, etc. in boiling or stewing.

[8] Fr. *m'enrime* (= take cold), used with a pun on *rhume* and *rime* (cf. v. 47), probably borrowed from Cl. Marot, *Epistre au Roy* (vii):

> "En m'esbatant je fais rondeaulx en rithme,
> Et en rithmant bien souvent je m'enrime."

Cf. also: "Las d'estre debout, je m'assied,

                    Sh—ard,
                    Squittard,
                    Crackard,
                       Turdous,
                    Thy Lard
                    Off guard
                    Has tarred
                       All us.
                    Filthard,
                    Cackard,
                    Drenchard,
        Be by St Anthony's Fire burnt and charr'd,
                       If thus
                    Thy truss
                    Porous
        Thou clearest not ere thou from here depart.

Would you like some more of it?"
    "Yea verily", said Grandgousier.
    "Then", said Gargantua:

                    Rondeau
            A—s—g I smelt t'other day
            Earth's Tribute I paid—but a mite;
            The Odour I thought was not right,
            Wherewith I was reeking away.
            O had there but come a kind Fay
            To bring her I wished to my Sight
                    A—s—g.
            For I would in my homely rough Play
            Have closed up her Water-way tight;
            Meantime with her Fingers she might
            Have guarded my Breech from its Spray,
                    A—s—g.

    "Now say that I know nothing therein. By'r Lady,[1] they be
none of my making; but hearing them recited by the great Lady
you see there I have retained them in the Budget of my Memory."
    Said Grandgousier, "Let us return to our Subject".

            Pour composer en prose ou rime
            Où le plus souvent je m'enrime
            Si je n'ay un peu vin humé".
                            Le Varlet à tout faire, A.P.F. i. 85.
    [1] Fr. *par la merdé* (G. 25, 35). It is the equivalent of *m'armes* and *merdigues* (iv
N.P. *briefve decl.*) and suggested no doubt by the subject-matter of this chapter
(Duchat). ? = *merci Dieu.*

"Which?" said Gargantua, "Skiting?"

"No", said Grandgousier, "but wiping."

"But", said Gargantua, "will you pay a Puncheon of Breton Wine if I gravel[1] you in this Matter?"

"Yes, indeed", said Grandgousier.

"There is no Need", said Gargantua, "to wipe one's Tail unless Ordure be there. Ordure there cannot be, unless one hath skited. Therefore we must skite before we wipe our Tail."

"Oh!" said Grandgousier, "what good Sense thou hast, my Laddikin. The first day I can I will have thee passed Doctor in gay science;* for (perdy!) thou hast more Wit than Age.

"Prithee go on with this breech-wiping Discourse: by my Beard; instead of a Puncheon thou shalt have sixty Pipes, I mean of this good Breton Wine which grows, not in Brittany, but in this good Land of Verron."[2]

"Afterwards", said Gargantua, "I wiped myself with a Kerchief, with a Pillow, with a Slipper, with a Pouch, with a Pannier; but oh dear! it *was* an unpleasant Wipe.

"Then I used a Hat. And note that Hats are some shorn, others hairy, some velveted, some covered with Taffeta, some with Satin. The best of these is that covered with Hair; for it maketh a very neat Abstersion of faecal Matter.

"Then I wiped myself with a Hen, with a Cock, with a Pullet, with a Calf's skin, with a Hare, with a Pigeon, with a Cormorant, with a Lawyer's Bag, with a Montero,[3] with a Coif, with a Falconer's Lure.

"But in conclusion I say and maintain that there is no such Tailwipe as a Gosling that is well covered with Down, provided

---

* *en Sorbone*, ABC.

[1] Fr. *fais quinault* (*P.* 10, 18, 19).

[2] *Verron* (iv. *A.P.*) is the name of the tongue of land formed by the confluence of the Loire and the Vienne near Chinon. The *vin breton* of this country, so called because it was *bought* by the Bretons, was renowned as good, while the wine of Brittany was a poor sour drink. Cf. iii. 45; iv. 15. *Quinquenois*, which according to Rabelais produced good wine, is in Verron. Cf. iv. 14, 15. Verron comprised the communes of Avoine, Beaumont, Saint-Louans and Savigny (*R.E.R.* v. 81). *Vin gros cabernet* or *breton* is still cultivated in Touraine. It is a red wine of deep colour and much body (*R.E.R.* vii. 100).

[3] Fr. *barbute* (*P.* 7; iv. 31, 52).

you hold it with its Head between your Legs. For you feel in your Nockhole a mirific Pleasure, both by reason of the Softness of the aforesaid Down and also from the temperate Heat of the Gosling, which is easily communicated to the Rectum and the other Intestines until it reaches the Region of the Heart and the Brain.

"And think not that the Beatitude of the Heroes and Demi-gods whose Abode is in the Elysian Fields consisteth in their Asphodel, or Ambrosia, or Nectar, as these old women here tell you. In my Opinion it consisteth in this that they wipe their Tail with a Gosling. And such is the Opinion of Master John of Scotland."[1]

---

[1] *Master John of Scotland.* Johannes Duns Scotus (*doctor subtilis*), born at Dunston in Northumberland in 1274, was a Franciscan teacher of great repute. He was at Merton College, Oxford, where he taught, and afterwards at Paris and Cologne, where he died in 1308. He founded the Scotists (*realists*), who were opposed to the Thomists (*nominalists*), followers of St Thomas Aquinas. The subtleties of his logic got for him the name Scotine (σκοτεινός). Cf. *P.* 7; iii. 17; v. prol. 15.

CHAPTER XIV

How Gargantua was instructed in Latin by a Sophist*[1]

HAVING heard this Discourse, the Good man Grandgousier was ravished with Admiration, considering the high Reach and marvellous Understanding of his Son Gargantua. So he spake thus to his Governesses:

"Philip, King of Macedon,[2] discovered the good Wit of his Son Alexander by his dexterous Managing of a Horse. For the said Horse was so terrible and unruly that no one dared mount upon him, because he gave a Fall to all his Riders, breaking the Neck of one, the Legs of another, braining one and breaking the Jawbone of another. Considering this, Alexander in the Hippodrome (which was the Place where Horses were exercised and trained) observed that the Wildness of the Horse proceeded only from the Fear he had of his own Shadow. Whereupon, getting on his Back, he made him run towards the Sun so that his Shadow fell behind, and by this Means rendered the Horse gentle as he could wish. Whereby his Father recognised the divine Understanding that was in him, and had him very carefully instructed by Aristotle, who at that time was esteemed above all Philosophers of Greece.

"But I assure you that in this single Discourse which I have just held before you with my Son Gargantua, I discover that his Understanding partakes of some divine Power, to such a Degree do I find him acute, subtle, profound and sedate. And he will arrive at a sovereign Degree of Wisdom if he is well instructed. Therefore I

---

* *Sophiste*, D; *Théologien*, ABC.

[1] *Sophist.* From Erasmus onwards it was the fashion to speak of the theologians under the transparent disguise "Sophist" (*R.E.R.* viii. 299). In this chapter is given a list, more or less complete, of the text-books of instruction which were in vogue in Rabelais' time, and which he holds up to ridicule.

[2] *Philip, King of Macedon*, etc. This paragraph is apparently taken from Plutarch's *Life of Alexander*, c. 6. 667 C–D, one of the few "Lives" which Rabelais used. The story is told also in Erasmus, *Apoph.* lib. iv (Alex. 41), but with different details.

wish to entrust him to some learned Man to indoctrinate him according to his Capacity; and therein will I spare no Cost".

Accordingly they assigned to him a great Doctor Sophist* named Thubal Holofernes,[1] who taught him his Alphabet[2] so well that he said it by Heart backwards, and he was about it five Years and three Months.

Then he read to him Donatus,[3] Facetus,[4] Theodolet[5] and Alanus *in Parabolis*,[6] and about this he was thirteen Years six Months and two Weeks.

---

* *Docteur Sophiste*, D; *Docteur en Théologie*, ABC.

[1] *Holofernes* is the name given to the schoolmaster in Shakespeare's *Love's Labour's Lost*, but Tubal Holofernes occurs in the *Pronostication nouvelle*, *A.P.F.* xii. 148:

"Pronostication moderne
Du temps futur qu'il adviendra,
De maistre Tubal Holoferne,
Pour quelque année qu'on voudra".

The oldest copy known of this work was published at Lyons about 1545, but M. de Rothschild shews that this was not the original, which must have been composed about 1525. Du Verdier mentions this as a *Prognostication nouvelle et joieuse pour trois jours après jamais composée par Thubal Holoferne et imprimée à Paris l'an* 1478, a date evidently supposititious according to M. de Rothschild.

[2] *Alphabet*, Fr. *carte*, because the ABC was ordinarily stuck on a piece of cardboard.

"Cartam compraverat illi,
Sive quadernellum, supra quam disceret a. b."
Merl. Coc. *Baldus*, ii. 23.

[3] *Aelius* DONATUS, *de octo partibus orationis libellus*, was one of the first books printed (Moguntiae, Gutenberg, 1455; Romae, Pannartz and Sweynheym, 1465). Donatus was the celebrated grammarian of the fourth century and preceptor of St Jerome. The word *Donat* in Early English and French became a synonym for a grammar-book or a lesson.

[4] *Liber* FACETI, *docens mores hominum in supplementum eorum qui a Cathone sunt omissi* (Daventriae, Jac. de Breda, 1494), perhaps written by Reinerus Alemanni, a German Benedictine (1155–1230). Cf. Chaucer, *C.T.* (A. 3227), and Skeat's note.

[5] THEODULI, *Egloga sive dialogus Pastorum* (Henr. Quentell, Coloniae 1492), is an allegorical dialogue in 345 leonine hexameters between Truth and Falsehood, judgment being given by Wisdom.

[6] ALANI DE INSULIS, *liber Parabolarum* (Lugd. 1492; Coloniae 1497). Alain de Lisle was a monk of Cîteaux (1114–1203), also author of *Anti-Claudianus*. Cf. Skeat's *Chaucer*, vol. i. p. 516. The last three books form part of the *Autores octo morales*, libros subscriptos continentes, videlicet: Catonis, *Faceti*, *Theodoli*, Cartule, alias de contemptu mundi, Thobiadis, *Parabolarum Alani*, Fabularum Esopi, Floretus Bernardi (Lugd. 1498).

But note that all this Time he taught him to write in Gothic[1]
Characters; and he wrote all his Books, for the Art of Printing was
not yet in Use.

And he generally carried a huge Writing-case weighing more
than seven thousand Quintals, the Pencil-case[2] of which was as
great and as long as the huge Pillars of Enay,[3] and the Ink-horn
was attached to it by great iron Chains, being large enough to hold
a Cask of Merchandise.

After that he read to him *De modis significandi*[4] with the Commentaries of Hurt-bise, of Fasquin, of Trop-diteux, of Gualhault,
of John Calf, of Billonio, of Brelingandus and a Rabble of others,
and at this he was more than eighteen Years and eleven Months.
And he knew it so well that in Examination[5] he would recite it by

---

[1] *in Gothic.* "Argumento sunt codices gothice scripti, quae magna multitudo
est. Veteres admiscebant linguae suae *graecam*, isti (legulei) admiscent *gothicam*",
L. Valla, *Elegant.* lib. iii. proem. Sir E. M. Thompson in *Shakespeare's England*,
c. 10, argues from the six signatures that have been preserved that Shakespeare
wrote "Gothic".

[2] Fr. *galimart* (iv. 32), from Lat. *calamarium* (*calamaria theca*, Suet. v. 35).

[3] *Enay* is the Abbey of Ainay (*Ataneum*) at Lyons, founded in the sixth century
on the site of a temple erected to the goddess Roma and to Augustus. Four old
pillars of the temple still survive in the chancel of the church of St Martin
d'Ainay (*R.E.R.* vi. 385). The spot had been occupied by the *ara Lugdunensis* set
up by Drusus in honour of Augustus 12 B.C. at the confluence of the Saône and
the Rhone and inscribed with the names of the sixty peoples of *Gallia comata*.
Cf. Juv. i. 44 and Mayor's note.

[4] *De modis significandi*, a grammar-book, the first author of which is unknown,
said by some to be Aquinas, by others Albertus de Saxonia, by others Duns
Scotus (Böcking's *Von Hutten*). Panzer gives: *Jo. Duns Scoti Ord. Min.*, *doctoris
subtilis*, de Modis significandi, seu grammatica speculativa (Vill. Alban. 1480;
Venet. 1491, 1499). Dr Mullinger, *Hist. Univ. Camb.*, attributes this book to
Jean Gerson, Chancellor of the University of Paris. Gerson's book is a concise
and clear exposition of Nominalism from the logical standpoint, while his *De
concordia Metaphysicae cum Logica* takes the metaphysical side. Of the commenta-
tors here fancifully assigned, *Hurt-bise* (Wind-beater) occurs in Coquillart, i. 81,
Trop-diteux in G. 25 and v. 4, *Gualhault* in P. 1; *Brelingandus* is the same as
Prelinguant, who occurs in G. 34 and iv. 40, and *Jean le Veau* is probably
Ioannes Kalb mentioned in *Epist. Obs. Vir.* ii. 48, on whom Cl. Marot wrote an
epitaph adapted from a Latin one:

> "O Deus omnipotens, Vituli miserere Joannis,
> Quem mors praeveniens non sinit esse bovem".

[5] Fr. *au coupelaud*, from *coupelle*, a vessel for assaying metals, hence testing. Cf.
Villon, *Test.* l. 708, *argent de coepelle*.

Heart backwards. And he proved on his Fingers to his Mother that *de modis significandi non erat scientia.*

Next he read to him the *Compostum,*[1] wherein he was engaged sixteen Years and two Months, when his said Preceptor died:

Deceased in fourteen hundred twenty
Of Boils and Blains that came in plenty.[2]

Afterwards he had another old coughing Fellow named Master Jobelin Bridé,[3] who read to him Hugutio,[4] Hebrard's Grecismus,[5] The Doctrinal,[6] The Parts of Speech, The *Quid est,*[7] The *Supple-*

---

[1] *Compostum* or *Computus* is the whole body of rules for finding the movable feasts, etc. in the Calendar. *Compotus manualis ad usum Oxoniensem cum commento* (Paris 1494). *Comp. cum comm. per Claudium Nourri* (Lugduni 1504).

[2] Lines from the 3rd epigram of Cl. Marot on John Bishop of Orléans:

"Cy gist, repose et dort leans
Le feu euesque de Orleans;
I'entens l'Euesque en son surnom,
Et frere Iehan en propre nom,
Qui feust l'an cinq cens et vingt
De la verolle qui luy vint".

[3] *Jobelin Bridé* is a sort of *Job in Harness.*

"Et voyla Trop tot maryé,
Qui en est Jobelin Bridé."

Roger de Collerye (p. 116), *Sermon pour une Nopce.*

[4] *Hugutio.* Agno Ugutio of Pisa, Bishop of Ferrara (†1210), composed his *Magnae derivationes* (1192) from the *Origines* of Isidore and the glossary of Papias. It was copied by Reuchlin: *Jo. Reuchlin (Capnio) Vocabularius Breviloquus cum arte diphthongandi Guarini Veronensis* (Basil. 1478). Dante, who styles the author "Uguccione", makes considerable use of this book (see Toynbee's *Dante Studies,* pp. 97–114).

[5] *Ebrardi Bethuniensis Graecismus,* seu liber carmine conscriptus de Figuris deque octo orationis partibus, editus Lugduni anno 1490 (Paris, Pet. Level, 1487; Joh. du Pré, 1493) (Wrobel, Vratislaviae 1887):

"Anno milleno centeno bis duodeno (1212)
Condidit Ebrardus Graecismum Bethuniensis".

[6] *Doctrinale puerorum cum sententiis notabilibus* (Basil. 1498), by Alexander Gallus, or *de Villa Dei.* A poem in leonine verses by Alexandre de Ville-Dieu, a Franciscan of Brittany (1242). A careful edition with an exhaustive introduction has been published by Dr Reichling (Berlin 1893). The *Graecismus* and *Doctrinale* were for three centuries the recognised books for teaching Latin grammar and prosody. Being written in verse (the *Graecismus* in hexameters and occasionally elegiacs, and the *Doctrinale* in hexameters, mostly leonine) they usurped the place of Donatus and Priscian, which were written in prose.

[7] The *Quid est* was a sort of catechism on the "Parts of Speech". Alexandre de Ville-Dieu also wrote a book called the "*partes orationis*" as well as a *Massa Computi* or *Compositum,* see above.

mentum,[1] Marmotret,[2] *De moribus in mensa servandis,*[3] Seneca[4] *de quatuor virtutibus cardinalibus,* Passavantus[5] *cum Commento* and *Dormi securè,*[6] for the Festivals; and some others of the same Kidney; by the Reading whereof he became "as wise as any since we ever baked in an Oven".[7]

---

[1] *Supplementum Chronicorum a venerando patre Jacobo Philippo Bergomate Ord. Erem. professo conscriptum.* Cf. *G.* 37. It was a kind of compendious history.

[2] *Mammotrectus sive expositio vocabulorum quae in Bibliis, Hymnis ecclesiasticis, Homiliis,* etc. *occurrunt* (Beromünster 1460). The first book printed in Switzerland. "*Mam.* authore Marchesio (Moguntiae 1470). *Et quia morem gerit talis decursus paedagogi qui gressus dirigit parvulorum, Mammotrectus poterit appellari.* Immo Mammothreptus ex Gr. μαμμόθρεπτος qua de voce prae ceteris Augustinus" (Serm. 2 in Psalm. 30) (Ducange). "*Mammothreptus* quasi dicas *aviae alumnum*", Erasm. *Colloq.* (*Synodus Grammaticorum*), p. 416. Rabelais has another gibe at it in *P.* 7: "*Marmotretus de baboinis et cingis*". There is also a ridiculous letter in *Epist. Obs. Vir.* i. 33 from *Mammotrectus Bunternantellus.*

[3] *Jo. Sulpitii Verulani de moribus puerorum in mensa. Carmen elegiacum* (Aquileiae 1483; Lips. 1503; Lugd. 1506). Johannes Sulpitius of Veroli in the Campagna, the oldest of the humanistic grammarians and a determined opponent of Alexander's *Doctrinale,* flourished at the end of the fifteenth century. The book is also called *La contenance de la table* (Paris, Trepperel) and *Quos decet,* because it begins with the lines:

"Quos decet in mensa mores servare docemus
Virtuti ut studeas litterulisque simul".

[4] *Seneca* is a pseudonym of Martin, Bishop of Braga (576), Archbishop of Mondonedo (†583) or Martinus Dumiensis, *de quattuor virtutibus cardinalibus* (Lovanii s. n. ann. Joh. de Westphalia), also called *Formula honestae vitae vel de verborum copia.* It was used by Chaucer in the *Tale of Melibeus:* cf. Skeat's note, *C.T.* B 2261. It is printed at the end of the Teubner *Seneca* (ed. Haase). This treatise was greedily accepted as Seneca's in the Middle Ages, but rejected by Petrarch, *Ep. Senil.* ii. 4 (Toynbee, *Dante Studies,* p. 155).

[5] *Jacobus Passavantus* (a Florentine Dominican: †1357): *Lo specchio di vera Penitentia* (Florentiae 1495). He also wrote silly notes on the *De Civitate Dei* (Erasm. *Ad.* ii. 5. 58). He was the Prior of Santa Maria Novella, and under his direction were painted the frescoes in the "Spanish Chapel".

[6] *Dormi secure, sermones dominicales et de sanctis,* by Richard Maidstone, a Carmelite (†1396), published at Lyons in 1494 and often reprinted in the sixteenth century. "Satis notabiles et utiles omnibus sacerdotibus qui *Dormi secure,* vel *Dormi sine cura,* sunt nuncupati, eo quod absque magno studio faciliter possint incorporari et populo praedicari." There is an account with extracts from this book in H. Estienne, *Apologie pour Hérodote,* c. 34, vol. ii, pp. 202, 209, etc.

[7] An expression become proverbial:

"A ceste heure suis aussi sage
Qu'oncques puis ne fourneasmes nous".

Farce du pont aux asgnes, A.Th.F. ii. 42.

The meaning clearly is "he was as wise as he was before". Laurentius Valla, *Elegantiarum Linguae Latinae libri sex* (1450), lib. ii, c. 1, after speaking of Donatus,

Servius and Priscian, goes on thus: "ut post eos quicunque de Latinitate scrip-
serunt balbutire videantur; quorum primus est Hisidorus indoctorum arro-
gantissimus, qui cum nihil sciat omnia praecipit; post hunc Papias aliique in-
doctiores: Eberardus, Hugutio, Catholicon, Aimo; et caeteri indigni qui
nominentur, magna mercede docentes nihil scire, aut stultiorem reddentes
discipulum quam acceperunt". Erasmus, *de Colloq. utilitate*, has: "Ex his,
si nihil aliud discerent pueri quam Latine loqui, quanto plus laudis mea
mereretur industria…quam illorum qui miserae juventuti *Mammotrectos,
Brachylogos, Catholicontas, et significandi modos obtrudebant*".

CHAPTER XV

How Gargantua was put under other Schoolmasters

MEANTIME his Father perceived that indeed he studied right well, and spent all his Time therein; nevertheless that he profited nothing, and, what is worse, that he became thereby foolish and simple and altogether doting and doltish.

As he was complaining thereof to Don Philippe Des Marays,[1] Viceroy of Papeligosse, he was told that it were better for him to learn nothing than to be taught such Books under such Preceptors; for their Knowledge was but Stupidity, and their Wisdom nought but Trifles, bastardising good and noble Spirits, and corrupting the whole Flower of Youth.

"To prove that this is so," said he, "take any one of these young Folk of the present Time, who has studied only two Years; if he have not better Judgment, better Terms and better Discourse than your Son, with a better Bearing and Courtesy to everybody, account me ever afterwards a Chaw-bacon of Brene."[2] This was well-pleasing to Grandgousier and he ordered it to be done.

In the Evening at Supper, the said Des Marays brought in a young Page of his from Villegongis,[3] called Eudemon,[4] so well

---

[1] *Don Philippe des Marays.* Erasm. *Epist.* 180 (ed. Allen) is addressed to Joh. Paludanus (= des Marays), who was a friend and host of Erasmus. It serves as an introduction to a panegyric, addressed to Don Felipe (Philip the Fair), Viceroy of Castile (*Papeligosse* = Pampeluna + Saragossa), father of Charles V. This letter and panegyric (1504) served as an introduction to the *Institutio Principis Christiani*, which Erasmus dedicated to Charles V in 1516 on his accession to the throne of Spain. Thus Rabelais, who is engaged on educational themes in these chapters (14–24), shews his acquaintance with the work of Erasmus.

[2] *la Brene* (G. 3) is in Berry, which is full of ponds and marshes (*R.E.R.* vii. 75), and therefore foggy. Hence the propriety of the name des Marays (Lat. *Paludanus*).

[3] *Villegongis* is also in Berry, between Buzançay and Chateauroux (*R.E.R.* vii. 352).

[4] The account of Eudemon seems to be derived from Erasmus (*Colloq.*), *Monita paedagogica*: "Quoties alloquitur te quisquam cui debes honorem, com-

curled, so trimly dressed, so well brushed, so comely in his Behaviour, that he far more resembled some little Angel than a Man. Then he said to Grandgousier:

"Do you see this young Boy? He is not yet twelve Years old: let us see, with your good Pleasure, what Difference there is between the Knowledge of your doting Mateologians[1] (*vain-babblers*) of times gone by and the young People of to-day."

The Trial pleased Grandgousier, and he commanded the Page to begin.

Then Eudemon, asking Leave of the said Viceroy his Master to do so, with Cap in Hand, an open Countenance and ruddy Lips, his Eyes steadfast and Look fixed on Gargantua, with a youthful Modesty stood up on his Feet, and began to commend and exalt him, first for his Virtue and good Manners, secondly for his Knowledge, thirdly for his Nobility, fourthly for his personal Beauty: and in the fifth place he sweetly exhorted him to reverence his Father with every Observance, for that he took such Thought to have him well instructed; lastly, he prayed him of his Goodness to retain him as the least of his Servants; for other Favour desired he none of the Heavens at this present, save that Grace should be given him to be pleasing to Gargantua in some agreeable Service.

All this was delivered by him with Gestures so appropriate, Pronunciation so distinct, with a Voice so eloquent and Language so ornate, and in such good Latin, that he rather resembled a Gracchus, a Cicero, or an Emilius[2] of the past Time than a Stripling of the present Age.

But all the Countenance that Gargantua kept was that he took

---

pone te in rectum corporis statum, operi caput. Vultus sit nec tristis nec torvus nec impudens, nec protervus nec instabilis, sed hilari modestia temperatus; oculi verecundi, semper intenti in eum cui loqueris; juncti pedes, quietae manus.... Vestis item ad decorum componatur, ut totus vultus, gestus et habitus corporis ingenuam modestiam et verecundam indolem prae se ferat. Cum loquaris... distincte, clare, articulate consuescito proferre verba tua".

[1] *Mateologians* (iv. 10, A), ματαιολόγοι, vain-babblers, with a sly hint at *Théologiens*.

[2] *Emilius* refers to M. Aemilius Lepidus, called Porcina (Cic. *Brutus*, 25. § 95), a consummate orator, instructor of T. Gracchus and C. Carbo. "Aemilian eloquence" occurs in *Hyp*. c. 10. g. vii recto; in Plut. *Numa*, c. 8. 65D, the punning quality αἰμυλία = deftness is attributed to the *gens Aemilia*.

to crying like a Cow, and hid his Face in his Cap; nor was it possible to get a Word from him more than a f—t from a dead Ass.

At this his Father was so enraged that he wished to slay Master Jobelin. But the said Des Marays kept him from it by fair Persuasion which he made to him, in such wise that his Anger was moderated. Then Grandgousier ordered that his Wages should be paid him and that he should be made to ply the Pot soundly like a Sophist;[1] this done, that he should go to all the Devils.

"At least", he said, "for this Day he shall not cost his Host much if perchance he should die as bloated as an Englishman."[2]

Master Jobelin having gone out of the House, Grandgousier consulted with the Viceroy what Preceptor they could give him, and it was agreed between them that Ponocrates,[3] the Tutor of Eudemon, should be assigned to this Office, and that they should all go together to Paris to learn what was the Study of the Young men of France at that time.

---

[1] Fr. *chopiner Sophistiquement* (theologalement, ABC). H. Estienne, in *Apol. pour Hérod.* c. 22, explains *vin théologal* as the best wine and flowing freely, citing Horace's *dapibus Saliaribus* and *Pontificum potiore cenis*. Erasmus writes (*Pontificalis coena, Ad.* iii. 2. 37): "Ab eo quod scripsit Horatius non abhorret quod hac tempestate apud Parisios vulgari joco vinum *theologicum* vocant quod sit validissimum minimeque dilutum".

[2] *bloated as an Englishman*. Cf. Erasm. *Ad.* ii. 2. 68 *fin.*: "vulgatissimum apud Gallos proverbium ut, cum hominem vehementer cibo distentum velint intelligi, dicant *tam satur quam est Anglus*. Verum iidem ut illis attribuant πολυφαγίαν ita nobis πολυποσίαν adscribunt".

[3] *Ponocrates* (iv. 22), the hard worker. Ponocrates and Epistemon, the tutors respectively of Gargantua and Pantagruel, are mentioned in iii. 34 as having been fellow-students of Rabelais at Montpellier.

CHAPTER XVI

How Gargantua was sent to Paris, and of the huge Mare that he rode on, and how she destroyed the Ox-flies of la Beauce

AT this same Season Fayolles,[1] fourth King of Numidia, sent from the Land of Africa to Grandgousier a Mare,[2] the most enormous and huge that ever was seen, and the most monstrous; as you know well enough that Africa always produces something new.[3] She was as large as six Elephants, and had her Feet cloven into Toes like the Horse of Julius Caesar, her Ears as slouching as the Goats[4] of Languedoc, and a little Horn on her Rump.

Moreover, she was of a burnt-sorrel Hue with dapple-grey Spots; but above all she had a horrible Tail, for it was (be the same more or less) as large as the Pillar of St Mars[5] near Langeais,[6] and as

---

[1] M. le Marquis de Fayolle makes it highly probable that "Fayolles, fourth King of Numidia", is intended to represent François, second son of Jean de Fayolles, captain of Coulonges-les-Royaulx (iv. 30), who had taken part in an expedition against the Turks and had received letters of indulgence for this from Leo X, April 5, 1518. He did not marry till 1533 and founded a branch of his family in Périgord (cf. iii. 31). He was related to the Estissac (*R.E.R.* vii. 389).

[2] In the *Grandes Cronicques*, c. 4, Merlin compounds a huge mare to carry Grand Gousier and Galemelle.

[3] ἀεί τι καινὸν φέρει ἡ Λιβύη (v. 3) is recorded as proverbial by Aristot. *Hist. An.* viii. 27. § 7 and Pliny, 8. 42. Cf. Erasm. *Ad.* iii. 7. 10.

[4] The enormous pendent ears of the goats in Syria are noted in Aristot. *Hist. An.* viii. 27. § 3.

[5] *La pile Sainct Mars* (also *de Cinq Mars*) is a square monument 86 feet in height, with four small turrets, on the north side of the Loire, 2 miles from the town Cinq-Mars, and about 5 miles from Langeais. "Upon each face towards the top are wrought in bricks in different colour from the main structure various devices.... These can be nothing else than the 'armorial bearings' of the several cities or tribes that combined together for the erection of so costly a monument; which we may safely suppose intended for one of those *plurima simulacra* of Mercury which Caesar noticed in Gaul (*B.G.* vi. 17)," King, *Gnostics and their Remains*, p. 429, 2nd ed.

[6] *Langeais* is the chief town of a canton in the arrondissement of Chinon, on the right bank of the Loire, about 15 miles from Tours and a little less from Chinon. It has a fine château of the fifteenth century.

much squared with Plaits, neither more nor less worked in together than Ears of Corn.

If you wonder at this, wonder rather at the Tails of the Rams[1] of Scythia which weighed more than thirty Pounds, and of the Sheep of Syria, for which (if Tenauld[2] says true) men have to fasten a little Truck behind them to bear up their Tail, so long and heavy is it. You have none such, you Rustics of the low Countries.

And she was brought by Sea in three Caracks[3] and a Brigantine, as far as the Harbour of Olonne[4] in Thalmondais. When Grandgousier saw her he said: "Ha! here is just the Thing to carry my Son to Paris! Ha! Perdy! all will go well. He will be a great Scholar in times to come. Were it not for the Dunces we should all live as Doctors".[5]

The next Day (after drinking, you understand) they set out on their way, Gargantua, his Tutor Ponocrates, and his People, and together with them Eudemon the young Page; and because the Weather was serene and temperate, his Father had made for him dun-coloured Boots; Babin[6] calls them Buskins.

So they joyously went along their Highway, and always in high

---

[1] *Rams' tails.* Herodotus (iii. 113) records all this of the rams in Arabia. The gigantic tails of the Syrian rams are mentioned in Aristotle, *Hist. An.* viii. 27. § 3; Pliny, 8. 198: "Syriae cubitales ovium caudae". Cf. Pierre Gilles, *ex Aeliani historia*, vi. 34 (Gyllii accessio: Aelian, *Nat. An.* x. 4): "In Scythia arietes sunt cauda tam longa et lata ut ad triginta libras accedat".

[2] *Le voyage et itinaire* (sic) *de oultre mer faict par frère Jehan Thenauld maistre es ars docteur en theologie et gardien des frères mineurs d'Angoulesme* (Paris, *ca.* 1530) contains the following passage (p. 43): "Le Souldan nous envoya presens, c'est assavoir moutons à la grande queue, et fault sçavoir qu'il n'est si petit mouton dont en la queue n'ait plus de x livres de chair... au porter et traisner desquelles les moutons travaillent moult: pour ce on leur faict petites charettes esquelles reposent leurs queues, qu'ilz traisnent par leurs cornes" (*R.E.R.* viii. 353).

[3] *Caracks. Carrik* is first used by Chaucer, *Somnour's prologue*, 24. D. 1688. It is a large trading-ship (*R.E.R.* viii. 47). Cf. *Shakespeare's England*, i. 153.

[4] *Olonne* (*G.* 50; iii. 49; iv. 1; v. 48; *P.P.* 6) is a port of Talmondais, a principality in Poitou. Talmont is a little town in the centre of the district (*R.E.R.* ii. 251).

[5] A transposition of the sentence in Froissart, ii. 173 (R), iii. 28 (M–L): *Les seigneurs seroient comme bestes si le clergé n'estoit.* Berners' translation gives: "the lordes could not lyve but as beestes and the clergy were not" (a. 1384) (Tudor translation, vol. iv. p. 240.) Cf. εἰ μὴ ἰατροὶ ἦσαν οὐδὲν ἂν ἦν τῶν γραμματικῶν μωρότερον, Athen. xv. 666A.

[6] *Babin* was the name of a family of shoe-makers at Chinon (Le Double, p. 413, n. 4; *R.E.R.* i. 80).

Feather until just above Orleans, in which Place was a spacious Forest five-and-thirty Leagues long and seventeen wide, or thereabouts. This Forest was horribly fertile and abounding in Gadflies and Hornets, so that it was a very Brigand's Den for the poor Mares, Asses, and Horses.

But Gargantua's Mare did handsomely avenge all the Outrages therein perpetrated on the Beasts of her Kind, by a Trick which they did not in the least suspect. For as soon as they had entered the said Forest and the Hornets had given the Assault, she drew out her Tail, and so well did she smouch them in skirmishing that she threw down the whole Wood along and athwart, this side and that side, here and there, longways and sideways, over and under, and knocked down the Trees as a Mower does Grass; in such sort that since then there has been neither Wood nor Hornets, but the whole Land was reduced to a Plain.

Seeing this, Gargantua took mighty great Pleasure thereat, without otherwise vaunting himself. And he said to his People: "I find This fine" (*Beau ce*). Whence this Country has since been called la Beauce. But all they got for Breakfast was Yawning; in memory of which still to this day the Gentlemen of Beauce do break their Fast[1] by Yawning, and find themselves well off therein and only spit the better for it.

At last they arrived at Paris, in which Place he refreshed himself two or three Days, making very merry with his Folk, and enquiring what Learned men there were then in the Town, and what Wine they drank there.[2]

---

[1] The poverty of the province of Beauce (Lat. *Belsa*: *R.E.R.* vii. 86) was proverbial in Rabelais' time:

"Et desjeuner tous les matins
Comme les escuiers de Beaulce".

Coquillart, *Mon. des Perr*. ii. 289.

Yawning was also the breakfast of the Quaver-brothers in v. 27.

[2] *what Wine they drank there*. In the sixteenth century each town had its *crieurs de vin* to advertise the taverns and their wines. (Fr. ed.)

CHAPTER XVII

How Gargantua paid his Welcome to the Parisians, and how
he took away the great Bells of the Church of Our Lady[1]

SOME days after that they had refreshed themselves, he paid a
Visit to the City and was looked upon with great Admiration by
everybody; for the People of Paris are by nature so silly, such
Cockneys and such Oafs, that a Mountebank, a Carrier of Indulgences, a Mule with its Bells, a Fiddler in the middle of Cross-
ways will bring together more People than a good Preacher of the
Gospel.[2]

And so troublesome were they in pursuing him that he was constrained to take his Rest on the Towers of the Church of Our Lady.
And being at this Place, and seeing so many People round about
him, he said in a clear Voice:

"I believe these Chuffs wish that I should pay them here my
Welcome and my *proficiat*.[3] There is good Reason therein. I am
going to give them their Wine,[4] but it shall be only in Sport" (*par
ris*).

Then smiling, he untied his fine Cod-piece, and drawing his
Mentula forth into the Air he bep—d them so bitterly that he
drowned two hundred and sixty thousand four hundred and
eighteen, besides Women and little Children.

---

[1] The main incidents of this chapter are developed from the *Grandes Cronicques*,
c. 9.

[2] Cf. Lucian, *Alex*. c. 9 (Erasm. trad. 1505): "cujusmodi Paphlagonas
affirmabat esse hos qui supra Aboni murum incolunt, nempe superstitiosos
plerosque ac stolidos, qui si quis tantum apparuisset tibicinem aut tympanistam
aut qui cymbala pulsaret secum adducens, cribro (quod aiunt) vaticinans,
illico vehementer omnes in illum inhient et perinde ut caelitum quempiam
intuerentur".

[3] *proficiat* (*G*. 34; *P*. 30), a fee or benevolence, bestowed on bishops by ecclesi-
astics after their installation. It was one of the *consuetudines laudabiles*. Also =
pourboire.

[4] Fr. *donner le vin*, give them a *pourboire*, a proverbial expression corresponding
to our "pay them out". Cf. "il aura son vin", *G*. 5; *P*. 18.

A certain Number of them escaped this P—s-flood by Fleetness of Foot. And when they were at the highest Part[1] of the University, sweating, coughing, spitting and out of Breath, they began to curse and to swear, some in Anger and some in Sport (*par ris*). "*Carimari carimara!*[2] By the Halidame, we are well washed *parris*."[3]

Wherefore the City hath since been called Paris, which before

---

[1] *the highest Part.* Mont Ste Geneviève, the highest point of the University quarter. (Fr. ed.)

[2] Cf. Patelin, l. 614:

> "Ostez ces gens noirs!...Marmara
> *Carimari carimara*".

Caurimauri is a coarse kind of cloth in *Piers Plowman*, A. v. 62: cf. Skeat's note. *Carimari, carimara* are some of the cries uttered by Patelin in his pretended delirium. Perhaps it was intended by Patelin to depreciate the Draper's cloth, like Falstaff's "Dowlas, filthy dowlas", Shakesp. 1 *Hen. IV*, iii. 3. 79. One of the seven greater arts in Florence was that of the dealers in foreign cloths, the *arte di Calimala* (Hallam, *Mid. Ages*, i. 422; *Camb. Mod. Hist.* i. 512). ABC give here in addition a number of confused exclamations and oaths: "les plagues Bieu, je renie Bieu, Frandiene, vez tu ben, la mer Dé, po cab de Bious, das dich Gots leyden schend, pote de Christo (BC: ia martre schend), ventre sainct Quenet, vertus guoy, par sainct Fiacre de Brie, sainct Treignant, je foys veu à sainct Thibaud, *Pasques Dieu, le bon jour Dieu, le Diable m'emport, foy de Gentilhomme* (BC: carimary carimara), par sainct Andouille, par sainct Guodegrin qui feut martyrizé de pommes cuyttes, par sainct Foutin lapostre, par sainct Vit (BC: nè Dia, ma Dia), par saincte Mamye". The exclamations are those of several provinces or nations: Gascon, German (lansquenet), Italian, Breton, Scotch, etc. to shew the composite nature of the population of Paris. The expressions in italics are the historic adjurations of the four French kings, Louis XI, Charles VIII, Louis XII and Francis I. Brantôme (*Le grand Roy Francoys*, i. ii. c. 14) gives the following verse:

> "Quand la Pasques Dieu deceda,
> Par le jour Dieu succeda;
> Le Diable m'emporte s'en tint près;
> Foy de Gentilhomme vint après".

"St Guodegrin qui feust martyrizé de pommes cuyttes" is from *La vie de saint Christophle* (Chevallet, Grenoble 1530), in which the following lines occur:

> "Du glorieux martir sainct Pran
> Qui fut jadis bouilli en bran
> Et lapidé de pommes cuictes".

A pun also is intended on *Grand godet*, hard drinking. It serves as the name of a tavern in Villon, *Test.* 91. 2. (*R.E.R.* viii. 362.)

[3] *Parris.* Cf. Cretin, p. 220:

> "Auront de moy vieulx aulx pourriz, pour riz".

was styled Leucetia, as Strabo saith *lib. iiij.*,[1] that is to say, in Greek, Whitehall, because of the white Thighs of the Ladies of the said Place.

And forasmuch as at this Imposition of a new Name, all the people present swore, each by the Saints of his Parish; the Parisians (who are made up of all Kinds of People and all Sorts of Men) are by nature good Jurors and good Jurists, and a little overbearing; wherefore Joaninus de Barranco[2] holds, *Libro de copiositate reverentiarum*, that they are called *Parrhesians* from the Greek,[3] that is to say, bold in Speech.

This done, he considered the great Bells which were in the said Towers and made them ring very harmoniously. Whilst he was so doing, it came into his Thoughts that they would do well for Cowbells to hang on the Neck of his Mare, which he wished to send back to his Father laden with Brie Cheeses[4] and fresh Herrings. Accordingly he carried them off to his Abode.

Meantime there came a Knight Commander of Hams of the

---

[1] In Strabo (iv. 194) Paris is called Lucotokia ($\pi\epsilon\rho\grave{\iota}\ \delta\epsilon\ \tau\grave{o}\nu\ \Sigma\eta\kappa o\acute{a}\nu a\nu\ \pi o\tau a\mu\acute{o}\nu$ $\epsilon\grave{\iota}\sigma\iota\ \kappa a\grave{\iota}\ o\acute{\iota}\ \Pi a\rho\acute{\iota}\sigma\iota o\iota,\nu\hat{\eta}\sigma o\nu\ \check{\epsilon}\chi o\nu\tau\epsilon\varsigma\ \kappa a\grave{\iota}\ \pi\acute{o}\lambda\iota\nu\ \Lambda o\nu\kappa o\tau o\kappa\acute{\iota}a\nu$). Julian's $M\iota\sigma o\pi\acute{\omega}\gamma\omega\nu$ (340D) gives $\Lambda o\nu\kappa\epsilon\tau\acute{\iota}a$ and in a bad MS. $\Lambda\epsilon\nu\kappa\epsilon\tau\acute{\iota}a$. Rabelais' copy of Strabo may have had a similar faulty reading.

[2] *Joaninus de Barranco*, probably, like Bragmardo, invented to resemble a logical term. The reference may be to the *Philippide* of Guillaume le Breton, who says of the Parisians:

"Et se *Parrhisios* dixerunt nomine Graeco,
Quod sonat expositum nostris *audacia* verbis".

Pasquier, *Recherches*, ix. 2.

Later he gives another derivation:

"Nullus in orbe locus, quoniam tunc temporis illam
Reddebat palus et terrae pinguedo lutosam
Aptum Parisii posuere *Lutetia* nomen".   Id. *ibid.*

In the letter dedicating Marliani's *Roman Topography* to Bishop du Bellay, Rabelais says: "*antistitem Parisiensem vere* $\pi a\rho\rho\eta\sigma\iota\acute{a}\zeta\epsilon\iota\nu$". The source probably is Seneca, *de Ira*, iii. 23. § 2: "Demochares *Parrhesiastes*, ob nimiam et procacem linguam, appellatus".

[3] Fr. *en grecisme*. Cf. *Epist. Obs. Vir.* ii. 8: "docui eum *in grecismo*". "In *Grecismus*" (*G.* 14). Cf. Eberardi *Graecismus*, viii. 176:

"Sicut Parisius sonat, introductio Graece
Est is is, ast alibi sit tibi numen Isis".

[4] *Brie cheeses* are called in Davenant, *The Wits*, Act. iv. Sc. 1, "Your *angelots* of Brie". They are round cream cheeses covered with tinfoil and stamped like a coin, so *angelots*.

Order Saint Anthony,[1] to carry on his porkish Quest; who, to make himself heard from a Distance, and to make the Bacon tremble in the Larder, wished to carry them off by stealth. But he left them behind from a feeling of Honesty, not because they were too hot, but because they were somewhat too heavy for him to carry.[2] This was not he of Bourg,[3] for he is too good a Friend of mine.

All the City was moved and in uproar, as you know that for this they are so ready,[4] that foreign Nations do marvel at the Patience[5]* of the Kings of France, who do not by strict Justice rein them in from such Courses, seeing the Inconveniences that proceed therefrom from day to day. Would to God I knew the Shop in which are forged these Divisions and factious Combinations, that I might bring them to Light in the Meetings of my Parish! Be assured that the Place, at which were assembled the People all befooled and befouled,[6] was Nesle,[7]† where was, but now is no more, the Oracle of

---

* *De la patience ou pour mieux dire de la stupidité des Roys de France*, A.
† *Nesle*, D; *Sorbonne*, A.

[1] Fr. *commandeur jambonnier de Saint Antoine*. Saint Antony of Coma in Egypt (251–356), not of Padua, is represented with a pig at his feet, supposed to be the devil, who tempted him in that form. Cf. Dante, *Par.* xxix. 124:
    "Di questo [indulgences] ingrassa il porco Sant' Antonio".
Contes d'Entrapel, No. 20: "Il n'y a andouille à la cheminée, ne jambon au charnier, qui ne tremble à la simple prononntiation et voix d'un petit et harmonieux *Ave Maria*".

[2] In Lucian (*Deor. dial.* vii. 3) Apollo tells how the new-born Hermes stole Zeus' sceptre, and would have stolen the thunderbolt had it not been too hot and too heavy. Cf. *G.* 27; iv. 14; Skeat's *Chaucer, C.T.* notes, vol. v. p. 326.

[3] Frai Antoine du Saix, commandeur de Saint-Antoine, de Bourg en Bresse, in 1532 wrote an *Esperon de discipline* (cf. *P.* 7), at the end of which he styles himself *jambonnier* (Fr. ed.). He is mentioned as the writer of this in *Les Mots dorés de Cathon* (*A.P.F.* vii. 16). Cf. *R.E.R.* ix. 221.

[4] The fickle, inquisitive and turbulent nature of the Gauls is well pointed out by Caesar, *B.G.* iv. 5, to which reference is made in *P.P.* prol.

[5] *Patience*, etc.: "ut nescire cogamur episcoporumne impudentia an plebis patientia hactenus fuerit ineptior", Agrippa, *de van. scient.* c. 64 *fin.*

[6] Fr. *folfré et habeliné*. The meaning of these words is difficult to determine exactly.

[7] *L'hostel de Nesle* was on the site now occupied by the Mint of Paris. For *Nesle* ABC read *Sorbonne*. Francis I had established a bailiff at *Nesle* in 1522 to take cognisance of University jurisdiction (*R.E.R.* viii. 288). The *Oracle of Leucetia* means the pillars of Isis, the protecting goddess of Paris, which in 1514 were in

Leucetia. There the Matter was proposed and the Inconvenience set forth of carrying away the Bells.

After having thoroughly *ergoed pro* and *contra*, it was concluded in *Baralipton*[1] that they should send the oldest and most competent of the Faculty* to Gargantua to point out to him the horrible Inconvenience caused by the Loss of the said Bells. And notwithstanding the Remonstrance of certain Members of the University, who declared that this Duty was more suited to an Orator than a Sophist,† there was chosen for this Business our Master Janotus de Bragmardo.[2]

---

* *La Faculté*, D; *la Faculté Théologale*, ABC.
† *Sophiste*, D; *Théologien*, ABC.

the Church of St Germain des Prés. There was also a *Tour de Nesle*, now replaced by the *Institut de France*. From this tower, according to an old legend, Mary of Burgundy, wife of Louis X (*le Hutin*), used to have scholars, whom she had enticed there, thrown into the Seine. Cf. Villon, *Ballade* (after *Test.* 41) and *P.* 28 *fin*. There is a play of Alexandre Dumas, *La Tour de Nesle*.

[1] *Baralipton* is the designation of a syllogism of the first figure in the wellknown *memoria technica*:

bArbArA cElArEnt, dArII, fErIO, bArAlIpton.

[2] *Bragmardo* is a name coined from *Bracquemart* or *Bragmard*, a cutlass, and made to resemble the designation of an impossible syllogism (AAO).

CHAPTER XVIII

How Janotus de Bragmardo was sent to recover the great Bells from Gargantua

MASTER JANOTUS, with his Hair cut in the Caesarian[1] fashion, clad with his Liripipion[2]* in the ancient manner, and his Stomach well antidoted with Bakehouse Condiments and Holy Water from the Cellar, betook himself to the Lodging of Gargantua, driving before him three red-muzzled Calves of Bedels, and dragging after him five or six artless Masters,[3] thoroughly[4] bedraggled with Mire.

At their Entry Ponocrates met them and was afraid, seeing them thus disguised, and thought they were some Maskers out of their Wits;[5] then he enquired of one of the said artless Masters in the Company, what was the Meaning of this Mummery. It was answered him that they desired their Bells to be restored to them.

Immediately that he heard this, Ponocrates ran to tell the News to Gargantua, so that he might be ready with his Answer and determine at once what he had to do. Gargantua being advised of the matter, called aside Ponocrates his Preceptor, Philotomie[6] his

---

* *liripipion à l'antique*, D; *l. théologal*, ABC.

[1] *Caesarian, i.e.* after the manner of the Roman Emperors, cropped short (cf. Suet. i. 45). Servius, *in Aen.* i. 590, has "a caedendo dicta caesaries". The fashion of wearing the hair short was adopted by Francis I, first among the French Kings. He also grew a beard to conceal a scar which he received while snow-balling.

[2] *Liripipion* is properly the pig-tail to a hood (Ducange). "Est autem habitus magistrorum nostrorum caputium magnum cum *liripipio*", *Epist. Obs. Vir.* i. 26.

[3] *artless Masters.* Fr. *maistres inertes* instead of *ès arts.*

[4] Fr. *à profict de mesnaige* (G. 5; iv. 9), soundly, thoroughly (Cotgrave); so as not to lose any dirt they had gathered.

[5] Cf.

> "*Dion.* (to *Xanthias*): Did you observe? *X.* What? *D.* How alarmed He is? *X.* Aye truly, lest you've lost your wits".

Aristoph. *Ran.* 40.

[6] *Philotomie* (φιλοτομία), not *Philotime* as in ABC.

Steward, Gymnast his Esquire, and Eudemon, and summarily conferred with them on what he was to do as well as to answer.

They were all of Opinion that they should be taken to the Buttery[1] and there made to drink like Roysterers;* and in order that this Cougher might not be puffed up with Vainglory, because the Bells had been given up at his Request, while he was boozing they should send for the Provost of the City, the Rector of the Faculty and the Vicar of the Church,[2] to whom they would deliver up the Bells before the Sophister[3]† had set forth his Commission. After that, in the Presence of these they would hear his fine Harangue. This was done; and the aforesaid Persons having arrived, the Sophister was introduced in the Hall, where they were in full Assembly, and began as follows, coughing:

---

* *rustrement*, D; *théologalement*, ABC.
† *Sophiste*, D; *Théologien*, ABC.

[1] *Le retraict du Guobelet*, the buttery (Cotgrave). Cf. iv. 35.
[2] The Vicar-general of the Bishop of Paris in 1534 was René Du Bellay, afterwards Bishop of Le Mans.
[3] With regard to the word *Sophists* substituted for the word *Theologians* we may compare the following passage of Erasmus: "meo judicio saperent Christiani si...clamosissimos Scotistas et pertinacissimos Occamistas et invictos Albertistas, una cum tota sophistarum manu mitterent in Turcas et Saracenos", *Mor. Enc.* c. 53.

CHAPTER XIX

*The Harangue of Master Janotus de Bragmardo made to
Gargantua for the Recovery of the Bells*

AHEM, hem, hem,[1] gudday,[2] Sir, gudday, *et vobis*, my Masters.
It could not be but good that you should give us back our Bells, for
we have sore Need of them. Hem, hem, hasch. We had oftentimes
heretofore refused good Money for them from those of London[3] in
Cahors, yea and from those of Bordeaux in Brie, who would have
bought them for the substantific Quality of the elementary Complexion which is intronificated in the Terrestreity of their quiddita-
tive Nature, to extraneise[4] the Hail-storms and Whirlwinds from
our Vines, not indeed ours, but those hard by. For if we lose the
Drink we lose everything, Sense and Law.[5]

If you restore them to us at my Request, I shall gain thereby ten
Links of Sausages and a fine Pair of Breeches, which will do great
good to my Legs—or else they will not keep their Promise to me.
Ho, ho, Gad! *Domine*, a Pair of Breeches is good *et vir sapiens non
abhorrebit eam*. Ha, ha, 'tis not every one who wishes has a Pair of

---

[1] *Ahem*, etc. In ridicule of the style of the preachers of that time, especially of
Olivier Maillard, a Franciscan Observantin, †1502 (iv. 8), who marked in his
sermons the places where the preacher was to cough, and who spoke of *l'élo-
quence tousseuse*. In d'Aubigné's *Baron de Faeneste*, iv. c. 8 (*fin.*), the sermon of
Père Ange is thus introduced: "Après les croix, les révérences et le plonge,
ayant fait branler la pointe du capuchon et celle de la barbe, toussé en E-la,
mis le haut mont devotieusement et craché trois fois, il commença d'une haulte
voix".

[2] *gudday*. Fr. *mna dies*, a corrupt pronunciation of *bona dies*. *Na dies* occurs in
Farce nouvelle, A.Th.F. iii. 200. Cf. Cordier, 21. § 10: "Non dicit *bona dies*
transeuntibus, Il ne salue pas les passans".

[3] There is a small *Londres* near Marmande (Lot-et-Garonne), and a Bordeaux
near Ville-Parisis (Seine-et-Marne) (M), but it seems better to consider these
as geographical blunders of the blockhead Janotus.

[4] *extraneise*, etc. Alluding to the practice of ringing church bells to drive
away or modify the effect of hail and thunderstorms, as indicated by the motto
of Schiller's "Bell": *Vivos voco: mortuos plango: fulgura frango*.

[5] Cf. "Qui pert le sien il pert le sens" (Cretin, p. 204), explained in Cordier as *vix in damno quisquam sapit*, 58. § 212. Cf. Ovid, *ex Ponto*, iv. 12. 48: "Et
sensus cum re consiliumque fugit". Old Engl. proverb: "Loss of pence is loss
of sense".

Breeches: I know it well of myself. Consider, *Domine*, I have been these eighteen Days matagrabolising this fine Harangue: *Reddite quae sunt Caesaris Caesari et quae sunt Dei Deo. Ibi jacet lepus.*[1]

By my Faith, *Domine*, if you will sup with me *in camera*, Copsbody, *charitatis,*[2] *nos faciemus bonum cherubin.*[3] *Ego occidi unum porcum et ego habet bonum vino.*[4] But of good Wine we cannot make bad Latin.

Well now, *de parte Dei date nobis Clochas nostras.* Hold, I give you in the Name of the Faculty a *Sermones de Utino,*[5] that *utinam* you would give us our Bells. *Vultis etiam Pardonos? Per diem vos habebitis et nihil payabitis.*

O Sir, *Domine, clochidonaminor nobis.* Verily, *est bonum urbis.* Every one uses them. If they fit your Mare well, so they do our Faculty, *quae comparata est jumentis insipientibus et similis facta est eis. Psalmo nescio quo;* and yet I quoted it well in my Note-book *et est unum bonum Achilles.*[6] Hem, hem, ahem, hasch.

See here, I prove to you that you ought to give me them. *Ego sic argumentor: Omnis clocha*[7] *clochabilis in clocherio clochando, clochans clochativo clochare facit clochabiliter clochantes. Parisius habet clochas. Ergo gluc.*[8]

---

[1] *Ibi jacet lepus* (cf. iii. 41) = *Cy gist le lievre,* from the difficulty of seeing a hare in her form. From this comes the English word *gist*. Cf. Chaucer, *C.T.* B. 1886: "Thou lokest as thou woldest find an hare".

[2] *In camera charitatis* is the refrain of some lines spoken by *Devocion* against *Papelardize* in Gringore, *Les folles Entreprises* (vol. i. p. 107, ed. Elz.). A pun is intended between *charitatis* and *caro*, meat.

[3] *faciemus hodie bonum cherubin*, Cordier, 28. § 15 and 58. § 190, who explains *cherubin = chere*, good cheer.

[4] *ego habet bonum vino.* Cf. Basselin, *Chanson* 21:

"Certes hoc vinum est bonus,
De mauvais latin ne vous chaille".

[5] Fr. *Leonardi de Utino* (Udine) *sermones aurei de Sanctis* (Lugd. Joh. Trechsel, 1494). This gives the pun on *utinam*. These sermons were composed in 1446 and first printed at Venice, 1473 (*Menagiana*, ii. 406).

[6] *Achilles, i.e.* an unanswerable argument (*argumentum Achilleum*, Erasm. *Ad.* i. 7. 41), with reference to the Eleatic puzzle of Achilles and the tortoise. "Les prelats faisoyent d'icelles leur Achilles", H. Estienne, *Apol. pour Hérod.* ii. 168; "Les femmes faisoyent leur Achilles de ce qu'il avoit dict", Hept. *Nov.* 46; "Their Achilles and strongest argument", Sir T. Browne, *Pseud. Epid.* ii. 2 (p. 49).

[7] *clocha*, etc. Cf. Cordier, 34. § 1: "Non ibis hodie perostium, sed perclochetum (*clochier*), Hodie claudicabis".

[8] *Ergo gluc*, an ancient formula to express a conclusion that concluded nothing.

Ha, ha, ha, 'tis well put, that! It is *in tertio primae*,[1] in *Darii*, or
elsewhere. By my Soul, I have seen the Time when I could play
the Devil in arguing, but for the present I do nothing but dote.
And henceforward I want nothing but good Wine,[2] a good Bed,
my Back to the Fire, my Belly to the Table, and a good deep Dish.

Hei, Domine, I beseech you, *in nomine Patris et Filii et Spiritus
Sancti, Amen*, to restore us our Bells, and God keep you from Harm
and our Lady from Health,[3] *qui vivit et regnat per omnia saecula saecu-
lorum. Amen.* Hem, hasch, ehasch, grrenhen, hasch.

*Verum enim vero, quando quidem, dubio procul, edepol, quoniam, ita
certe, me Deus fidius,* a City without Bells is like a Blind man without
a Stick, an Ass without a Crupper, and a Cow without Cymbals.
Until you have restored them to us we will not cease to cry after
you like a Blind man who has lost his Stick, to bray after you like
an Ass without a Crupper, and to bellow after you like a Cow
without Cymbals.

A certain Latiniser[4] dwelling near the Hospital said once,

---

[1] In the third mood of the first figure of syllogisms, according to the *memoria*:
bArbArA cElArEnt dArII, fErIO bArAlIpton.

[2] *good Wine*, etc. Cf. Cretin, p. 243:

"Plus n'a besoing, tant sa force amolit,
Que de profonde escuelle et de mol lict";
and

"Boire souvent de grand randon,
Le dos au feu, le ventre à table,
Avant partir de la maison,
C'est opiate prouffitable".
Cl. Marot, *Remede contre la peste, Epig.* 266.

[3] Fr. *Dieu vous garde de mal et Nostre Dame de santé.* A double interpretation is
evidently intended. Cf. *Watelet de tous mestiers, A.P.F.* xiii. 156:

"Bonnes gens, Dieu vous garde de foye
Et Nostre Dame de santé".

There is a N.D. de Santé at Carpentras and other places in the South of France
(*R.E.R.* vii. 441).

[4] *A certain Latiniser*, etc. In 1529–30 a new prose translation of Sebastian
Brandt's *Narrenschiff* (1494) was published by Juste at Lyons and at Paris by
Ph. le Noir and Denis Janot. At the end of the preface occur the following
words: "*translatée de latin en françoys et imprimée à Paris par Denis Janot, De-
mourant devant l'hostel dieu*, a lenseigne de la Corne de Cerf" (*R.E.R.* i. 224). It
seems then that this passage refers to the translator of the *Narrenschiff*, which

quoting the Authority of one Taponnus[1]—I lie, it was Pontanus, a
secular Poet[2]—that he wished they were made of Feathers and the
Clapper of a Fox-tail, because they engendered the Colic[3] in the
Bowels of his Brain when he was composing his carminiform Lines.
But

> *Nac petetin petetac,*[4]
> *Tique, torche lorne,*

he was declared a Heretic. We make them as of Wax.[5] And
further the Deponent saith not. *Valete et plaudite.* *Calepinus recensui.*[6]

---

contains in c. 41 the reference to the bell with a fox's brush for a clapper, and
that he is intended by Janotus de Bragmardo.

> "Whether that a bell be hangyd or lye aground,
> If unto the same a clapper lacke or fayle,
> The bell shall make but sympyll noyse or sound
> Though thou in it do hang a Foxe's tayl."

Barclay's *Shippe of Fools.*

[1] *Taponnus,* a bung, anagram on John Jovian *Pontanus* (1426–1503), head of
the Neapolitan "Academy", who had written a dialogue entitled *Actius* from
which had been extracted a Latin bill of sale. This was published by Rabelais,
together with a will of Cuspidius composed by Pomponius Laetus, as genuine
relics of antiquity. Cf. *Epist. Nuncup.* ad Almaricum Bouchard.

[2] *a secular Poet.* All writers who were not Roman Catholics—Virgil, Cicero,
Homer, etc. included—were styled secular *poets,* cf. *Epist. Obs. Vir.* Petrarch
(*Epist. Fam.* iv. 15) twits Giovanni Andreae, the great canonist, with this.

[3] *Colic.* Fr. *chronique.* In the dialogue *Charon* (Dialogi II, Charon et Antonius:
Neapoli 1491) Pontanus has the following passage: "CHARON Nescis, Mercuri,
paulo ante quam mihi animum pupugeris ubi *Campanos* nominasti. Nimio enim
sum veritus ne de *campanis* dicturus esses aliquid, quarum non modo sonitum
verum etiam nomen odi".

[4] *Nac petetin petetac,* etc. (cf. iv. 56) is from Jannequin's song, *Deffaicte des
Suisses à Marignan.*

[5] Fr. *Nous les faisons comme de cire, i.e. les hérétiques.* Cf. Patelin, l. 627: "Ils en
oeuvrent comme de cire".

[6] The three endings given here are (1) that of depositions, (2) that of Latin
comedies, (3) that of a copyist at the end of a manuscript. In *Epist. Obs. Vir.*
ii. 40 a letter from Joannes Crapp ends thus: "Laus Deo. Valete. Et sic est
finis. Telos. Tetragrammaton. Datum Rhomanae Curiae". In old editions of
Terence at the end of each play occurs: "Vos valete et plaudite: ego Calliopius
recensui". Cf. Burton's *Anat.* ii. 3. 5. Calliopius was some old grammarian,
but Rabelais substitutes Calepinus the lexicographer as more familiar and
necessary to the dunce Bragmardo. Ambrosio Calepino (1435–1510), an
Augustinian of Bergamo, composed a polyglot lexicon. It was first published
at Reggio (1502) and was constantly enlarged by its author, Passerat and others,
till it comprised eleven languages. An edition was published by Gryphius in
1540. It appeared last at Padua in 1758 and 1772 (Lacroix). *Calepin* is now
used in French for a note-book. The verb *calepiner* also existed.

CHAPTER XX

How the Sophist* carried off his Cloth,[1] and how he had a Suit at Law against the other Masters†

THE Sophist had no sooner finished, than Ponocrates and Eudemon burst out laughing so heartily that they nearly gave up the Ghost; neither more nor less than Crassus[2] did, on seeing a Jackass eating Thistles, and as Philemon,[3] on seeing an Ass eat some Figs which had been prepared for his Dinner, died by dint of Laughing.

Together with them began Master Janotus to laugh his very best, so that the Tears came into their Eyes from the vehement Concussion of the Substance of the Brain, from which were expressed these lachrymal Humidities and flowed down along the optic Nerves; wherein was represented by them Democritus Heraclitising and Heraclitus Democritising.

This Laughter being quite appeased, Gargantua consulted with his People what was to be done hereupon. Thereupon Ponocrates was of opinion that they should make this fine Orator drink again; and, seeing that he had given them Amusement and made them

---

* Sophiste, D; Théologien, ABC.
† Les aultres maîtres, D; les Sorbonistes, ABC.

[1] carried off his Cloth. Throughout this episode runs a covert reference to the rascally Patelin of the farce, carrying off the cloth of which he cheated the draper. Cf. Patelin, ll. 848–9.

[2] Crassus ἀγέλαστος (grandfather of the triumvir). This trait is again referred to in iv. Ep. Ded. and v. 25, the information being derived from Erasmus (Ad. i. 10. 71: Similes habent labra lactucas), who refers to Cic. Tusc. iii. § 31, de Fin. v. § 92, Pliny, 7. 79, Macrob. Sat. ii. 1. 6, and quotes St Jerome, Epist. ad Chromatium (i. p. 340, Migne): "Secundum illud quoque de quo semel in vita Crassum ait risisse Lucilius: similem habent lactucam labra, comedente asino carduos'". Cf. "Like lettuce like lippes; a scabbed horse for a scald squire", New Custome, Act ii. Sc. 2 (1573) (Dodsley, vol. i. p. 283). Milton (Sonnet on Tetrachordon) has a curious allusion to this: "Those rugged names to our like mouths grow sleek".

[3] Philemon (G. 10; iv. 17; v. 7). This story is from Lucian's Macrobii, c. 25, but in iv. 17 it is derived from Valerius Maximus, as is indicated by the reading "Philomenes"—that of the Paris editions of that writer.

laugh more than ever did Songe-creux,[1] that they should give him
the ten Links of Sausages mentioned in his merry Harangue, with
a pair of Breeches, three hundred regulation Billets of Wood, five-
and-twenty Hogsheads of Wine, and a Bed with three Courses of
Goose-down, and a Dish mighty capacious and deep; all which
things, he said, were necessary for his Old age.

All this was done as had been determined, except that Gargantua, doubting that they could not at once find Breeches that
would suit his Legs; doubting also what Fashion of them would
be most convenient for the said Orator, [whether the Martingale
fashion, which is a Drawbridge, for his greater Ease; or the
Mariner fashion, for the greater Solace of his Kidneys; or the Swiss
fashion, which keeps warm the Belly-tabret; or the Cod's-tail
fashion, to prevent overheating his Reins], caused to be given to
him seven Ells of black Cloth, and three of white for the Lining.
The Wood was carried by the Porters; the Masters of Arts carried
the Sausages and the Dish; Master Janotus himself would carry the
Cloth.

One of the said Masters, named Master Jousse Bandouille,
pointed out to him that this was neither seemly nor decent for one
of his Degree, and that he should deliver it to one of them.

"Ha!" said Janotus, "Blockhead, Blockhead, thou dost not
conclude *in modo et figura*. See whereto serve the *Suppositions* and
Parva logicalia.[2] *Pannus pro quo supponit?*"

---

[1] *Songe-creux* was the name given to Jehan de l'Espine de Pontalais, a player
of farces, moralities, etc. before Francis I. The name was probably derived from
pieces he wrote: *Prenostication de Maistre Albert Songe-creux bisscain* (*A.P.F.* xii.
172) and *Les Contredictz de Songe-creux* (*autrement du prince des sots*) *par Pierre
Gringore* (Galliot du Pré, Paris 1530). He is mentioned in the *Dizain* at the beginning of *Pantagruel*, and as *M. n. Songecrusion* in *P.* 7. *Le Seigneur du Pont Alletz*
is one of the characters in a *Sottie* of Gringore (vol. i. p. 207, ed. Elz.).

[2] *Petri Hispani Ulyssiponensis Summulae Logicales*, of which the *parva logicalia*
form a portion, "treats of ambiguities attaching to the use of words with a
varying connotation", Mullinger, *Hist. Univ. Camb.* i. 178, 350. Agrippa, *de
van. scient.* c. 8, speaks with the utmost contempt of this and similar treatises.
Petrus Hispanus was afterwards Pope John XXI (†1277). "*Suppositio* est ac-
ceptio termini substantivi pro aliquo", Petr. Hisp. *Tract.* vi; "Terminus in-
finitatis communiter tentus supponit confusè et distributivè ut homo currit, ibi
homo supponit confusè et distributivè", *Tract.* vii. "The Suppositions" are a
section of the *parva logicalia*, and perhaps the reading should be "suppositions
ès parva logicalia", not *et*.

"*Confusè*", said Bandouille, "*et distributivè.*"

"I ask thee not, Blockhead," said Janotus, "*quomodo supponit* but *pro quo*? It is, Blockhead, *pro tibiis meis.* And therefore I will carry it *egomet, sicut suppositum portat appositum.*"[1]

And so he did carry it off stealthily,[2] as Patelin did his Cloth.

The best Part of it was when this Cougher, in full Assembly[3] held at the Mathurins, confidently demanded his Breeches and Sausages. For they were peremptorily refused him on the ground that he had them of Gargantua, according to the Informations given thereupon. He pointed out to them that this had been *gratis* and out of his Liberality; by which they were not in any way absolved from their Promises.

This notwithstanding, it was answered that he should be content with Reason, and that no other Scrap should he get therefrom.

"Reason!" said Janotus; "we use none of that here; wretched Traitors, you are good for nothing; the Earth doth not bear more wicked Folk than you are; I know it well. Do not hobble[4] in the Presence of Cripples; I have practised Villainy with you. 'Ods Spleen! I will inform the King of the enormous Abuses that are forged here, and by your Hands, and carried out. May I turn Leper, if he do not have you all burnt up alive as Bougres, Traitors, Heretics, and Seducers, Enemies of God and of Virtue".

At these Words, they framed Articles[5] against him; he on the other side cited them to appear. The End of it was that the Suit

---

[1] *sicut suppositum,* etc. Cf. iii. 40, *accessorium naturam sequitur principalis,* from Sext. V, *Reg. Jur.* 42.

[2] *stealthily.* Fr. *en tapinois.*

> "Dea, il s'en vint *en tapinois*
> A tout mon drap soubz son aisselle."
>
> Patelin, ll. 848–9.

[3] *en plein acte de Sorbonne,* ABC. It was customary in the University of Paris to assemble in the temple of the Mathurins to hear the rector harangue.

[4] *Do not hobble,* etc. Cf. "Loripedem rectus derideat" (Juv. ii. 23); "Devant boiteux ne faut clochier", *Le debat des deux demoiselles, A.P.F.* v. 278; "Quasi claudus claudo claudicationis vitium per contumeliam objiciat", Erasm. *Ad.* iii. 2. 21.

[5] *framed Articles, i.e.* laid plaints against him. "*Articuli* dicuntur capitula in judicio probando". Numberless were the charges that could be brought in the matter of heresy. "Salutes vobis plures opto quam sunt...in Parrhisia *articuli*", says a correspondent to Ortuinus Gratius in *Epist. Obs. Vir.* ii. 16.

was retained by the Court, and is there still. On this Point the Masters* made a Vow[1] never to cleanse themselves; and Master Janotus with his Adherents made a Vow never to blow their Noses until Judgment should be given on this by definitive Sentence.

Bound by these Vows, they have to this day remained dirty and rheumy; for the Court has not yet fully examined[2] all the Proceedings. The Sentence will be given at the next Greek Calends,[3] that is to say, never. For you know that they do more than Nature doth, and act contrary to their own Articles. The Articles of Paris proclaim that God alone can do Things that are infinite. Nature produceth nothing that is immortal, for she putteth an End and Period to all Things produced by her, seeing that *omnia orta cadunt*, etc.[4]

But these Swallowers of Fog[5] make the Suits pending before them both infinite and immortal;[6] and in so doing they have given Occasion to and verified the Saying of Chilon the Lacedaemonian, consecrated at Delphi, that Misery is the Companion of Law-suits,[7] and that Suitors are miserable, for that they sooner come to the End of their Lives than to the Rights they put forward.

---

* *Les Magistres*, D; *Les Sorbonicoles*, ABC.

[1] *made a Vow*, etc. (cf. iii. 24). This is a parody of the vow of the Argives never to wear their hair long till they had regained Thyrea (Herod. i. 82).

[2] *examined.* Fr. *grabeler* (P. 7, 10, 13, 16; iii. 16; iv. 18), said to be from *grabeau*, a small substance in pharmacy; but cf. Pasq. *tomi duo*, p. 142: "propositiones per *cribrum* separem". Also *cribellationes* occurs in a Latin translation of Avicenna.

[3] *Greek Calends* (P. 1). "(Augustus) cum aliquos numquam soluturos significare vult, *ad Kal. Graecas soluturos ait*", Suet. ii. 87. Quoted Erasm. *Ad.* i. 5. 84; Cordier, 58. § 151.

[4] "Videtur secutus Epicurum, qui ait: Omnia, quae orta, cadunt atque aucta senescunt", Serv. *in Georg.* ii. 336 and Sall. *Bell. Jug.* 2. § 3. Quoted by Ioh. Nev. *Sylv. Nupt.* fo. 179. 3.

[5] *Swallowers of Fog* (G. 54; iii. prol.). Lawyers are called also in English "pettifoggers". Milton has "this petty fog of witnesses", *Prel. Epis.* and Aristophanes, *Ach.* 684, δίκης ἠλύγην, the mist of a law-suit.

[6] *Suits...infinite and immortal.* Cf. Justinian, C. iii. 1. 13: "Properandum nobis visum est ne lites fiant paene immortales et vitae hominum modum excedant"; Δ, ii. 14. 10: "Volentes finem imponi litibus, ne immortales existant".

[7] "Chiloni Lacedaemonio praecepta....Delphis consecrando aureis literis ...comitem aeris alieni atque litis esse miseriam", Pliny, 7. 119.

CHAPTER XXI

The Study and Manner of Life of Gargantua according to the Discipline of his Sophistical Preceptors*

THE first Days being thus spent and the Bells put up again in their Place, the Citizens of Paris in acknowledgment of this Courtesy, offered to maintain and feed his Mare as long as he should please. This Gargantua took in good Part, and they sent her to live in the Forest of Bière.[1] I believe she is not there any longer now.

This done, he wished with all his Mind to study at the Discretion of Ponocrates. But he, for the Beginning, ordered that he should go on in his accustomed Manner, in order to understand by what Means, in so long a Time, his former Preceptors had made him so foolish, simple and ignorant.

Accordingly he arranged his Time in such Fashion that ordinarily he awaked between eight and nine of the Clock, whether it was Daylight or not; for so had his former Governors† ordered, citing that which David saith: *Vanum est vobis ante lucem surgere.*

Then he did tumble and toss, stretch his Legs, and wallow in the Bed some time, the better to stir his animal Spirits; and he apparelled himself according to the Season; but he did willingly wear a great long Gown of coarse Frieze furred with Fox-skins; after-

---

* *Sophistes*, D; *Sorbonagres*, ABC.
† *Regens antiques*, D; *Regens théologicques*, ABC.

[1] *The Forest of Bière* (Lat. *foresta Bierrae*) must have been the forest of Fontainebleau. Cf. *R.R.* 16,266:

"En sa main tint une fort lance
. . . .
Il n'en croist nule tele en Biére".

In *P.* 15 it is called the *forest de Bièvre*. A poem celebrating the birth of a prince (afterwards Francis II) at Fontainebleau begins *En la forestz de Bièvre, A.P.F.* i. 229. The river Bièvre falls into the Seine just before the Pont d'Austerlitz.

wards he combed himself with a Comb in the Almain[1] Fashion, which is with his Thumb and four Fingers, for his Preceptors said that to comb himself in any other Way, to wash or make himself clean, was to lose Time in this World.

Then he...., ..., ..., ..., ..., yawned, spat, coughed, hawked, sneezed, blew his Nose like an Archdeacon;[2] and breakfasted, so as to abate the Effect of the Dew and the bad Air, on good fried Tripes, fair Carbonadoes, fine Hams, good Ragout of Game, and a Store of Soup of Prime.[3]

Ponocrates pointed out to him that he ought not to eat so immediately after leaving his Bed, without having previously taken some Exercise.

Gargantua answered: "What! have I not taken sufficient Exercise?[4] I have rolled myself round six or seven times in my Bed before I rose. Is not that enough? The Pope Alexander did use to do so by the Advice of his Jew Physician[5] and lived till his Death in spite of his Detractors. My first Masters have thereto accustomed me, saying that to break one's Fast caused a good Memory; therefore they drank thereat first. I find myself very well for it and only dine the better therefor.

"Also Master Tubal told me (he was first as a Licentiate at Paris) that it is not every Advantage to run apace, but to set forth

---

[1] *Jacques Almain* was a doctor of the University of Paris. There was a book, Jacobi Almain, *Questiones a decima quarta distinctione Scoti* (Paris 1526). The editions of Juste of 1535 and 1542 (B, D) read *Almain*, that of C (1537) and others read *Aleman*.

[2] *Archdeacon*, as richer and more self-indulgent than ordinary Churchmen.

[3] *Soup of Prime* (iii. 15) = of the first monastical *hour*. This consisted, according to Cotgrave, of "Cheese and bread put into pottage; or chopped Parseley strewed or layed together with the fat of the Beefe-pot, on the bread".

[4] *Exercise.* "Assiduitatem concubitus velut exercitationis genus *clinopalen* vocabat", Suet. *Dom.* c. 22.

[5] *Jew Physician.* This was Bonnet de Lates, a converted Jew of Provence, established at Rome at the beginning of the sixteenth century. He was physician to Alexander VI, to whom he dedicated a treatise: *Boneti de Latis medici provenzalis, annuli per eum compositi, super astrologiam utilitates.* Cf. Gringore, *Sottie* (p. 226, ed. Elz.):

> "*Mere Sotte.*   Mon medecin Juif prophetise
> Que soye perverse et que bon est.
>
> *Sotte Fiance.* Et qui est-il?
> *M.S.*   Maistre Bonnet".

betimes. So the Sum-total of the Health of our Humanity is not to drink switter-swatter[1] like Ducks, but rather to drink early in the Morning; *Unde versus*:

> To rise betimes doth not give Rest;
> To drink betimes is far the best".[2]

After having breakfasted right well, he went to Church and they carried for him in a great Basket, a huge Breviary enslippered[3] in its Case, weighing, what with Grease, Clasps and Parchment-cover, little more or less than eleven Quintals six Pounds. There he heard twenty-six or thirty Masses. Meantime came his Matins-mumbler to his Place, muffled and crested like a Hoopoe, and with his Breath well antidoted with a Store of Vine-tree Syrup; with him Gargantua mumbled all his Kyrielles[4] (*Litanies*), and so curiously did he pick them over, that not a single Grain (*bead*) thereof fell to the Earth.[5]

As he came from Church, they brought him on an Ox-wain a Pile of Paternosters of Saint Claude,[6] each one as big as is a Hat-block;[7] and as he walked through the Cloisters, Galleries or Garden he said more of them than sixteen Hermits.

Then he studied some miserable Half-hour, with his Eyes fixed

---

[1] *switter-swatter*. Fr. *à tas, à tas*. Cf. Coquillart, i. 180:

> "Injures trop, *à tas, à tas*".

[2] A parody of the verses of Pierre Grosnet's *Les Mots dorés de Cathon*:

> "Lever matin n'est point bon heur
> Mais venir à poinct est meilleur".

In the *Proverbia communia*, Joh. Aegidii Nivernensis, is

> "Lever matin n'est pas heure
> Mais desjeuner est la plus seure".

[3] Fr. *empantoflé*, *i.e.* having the authorisation of the Pope, sealed as it were with his slipper, *pantofla decretorum* (*P.* 7). (D.)

[4] *Kyrielle* from *Kyrie eleison* = the responses in the Litany. Coquillart (ii. 99) has "On est mis en la kyrielle", *i.e.* in the number of those who say "Lord have mercy upon us".

[5] "Crevit autem Samuel et Dominus erat cum eo, et non cecidit ex omnibus ejus verbis in terram" (1 *Reg.* ii. 19).

[6] *St Claude* is a place in Franche-Comté on the Bienne, about 27 miles north-east of La Cluse, which is on the line from Bourg to Geneva. A considerable trade in the manufacture of beads, etc. still continues at this place.

[7] Fr. *moulle d'un bonnet*, *i.e.* a head. Cf. *G.* 9.

on his Book; but as the Comic poet says, his Soul was in the Kitchen.[1]

Then voiding a full Official,[2] he sat down to Table; and because he was naturally phlegmatic, he began his Repast by some dozens of Hams, smoked Neats' tongues, Botargoes, Chitterlings and other Vaunt-couriers of Wine.

Meantime four of his People threw into his Mouth, one after another continuously, Mustard by the Bucketful; then he drank a horrific Draught of white Wine to relieve his Kidneys. After that, he ate, according to the Season, Meats agreeable to his Appetite, and then left off eating when his Belly was blown up.

For drinking he had neither End nor Rule; for he used to say that the Goals and Bounds[3] of drinking were when, as the Man drank, the Cork-sole of his Slippers swelled[4] to the Height of half-a-Foot.

---

[1] "Jamdudum animus est in patinis" (Ter. *Eun.* 816) is quoted by Erasmus in *Ad.* iii. 7. 30: *Animus est in coriis.*

[2] Fr. *plein urinal*, D. ABC give *official*, which has the same meaning, cf. *G.* 9.

[3] *Goals and Bounds.* Fr. *metes et bournes.* "The very old Whitechapel Hay Market is without 'metes and bounds'", *The Standard*, Aug. 23, 1911.

[4] *swelled, i.e.* by the wine that exuded from his pores into his slippers. *Pantophle*, according to Rabelais' *briefve declaration* at the end of the *Fourth Book*, is derived from the Greek παντόφελλος, all of cork. Cf. Pliny, 10. 153: "Scitum de quodam reperitur Syracusis tamdiu potare solitum, donec coöperta terra fetum ederent ova".

CHAPTER XXII

The Games of Gargantua[1]

THEN lumpishly mumbling over a Scrap of a Grace, he washed his Hands in fresh Wine, picked his Teeth with a Hog's foot and discoursed merrily with his People.

Then the green Cloth being spread, they displayed a store of Cards, a number of Dice, and an abundance of Chess-boards. There he played at:

Flush[2]	Slam[4]
Prime[3]	Robber[5]

---

[1] This collection of games is put together by Rabelais in conformity with the taste of those times, which delighted in long lists or "litanies" (cf. a "litany of Proverbs", *Don Quixote*, ii. c. 43). Here the beginning is made with games of cards, draughts, chess and backgammon, to the number of about thirty-five; afterwards games of forfeits and indoor games, but later on free reins are given to memory and imagination, and any kind of game seems to be put down at random. Sometimes the same game is repeated in various forms with names differing in the various provinces of France. Descriptions and explanations have been here taken from many sources. Several of the card-games are simple. In earlier times they provided sufficient interest, but afterwards they formed parts of more complex games, such as *primero* and *picquet* (known as *cent*, or in Spanish *cientos*). Thus *flus, prime, ronfle, sequence* form parts of *picquet*. Rabelais' purpose in putting down all these games was to shew the frivolity of such amusements, as contrasted with the scientific instruction to be gained from those allowed by Ponocrates in the next chapter (*R.E.R.* vi. 1–37). The same notions about frivolous and useful games may be found in John of Salisbury, *Policraticus*, i. 5, with the addition of profane swearing, which is treated of by Rabelais in v. 10. Cf. also Chaucer, *The Persone's Tale*, I. 793 and *The Pardonere's Tale*, C. 651.

[2] *Flush* (Fr. *au flux*, iii. 35; v. 7). A sequence of four cards of the same colour —the winning chance in *primero*.

[3] *Prime.* Four cards, all of different colours.

[4] *Slam* (Fr. *à la vole*), when a player takes all the tricks. *Vola* is the Latin for the palm of the hand, or the sole of the foot, Pliny, 11. 253; Macrob. *in SS*. i. 6. 80. Cf. G. 11; *volam pedis ostendere*, Erasm. *Ad*. iv. 10. 56.

[5] *Robber* (Fr. *à la pille*). In certain games *de triomphe* a player has sometimes the right to take all the cards of one suit and substitute others. This was called *piller les cartes*. Cf. *amusez à la pille; G*. 36.

Triumph[1]
Prick and spare not[2]
The Hundred[3]
The Spinet[4]
Poor Moll[5]
The Fib[6]

Pass ten[7]
Trente et un[8]
Pair and Sequence[9]
Three hundred[10]
Beggar my Neighbour[11]
Odd Man out[12]

---

[1] Fr. *à la triomphe*. Somewhat resembles *écarté*, but the leading idea is the *trump* suit dominating the rest. Mentioned *A.P.F.* viii. 307 and Shakesp. *Ant. and Cleop.* iv. 14. 20:

> "she, Eros, hath
> Pack'd cards with Caesar and false-played my glory
> Unto an enemy's *triumph*".

See also Bishop Latimer's sermons *On the card*.

[2] Fr. *à la Picardie*. Probably an old form of picquet.

> "J'avais cinquante et cinq de *roffle*
> En jouant à la Picardie."
>
> *Chicheface* in *A.P.F.* xi. 290.

[3] Fr. *au cent* (*jouer au cent*, Hept. *Nov.* 59). Ital. *centos*, Span. *cientos*, Engl. *cent, sant*, or The Hundred, are the old names for *Piquet*. Cf. Cavendish on *Piquet*. The game seems to have been developed from the simple forms *Flux, Point, Prime, Ronfle*, etc. The name *Picquet* is probably from *picques*, from *espees*, Span. *espada*, the earlier form of the English *spades*.

[4] Fr. *à l'espinay, Spineticum*, from *Spina*, the Sunday before Lent, a game called *Espinette* played in Dauphiné. It was a *hastiludium* or tournament. The names and arms of the *reges Spineti* up to 1526 (when they were abolished) were preserved in the *domus publica Insulensis* (Ducange).

[5] Fr. *à la malheureuse*. It is the same game as *au malheureux, au maucontent*, and *au cocu* or *à la hère* which occur lower down.

[6] Fr. *au fourby*.

[7] Fr. *à passe-dix*. Played with three dice with the object of exceeding ten by the aggregate number of points in a throw (cf. *Baron de Faeneste*, iv. 44; *R.E.R.* vi. 29).

[8] Practically the same game as *trente et quarante*, 31 points being the winning number while a forfeit is exacted for excess or defect.

[9] Fr. *pair et séquence*. Two cards of the same kind were to be got together, followed by a suit of the same colour.

[10] Fr. *à trois cens* (cf. iv. 14, *au trois cens trois*). Three hundred was the score aimed at.

[11] Fr. *au malheureux*. This is a variant of *à la malheureuse* and *au maucontent* (*infra*), sometimes called *la hère* and in Auvergne *l'asne*.

[12] Fr. *à la condemnade* (Ital. *condennata*). "Au *glic* ou *à la condemnade*", Coquillart, *Droits nouveaulx*, i. 85. Cf. Cl. Marot, *Epistre* (18): "qu'il perdit *à la condemnade*"; "Ilz passerent deux ou trois heures à jouer *au flus, à la sequence, à la condemnade, au trou madame* (cf. iv. 39), *à la clef, à remue menage* et aultres tels jeux qui ne sont pas defendus", de Cholières, *Contes*, fo. 174, quoted by Littré. One player called the card, the second cut, and the third dealt, till the card called for appeared.

The turned Card[1]	Who doth one doth the other[10]
Take Miss [2]	Sequences[11]
Lansquenet[3]	Cockall[12]
Cuckow[4]	Taroc[13]
Let him speak that hath it[5]	Losing Lodam[14]
Teetotum[6]	Gulls[15]
Marriage[7]	Torture[16]
I have it[8]	Snorer[17]
Opinion[9]	Gleek[18]

---

[1] Fr. *à la carte virade*, in "cutting for knaves", etc. One of the cooks in iv. 40 bears this name.

[2] Fr. *au maucontent*, another name for *le hère*, cf. *supra*, *au malheureux*.

[3] *Lansquenet*. Still known under this name, also as "lantern-loo", and now better as "loo".

[4] Fr. *au cocu*. Another form of *au maucontent*, when a player has the right to exchange a card with his right-hand neighbour, unless it be the king of the suit which he holds, when he calls *coucou*.　　　　[5] Fr. *à qui a si parle* (iv. 65).

[6] Fr. *à pille, nade, jocque, fore*, or P.N.J.F., marking the sides of the teetotum. *Pille*, Ital. *pigliar*. *Nade*, Span. *nada*, nothing. *Jocque*, Ital. *giuoco*, game. *Fore*, Ital. *fuora*, all over.

[7] Fr. *à mariaige*. Also known as *la mariée* and *la guimbade* or *brisque*, is a game of which the object is to get the King and Queen of Hearts into the same hand.

[8] Fr. *au gay*. The old French form for *j'ai* in the game *j'ai flus et sequence*. Cf. d'Aubigné, *Baron de Faeneste*, iv. 14.　　　[9] Fr. *à l'opinion*. Cf. *infra*, *au propous*.

[10] Fr. *à qui faict l'ung faict l'aultre*. The French word *faire* is used here of dealing cards.

[11] *Sequence* has much the same meaning as *flush*, a run of cards more than three of the same colour.

[12] Fr. *au luettes* (P. 5; v. 23). A Spanish card-game in which the names for the suits are Deniers, Coupes, Espées, Bastons (Span. *Dineros, Copas, Espadillos, Bastos*). Ducange, s.v. *Lucas*: "Ad aleas et taxillos vel etiam cum laicis ad *lucas* ludere nolite".

[13] Fr. *au tarau* (v. 23). A Spanish game so called because the backs of the cards were *tarotées*, or decorated with lozenge-shaped patterns.

[14] Fr. *Coquimbert, qui gagne perd* = Simple Simon, winner loses. Florio suggests that it is derived from the Italian game *carica l'asino*. Perhaps it should be spelt *Load'em*: cf. *Returne from Parnassus*, Prol. l. 14, "you that have been deepe students at post and paire, Saint (Fr. *cent*) and Loadum". Cf. Petronius, c. 59: "Semper in hac re qui vincitur vincit"; Strutt's *Games and Pastimes*, iv. 2. 9.

[15] Fr. *au beliné*. Cf. *P.* 7, *le beliné en Court*; iv. prol. *fin*.

[16] Fr. *le torment*. This game is quite unknown.

[17] Fr. *à la ronfle* (Ital. *ronfa*) is "the point" at *primero* or *piquet*. It consists of having four cards which make 55. It is also called *prime*. This however is beaten by a *flush*, or four cards of the same suit.

> "J'avais cinquante et cinq de *roffle*
> En jouant à la Picardie."　　　　*A.P.F.* xi. 290.

[18] Fr. *glic* (*glissis*, Ducange). Played by three persons, with 44 cards, each

Honours[1]   Black and white[6]
Morra[2]   Raffles[7]
Chess[3]   Mumchance[8]
Fox and Geese[4]   Three Dice[9]
Nine men's morris[5]   Tables[10]

---

hand having 12 cards and 8 being left for "Stock"; Nares's *Glossary*. The object
is to get 3 cards of a kind together, *e.g.* 3 knaves, 3 kings, etc. Cf. Coquillart,
i. 85: "au glic ou à la condemnade".

[1] Fr. *aux honneurs* = the honours or court-cards, which we count in whist, etc.

[2] Fr. *à la mourre* (iv. 14). An Italian game played by two players or by two
or three pairs. The adversaries sit opposite each other and both together thrust
forth their hands with any chance number of fingers extended, and *both together*
guess the aggregate number of fingers extended on both hands. The Roman
name was *micatia*: cf. Cic. *de Off.* iii. § 77; Erasm. *Ad.* i. 8. 23.

[3] Fr. *aux eschetz*. "Ludamus *ad scacos*, ludamus *latrunculis*", Cordier, 38. § 47.

[4] Fr. *au renard*. Cf. Ovid, *A.A.* iii. 358; *Trist.* ii. 478. *Vulpis* in John of
Salisbury, *de nugis curial.* i. 5 and Agrippa, *de van. scient.* c. 14.

[5] Fr. *aux marelles*. Played either on a piece of turf (scored to imitate the board,
which has one square within another (cf. Shakesp. *Mids. N. Dr.* ii. 1. 98)), or on
the board with counters called *Merrils*. See Strutt, *Games and Pastimes*, iv. 25.
13; Coquillart, *Droits nouveaulx*, i. 166 n.; *A.P.F.* ix. 162. In Ducange *marrellas*
or *merallus* is a counter.

[6] Fr. *au vasches*. Some game played with white and black counters. Cf.
Ducange, "Lesquels se prindrent à jouer aux Vaches au plus de blanches ou de
noires".

[7] Fr. *à la blanche*. "Ludendo inter se ad *Rafflam* cum taxillis." Germ. *Raffen*,
from Lat. *rapere*. Ballads are given in *A.P.F.* ii. 270–83 on two Chambrières
who have lost their chance of marriage *à la blanque*, and of one who has gained
in it. Chaucer, in his *Persone's Tale*, I. 793, speaks of "hasardrye with his appurtenances of *tables* and *rafles*", and there, as well as in the *Pardonere's Tale*,
C. 590, alludes to the blasphemy which accompanies gambling. Cf. v. 10.
Pasquier, *Recherches*, viii. 49, gives an account of the introduction of *la blanque*
from Italy.

[8] Fr. *à la chance*. Cf. Coquillart, i. 164:

"L'ung a les dez, l'aultre *la chance*".

Chance is used for "hazard": Rabelais uses *livrer chance*, iii. 37, *muer de chance*, iii.
36 and *tomber en chance*, iii. 44. From the *Moralité des enfans de maintenant* (*A.Th.F.*
iii. 52–5) we learn that the game was played with two dice and that winning
numbers were 7 or 14 (*R.E.R.* vi. 140).

[9] Fr. *à troys dez* (*P.* 7). Coquillart, ii. 269, has *à trois beaulx dez*, quoted by
Panurge in iii. 11.

[10] Fr. *au tables*, at "tables", *i.e.* draughts, backgammon or any game that is
played on a *tablier*. Cf. Ovid, *Trist.* ii. 475–8.

"When he plays at *tables*
He chides the dice in honourable terms."

Shakesp. *Love's Lab. Lost*, v. 2. 326.

Nick-nock[1]

Lurch[2]

Queen's Game[3]

Sbaraglino[4]

Backgammon[5]

All Tables[6]

Fell down[7]

Copsbody[8]

Needs must[9]

Draughts[10]

Mop and mow[11]

Primus Secundus[12]

---

[1] Fr. *à la nicque-nocque* (*P.* 7, *la nique-noque* des questeurs). Said to be a doublet of *nazardes* and *chinquenaudes*, *infra*, *i.e.* fillips on the nose or face with one's fingers.

[2] Fr. *au lourche*. Cf. iii. 12: "le Jan en vaut deux...je pensois au jeu *du lourche* et *trictrac*". This goes to shew that some game of backgammon is indicated, perhaps derived from Lat. *orca*, a dice-box ("angustae collo non fallier *orcae*", Pers. iii. 50). Later "lurch" meant "a love-set", cf. Shakesp. *Coriol.* ii. 2. 105: "He lurch'd all swords of the garland" and *Hudibras*, iii. 2. 1062:

"Was like to lurch you at backgammon".

This is perhaps from *lurcare*, to devour; "ut *lurcaretur* lardum", Lucil. ii. 47 (ed. Bachners).

[3] Fr. *à la renette* (*regineta* and *rianeta*, Ducange). Some backgammon game, probably referring to the *doublet*, *P.* 12 and *dames doublées*, Coquillart, i. 156:

"Jouent au glic ou à la roynette".

"Si jugares al *reinado*
Los cientos, ó la primera."
Don Quixote, ii. c. 57.

"Quilibet possit ludere ad *scacos* vel ad tabulas vel ad *Reginetam*", Statut. Massil. v. 10 (Ducange).

[4] Fr. *au barignin* = *sbaraglino*, an Italian name for backgammon.

[5] Fr. *au trictrac*. The comprehensive French name for backgammon—a word formed from the rattle of the dice.

[6] Fr. *à toutes tables*. A backgammon game in which the draughts instead of being piled up in one corner are placed in four heaps symmetrically at *all the tables*. (Fr. ed.)

[7] Fr. *au tables rabatues*. The draughts are piled to the number of 15 on the points of one side of the board and at each throw of the dice one or more is removed to the other side (*R.E.R.* vi. 147).

[8] Fr. *au reniguebieu* (*P.* 17). Except that it was played on a board or some flat surface, nothing is known of this game. The name probably has reference to cursing and swearing, which are the usual accompaniments of gambling. Cf. v. 10.

[9] Fr. *au forcé*. Cotgrave explains this as of a game at draughts when a player is forced to take a piece that is *en prise*, or be "huffed".

[10] Fr. *au dames*. "Ludamus *ad dominas*", Cordier, 38. § 46.

[11] Fr. *à la babou*. Cf. iv. 56: "Panurge lui fit *la babou* en signe de derision".

[12] Fr. *à primus secundus* (*P.* 18). A bundle of spilikins was laid on the table, and the game seems to have had for an object getting one's spilikin above, or past, that of the other players.

Shovel-board[1]   Billiards[8]
The Keys[2]   Hunt-the-Slipper[9]
Hop-scotch[3]   The moping Owl[10]
Odd or Even[4]   Coddling the Hare[11]
Heads or Tails[5]   Tug of War[12]
Huckle-bones[6]   Trudge-pig[13]
Spilikins[7]   Magpies[14]

---

[1] Fr. *au pied du cousteau*. A knife was set up on a table, or stuck in the earth, and counters were sped towards it from the edge of the table, the nearest being the winner. Cf. Ducange, s.v. *Cultellus*, Litt. remiss. ann. 1393: *au jeu appellé au plus près du Coustel*.

[2] Fr. *au clefz*. "Ludamus *clavibus*." Cordier, 38. § 43. Keys were placed near the edge of a table and counters were to be sent as near as possible to the keys without falling off.

[3] Fr. *au franc du carreau*. The counter or stone had to be thrown in the square marked out so as to be clear of the line, but it was probably kicked into some other square as in the game of hop-scotch. Ducange speaks of it in 1417, s.v. *Francum*; and Eloy Damerval, *Livre de la diablerie*, p. 133, has

> "Là jouent en toutes saisons
> Aux quilles, *au franc de carreau*,
> Au trine, au plus près du cousteau,
> Aux dès, au glic, aux belles tables".

[4] Fr. *au pair ou non*. Cf. Hor. *Sat.* ii. 3. 247; Cordier, 38. § 45: "Ludamus *par impar*".

[5] Fr. *à croix ou pille*. In old coins one side was called *pile*, the other *croix*. Cf. Macrob. *Sat.* i. 7. 22: "pueri denarios in sublime jactantes *capita aut navia* lusu, teste vetustatis, exclamant"; Ducange, s.v. *hochia*: "Ilz commencerent à jouer ensemble à hoissier *à plus crois à plus pile*".

[6] Fr. *au martres*. Huckle-bones or roundish stones thrown in the air.

[7] Fr. *au pingres* (iv. 14). The word is probably connected with *épingle* or *espine*, Lat. *spina*.

[8] Fr. *à la bille*. Seems to be a sort of lawn billiards which subsequently was adopted as an indoors game. The French editors are inclined to identify it with *croquet*. Cf. *R.E.R.* vi. 158.

[9] Fr. *au savatier*. "Ludamus *ad savatum*. Jouons à la savate. Ludamus *solea detrita*", Cordier, 38. § 25.

[10] Fr. *au hibou*. The game may be for the player to imitate the hoot of the owl, or to personify his melancholy habits.

[11] Fr. *au dorelot du lievre*. Seems to be hunting a hare when dazed, having just left its form.

[12] Fr. *à la tirelitantaine*. According to Le Duchat = *tirez-le un tantinet*.

[13] Fr. *au cochonnet va devant*. *Cochonnet* is the "Jack" at bowls, but here it probably refers to the picking up and throwing or kicking pebbles before one in the course of a walk, as is exemplified in the story of Scipio and Laelius on the seashore told in Cic. *de Orat.* ii. § 22 and repeated in Val. Max. viii. 8. 1; Erasm. *Ad.* v. 2. 20 and Montaigne, iii. 13 *ad fin.*

[14] Fr. *au pies*. Nothing is known of this game.

The Horn[1]
The shrove-tide Ox[2]
The Madge-owlet[3]
Hinch pinch and laugh not[4]
Pinpricks[5]
Unshoeing the Ass[6]
Pigs to Market[7]
Gee up, Neddy[8]
I sit down[9]

Gold-beard[10]
Buskins[11]
Draw the Spit[12]
Chucker-out[13]
Gossip, lend me your Sack[14]
Ramscod[15]
Thrust out[16]
Marseilles Figs[17]
At the Fly[18]

---

[1] Fr. *à la corne*, probably referring to the gesture made by the players.

[2] Fr. *au beuf violé*. The fat ox which the butchers led in procession at Shrovetide to the sound of a violin or other instruments. Villon, Lai 13: "Le beuf couronné qu'on veult vendre"; Juv. x. 65: "Duc in capitolia magnum Cretatumque bovem".

[3] Fr. *à la cheveche*. Perhaps a variety of backgammon.

[4] *Hinch pinch and laugh not* (Harsnet, *Dict. of Popish Imposture*, p. 134). *Je te pinse sans rire* (iv. 34), a children's game; holding one another's chin and grinning so as to make the other laugh, which scored against him. "Comme se sentans pinsez sans rire", Dolet's dedication of Marot's *Enfer*.

[5] Fr. *à picoter*, "prickle me, tickle me" (Urquhart).

[6] Fr. *à deferrer l'asne*. Equivalent to "go afoot". This game and the next two refer to the same subject.

[7] Fr. *à laiau tru*. The cry of the shepherds in Champagne to drive on their sheep.

[8] Fr. *au bourry, bourry zou*. A cry to drive on the asses in Languedoc. Cf. *G.* 11 *hari bourriquet*.

[9] Fr. *à je m'assis*. Nothing is known of this game.

[10] Fr. *à la barbe d'oribus*. The chin of one of the players who is blindfolded is smeared with filth (*oribus*, a pejorative diminutive from *or*, Le Duchat). *Poudre d'oribus* occurs in *P.* prol. and in *P.* 30 occurs *pouldre de diamerdis*. In *P.* 22 Matthieu Ory is called *nostre maistre Doribus*.

[11] Fr. *à la bousquine*. Nothing is known of this game.

[12] Fr. *à tire la broche*. Probably pulling the stick from between the arms and legs of a boy who had been trussed for "cock-fighting".

[13] Fr. *à la boute foyre*. Some game with filth analogous to *à la barbe d'oribus* (Cotgrave).

[14] Fr. *Compere, prestez moi vostre sac*. Probably similar to the games mentioned in the last note.

[15] Fr. *à la couille de belier*, a football made of a rams-cod. Brantôme, *des Dames* (disc. 5), speaks of one of these being furtively placed under one of the court-ladies' dress; when she arose, it bounded out into the room, causing great consternation.

[16] Fr. *à la boute hors*. A kind of racquet game (*pelote*) in which the ball was made to rebound beyond a certain point (cf. Ducange, s.v. *boutare*).

[17] Fr. *à figues de Marseilles*. These figs were celebrated, but the game has not been explained.

[18] Fr. *à la mousque* (*à la mousche*, iii. 40), a sort of hop-scotch. (Gk. μυῖνδα παίζειν, μυῖα χαλκή, Ital. *mosca cieca*, Pollux, ix. 110). *Ad muscam = Empusae*

Bowman Shot[1]	Quick and dead Judge[8]
Flay the Fox[2]	Unoven the Iron[9]
Tobogganing[3]	The false Clown[10]
Hold the Pass[4]	Nine-stones[11]
Oat-selling[5]	The hunchback Courtier[12]
Blow the Coal[6]	The Finding of the Saint[13]
Hide and seek[7]	Hinch-pinch[14]

---

ludus. "Empusa fuit monstrum *unius pedis*", Cordier, 38. § 12; Aristoph. *Ran.* 297.

[1] Fr. *à l'archer tru.* Probably a game representing an archer driving some thieves away. Cf. *laiau tru,* above. From its position in the list it can scarcely be a card-game (cf. Fr. ed.).

[2] Fr. *à escorcher le renard (P. 6, 12; G. 11) = evomere crapulam* (Cordier, 58. § 266).

[3] Fr. *à la ramasse (la r. des nommez et graduez, P. 7).* There is a spirited and detailed description of this game in Daudet's *Numa Roumestan,* c. 12. Montaigne, *Voyages* (p. 555, ed. d'Ancona), did not find it so formidable in his descent from Mont Cenis.

[4] Fr. *au croc madame.* Cf. *R.E.R.* xiii. 278; *A.P.F.* ix. 117:

> "Devant vous jouent *au croc madame*
> Puis ilz luictent, courent et saillent".

"A tenir le pas qu'on appelle *le croc madame*", Le Maire, *Illustrations de Gaule,* i. 21. Cf. Ducange, s.v. *passus.* Some violent game involving pushing and tugging.

[5] Fr. *à vendre l'avoine.* Cf. *infra, à semer l'avoyne.* "Le lendemain de ses noces l'un demandoit à ce nouveau marié—*combien valoit l'avoine*", G. Bouchet, *Serée* 5, vol. i. pp. 214–15. Cf. Engl. "sowing wild oats".

[6] Fr. *à souffler le charbon.* A lighted coal was suspended from the ceiling and children blew it to keep the sparks alight, with the words *petit bonhomme vit encore (R.E.R.* vi. 176).

[7] Fr. *au responsailles.* "Jeu de *cache-cache*" *(response) (R.E.R.* vi. 176).

[8] Fr. *au juge vif et juge mort.* "Inde venturus est judicare vivos et mortuos" (Apostles' Creed); "Nullum alium inter pueros ludum nisi *ad judices* exercuit", Spartianus, *Sept. Severus,* c. 1.

[9] Fr. *au tirer les fers du four.*

[10] Fr. *au fault villain.* Many names are given in Eloy Damerval, *Grande Diablerie, A.P.F.* x. 223:

> "Se vont jouant *à la chevrette,*
> *Au molinet, aux belles quailles,*
> *Au long festu, aux courtes pailles,*
> *Au faulx villain,* ou *champ estroit*".

[11] Fr. *au cailletaux = petits cailloux,* of which there were nine.

[12] Fr. *au bossu aulican.*

[13] Fr. *à Sainct trouvé.*

[14] Fr. *à pince morille.*

Pear-tree[1]
Bumbasting[2]
The Breton Jig[3]
Barlibreak[4]
The Sow[5]
Belly to Belly[6]
Cubes[7]
Pushpin[8]

Quoits[9]
The ball is mine[10]
Fouquet[11]
Nine-pins[12]
The return Course (Cot.)[13]
Flat Bowl[14]
Flying Dart[15]
Pick-a-back to Rome[16]

---

[1] Fr. *au poirier*. Probably the same as *poirier fourchu, l'arbre fourchu* (iv. 19) and *chesne forchu (infra)*, *i.e.* standing on one's head. Herod. vi. 129, τοῖσι σκέλεσιν ἐχειρονόμησε, is translated by Montaigne *faire l'arbre fourché sur une table*.

[2] Fr. *au pimpompet*. Three children thumped or kicked each other behind (Cotgrave).

[3] Fr. *au triori* (τριχορία, *saltatio trichorica*, iv. N.P., 38; v. 33). The well-known Breton jig (cf. *Contes d'Eutrapel*, c. 19).

[4] Fr. *au cercle*, barlibreak, kiss in the ring, *chorus circularis*. Cf. *The honest Whore*, Act. i. sc. 12; *Virgin Martyr*, v. 1; *The Guardian*, i. 1.

[5] Fr. *à la truye*. A game in which a wooden ball called *truye* (cf. *cochonnet*) was driven into a hole with a club. ? Golf.

[6] Fr. *ventre contre ventre* (iii. 12 (W); iv. 39; v. prol.), also called *le monde renversé*. A boy lies down with his legs in the air, another takes him round the waist and the two place themselves on the back of another boy and so play see-saw. (Fr. ed.)

[7] Fr. *au combes*. Probably at *cubes*, which were used for calculating (Godefroy). (Fr. ed.)

[8] Fr. *à la vergette* (P. 18).

[9] Fr. *au palet*. A flat and round piece of stone or metal was thrown as near as possible to a mark. (Fr. ed.)

[10] Fr. *au j'en suis*. A third player cuts in with his racquet and catches the ball, taking it from the other players, with the cry *J'en suis*, "the ball is mine". *Mea est pila*, Plaut. *Truc.* 4. 1. 7; Cordier, 38. § 52.

[11] Fr. *au fouquet* (Lat. *focus*, P. 12; iv. N.P. 40). The game consisted in plugging one nostril with a piece of tow and, when this has been lighted, blowing it out with the other nostril.

[12] Fr. *à la quille*. "*Ad quillam*, clava pilaria", Cordier, 38. § 39. Ducange on *Quillia* has: "Litt. remiss. ann. 1378...au jeu des grosses Quilles auquel jeu l'on jette de loing pour ferir les dittes Quilles, d'un baston de la longueur ou environ d'une aulne".

[13] Fr. *au rapeau*. (1) A stroke at nine-pins in which 3 pieces are knocked down at one throw, (2) a second throw, (3) taking the pool at cards (cf. Ducange s.v. *rapiarius*).

[14] Fr. *à la boule plate*. The bowl has one side smaller than the other and therefore runs in a curve (*R.E.R.* vi. 326).

[15] Fr. *au vireton*. A dart furnished with a paper set of screws at the end, curved a little so as to make it fly straight.

[16] Fr. *au picquarome*. A game *piquerommier* is mentioned in Ducange, s.v. *pica*, 1 (*sub fin.*), as of children playing with a stick pointed at one end (*R.E.R.* vi. 327).

Touch-clod[1]   Rush bundles[9]
Sly Jack[2]   Short Staff[10]
Short Bowls[3]   Shuttlecock[11]
Shuttlecock[4]   Hodman blind[12]
Dogs' ears[5]   Spur away[13]
Smash Crock[6]   Sweepstakes[14]
My Desire[7]   The Ferret[15]
Twirlywhirly[8]   The Pursuit[16]

---

[1] Fr. *rouchemerde* (= *ronger*). Cf. *supra*, *barbe d'oribus* and *boute foyre*.

[2] Fr. *à angenart*. An unknown game.

[3] Fr. *à la courte boulle*. "Ludamus *sphaera volubili*", Cordier, 38. § 7. This game of bowls was played in a court or a confined space, as opposed to *longue boule* (long bowls) mentioned in Scott's *Antiquary*, c. 29.

[4] Fr. *à la griesche* (*fol griays*, iii. 38). *G.* has the meaning of harsh, rough, disagreeable, and also "Greek" (pie grieche = *pica Graeca*). Littré suggests that *Greek fire* may have given it the sinister interpretation. Here it probably means "grey" because the shuttlecock was winged with feathers from the grey partridge (*perdrix griesches*). Gringore refers to this game. Cf. *R.E.R.* vii. 132.

[5] Fr. *à la recoquillette*. Probably some game of hide and seek. (Fr. ed.)

[6] Fr. *au cassepot*. "*Olla pertusa*", Cordier, 38. § 26. An old earthenware pot was tossed from one to another till it fell and was smashed. The player who let it fall paid forfeit. Cotgrave and Scarron, *Roman Comique*, agree in this description (*R.E.R.* vi. 331).

[7] Fr. *à mon talent*. Nothing is known about this game.

[8] Fr. *à la pyrouette*. Perhaps a kind of small windmill, or teetotum (*R.E.R.* vi. 331).

[9] Fr. *au jonchées*. "Le jeu des jonchetz, *ludus junculorum*", Cordier, 38. § 43. A sort of "spilikins" formerly played with rushes.

[10] Fr. *au court baston*. Two children seated on the ground both holding on to a short stick; each tries to make the other get up. It might perhaps = "tip-cat". Cf. *bille-boucquet* (*infra*).

[11] Fr. *au pyrevollet*. A kind of shuttlecock.

[12] Fr. *à cline muzete*. "Hodman blind, or are you all hid?" (Cotgrave). "Tant joua à *clugnes-mussectes*", *A.P.F.* v. 29; *C.N.N.* 87; ἀποδιδρασκίνδα, Pollux, ix. 117. One player was blindfolded and the others ran and hid.

[13] Fr. *au picquet*. Similar to *picquarome* (*supra*).

[14] Fr. *à la blancque*, a lottery-game with children. One opened with a pin a book, in which some pages had prizes and the others blanks; so it was *blanc ou benefice*. Pasquier, *Recherches*, viii. 49, gives an account of such a lottery in Italy (*bianca*).

[15] Fr. *au furon*. A ring was slipped on to a long cord and passed about by the players while another tried to find it.

[16] Fr. *à la seguette*. One player throws a ball a certain distance, another tries to hit it with his ball. This is continued by one or other of the players till one succeeds and so scores a point.

Cob-nut[1]	Scared face[8]
All in a Row[2]	Football[9]
The cherry Pit[3]	Fast and loose (*Cot.*)[10]
The Humming-top[4]	Fat-rump[11]
The Whip-top[5]	Cock-horse[12]
The Peg-top[6]	St Côme, I come to worship[13]
The Hobgoblin[7]	The brown Beetle[14]

---

[1] Fr. *au chastelet*. A fort is built up with walnuts and one of the players sends a walnut at it and claims all he may have thrown down. Cotgrave gives the name *Cob-nut*.

[2] Fr. *à la rengée*. Walnuts are placed in a row; a player with another walnut displaces as many as he can.

[3] Fr. *à la foussette*. A small hole is made in the earth and the object is to throw walnuts, or marbles, or little balls, so that as many as possible may remain in it.

[4] Fr. *au ronflart*.

[5] Fr. *à la trompe* (cf. iv. 9, "Dieu guard mon sabot, ma trompe, ma touppie"). "Veulx tu jouer à la trompe avecques moi? Vis mecum versare turbinem?" Cordier, 38. § 82.

[6] Fr. *au moyne*, a top shaped like a pear, a peg-top (*R.E.R.* vii. 131. 426). It has nothing to do with *donner le moyne* (cf. *G.* 12, 43, 45; iv. 16).

[7] Fr. *au tenebry*, playing the ghost. Eloy Damerval, *Livre de la Diablerie* (lib. ii. c. xvii), has

"*Au tonnebri, à la paulmette*
Et aussi à *monte eschelette*."

"A tant de joyeulx jeux, beau sire."   *A.P.F.* x. 223.

[8] Fr. *à l'esbahy*. The method of the game is unknown, but is mentioned by several writers, *e.g.* "Et pouvez croire...que M. vostre pere et MM. vos oncles jouerent tout un temps *à l'esbahi*", *Satyre Ménippée*, xii (*Harangue de M. d'Aubray*, p. 188).

[9] Fr. *à la soulle*. Played sometimes with a wooden ball which was driven by a club, or a leather ball stuffed with bran, or filled with air. The object was for one party, by kicking or striking or carrying, to get the ball into their opponents' goal. See Jusserand, *Les Sports, etc. dans l'ancienne France*, pp. 265–83. The game is of great antiquity in France.

[10] Fr. *à la navette*. *Navette* is a weaver's shuttle, which is sped backwards and forwards over the warp in a loom. If it were a card game it might be paralleled to a cross-ruff in whist, but it must here be an outdoor game of some kind.

[11] Fr. *à fessart*. Unknown.

[12] Fr. *au ballay*. Perhaps riding on a broom-stick. "Equitare in arundine longa", Hor. *Sat.* ii. 3. 248.

[13] Fr. *à Sainct-Cosme je viens t'adorer*. The reliques of SS. Cosma and Damianus (twin Arab martyrs and the patron saints of surgeons, cf. *Brev. Rom.* Sep. 27) were supposed to be at Luzarches, about 20 miles north of Paris, whither the Paris ladies used to go on a pilgrimage, *à l'église de S. Côme*, on the saint's day (*A.P.F.* xii. 28 n.). "Son compagnon vouloit gager que c'estoit un ramonneur de cheminée, ou bien que c'estoit quelqu'un qui avoit joué à *S.C. je viens t'adorer*", G. Bouchet, *Serée* 29. Perhaps the game was played by someone with a blackened face who personated the Moorish Saint.

[14] Fr. *à escharbot le brun*. To imitate the beetle one of the children went on all fours. (Fr. ed.)

I catch you napping[1]

Fair and gay goes Lent away[2]

The forked Oak[3]

Leap-frog[4]

The Wolf's Tail[5]

Nose in Breech[6]

William, give me my Lance[7]

The Swing[8]

Shocks of Corn[9]

The small Bowl[10]

Baste the Bear[11]

Tit, tat, toe, my first go[12]

Cross questions and crooked answers[13]

---

[1] Fr. *je vous prend sans verd* (iii. 11). "I catch you without a green leaf (as in England on oak-apple day, May 29), catch you napping".

"Jamais on n'y est pris sans vert."   *A.P.F.* iv. 257.

[2] Fr. *à bien et beau s'en va Quaresme.* Ch. d'Orléans, *Rond.* 206 (iv. prol.). This verse had to be repeated on Easter morning so as to anticipate one's comrade. Like *bon jour, Philippine.*

[3] Fr. *au chesne forchu* (iv. 19; v. 9). Cf. *supra, au poirier*; Shakesp. 2 *Hen. IV*, iii. 2. 332: "he was for all the world like a forked radish".

[4] Fr. *au chevau fondu.* "*Ad equum fundatum, equuleo depresso*", Cordier, 38. § 24. Erasmus in *Colloq. Lusus pueriles* has *saltus ranarum.*

[5] Fr. *à la queue au loup.* A boys' game in which one (the wolf) endeavours to carry off one of a string of boys who represent sheep. Another (the shepherd) guards them (*R.E.R.* vi. 352). The boys have to march like wolves putting their feet in the track of their predecessor.

[6] Fr. *à pet en gueulle.* Two boys holding tight to one another, with their bodies reversed so that the head of each appears between the legs of the other, roll down a grass slope. Cf. also Aristoph. *Ran.* 1074.

[7] Fr. *au Guillemin, baille my ma lance.* A boy blindfolded mounted on another boy asks for his lance. A staff smeared with filth is given him (Cotgrave).

[8] Fr. *à la brandelle.* This is simply a swing, constructed either by fastening together boughs of two trees or by hanging a cord from the bough of a high tree.

[9] Fr. *au treseau*, the wheat-shock, generally contains 12 sheaves (Skeat). A number of players (properly 12) range themselves in pairs one before the other. A thirteenth (*treiziau*) stations himself behind one of the pairs but is pursued by a fourteenth and takes shelter between another of the pairs, one of whom is obliged to become the pursued. (Fr. ed.)

[10] Fr. *au bouleau.* This game is unknown.

[11] Fr. *à la mousche* (iii. 40). Cordier in 38. § 13: "*Habuit muscam. Habet, i.e.* Percussus est*". This agrees with Rabelais and it would seem to be a game in which one player is buffeted by the others.

[12] Fr. *à la migne, migne beuf.* ? *Tit-tat-to*, which Prof. Skeat would make an East Frisian slate-game with the more intelligible words *tik-tak-tuk* (*Notes on Eng. Etymol.* p. 302).

[13] Fr. *au propous.* Players being seated in a circle, each, in a whisper, asks a question of his right-hand neighbour and answers that of his left-hand neighbour. This done, each player in turn repeats aloud the question he was asked and the answer he received, as if they corresponded. Cf. *Aresta Amorum*, No. 24.

Nine Hands[1]

Harry-racket[2]

The fallen Bridges[3]

Bridled Nick[4]

The Bull's Eye[5]

Battledore and Shuttlecock[6]

Blindman's Buff[7]

Bob-cherry[8]

Spy[9]

Frogs and Toads[10]

Cricket[11]

Pestle and Mortar[12]

Cup and Ball[13]

The Queens[14]

---

[1] Fr. *à neuf mains*. The players' hands one on top of another, up to nine, the owner of the topmost seizes that of one of the others crying, *Je retiens mon pied de boeuf*. Littré (*pied*).

[2] Fr. *au chapifou* (v. 27). A form of *Blindman's buff* like *colin-bridé*, *colin-maillard* and *cligne-musette*. κολλαβίζω is given in Pollux, ix. 129, of a game in which one player is blindfolded and given a box on the ear and told to guess which hand struck him, left or right.

[3] Fr. *au pontz cheuz*. Children balanced themselves on a sort of elevated point till there was a collapse (Regis).

[4] Fr. *à Colin bridé*. Another form of Blindman's buff. *Colin* was employed to denote a *ninny*. Cf. *Jobelin bridé* in *G.* 14.

[5] Fr. *à la grolle* (iv. 52). This game recurs later in the list. It seems to be "a rook" painted in the middle of a target instead of a "bull's-eye". In *G.* 38 and iii. 32 occurs *noyau grollier*, perhaps = a walnut-tree in which "a rook" was set up for the archers.

[6] Fr. *au cocquantin*. Ducange, *Glossaire Français*, s.v. quotes:

> "Mais ne feroit pour lui un coquentin.
> Plus het l'un l'aultre que triacle venin".

It is a kind of shuttle-cock. Cf. *picandeau*, *infra*.

[7] Fr. *à Colin maillard*. Cf. *supra*, *Colin bridé*.

[8] Fr. *à myrelimoufle*. The method of the game is unknown, but a rime survives, *R.E.R.* vi. 361:

> "Et d'où venez vous, *mire ly moufle?*
> Je viens du marché, soufle ly soufle".

[9] Fr. *à mouschart*, the eavesdropper.

[10] Fr. *au crapaud*, a rattle, or some instrument that imitates the croaking of a frog or toad. Perhaps it is produced by a horsehair inserted in a piece of parchment that covers tightly the orifice of a reed.

[11] Fr. *à la crosse*. "Ad crossam, ludere clava. Hic ludus *clava et pila* constat", Cordier, 38. § 40. "*Crossare*, baculo recurvo pilam propellere" (Ducange). *Lacrosse* is the ancestor of hockey, polo, golf, cricket. Cf. Jusserand, *Les Sports etc. de l'ancienne France*, pp. 284, 599. Cotgrave gives "Crosse: a cricket staffe, or the crooked staffe wherewith boyes play cricket".

[12] Fr. *au piston*. An unknown game.

[13] Fr. *au bille boucquet*, cup and ball; but Le Duchat, vol. i, p. 86, describes it as a game that is evidently our "tip-cat", which is perhaps intended by *court baston* above (*R.E.R.* vii. 51).

[14] Fr. *au roynes*. Perhaps alluded to in Adam de la Halle, *Jeu de Robin et de Marion*, "as roys et *as roïnes*" (*R.E.R.* vii. 51).

The Trades[1]
Heads and Points[2]
Dot and go one[3]
Wicked Death[4]
Fillips[5]
Lady, I wash your Cap[6]
The boulting Cloth[7]
Oat-sowing[8]
Greedy Glutton[9]

Windmills[10]
Defendo[11]
Pirouetting[12]
Bascule[13]
Hind the Ploughman[14]
The Madge-Owlet[15]
Butting Rams[16]
The dead Beast[17]
Climb the Ladder[18]

---

[1] Fr. *aux mestiers*. "A game in which trades are counterfeited by signs" (Cotgrave). Perhaps = "deaf and dumb motions".

[2] Fr. *à teste à teste bechevel*. Pins are placed head and point together and held in the closed fist, for another player to guess the arrangement. *Bechevet* is a double arrangement in a bed, head to feet.

[3] Fr. *au pinot*. Nothing is known of this game. Regis translates *Hinkebein*, Limping leg.

[4] Fr. *à male mort*. Perhaps the amusement of tapping on the hand of a child and repeating the verse:

> "Main morte, main morte
> Frappe à la porte".   (Fr. ed.)

[5] Fr. *au croquinolles*. A kind of filliping on the nose. Cf. *infra, nazardes, allouettes* and *chinquenaudes*.

[6] Fr. *à laver la coiffe, Madame*. Unknown.

[7] Fr. *au belusteau*. Two children take hands and swinging them from side to side pretend to be boulting flour in a sieve. Cf. iv. 31 and *Hept.* 69.

[8] Fr. *à semer l'avoyne*. Cf. *supra, à vendre l'avoine*.

[9] Fr. *à briffault*, from *briffer*, to gormandise.

[10] Fr. *au moulinet*. Perhaps "quarter-staff", from the *wind-mill* play of various strokes. Cf. *G.* 35. Or it may be the common game of two children holding each other's feet and rolling down a hill.

> "Se vont jouant *à la chevrette*
> Au molinet aux belles quailles".   *A.P.F.* x. 223.

[11] Fr. *à defendo*. A child has a number of pieces of bread in a line before him, and has to repeat a form of words over them and to take the piece which he comes to with his last word.

[12] Fr. *à la virevouste*, or the whirligig. Cf. Chaucer, *The Miller's Tale*, A. 3770: "Have brought you thus upon the *viritoot*" and Scott's *Fortunes of Nigel*, c. 18: "Have you come on the viretot?" Cf. also *P.* 7, *virevoustatorium nacquettorum*.

[13] Fr. *à la bacule*. Cotgrave and Ducange (*baculare*) agree in describing this as a beating on the rump with a stick or flinging on to the ground.

[14] Fr. *au laboureur*. Probably a child's game of dragging another by his legs along the ground and so *labourer la terre*. (Fr. ed.)

[15] Fr. *à la cheveche*. Already given, cf. *supra*.

[16] Fr. *au escoublettes enragées*. Butting like rams, which thus entangle their horns (*R.E.R.* vii. 57).

[17] Fr. *à la beste morte*. Carrying a boy on one's back with his head downwards (*R.E.R.* vii. 57).

[18] Fr. *à monte, monte l'eschelette*. One player places his closed fist on his knee

The dead Pig[1]	The Buzzard's Nest[10]
The salt Doup[2]	Hark forward[11]
The Pigeon has flown[3]	Figs[12]
Twos and Threes[4]	Gunshot Crack[13]
Faggots[5]	Mustard-pounder[14]
The bush Jump[6]	Out of School[15]
Crossing[7]	The Relapse[16]
Hide and seek[8]	The feathered Dart[17]
Coin in the Tail-pocket[9]	Duck your Head[18]

with the thumb upwards; another closes his fist on this thumb, keeping *his* thumb upwards. Another plays the same game and so on. They call out at each relay *Monte, monte echelette, monte en haut*. (Fr. ed.) But cf. Robinet, v. 33.

[1] Fr. *au pourceau mory*. Cf. *supra, à la beste morte*.

[2] Fr. *à cul sallé*. Unknown.

[3] Fr. *au pigonnet*. Well known as *le pigeon vole*.

[4] Fr. *au tiers*. This game is like *au treseau, supra*. Players group themselves in twos, and two others run around trying to find places. Ducange (s.v. *tertium*) explains thus, and the game is mentioned in the *Aresta Amorum*, No. 24.

"Mieux eusses faict de te jouer aux noix,
        Ou bien *au tiers*, courant comme un formi."   *A.P.F.* iv. 293.

[5] Fr. *à la bourrée*. A number of boys form a circle looking inwards. They interlace their arms above the shoulders and so form a vault, on to which other boys leap till they break it down (*R.E.R.* vii. 426).

[6] Fr. *au sault du buisson*. Jumping into a bush. (Fr. ed.)

[7] Fr. *à croyzer*. When one player is pursuing another, one who crosses or runs between becomes the object of pursuit.

[8] Fr. *à la cutte cache*. *Cuta* in Ducange is *latebra*, a hiding place, so that the game would be "hide and seek" like *responsailles, supra*.

[9] Fr. *à la maille, bourse en cul*. Unknown. Perhaps the game in which one player has a whistle or something fastened on his coat-tail and vainly seeks to find which of the circle around him blew it.

[10] Fr. *au nid* (*nic*, A, B) *de la bondrée*. The buzzard's nest. Probably something was hidden that had to be found.

[11] Fr. *au passavant*, a thump. Cf. *nicnocque, chinquenaude*, etc.

"Tire avant, tire malheureux
        Ou tu auras ung *passavant*."
                        Mistere du vieil Testament. (Fr. ed.)

[12] Fr. *à la figue*. Thrusting the thumb between the index and middle fingers. Cf. iv. 45.

[13] Fr. *au petarrades*. A noise made with the mouth to express contempt (*R.E.R.* vii. 62). Cf. iii. 20.

[14] Fr. *à pille moustarde*, at "Sim Slapsauce" (Thos. Becon).

[15] Fr. *à cambos* (? *campos*, P. 5). A holiday in the country. "Primarius hodie dabit *campos*", Cordier, 33. § 2.   [16] Fr. *à la recheute*. Unknown.

[17] Fr. *au picandeau*. A flying dart furnished with paper wings at the end. Cf. *supra, la griesche* and *cocquantin*.

[18] Fr. *à croque-teste*. Leap-frog, in which the boy who is leapt over has to duck his head.

The Bull's Eye[1]   Flirts on the Nose[4]
Crane-dance[2]   Larks[5]
Slash and cut[3]   Filliping[6]

After having well played and littered and frittered and sifted[7]
away his Time, it seemed fitting to drink some little: it was eleven
Quarts[8] a head; and immediately after to bench it, that is, on a
fair Bench or a good large Bed, to stretch himself and sleep for two
or three Hours without thinking ill or speaking ill.[9] After he was
awakened, he would shake his Ears a little; meantime fresh Wine
was brought him; thereupon he drank better than ever.

Ponocrates pointed out to him that it was an ill Diet[10] to drink
thus after sleeping.

"It is", answered Gargantua, "the true Life of the Fathers.[11]
For naturally I do sleep salt, and sleeping has been worth to me so
much Ham."

Then he began to study some little, and Paternosters were to the
front; in order the better to despatch them in Form, he got upon
an old Mule which had served nine Kings; and so, mumbling with

---

[1] Fr. *à la grolle* (iv. 52). Cf. *supra*.

[2] Fr. *à la grue*. Probably standing on one leg to imitate the cranes.

[3] Fr. *à taille-coup*.

[4] Fr. *au nazardes* (*P.* 30; iv. 30).

[5] Fr. *aux allouettes* (*P.* 30). Thumps, etc.

[6] Fr. *aux chinquenaudes* (*P.* 30, iii. 20, iv. 14, 30). Filliping with the middle
finger when released from the thumb which had held it in check (cf. iv. 14).
Cordier, 38. § 22: "Ludamus *pro chiquenodis*, jouons pour les chiquenauldes.
Certemus *talitris*. Certemus poena talitrorum." Cf. Suet. *Tib.* 68.

[7] Fr. *sassé, passé et beluté* (v. 21). "Passait le temps à travers l'estamine",
A.Th.F. iii. 250. (Plattard.)

[8] Fr. *peguadz* (veguade, *G.* 6). From *pega* in Gascony, a measure of 8 *livres*.
Ducange has *picarium* and *bicarium* = beaker.

[9] Fr. *sans mal penser ny mal dire*. Cf. *P.* 12 (*init.*).

> "And then to sleep but three hours in the night
> And not be seen to wink of all the day—
> When I was wont to think no harm all night
> And make a dark night too of half a day."
>   Shakesp. *Love's Lab. Lost*, i. 1. 42. (R.)

[10] *an ill Diet*, etc. Cf. c. 41.

[11] *Life of the Fathers*. Cf. *Reg. S. Bened.* c. 42: "Mox ut surrexerint a cena se-
deant omnes in unum et legat unus *Collationes* vel *Vitas Patrum*, aut certe aliquid
quod aedificet audientes". After this they took a cup at the refectory. The
reading produced thirst in the holy Fathers, sleeping did the same for Gargantua.
(D.)

his Mouth and doddling with his Head, he went to see some Coneys taken with Nets.

On his Return he betook himself into the Kitchen, to know what Roast was on the Spit.

And he supped very well, on my Conscience, and did willingly invite some Topers from among his Neighbours, with whom carousing merrily, they told Stories of all sorts from the old to the new.

Among others, he had for his Servants the Lords of Fou, of Gourville, of Grignault and Marigny.[1]

After Supper, were brought in the fair wooden Gospels,[2] that is to say many Chess or Backgammon Boards, also the fair Flusse, "One, two, three"; or Primero,[3] to kill Time; or else they went to see the Wenches thereabouts, and had small Banquets among them, Collations and After-collations. Then he would sleep without unbridling till eight o'Clock the next Morning.

---

[1] *Jacques du Fou*, maître d'hôtel to Francis I, Sept. 8, 1536, seneschal of Poitou, owner of La Motte (iii. 41) (*R.E.R.* ii. 160, 230). Cf. *A.P.F.* vi. 121 n. *Gourville*, three members of this family were known at this time. They were of Angoulême. The Seigneur de *Grignaux* was of Périgord and advised Francis I when he was a young man. Cf. Brantôme, ix. 640 (*R.E.R.* ix. 174). *Marigny* was in Normandy.

[2] *wooden Gospels*. Boards for draughts, backgammon, etc., made to resemble *livres d'Évangiles*. Budé (*de Asse*, v. p. 717) speaks of the Gospels as *Jus quatuor tabularum*.

[3] Fr. *à toutes restes*. Cf. *supra* and *G.* 3. "To set up all rests" was a part of the play in *primero*; when thinking to have a winning position a player throws down his cards. He can only be defeated by his adversary producing a "flush".

CHAPTER XXIII

How Gargantua was trained by Ponocrates in a Discipline such that he lost one Hour of the Day

WHEN Ponocrates knew Gargantua's vicious Manner of Living, he determined to instruct him in Letters in a far different Fashion; but for the first few Days he bore with him, considering that Nature doth not endure sudden Changes[1] without great Violence.

Therefore, the better to begin his Work, he entreated a learned Physician of that Time, named Master Theodorus,[2] to consider if it were possible to change Gargantua to a better Course. He purged him *secundum artem* with[3] Hellebore of Anticyra,[4] and by this Medicament cleared him from all this Corruption and perverse Habit of Brain. By this means also Ponocrates caused him to forget all that he had learned under his ancient Preceptors, as Timotheus[5] did to his Pupils, who had been instructed under other Musicians.

To do this the better, he brought him into the Company of Learned men who were there, in emulation of whom his Wit

---

[1] *sudden Changes.* πάντα ἐξαπίνης μέζον πολλῷ τοῦ μετρίου μεταβαλλόμενα ἐπὶ τὰ καὶ ἐπὶ τὰ βλάπτει, Hipp. *de vict. rat. in acutis*, § 46.

[2] *Theodorus*, D. ABC read *Seraphin Calobarsy*, an anagram of Phrancoys Rabelais. Theodorus (*P.* 17) was a Cyrenaic philosopher who made happiness depend entirely on intelligence. Happiness should consist (he said) not in individual pleasures but in a happy state of mind, unhappiness in the contrary (Diog. Laert. ii. 8. § 13). Thus *in contemptu rerum fortuitarum* he was a Pantagruelist.

[3] Fr. *purgea canonicquement.* A sly allusion to the enactments *de purgatione canonica* in *Δ.* v. 34; medically it would be *secundum artem.*

[4] *black Hellebore* was the specific against paralysis, insanity, dropsy, gout of long standing and arthritic diseases. It was a strong purgative and grew in Anticyra. Theoph. *H.P.* ix. 10; Pliny, 25, 48–53; Paus. x. 36. 7 (cf. Frazer's note); Hor. *Sat.* ii. 3. 83, 106; *A.P.* 30. Carneades before disputing with Chrysippus (or Zeno) purged himself with hellebore to clear his brain (Pliny, 25, 51). Lucian's *Hermotimus* (c. 86) is for ridding himself thus of all the Stoic notions of Chrysippus. Cf. Erasm. *Ad.* i. 8. 51–3.

[5] "Timotheus clarus in arte tibiarum duplices ut ferunt ab iis quos alius instituisset solebat exigere mercedes quam si rudes traderentur", Bud. *in Pand.* i. p. 474. It is derived from Quint. ii. 3. 3.

increased and his Desire to study otherwise and to make known his Worth.

Afterwards, he put him in such a Course of Study that he lost no Hour whatever of the Day, but spent all his Time in Literature and sound Knowledge.

So then, Gargantua awoke about four o'Clock in the Morning. Whilst he was being rubbed there was read to him some Page or other of Holy Writ, aloud and clearly, with Pronunciation suited to the Matter; and hereunto was appointed a young Page, a native of Basché,[1] named Anagnôstes.[2] According to the Purpose and Argument of that Lesson, he oftentimes gave himself to revere, adore, pray and beseech the good God, whose Majesty and marvellous Judgments the Reading shewed forth.

Then went he into the secret Places to make Excretion of his natural Digestions. There his Preceptor repeated to him what had been read, expounding unto him the most obscure and difficult Points.

On their Return they considered the Condition of the Sky, if it were such as they had observed it the Night before, and into what Signs the Sun was entering, as also the Moon, for that Day.

This done, he was dressed, combed, curled, trimmed and perfumed, during which time were repeated to him the Lessons of the Day before. He himself said them by Heart, and founded thereon certain Cases that were practical and bearing on the State of Man; this they continued sometimes for two or three Hours, but generally they ceased as soon as he was fully clothed.

Then he was read to for three good Hours.

This done, they went forth, still conferring on the Subjects of Lecture, and betook themselves to the Bracque,[3] or to the Meadows,

---

[1] *Basché* (iv. 12–15), a hamlet in the commune of Assay. The lands belonged in 1507 to René du Pay, Seigneur de Basché (iv. 12–15), whose daughter Louise has a tomb in the church of Rivière near Chinon (*R.E.R.* v. 57).

[2] *Anagnôstes.* Greek for "a reader". Cf. Mayor's *Juvenal*, xi. 180. This may be intended for Pierre Duchatel, reader to Francis I. Cf. iv. *Ep. Ded.*

[3] Fr. *en Bracque.* The *Carrefour de Bracque*, now *la place de l'Estrapade*, where was a tennis-court. In a dialogue of Lud. Vivès it is stated that there were several private tennis-courts in Paris, "et in ipsa civitate famosissimum quod vocant *Bracchae*".

and played at Ball or Tennis or the Triangular[1] Ball-game, gaily
giving Exercise to their Bodies, as they had before to their
Minds.

Their Sports were always taken in perfect Freedom, for they left
off their Game when it pleased them; and they mostly gave over
when they sweated[2] all over their Body, or were otherwise tired.
Then they were well dried and rubbed, changed their Shirts, and
walking gently, went to see if the Dinner was ready. Whilst they
were there waiting, they did clearly and eloquently pronounce
some Sentences retained from their Lecture.

Meantime Master Appetite came, and as good Occasion served
they sat them down at Table.

At the Beginning of the Repast there was read some pleasant
Story of the ancient Feats of Arms, until he had taken his Wine.[3]
Then (if they thought good) the Reading was continued, or they
began to discourse merrily together, speaking for their first Discourse of the Virtue, Property, Efficacy and Nature of all that was
served them at Table; of the Bread,[4] Wine, Water, Salt, Meats,
Fishes, Fruits, Herbs, Roots, and of their Dressing. And in doing
this he learned in a short time all the Passages bearing on this in
Pliny, Athenaeus, Dioscorides, Julius Pollux,[5] Galen, Porphyrius,[6]

---

[1] Fr. *pile trigone*. Cf. Hor. *Sat.* i. 6. 126:

                "Fugis campum lusumque trigona";
Mart. iv. 19:   "Seu lentum ceroma fugis tepidumve trigona."

[2] ...*when they sweated*. Cf. Hippoc. *Epid.* vi. § 3: "Exercitationis modum
indicat sudor guttatim effluens".

[3] In the sixteenth century the wine was placed on a *buffet*, not on the table,
and was called for by the guests. (Fr. ed.)

[4] *Bread, Wine*, etc. In Macrobius' *Saturnalia* are discourses on singing and
dancing at the *triclinia*, on various fish, nuts, apples, pears, figs, olives and
grapes. In Athenaeus (i, ii, iii) wines, waters, meats, etc. are discussed.

[5] *Julius Pollux* of Naucrates in Egypt (iv. prol.; v. 33) was a Greek sophist
who lived at Athens about A.D. 180. His *Onomasticon*, a treatise on every variety
of subject in ten books, was dedicated to the Emperor Commodus A.D. 177. It
was published by Aldus in 1504. The 5th book treats of hunting, animals, etc.
the 6th of meals.

[6] *Porphyrius* (v. 31), a great Neo-Platonist, pupil and biographer of Plotinus.
His treatise on abstinence from meat that has had life is probably in view
here.

Oppian,[1] Polybius,[2] Heliodorus,[3] Aristotle, Aelian[4] and others. After holding these Discourses, they often, to be better assured, had the before-named Books brought to Table. And so well and perfectly did he retain in his Memory the things spoken of, that in those days there was not a Physician who knew therein half as much as he did.

Afterwards they discoursed of the Lessons read in the Morning, and finishing their Repast by some Confection of Quinces,[5] he picked his Teeth with Tooth-picks of the Mastick-tree;[6] washed his Hands and his Eyes with fair fresh Water, and they returned Thanks to God in some fine Canticles made in praise of the Divine Bounty and Munificence.

This done, Cards were brought, not to play with, but to learn from them a thousand pretty Tricks and new Inventions, all of which proceeded from Arithmetic. By this means he fell in love with the said Numerical Science, and every day after Dinner and Supper, passed his Time as pleasantly as he had been wont at Dice or at Cards; insomuch that he knew the Theory and Practice of it so well, that Tunstal, the Englishman,[7] who had written largely

---

[1] *Oppianus* (v. 31), a Cilician poet of the second century A.D., who wrote on hunting and fishing.

[2] *Polybius*, probably not the historian, but a pupil and son-in-law of Hippocrates. Several treatises are attributed to him, such as *De salubri diaeta, De principiis aut carnibus.* (Fr. ed.)

[3] *Heliodorus* (v. 31), probably not the author of the romance (cf. iv. 63), but an Athenian called ὁ περιηγητής mentioned in Athen. ii. 45 C, vi. 229 E, ix. 406 C.

[4] *Aelian* (G. 36; iii. 22; iv. prol.; v. 30) was a rhetorician at Rome in the time of Hadrian. There survives of him *De natura animalium* in seventeen books and *Varia Historia* in fourteen books, mostly derived from Alexander of Myndos. These books are mostly on points of natural history of a desultory kind. Excepting in the *Fourth Book* and the second edition of the *Third Book*, Rabelais seems indebted to an adaptation of this writer by Pierre Gilles of Albi (v. 31) published by Seb. Gryphius in 1533.

[5] Fr. *cotoniat* (P. 28; iv. 32); *coudignac* (G. 18); *pasté de coings* (iii. 32). Cf. Pliny 15. 37: "Mala quae vocamus *cotonea* et Graeci *cydonia* ex Creta insula advecta"; Avicenna, *Canon*, v. 1. 8: "Cydonia condita quae conveniunt ad confortandum stomachum et stringunt naturam". Cf. also *R.E.R.* iii. 181.

[6]   "Lentiscum melius: sed si tibi frondea cuspis
          Defuerit, dentes penna levare potest."
                              Mart. xiv. 22, quoted Erasm. *Ad.* i. 8. 33.

[7] Cuthbert Tunstal (1476–1559), Master of the Rolls, Bishop of London, translated to Durham (1529) in succession to Wolsey. He published *C. Tonstalli*

thereon, confessed that verily, in comparison with him, he understood no more therein than the High-Dutch.[1]

And not only in this, but also in the other Mathematical Sciences, as Geometry, Astronomy and Music;[2] for, as they waited for the Concoction and Digestion of his Repast, they made a thousand pretty Instruments and Geometrical Figures, and likewise practised the Astronomical Canons.

Afterwards they recreated themselves with singing musically in four or five Parts, or on a set Theme, to the full extent of their Throat. With regard to musical Instruments, he learned to play on the Lute, the Spinet, the Harp, the German Flute,[3] and the Flute with nine Holes, the Viol and the Sackbut.[4]

This Hour thus spent and his Digestion finished, he did purge his Body of natural Excrements; then betook himself to his principal Study for three hours or more, as well to repeat his morning Lesson as to go on with the Book he had in hand, as also to write and draw and trace carefully the antique[5] and Roman Letters.

This done, they went out, and with them a young Gentleman of Touraine, named the Esquire Gymnast, who taught him the Art of Riding. Changing then his Clothes, he mounted a Charger, a Courser, a Gennet, a Barb, a light Horse, made him run a hundred Courses,[6] leap in the Air, clear the Ditch, leap over the Barrier, caracole sharply to the right or the left.

---

de arte supputandi libri quatuor, Lond. R. Pynson, 1522; Paris, Rob. Estienne, 1529. Cf. Mullinger, *Hist. Univ. Camb.* i. 591 *sq.*; Allen, *Epist. Erasm.* i. 428.

[1] *High-Dutch = Hoch Deutsch.* The French had little communication with North Germany at that time.

[2] Arithmetic, Geometry, Astronomy and Music are the four "Arts" of the *Quadrivium*. They are alluded to in *P.* 8, the chapter on education in that book, here further developed probably on the lines of Vittorino da Feltre, the great Mantuan instructor (1378–1446). Cf. Creighton's *Historical Essays*, p. 118.

[3] *The German* (or transverse) *Flute* was so called (G. Bouchet, *Serée* 35, vol. v. p. 96) to distinguish it from the common flute which was a kind of flageolet (Rogers, *Birds of Aristophanes*, p. lxxxvi).

[4] Fr. *la sacque boutte*, a trombone. In old French it was a kind of lance with a hook to unseat knights on horseback. (Fr. ed.)

[5] *the antique* (*i.e.* Gothic) letters, which were in use from the thirteenth till the middle of the sixteenth century. Cf. *G.* 14.

[6] *Courses.* Fr. *quarieres.* Cf. Shakesp. *Rich. II*, i. 2. 49 and Madden, *Diary of M. William Silence*, p. 286:

"Or, if misfortune miss the first *career*".

There he broke, not his Lance, for it is the greatest Folly in the World to say: I have broken ten Lances at Tilt or in Battle—a Carpenter could easily do it—but 'tis a laudable Boast to have overthrown ten Enemies with one Lance. With his Lance then, tipped with Steel, tough and strong, he would break down a Door, pierce a Harness, uproot a Tree, spike a Ring, carry off a Cuirassier-saddle, a Coat-of-mail, a Gauntlet. All this he did, armed from Head to Foot.

With regard to prancing Flourishes and little Chirrups[1] on horseback, no one did it better than he. The Vaulter of Ferrara[2] was but an Ape in comparison. He was singularly accomplished in leaping nimbly from one Horse to another without putting Foot to the Ground—these Horses were called *desultorii*[3]—and leaping on horseback on both Sides, Lance in hand, and without Stirrups; and guiding his Horse at pleasure without a Bridle; for such things are useful for military Discipline.

Another day he practised with the Battle-axe, which he wielded so well, so lustily recovered it from every Thrust, so nimbly lowered it with a sweeping Stroke, that he was passed Knight-at-arms in the Field and in all Trials.

Then he brandished the Pike, played with the two-handed Sword, or the Back-sword, the Spanish Rapier, the Dagger, the Poniard, armed or unarmed, with a Buckler, Cloak or Target.

He hunted the Stag, the Roe-buck, the Bear, the Fallow-deer, the wild Boar, the Hare, the Partridge, the Pheasant, the Bustard.[4]

He played with the large Ball and made it bound in the Air with Foot as well as with Fist.

---

[1] Fr. *poppismes*, Gk. πόππυσμα. Cf. Pliny, 35. 104: "cum pingeret Nealces *poppyzonta* retinentem par equum".

[2] *the Vaulter of Ferrara.* Rabelais with Bishop du Bellay stayed a few days at Ferrara on their first visit to Rome in Jan. 1534 (V. L. Bourrilly, *Lettres de R. d'Italie*, p. 8). Cf. Ferrara Coaches, v. 23. Perhaps Rabelais alludes to Cesare Fiaschi, a celebrated Italian acrobat of the time. (Fr. ed.)

[3] *desultorii.* Hom. *Il.* xv. 679–84; Livy, xxiii. 29. § 5; Suet. i. 39 and Prop. v. 2. 35 (cited Bud. *in Pand.* p. 354):

"Est etiam aurigae species Vertumnus, et ejus
Trajicit alterno qui leve pondus equo".

[4] Fr. *l'ostade*: in c. 37 it is spelt *autarde*, conforming nearer to Pliny's name *avistarda* (10. 57). Cf. *P.* 11.

He wrestled, ran, jumped, not at three Steps and a Leap, not with a Hop, nor with the German Leap (for Gymnast said such Leaps are useless and of no good in War), but with a single Bound he would clear a Ditch, fly over a Hedge, mount six Paces up a Wall and clamber in this manner up to a Window of the height of a Lance.

He would swim in deep Water on his Belly, on his Back, on his Side, with all his Body, with his Feet only, with one Hand in the Air, wherein holding a Book he would cross the whole breadth of the River Seine* without wetting the Book, and dragging his Cloak with his Teeth as did Julius Caesar.[1] Then with one Hand he got into a Boat with great Strength; from there he would again throw himself into the Water head-foremost, sounded the Depths, explored the Hollows of the Rocks,† plunged into the Pits and Gulfs.[2] Then he turned the Boat about, steered it, rowed it quickly, slowly, with the Stream, against the Current, stopped it in full Course, steered it with one Hand and with the other laid about him with a huge Oar, hoisted the Sail, climbed aloft on the Mast by the Shrouds, ran along the Rigging, adjusted the Compass, tackled the Bowlines,[3] handled the Helm.

Coming out of the Water, he sturdily climbed up a Mountainside and came down again as easily; he clambered up Trees like a Cat, leaped from one to another like a Squirrel and knocked down the great Boughs like another Milo.

With two well-steeled Poniards and two well-tried Bodkins he

---

* *riviere de Seine*, D; *riviere de Loire a Montsoreau*, A.

† *creuzoit les rochiers*, D; *creuzoit les rochiers et gouffres de la fosse de Savigny*, A. •

[1] In the Alexandrian war, during a battle for the possession of Pharos, Caesar, being driven by a sudden sally of the enemy from a bridge into a boat together with many more, leaped into the sea and swam to the nearest ship 200 paces distant, carrying his papers in his left hand above the water and dragging his cloak with his teeth. Cf. Suet. i. 64; Plut. *Caes.* c. 49. 4; Dio Cass. xlii. 40; Caes. *Bell. Alex.* c. 21.

[2] In the first edition (A) here and in the passage about swimming, and in the one about St Victor and Montmartre, Rabelais forgets that he is in Paris and gives places in Touraine. See the variants. *Savigny-en-Veron* is now a huge marsh about 3 miles square in surface, filled with water nearly all the year. The "rocks and pits" are an invention of Rabelais. (Fr. ed.)

[3] *tackled the Bowlines*. Fr. *contreventoit les bulines* = to hold up the cordage against the wind. Cf. *R.E.R.* viii. 24.

climbed to the Top of a House like a Rat, then came down from the Top to the Bottom, with his Limbs so arranged that he got no Hurt by his Fall.

He hurled the Dart, threw the Bar, put the Stone, threw the Javelin, the Boar-spear, the Halbert; drew a Bow to the full, bent against his Breast strong rack-bent Cross-bows, took Aim by his Eye with an Arquebuss,[1] planted the Cannon, shot at the Butt, at the Popinjay, going up a Hill, coming down it, frontways, sideways, and behind him like the Parthians.[2]

They tied a Cable-rope for him on to the Top of some high Tower, with the other End hanging to the Ground; by this he climbed hand over hand to the Top, and then came down again so sturdily and firmly that you could not have done it better on a well-levelled Plain.

They placed for him a great Pole supported by two Trees; from this he would hang by his Hands, and go along it to and fro without touching anything with his Feet, so swiftly that you could not overtake him by running at full Speed.

And to exercise his Chest and Lungs he would shout like all the Devils. I heard him once calling Eudemon from the Gate of St Victor to Montmartre.[3] Never had Stentor such a Voice at the Siege of Troy.

Moreover, to strengthen his Sinews, they had made for him two great Sows of Lead, each weighing eight thousand seven hundred Quintals, which he called *haltères*:[4] these he would take from the Earth, one in each Hand, and hoist them in the Air above his

---

[1] *an Arquebuss* (Ital. *archibuso*, Fr. sixteenth century *haquebute*) was a very heavy piece, fired from a rest; it required portentous strength to hold it so as to take aim as with a fowling-piece. (From Fr. ed.)

[2] The Parthians shooting behind them afforded a commonplace to the Latin poets. Cf. Virg. *G*. iii. 31; Hor. *Od*. i. 19. 11; Ovid, *A.A*. i. 209.

[3] From St Victor to Montmartre is practically from the extreme south-east to the extreme north-west of Paris. In A the reading is "*depuy* la porte de Bessé jusqu'à la fontaine de Narsay". The fountain still exists in the canton of *l'Isle Bouchard*, 4½ kilometres from the Bessé gate in the centre of Chinon.

[4] Gk. ἁλτῆρες (ἅλλομαι), weights like dumb-bells used in jumping and thrown backwards at the moment of taking a leap. Cf. Mart. xiv. 49; Bud. *in Pand*. p. 349; Paus. v. 26. 2. In mod. French they are dumb-bells, Indian clubs and the like.

Head, and hold them so without stirring for three-quarters of an Hour and more, which shewed inimitable Strength.

He could play at Barriers[1] with the stoutest, and when the Tussle came, he kept himself on his Feet so firmly that he would let the hardiest of them try, to see if they could make him budge from his Ground, just as Milo did formerly, in imitation of whom also he held a Pomegranate in his Hand and gave it to whosoever could take it from him.[2]

His Time being thus bestowed and himself rubbed, cleansed and refreshed with a Change of Apparel, he returned fairly and softly; and passing by some Meadows or other grassy Places, they inspected the Trees and Plants, comparing them with the Accounts of them in the Books of the Ancients who have written thereon, such as Theophrastus,[3] Dioscorides,[4] Marinus,[5] Pliny, Nicander,[6] Macer[7] and Galen; and carried to the House whole Handfuls of them, whereof a young Page named Rhizotomus[8] had charge, and

---

[1] *at Barriers.* Fr. *aux barres*; "ad metas", Cordier, 38. § 15. It is to be noted that none of the games given here are included in the list of c. 22. (Fr. ed.)

[2] "Milonem...cum constitisset nemo vestigio educebat; malum tenenti nemo digitum corrigebat", Pliny, 7. 83. Cf. also Paus. vi. 14. 5–8.

[3] *Theophrastus* wrote in Greek two treatises on plants, *de historia plantarum* and *de causis plantarum* (ed. princ. Venet. 1497).

[4] *Dioscorides Pedacius,* a physician and herbalist, prob. second century A.D. He wrote a *Materia medica,* containing an account of plants as well as other medicaments. It was translated by Gerard of Cremona (ed. princ. Venet. 1499).

[5] *Marinus,* a celebrated physician and anatomist, tutor to Galen, who speaks of him with great respect (*de anatom. admin.* ii. 2). But Rabelais here seems to confound him with Pietro Marini of Foligno, who translated the *de re rustica et hortensi* of Palladius (Venet. 1528). (Fr. ed.)

[6] *Nicander of Colophon* (iii. 25, iv. 34), a priest of the Clarian Apollo (*circa* 185–135 B.C.), a physician and a poet. Cf. Cic. *de Orat.* i. § 69. He wrote on toxicology. Two of his poems survive, Θηριακά and Ἀλεξιφάρμακα. He also wrote the Ἑτεροιούμενα, which was the basis of Ovid's *Metamorphoses* (ed. princ. Venet. 1499).

[7] *Macer* is *not* Aemilius Macer of Verona referred to in Ovid, *Trist.* iv. 10. 43, but an obscure writer of the ninth or tenth century. Cf. Macer, *de usibus herbarum, versu heroico* (Anton. Zanotus Parmensis Mediol. 1482, Basil. 1527).

> "Quod si mage nosse laboras
> Herbarum vires Macer tibi carmine dicet."
>
> Dion. Cato, *Dist. Mor.* lib. ii. praef.

[8] *Rhizotomus* = "herbalist" in Greek (Theoph. *H.P.* ix. 8. 1). In Lucian, *Deor. Dial.* 13, Heracles tauntingly calls Asclepius ῥιζοτόμος.

together with them of Mattocks, Pickaxes, Grubbing-hooks, Spades, Pruning-knives and other Instruments requisite for good botanizing.

When they had arrived home, while Supper was being got ready, they repeated certain Passages of that which had been read, and then took their Place at Table. And here note that Gargantua's Dinner was sober and frugal; for he only ate enough to restrain the Cravings[1] of his Stomach; but his Supper was copious and ample, for he took then as much as was needful to maintain and nourish him. This is the true Diet prescribed by the Art of good and sound Medicine, although a Rabble of foppish Physicians, fagged in the Wrangling-shop of the Sophists,[2] counsel the Contrary.

During the said Repast the Lesson read at Dinner was continued as long as they thought good; the rest was taken up in good Discourse, learned and profitable.

After they had given Thanks, they set themselves to sing melodiously, and play on harmonious Instruments, or with those pretty Sports one has with Cards or Dice or Thimblerig; and there they remained making good Cheer and frolicking sometimes till Bedtime; sometimes they went to seek the Company of Learned men or such as had seen foreign Countries.

When it was full Night, before retiring, they went to the most open place of the House to see the Face of the Heavens; and there took note of the Comets, if there were any, likewise the Figures, Situations, Aspects, Oppositions and Conjunctions of the Stars.

Then with his Master he did briefly recapitulate, after the manner of the Pythagoreans,[3] everything which he had read, seen, learned, done and heard in the Course of all that Day.

And so they prayed unto God the Creator, worshipping Him

---

[1] *Cravings*. Fr. *abois* = barking. Cf. iii. 15 and Hor. *Sat.* ii. 2. 18:

"Cum sale panis
Latrantem stomachum bene leniet".

[2] *Sophistes* D, *Arabes* ABC. The change is probably made in consideration of physicians who were partisans of Avicenna. The revival of the Greek medical classics led to a declaration of war against the Arabians (J. F. Payne, *Harv. Orat.* p. 19).

[3] "Pythagoreorum more exercendae memoriae gratia, quid quoque die dixerim, audierim, egerim, commemoro vesperi", Cic. *de Sen.* 11. § 38.

and ratifying their Faith towards Him, and glorifying Him for His infinite Goodness; and returning Thanks to Him for all the Time past, they recommended themselves to His divine Clemency for all the Time to come.

This done, they betook themselves to their Repose.

CHAPTER XXIV

How Gargantua spent his Time in rainy Weather

IF it happened that the Weather was rainy and unsettled, all the Time before Dinner was employed according to custom, except that he had a good clear Fire lighted, to correct the Distempers of the Air.

But after Dinner, instead of their Exercise they stayed indoors, and by way of healthful Recreation[1] (*apotherapic*) amused themselves in trussing of Hay, cleaving and sawing of Wood and in threshing Sheaves of Corn in the Barn. Then they studied the Art of Painting and Sculpture, or brought back into use the ancient Game of *Tables*,[2] as Leonicus[3] has written of it and as our good Friend Lascaris[4] doth play it. In playing at it they recalled to mind the Passages of the ancient Authors in which Mention is made or some Metaphor taken from this Game.

Likewise, they either went to see the Drawing of Metals[5] or the Casting of Artillery; or they went to see the Lapidaries,[6] Goldsmiths

---

[1] Fr. *apotherapie*, from ἀποθεραπεία in Galen's *Thrasybulus*, c. 47 (v. 898). It means recreation *after* exercise. "*Praeparatoria*, quae dicitur, ad exercendum corpora praeparat; *apotherapeuticen* Latine *recuratoriam* dixeris haud inepte", Cael. Rhod. *Ant. Lect.* xi. 4.

[2] *Tables* (*Tales*, AB) (iii. 11; iv. 7) = ἀστράγαλοι. *Tali* had two sides round and the other four marked 1, 3, 4, 6. *Tesserae*, = κύβοι, were ordinary dice with all six sides numbered.

[3] Niccolo Tomeo Leonico (*i.e.* of Lonigo) (1457–1533), a pupil of Chalcondylas, taught Greek at Venice 1504–6. The rest of his life was passed at Padua, where he became acquainted with Longolius. His most important work was a translation of Aristotle's *Parva Naturalia*, *Opuscula* (containing *Sannutus* sive *de ludo talaris*), and *Dialogi* (Paris, Simon Colinaeus, 1530). He also wrote *De varia historia libri tres* (Lugd. Seb. Gryphius, 1532). He was a friend of Cardinal Bembo, very witty and well-read in classical literature and philosophy (Castiglione, *Corteg.* ii. 71).

[4] Andreas Janus Lascaris (v. 19), a celebrated scholar (1445–1535) and a friend of Rabelais. He gave instruction in Greek to Erasmus and Budé, and was employed as ambassador to Venice by Louis XII, afterwards as librarian to Francis I (Roscoe, *Leo X*, c. 10). Lascaris' tomb with epitaph in Greek is in the church of St Agatha de' Gothi in Rome. Cf. Allen, *Epist. Erasm.* i. 269 (p. 523).

[5] Fr. *tiroit les metaulx*. Cf. Virg. *Aen.* viii. 421, *Stricturae Chalybum*.

[6] *Lapidaries*, etc. μάλιστα δὲ πρὸς τοῖς ἀργυροκοπείοις εὑρίσκετο καὶ χρυσοχοείοις, εὑρησιλογῶν καὶ φιλοτεχνῶν πρὸς τοὺς τορευτὰς καὶ τοὺς

and Cutters of precious Stones; or the Alchymists and Minters of Coin, or the Makers of Tapestry, Weavers, Velvet-workers, Watch-makers, Mirror-makers, Printers,[1] Instrument-makers, Dyers and other such kinds of Workmen, and everywhere giving them Wine, they did learn and consider the Skill and Invention of the Trades.

They went also to hear the public Lectures, the solemn Acts, the Repetitions,[2] the Declamations, the Pleadings of the noble Advocates, and the Harangues of the Preachers of the Gospel.[3]

He went through the Halls and Places appointed for Fencing, and there played against the Masters at all Weapons, and taught them by Experience that he knew as much, yea more in it than they.

Also, instead of botanizing, they visited the Shops of the Druggists, Herbalists and Apothecaries, and diligently considered the Fruits, Roots, Leaves, Gums, Seeds, foreign Unguents,[4] therewith also how men did adulterate them.

He went to see the Jugglers,[5] Conjurors and Quack-salvers, and paid Attention to their Antics, their Tricks, their Somersaults and their smooth Tongue, especially those of Chauny[6] in Picardy; for they are by nature great Jabberers and fine cogging Praters[7] in the matter of green Apes.[8]

ἄλλους τεχνίτας. ἔπειτα...ὡμίλει ᾧ τύχοι καὶ μετὰ τῶν παρεπιδημούντων συνέπινε τῶν εὐτελεστάτων, Athen. v. 193 D (of Antiochus Epiphanes).

[1] *Printers.* Francis I set up a press in the Louvre (cf. *G.* 51), as Prince Massimi had done in his palace in Rome for Pannartz and Sweynheym.

[2] *Repetitions.* Ample discussions on debatable points of law.

[3] Fr. *les prescheurs evangeliques* (cf. *G.* 17). In these words may be seen a tendency to the doctrines of the Reformers, who based their opinions on the study of the Bible.

[4] Fr. *axunges peregrines.* Cf. *P.* 24 and Pliny, 28. 141.

[5] *Jugglers,* etc. ἡμεῖς οὖν ἅμα ἀκροώμενοι τῶν γελωτοποιῶν τούτων καὶ μίμων ἔτι δὲ τῶν ἄλλων τεχνιτῶν ὑποπίνωμεν. Athen. xi. 464E: cf. also i. 19D-F.

[6] *Chauny* was a yearly resort for such actors, acrobats, etc. (Pasquier, *Recherches,* vii. 5). (Fr. ed.)

"Femme qui fait les soubressaulx
Comme un basteleur de Chaulny."
Jamet, *Resp. à l'ép. du coq à l'asne.* Cl. Marot.

[7] Fr. *bailleurs de baillivernes.* Cf. Patelin, l. 810:

"Ha! quels bailleurs de baillivernes
Sont ce cy?"

[8] *green Apes* (iv. 32) = anything fantastic. It is the *simia Sabaea* of Linnaeus or the *cercopithecus Sabaeus* of Cuvier (Le Double, p. 885).

When they had returned Home for Supper they ate more soberly than on other Days, and Meats more desiccative and attenuating;[1] to the end that the humid Distemper of the Air, communicated to the Body by necessary Proximity, might by this means be corrected, and that they might suffer no Prejudice through not taking Exercise as was their Custom.

Thus was Gargantua tutored, and he kept on this Course from day to day, profiting as you understand a Young man can do, according to his Age, with good Sense[2] and Exercise of this kind thus continued; which although at the Beginning it seemed difficult, as it went on was so sweet, easy and delectable that it resembled rather the Recreation of a King than the Study of a Scholar.

Nevertheless Ponocrates, to give him Rest from this vehement Intention of the Spirits, marked out once in a Month some Day that was very clear and serene; on which they started in the Morning from the City and went either to Gentilly,[3] or to Boulogne, or Montrouge, or Charanton-bridge, or Vanves, or Sainct-Cloud. And there they spent all the Day in making the greatest Cheer they could devise; gibing, making merry, drinking Healths, playing, singing, dancing, tumbling[4] in some fair Meadow, unnestling of Sparrows, taking of Quails, fishing for Frogs[5] and Crayfish.

But although that Day was spent without Books and Reading, in no way was it spent without Profit. For in a fair Meadow they would repeat by Heart some pleasant Lines of Virgil's *Agriculture*, of Hesiod, of the *Rusticus* of Politian;[6] set abroach certain witty

---

[1] There is a treatise of Galen, *de victu attenuante*.

[2] Fr. *un jeune homme selon son age de bon sens*, D. ABC omit *selon son age*, which here disturbs the sense. Des Marets thinks the words have been disarranged in printing and would read *que peut faire selon son age un jeune homme de bon sens*. Scott has in *Redgauntlet* (c. 2 of *The Narrative*) "the duties of a solicitor to age as accords".

[3] *Gentilly*, etc., villages to the south and west of the University quarter of Paris, where it was usual to take a day's outing (*campos* in the University slang). Cf. Cordier, 33. § 2.

[4] Fr. *se voytrans*.

[5] *fishing for Frogs*. Cf. *depiscando grenoillibus, P.* 12.

[6] Politiani *Silvae* (Bononiae 1492, Lugd. Seb. Gryphius, 1537) were Latin poems by this scholar (cf. *G.* 1) highly prized at the time, entitled *Manto* (1482) on Virgil's *Bucolics*, *Rusticus* (1483) on the *Opera et Dies* of Hesiod and the *Georgica* of Virgil, *Ambra* (1485) on Homer, and *Nutritia* (Θρεπτηρία: 1486) on

Epigrams[1] in Latin and then turn them into Roundelays and Ballads in the French Tongue.

In their Feasting, they would separate the Wine[2] from the Water that was therewith mixed, (as Cato teacheth *De re rust.*, as doth Pliny also[3]) with a Cup made from Ivy; they would wash the Wine in a Bason full of Water, then take it out again with a Funnel. They made the Water go from one Glass to another, and contrived many little *automatic* Machines,[4] that is, Machines that moved of themselves.

---

poetry and the poets. They are composed in excellent Virgilian hexameters· *Ambra* derives its name from a country-house of Lorenzo Tornabuoni, to whom it is dedicated.

[1] *Epigrams,* etc. Among the epigrams of Cl. Marot are several translations from Martial and other Latin poets. See especially *Epig.* 24, 52, 103, 166, 221. In v. 17 Pantagruel is represented as writing elegies on the adventures of his shipmates before Grippeminaud.

[2] Fr. *vin aisgue,* wine mixed with water; *aigue, iau* and *eve* all occur in old French as equivalents for *eau.* Cf. *aiguade* in iv. 66 and *Aigues-mortes* on the coast of Languedoc.

[3] "Si voles scire in vinum aqua addita sit necne, vasculum facito de materia hederacea. Vinum id quod putabis aquam habere eo demittito. Si habebit aquam vinum effluet, aqua manebit", Cato, *de Agricult.* c. cxi; "Hederae mira proditur natura ad experienda vina, si vas fiat e ligno ejus, vina transfluere ac remanere aquam, si qua fuerit mixta", Pliny, 16. 155. Sir T. Browne, *Pseud. Epid.* ii. 7. § 9, disproved this by experiment, as I have done. Cf. also iii. 52. A curious mention of this is in *Hyp.* c. 5, c. 8 verso: "edera...il ligno cui poculato divide Bacco da Thetide".

[4] *automatic Machines.* Cf. *Epist. à Aymery Bouchard.* Margaret o Austria, daughter of Maximilian, is recorded to have given 20 Carolus for an automatic doll (Altmeyer, ii. 107 n.). Politian, *Epist.* x. 8 (Lugd. Seb. Gryphius, 1539), mentions an Orrery or *Planetarium,* which he styles *machinula automatos.* He also mentions *automata* in his Miscellanies, No. 97, in a note on Suet. *Claud.* 34 (*automaton et pegma*). Galen speaks (*de usu part.* iv. 2) of the αὐτόματα of Homer, *Il.* xviii. 471.

CHAPTER XXV

How was stirred between the Cake-bakers of Lerné[1] and those of Gargantua's Country the Great Strife,[2] whereby were waged great Wars

At that Time, which was the Season of Vintage at the Beginning of Autumn, the Shepherds of the Country were set to guard the Vines and hinder the Starlings from eating the Grapes.

At which Time the Cake-bakers of Lerné were passing on the great Highway, taking ten or twelve Loads of Cakes to the Town.

The said Shepherds asked them courteously to give them some in return for their Money, at the Market-price. For note that it is celestial Food to eat for Breakfast, Grapes with fresh Cake, especially Pine-apple Grapes,[3] Fig-grapes, Muscadines, Verjuice-Grapes, and the Luskard for those who are constipated in their Belly. For they make men go off to the length of a Hunter's Spear; and *thinking* to let off a Squib, men do often bewray themselves, wherefore they are called the Vintage-*thinkers*.[4]

---

[1] *Lerné* (iv. 23), a village in Touraine about 4 miles south-west of Chinon and 1 kilometre east of La Devinière. The manufacture of these cakes (*fouaces, panis subcinereus* from Lat. *focus*) was a great industry at Lerné (cf. c. 32) and was still carried on in 1821. There was a corporation of *fouaciers* and a *bâtonnier* of *la confrérie* (*R.E.R.* x. 73).

[2] *the Great Strife.* It seems very probable that at the time when Rabelais was visiting Chinon in September 1532 (cf. *P.* 34) an actual collision took place between the inhabitants of Lerné and Seuilly, who took the sides of Gaucher Sainte-Marthe and Antoine Rabelais in the law-suit which was now embittered, and that this is represented here and continued through the *Gargantua* allegorically as a tremendous war.

[3] *Pine-apple Grapes.* Fr. *pinau* (Touraine), *G.* 38. *Fig-grapes.* Fr. *fiers* (Anjou). *Verjuice-grapes.* Fr. *bicane* (Orléans), Lat. *omphacium*: Pliny, 12. 131, 14. 98. For details cf. *R.E.R.* vii. 103, x. 263.

[4] *Vintage-thinkers* (*P.P.* 6). Cf. Joh. Aegid. *Ad.*: "*Cuideurs* sont en *vendange.* Reddit complures vindemia laeta *putantes*". Perhaps a double meaning is intended between "pruners" and "thinkers".

> "J'ay assailly en Paris les jaloux
> Et les jalouses par voyes aspres, estranges;
> Tous les *cuideurs* ne sont pas *en vendanges.*"
>
> Gringore, *La Coqueluche* (vol. i. p. 493, ed. Elz.).

The Cake-bakers were in no way inclinable to their Request, but, what is worse, they insulted them hugely, calling them:

Babblers,[1] Broken-mouths, Carrot-pates, scurvy Fellows, Stinking Jacks, Drunken Roysters, sly Knaves, lazy Loons, slapsauce Fellows, Tunbellies, Gawkies, Ne'er-do-wells, Loggerheads, Paltry customers, Smell-feasts, Drawlatch Hoydens, strutting Coxcombs, Grimacers, Ninnies, Woe-begone Sneaks, gaping Noodles, Bog-trotters, Shaven-polls, Gluttons, Hickscorners, Rattle-tooths, Dung-drovers, sh—n Shepherds, and other such defamatory Epithets; adding that it was not for them to eat of these dainty Cakes, but that they ought to content themselves with coarse lumpy Bread, and Rye-loaf.[2]

To this Outrage one of them named Forgier,[3] a very honest man in his Bearing and a notable Springall, replied gently:

"Since when have you put on Horns,[4] that you have become so malapert?[5] Why, formerly you were wont to give them us freely, and now do you refuse? 'Tis not the Act of good Neighbours, and it is not thus that we treat you when you come here to buy our good Corn, whereof you make your Cakes and Buns. Moreover, we would have given you of our Grapes into the Bargain; but by the Halidame, you may chance to repent it, and some day you will have a Dealing with us, when we will act with you in like manner; therefore remember it".

---

[1] *Babblers*, etc. Regis aptly quotes a passage from Sterne's *Tristram Shandy*, ix. 25, in imitation of this.

[2] *Rye-loaf.* Fr. *tourte*, Lat. *torta panis* in the Vulgate, 1 *Reg.* ii. 36, x. 3. See Ducange, *panis tortus*. It may be intended for the circular loaves such as in Dauphiné are carried by the peasants into the mountains on a stick thrust through the hole in the middle.

[3] *Forgier*, a name still occurring in the neighbourhood of Chinon. One of this name was tenant of the Abbey of Seuilly (1549–56) (*R.E.R.* ii. 44).

[4] *put on Horns.* Fr. *pris cornes*. A metaphor to be found in the Psalms: cf. Ovid, *A.A.* i. 239: "Tunc veniunt risus, tunc pauper cornua sumit"; Hor. *C.* iii. 21. 18; Erasm. *Ad.* i. 8. 68.

[5] *malapert.* Fr. *rogues*. Cf. *R.R.* 12,569:

"Cum fiers et orguilleus et *rogues*".

Gringore, *La chasse du cerf des cerfs* (i. 165):

"Aussi rogue que ung chien sur son pallier".

Then Marquet,[1] grand Mace-bearer of the Guild of Cake-bakers, said to him: "Verily thou art rarely crest-risen this morning; thou didst eat too much Millet[2] yestreen; come hither, Sirrah, come hither, and I will give thee of my Cake".

Upon this Forgier in all Simplicity went towards him drawing a Shilling[3] from his Fob, thinking that Marquet was going to draw out of his Pouch some Cakes; but he gave him with his Whip such a rough Lash across his Legs that the Weals shewed. Then he would have made off in flight, but Forgier cried out "Murder! Help!" with all his might, and at the same time threw at him a great Cudgel which he carried under his Arm, and struck him on the coronal[4] Joint of his Head, on the crotaphic[5] Artery on the right Side; in such sort that Marquet tumbled from his Mare, more like a dead than a living Man.

Meantime the Countrymen, who were shelling Walnuts hard by, ran up with their long Poles and laid on these Cake-bakers as though they were threshing green Rye.[6] The Shepherds and Shepherdesses besides, hearing the Cry of Forgier, came up with their Slings and Cudgels,[7] and followed them with great Throwing of Stones, which fell so thick that it seemed as though it were Hail.

At last they came up with them and took from them about four or five Dozen of their Cakes; nevertheless they paid for them at the usual Price and gave them besides a hundred Walnuts[8] and three

---

[1] *Marquet* was father-in-law of Gaucher Sainte-Marthe (*Picrochole*) and was wounded on the head by a blow of a *tribart*, which is a stick hung on the necks of the dogs at vintage time (Notes of Bouchereau, *R.E.R.* iii. 406).

[2] Millet and maize were given to cocks to make them pugnacious. Garlic is so used in Aristophanes.

[3] Fr. *unzain*, a silver piece raised from the value of *ten* to *eleven* deniers Jan. 4, 1473 and from *eleven* to *twelve* April 24, 1488. It was at different times *dizain*, *douzain* and even *treizein* according to the different values. It was properly *un blanc* and degenerated from the old *gros tournois* or *sol* of 12 *deniers* (Cartier, *Numismatique de Rabelais*).

[4] The coronal suture ($\sigma\tau\epsilon\phi\alpha\nu\iota\alpha\iota\alpha\ \dot{\rho}\alpha\phi\dot{\eta}$ of Galen) is the fronto-parietal one, crossing the *sinciput* and coming down towards the middle of the temple. On the *sutures* see Galen, *de usu part.* ix. 7 (iii. 711); Paré, iii. 3.

[5] *crotaphic* ($\kappa\rho\sigma\tau\acute{\alpha}\phi\iota\sigma$), belonging to the temple. Galen, *de usu part.* ix. 7.

[6] *green Rye* (*P.* 17; iv. 12) would require more threshing to get the corn out.

[7] *Cudgels* (Fr. *brassiers*), Cotgrave; but it may well be some sort of *sling*.

[8] *Walnuts*. Fr. *quecas*, still used in Sologne and Berry. *Cacos* is used in Saintonge.

Basketfuls of white Grapes.[1] Then the Cake-bakers helped Marquet, who had an ugly Wound, to mount again, and returned to Lerné, without going on the Road to Pareillé,[2] venting stout and sturdy Threats against the Neatherds, Shepherds, and Countrymen of Seuillé and Sinays.

This done, the Shepherds and Shepherdesses made right merry with these Cakes and fine Grapes, and disported themselves together to the sound of the fair Bagpipe, scoffing at those fine, vainglorious Cake-bakers, who had met with Mischief for want of crossing themselves with the Right hand[3] in the Morning. And with great common Grapes[4] they carefully dressed Forgier's Legs, so that he was quickly healed.

---

[1] Fr. *francs aubiers*, Lat. *albus*. Cf. *R.E.R.* vii. 106. They were sweet white grapes, with round berries.

[2] *Pareillé* (a hamlet of Chinon), *Sinays* and *Seuillé* or Seuilly, villages on the road from Chinon to Lerné (cf. *G.* 4).

[3] *Right hand*. Fr. *la bonne main*. So the left is called *la male main*. Cf. Mayor's *Juvenal*, x. 5, *dextro pede*.

[4] An application made chiefly with the juice of unripe white grapes is given in Hippoc. *de ulceribus*, ii. 315. K.

CHAPTER XXVI

How the Inhabitants of Lerné, by the Command of Picrochole[1] their King, unexpectedly assaulted the Shepherds of Grandgousier[2]

THE Cake-bakers, being returned to Lerné, at once, before eating or drinking, betook themselves to the Capitol,[3] and there before their King Picrochole, third of that Name,[4] set forth their Complaint, shewing their Baskets broken, their Caps all crumpled, their Garments torn, their Cakes ransacked, and above all, Marquet enormously wounded; declaring that all had been done by the Shepherds and Countrymen of Grandgousier near the broad Highway beyond Seuillé.

Picrochole incontinently went into a furious Rage, and without questioning any further why or how, had proclaimed throughout

---

[1] *Picrochole* = choleric, passionate. πικρόχολος occurs in Hipp. *de morbis acutis*, c. 9 (ii. 43) and Galen, *Fac. Nat.* ii. 10 (ii. 124). The identification of Picrochole with Scévole, or Gaucher, Sainte-Marthe, physician to the Abbess of Fontevrault, was a tradition in the Sainte-Marthe family maintained by two great-nephews, MM. Sainte-Marthe, who edited Rabelais' Letters from Rome, and it was believed by Mènage. It was tentatively put forward in the edition of Marty-Laveau and has been investigated by M. Lefranc, supported by documentary evidence, and now finds general acceptance. Sainte-Marthe owned two estates adjoining those of Antoine Rabelais, one at Le Chapeau near Chavigny-sur-Loire, another at Lerné near La Devinière. He had constructed a mill and made enclosures by piles and dams and otherwise, to the prejudice of owners of land on the rivers Vienne and Loire. These owners formed a company and chose Maistre Antoine Rabelais, the senior *avocat*, to defend their rights. The result was a protracted law-suit, which François Rabelais describes under the guise of a war with all its accompaniments of artillery, alarms, excursions, etc.

[2] *Grandgousier* should evidently be read here instead of *Gargantua*. He was studying at Paris, while it is his father's country that is being invaded. The same change should be made in the heading of c. 25, "*the country of Gargantua*".

[3] Fr. *Capitoly*. This was the title of the Council-house at Toulouse and some other places in France, and the magistrates were called *capitouls*. Perhaps a mock heroic comparison with the Capitol of Rome is intended.

[4] *third of that Name.* His father and grandfather had been physicians to the Abbess of Fontevrault.

148

his Country Ban and Arrier Ban,[1] and that every one, under pain
of the Halter, should assemble in Arms in the Great Square before
the Castle at the hour of Noon.

The better to strengthen his Design he sent Orders that the
Drum should be beat about the Town. He himself, whilst his
Dinner was making ready, went to see his Artillery limbered up,
his Ensign and Oriflamme displayed, and Wagons loaded with
store of Ammunition, of Arms as well as of Provisions.

While he was dining he made out his Commissions, and by his
Edict Lord Shagrag[2] was appointed to command the Vanguard,
wherein were numbered sixteen thousand and fourteen Hacque-
busiers, thirty-five thousand and eleven Volunteers.[3]

The Charge of the Artillery was given to the grand Master of the
Horse Toucquedillon; in this were reckoned nine hundred and
fourteen great bronze Guns in Cannons, Double-cannons, Basilisks,
Serpentines, Culverins, Bombards, Falcons, Passevolans, Spiroles
and other Pieces.[4]

The Rear-guard was given to the Duke of Rake-penny; in the
Main battle were posted the King and the Princes of his Kingdom.

When they were thus hastily equipped, before they set forward,
they sent three hundred light Horsemen under the Direction of

---

[1] *Bannum* (L. Lat.) is a proclamation or summons, *Heer* German for "army".
Herebannum became corrupted to *arbannum* and subsequently into *arrière ban* and
again into *retrobannum*.

[2] Fr. *Trepelu* (*G.* 9; iii. 42), a poor ragged creature. The early edd. ABC read
Grippeminaud, who figures in v. 11 *sqq.* as Archduke of the Furred Cats. The van
was usually commanded by the Constable or a prince of the blood (*R.E.R.*
v. 10 n.).

[3] *Volunteers.* Fr. *avanturiers.* Companies of musketeers employed by Louis XII
and Francis I after the first Italian campaign, with no pay save what they got
by plunder. They became outrageous even in peace-time and very troublesome
to Francis. Cf. *J.B.P.* (1526).

[4] Paré in his *Apologie et Voyages* (vol. iii. p. 692) gives the following list of
pieces of ordnance: "*Canons, double canons,* bastardes, mousquets, *passe-volants;*
pieces de campagne, *couleuvrines, serpentines, basilisques,* sacres, *faulcons,* faulcon-
neaux, flustes, orgues, harquebuses à croc". Cf. Marco Polo, ii. 60 and Yule's
note. A *bombard* is a sort of mortar, so called from the noise it made, carrying
balls of metal or stone varying in weight—"tormentum quod novo vocabulo
bombardam vocant", Erasm. *Epist.* vol. iii. 919. 18 (ed. Allen), 1519. The *passe-
volant* and *spirole* are small pieces.

Captain Swill-wind[1] to reconnoitre the Country, and to see if there
was any Ambush on the Country-side. But after they had made
diligent Search they found all the Land around in Peace and Quiet,
without any Gathering of People whatever.

Learning this, Picrochole commanded that every one should
march under his Colours in all Haste.

Thereupon, without Order or Measure, they took the Fields one
with the other, ravaging and wasting everything wherever they
passed, without sparing Poor or Rich, places Sacred or Profane;
they drove off Oxen, Cows, Bulls, Calves, Heifers, Ewes, Wethers,
She-goats, He-goats, Fowls, Capons, Chickens, Goslings, Ganders,
Geese, Hogs, Sows, Porkers; bashing the Walnuts, stripping the
Vines, carrying off the Vine-stocks, knocking down all the Fruit
from the Trees.

It was an unparalleled Disorder that they wrought; and they
found no one to resist them, but every one put himself at their
Mercy, beseeching that they might be treated with more Humanity,
in regard that they had in all Time past been good and loving
Neighbours; and that they had never been guilty of any Excess or
Outrage against them that they should so suddenly be evil-en-
treated by them; and that God would punish them for it shortly.
To these Remonstrances the others answered nothing more than
that they would teach them to eat Cakes.

---

[1] *Swill-wind.* Fr. *Engoulevent.* He is one of the giants in *P.* 1. It is a good name
for a light-armed scout.

"Noble Seigneur d'Angoullevent."
Le Monologue des Nouveauz Sotz, A.P.F. i. 11.

CHAPTER XXVII

How a Monk of Seuillé[1] saved the Close of the Abbey from being sacked by the Enemy

So they went on harrying, pillaging and stealing, till they came to Seuillé, where they spoiled Men and Women alike, and took all they could; nothing was too hot or too heavy for them. Although the Plague[2] was in almost all the Houses, they went in everywhere and plundered all that was within, and yet none of them ever took any Hurt. Which is a Case wonderful indeed; for the Curés, Vicars, Preachers, Physicians, Surgeons and Apothecaries who went to visit, dress, heal, preach to and admonish the Sick were all dead of the Infection; and these devilish Robbers and Murderers never caught any Harm at it. Whence comes that, my Masters?[3] Think upon it, I beseech you.

The Town thus pillaged, they went on to the Abbey with a horrible Tumult, but they found it well barred and made fast; whereupon the main Body of the Army marched on towards the Ford of Vede, except seven Companies of Foot and two hundred Lances, who remained there and broke down the Walls of the Close so as to waste the whole Vineyard.

---

[1] *Seuillé (G. 4, 25).* Here was an abbey of Benedictines. There are still some remains of it, and the immortal Close was still to be seen in 1891. It is quite near La Devinière, Rabelais' birthplace, and it is probable that he went to school there as a boy.

[2] *The Plague (P. 32)* ravaged France in 1510 and seems to have visited various places in the first half of that century. It was at Auxerre in 1531. Cf. R. de Collerye (p. 280, ed. Elz.).

[3] *Whence comes that?* Cf. Pliny, 26. 4: "Quo mirabilius quid potest reperiri? aliqua gigni repente vitia terrarum in parte certa, membrisque hominum certis, vel aetatibus aut etiam fortunis, tamquam malo eligente, haec in pueris grassari, illa in adultis, haec proceres sentire, illa pauperes". Cf. also Alex. Aphrodisiensis, *Probl.* 89 (transl. Politian): "Cur in pestilentia alii pereunt alii minime? Hoc nimirum ex habitudinis convenientia accidit etc."

"Inque ipsos saeva medentes
Erumpit clades: obsuntque auctoribus artes."
Ovid, *Met.* vii. 561.

The poor Devils of Monks knew not to which of their Saints to devote themselves. At all risks they had the Bell rung *ad Capitulum capitulantes*.[1] There it was decreed that they should form a fair Procession reinforced by fine Chants and Litanies *contra hostium insidias* and fine Responses *pro pace*.[2]

In the Abbey at that time was a Cloister Monk named Friar John of the Trencherites,[3] young, gallant, frisky, lusty, very handy, bold, adventurous, resolute, tall, lean, with a rare gaping Mouth and a mighty prominent Nose, a fine Mumbler of Matins, Unbridler of Masses[4] and a Scourer of Vigils; to say everything summarily, a very Monk, if ever there was one, since the monking World monked a Monkery.[5] Moreover, he was a Clerk to the very Teeth in matter of Breviary.[6]

---

[1] A certain small bell summoned to the Chapter those who had a voice in affairs, not the novices. "Ad secreta capituli nemo interesse debet nisi canonici professi, nec eciam ipsi novicii in primo anno probationis" (*Augustin. Observ.* c. 29).

[2] *Da pacem, Domine, in nostris diebus.* There was a short subsidiary service *pro pace Ecclesiae.* Also "quotiescunque fiet *processio* pro aeris serenitate, *pro pace*, vel ad pluviam postulandam" (*Augustin. Observ.* c. 30). Cf. *P.* 2.

[3] *Entommeures* (iv. 66), minced-meat from *entamer*, L. Lat. *intaminare* (cf. Skeat's *Chaucer*, vol. v. p. 248 and Brachet on *entamer*), to cut in, carve and eat. Cf. Macrob. *Sat.* vii. 8. 1: "quae causa difficile digestu facit *isicium*, quod ab insectione *insicium* dictum?" Varro, *Lat. Ling.* v. § 110: "Insicia ab eo quod insecta caro". "Trencherites" has been adopted to convey these meanings, if possible. Friar John is probably to be identified with the Prieur de Sermaise in the following poem, *à Monseigneur Buinard*:

> "Quand Rabelais t'appelloit moine,
> C'estoit sans queue et sans doreure:
> Tu n'estois prieur ne chanoine,
> Mais frere Jehan de Lecitanmeure.
> Maintenant es en la bonne heure
> Pourveu et beaucoup mieux à l'aise
> Puis que fais paisible demeure
> En ton prieuré de Sermaise".

Ménage, who gives this in his *Dict. étymologique*, would read *l'entammeure.*

[4] Fr. *beau desbrideur de messes. Les menus propos, A.P.F.* xi. 381. Cf. Merl. Coc. *Baldus*, vii. 223:

> "Incipiebat enim nec adhuc *in nomine Patris*
> Quod tribus in saltis veniebat ad *Ite misestum*".

[5] In the legend of *Geoffrey of the long Tooth*, c. 18, occurs the following parallel: "Moynes ribaulds!...qui donques vous a donné ceste hardiesse d'ensorceler mon frere...et de le faire *moyne moynant de moynerie* comme vous?"

[6] *in matter of Breviary.* A phrase often recurring in the mouth of this Monk

This Monk, hearing the Noise which the Enemies made in the Close of their Vineyard, started out to see what they were doing; and finding that they were gathering the Grapes of the Close, on which depended their Supply of Drink for the whole Year, he returns to the Choir of the Church, where the other Monks were all amazed like so many Bell-founders,[1] and seeing them chant *im, im, pe, e, e, e, e, e, tum, um, ini, i, mi, i, co, o, o, o, o, o, rum, um,*[2] "This is", said he, "well cackled, well sung. By the Powers, why don't you sing

> Panniers farewell, Vintage is done?[3]

Devil take me if they are not in our Close, and cutting up so thoroughly both Vines and Grapes that, S'body! there will be nothing for four Years but gleaning for us there. By the Belly of St James,[4] what shall we poor Devils drink the while? O Lord! *da mihi potum*".

Then said the Prior of the Convent: "What will this drunken Fellow do here? Let one take me him to Prison. Thus to disturb divine Service!"

"But", said the Monk, "the Wine Service! Let us do our best that that be not disturbed; for you yourself, my Lord Prior, like to drink of the best. So does every honest Man. Never did a worthy Man hate good Wine; it is an Apophthegm of the Cloister. But these Responses that you are chanting here, pardy! they are not in Season.

(iii. 26; iv. 8, 10, 23, 27, 39, 54), who in this respect is certainly *homo unius libri*. It should be remembered that his quotations are not from the Vulgate but from the Breviary, and as they are often "responds" or from the Psalms he probably intones them.

[1] Bell-founders are proverbially dumfounded when a casting goes wrong (cf. *P.* 29).

[2] *Impetum inimicorum ne timueritis* is one of the Responds in the Breviary on all Sundays throughout October.

[3] *Panniers farewell*, etc. Brantôme, *des Dames*, disc. 5 (vol. ix. p. 463), tells a story of an old salt *le capitaine Panier*, who when struck by a cannon-shot had just time to quote this line:

> "Adieu paniers, vendanges sont faites".

Brantôme adds: "Sa mort fut plaisante par ce bon mot".

[4] *St James*. Referring probably to the pilgrim's gourd on the pilgrimage to St James of Compostella.

"Why are our Devotions short in time of Harvest and Vintage, and long during Advent and all the Winter?[1]

"The late Brother Macé Pelosse[2] of holy Memory, a truly zealous Man (Devil take me else!) of our Religion, told me, I remember, that the Reason was, in order that in this Season we might well press and make the Wine, and that in Winter we might drink it down.

"Hark ye, my Masters! ye that love Wine, in Heaven's Name follow me; for boldly I say it, Saint Anthony burn me if those taste the Liquor who have not succoured the Vine. The Goods of the Church, quotha! Ha! no, no. Devil take it! St Thomas of England[3] was ready and willing to die for them; if I should die for them, should I not be a Saint likewise? Yet will I not die for all this; for it is I who will make the others die."

Saying this, he threw down his great Monk's Habit and laid hold on the Staff of the Cross, which was of the Heart of Service-tree, as long as a Lance, rounded for a good Grip, and a little decorated with *Fleurs-de-Lys* almost all effaced.

Thus he set forth in a fine Cassock, put his Frock scarf-wise, and with his Staff of the Cross laid about him lustily on his Enemies, who without Order or Ensign, Trumpet or Drum, were gathering Grapes in the Vineyard; for the Standard-bearers and Ensigns had laid down their Standards and Colours by the Walls, the Drummers had knocked in their Drums on one side to fill them with Grapes, the Trumpeters were laden with Bunches of Grapes; every one was in Disorder—he fell upon them, I say, so stiffly without giving Warning that he overthrew them like Hogs, striking all at random in the old Fencing-fashion.

For some, he beat out their Brains;[4] for others, he broke their

---

[1] The services in the Breviary are shorter in autumn and winter till Advent, and especially short in October.

[2] *Macé* (= *Mathieu*, Coquillart, i. 117) *Pelosse*, René Macé, a native of Vendôme, a learned Benedictine and an Inquisitor. He was called *le petit Moine*. He is alluded to in *G.* 5 as *Prebstre Macé*. *Pelosse* seems to be derived from πέλος, πέλοψ, etc., alluding to the black dress of the Benedictines.

[3] "*licet S. Thomas voluerit mori pro defensione rerum ecclesiae*, non tamen propterea movit arma", Ioh. Nev. *Sylv. Nupt.* fo. 166. 3. St Thomas Becket was canonised by Pope Alexander III.

[4] For this anatomical passage cf. Le Double in *Rabelais anatomiste*, pp. 304–5.

Arms and Legs; for others, he disjointed the Bones of their Neck; for others, he demolished their Kidneys, slit their Nose, blackened their Eyes, gashed their Jaws, knocked their Teeth down their Throat, shattered their Shoulder-blades, mortified their Shanks, dislocated their Thigh-bones, disabled their Fore-arms.

If any one tried to hide himself where the Vines were thickest, he mangled the whole Ridge of his Back and dashed his Reins like a Dog.

If any wished to save himself by Flight, he made his Head fly into Pieces by the *Lambdoidal Commissure*.[1]

If any one climbed up a Tree, thinking there to be in Safety, he impaled him through the Body with his Staff.

If any of his old Acquaintance cried out to him: "Ha, Friar John, my Friend, Friar John, I yield myself".

"Why, thou needs must," he said, "but at the same time thou shalt yield thy Soul to all the Devils"; and at once he gave him *dronos*.[2]

And if any person was so far seized with Rashness as to withstand him to the Face, he at once shewed him the Strength of his Muscles; for he ran him through the Breast by the Mediastine[3] and the Heart; with others, laying on under the Hollow of their Ribs[4] he overturned their Stomachs, so they died immediately; others he thrust so fiercely through the Navel that he made their Puddings gush out; with others he drove into their Rectum through their Cods.

Believe me it was the most horrible Spectacle that ever was seen.

Some cried out on St Barbe, others on St George, others on Ste

---

[1] The *Lambdoidal Commissure* is the occipitoparietal suture between the *occiput* and *sinciput*, dividing the skull lengthwise. It is so called from its resemblance to a Greek Lambda (Λ). The three true sutures are *Coronalis*, *Sagittalis* and *Lambdoeides*. Cf. Paré, iii. 3; Galen, *de usu part.* ix. 7.

[2] *dronos* (P. 14), a word formerly used at Toulouse signifying thwacks (Fr. ed.). The phrase "bailler dronos" is used with reference to this by Brantôme, *Rodomontades*, vol. vii. p. 155.

[3] *Mediastine* (iv. 30), the membranous division of the chest into right and left, formed by the duplicature of the ribs under the sternum towards the vertebrae. The anterior mediastine contains the heart, the posterior the aorta, oesophagus, etc. (Le Double, p. 81).

[4] *the Hollow of their Ribs* = the intercostal space.

Nytouche,[1] others on Our Lady of Cunaut,[2] of Loretta,[3] of Good
Tidings,[4] of Lenou,[5] of Rivière.[6] Some devoted themselves to
St James, others to the holy *sudarium*[7] of Chambery (but it was
burnt up three Months afterwards so thoroughly that they could
not save a single Thread), others to Cadouin,[8] others to St John of
Angely,[9] others to St Eutropius of Saintes,[10] St Mesmes of Chinon,[11]

---

[1] *Ste Nytouche* (*Noli me tangere*). Cf. St-Gelais, ii. 276 (ed. Elz.):

> "Agnes se dore et va egorgetée,
> Cheveux frisés, et à cornette ostée,
> La voix fait gresle, et si quelqu'un luy conte
> Quelque folie elle rougit de honte,
> Et va si dru qu'il pert qu'elle *n'y touche*,
> Et a sa mère à toute heure à la bouche,
> Et n'oseroit, ce croy-je, avoir songé
> De faire un pas sans elle et sans congé".

[2] *Cunaut*, a celebrated priory in Anjou. For the different localities in which
Our Lady was worshipped cf. H. Estienne, *Apol. pour Hérod.* c. 38.

[3] *Laurette*, a chapel near Angers in Brittany.

[4] *de Bonnes Nouvelles*, an abbey near Orléans. Here was a chapel where the
students heard Mass (*R.E.R.* vii. 309).

[5] *Lenou*, an ancient parish between Chinon and Richelieu.

[6] *Rivière* (*G.* 47, 49), a commune of the canton of l'Isle Bouchard on the
Vienne (*R.E.R.* v. 75).

[7] *sudarium of Chambéry*, a celebrated relic mentioned in H. Estienne's *Apol.
pour Hérod.* c. 24 (vol. ii. p. 59, ed. Liseux). It was said to have been miraculously preserved. Cf. v. 10. There was a controversy on this subject in 1902,
when it was maintained that the "Holy shroud of Turin" is still in existence.
According to a report given by Cardinal Vaughan in *The Standard*, May 6,
1902, "it was brought by Margaret, widow of King John of Jerusalem to
Chambéry, where she reluctantly gave it to her sister-in-law Anna, Duchess of
Savoy....It was probably fabricated by some unscrupulous Moslem and sold
as a genuine relic to the devout chiefs of the early Crusades".

[8] *Cadouin*, *i.e.* the *sudarium* preserved at Cadouin, a Cistercian abbey in Périgord about 20 miles from Cahusac. The church founded in 1115 still exists. The
sudarium was taken to Cadouin in 1117. Bishop Arculf had seen it in the eighth
century. It was discovered at Antioch by the crusaders and brought by Bishop
Adhemer's chaplain to Puy, where it was saved from the fire which destroyed
the church. It was then presented to the Abbey of Cadouin. Geoffroi d'Estissac
was Abbot of Cadouin (*R.E.R.* vii. 400).

[9] At *St Jean d'Angely* in Saintonge was preserved a head of the Baptist, but it
was publicly burned by the Huguenots in 1572. The Benedictine abbey was
also destroyed.

[10] *St Eutropius of Saintes* in Saintonge was its first bishop and martyr in the third
century; he was specially invoked to heal dropsy (*Sanctus Eutropius facit hydropicos*,
cf. *G.* 45). His church (restored) still exists, having his tomb behind the high altar.

[11] *St Mesmes* = St Maximus (so *presme* = Lat. *proximus*, *P.* 2), an ancient parish
of Chinon.

St Martin of Candes,[1] St Clouaud[2] of Sinays, the holy Relics of Javrezay,[3] and a thousand other good little Saints.

Some died without speaking,[4] others spoke without dying; some died speaking, others spoke dying. Others cried with a loud Voice: "Confession, Confession! *Confiteor. Miserere. In manus*".

So great was the Outcry of the wounded, that the Prior of the Abbey with all his Monks came forth; who, when they saw these poor Wretches thus overthrown among the Vines and wounded to Death, confessed some of them.

But while the Priests were busied with confessing them, the little Monklings ran to the Place where Friar John was, and asked him wherein he wished they should help him. To this he replied that they should cut the Throats of those who were thrown down on the Earth.

Then, leaving their great Capes upon the nearest Rails, they began to cut the Throats of and to finish those whom he had already crushed. Do you know with what Instruments? With fair Whittles, which are little Half-knives, wherewith the little Children of our Country shell Walnuts.

Meantime with his Staff of the Cross he reached the Breach which the Enemy had made. Some of the Monklings carried off the Ensigns and Standards into their Cells to make Garters of them.

But when those who had been shriven tried to get out by this Breach, the Monk felled them with Blows, crying out: "These Men are shriven and repentant and have gained their Pardons; they

---

[1] *St Martin*, Archbishop of Tours, died at Candes (iii. 47) near the junction of the Vienne with the Loire. His tomb is there. Cf. *Legenda Aurea*, c. 166. *Candes* (*G.* 47, 51; iii. 47; iv. 19, 29) and Montsoreau are contiguous.

[2] *St Clouaud*, grandson of King Clovis. He is mentioned by Bouchet (D). In the ancient church of Cinais was an altar and statue of St Cloud (*R.E.R.* v. 62).

[3] *Lavresay* (D), a misprint for *Javresay* (ABC). Javresay or *Javarsay* is a hamlet in Poitou near Chef-Boutonne. In the parish church were preserved, among other relics, the bones of St Chastier (*R.E.R.* ii. 161).

[4] In Hippoc. *Prorrhet.* § 30, occurs: "Do not those whose body throbs throughout *die without speaking*?" (also *Coac.* § 347); and in § 128: "In the case of wounds accompanied by haemorrhage and slight perspiration throughout the patients *die speaking*" (also *Coac.* § 328).

will go at once into Paradise as straight as a Sickle,[1] or as the Road to Faye".[2]

Thus by his Prowess were discomfited all those of the Army who had got within the Close, to the number of thirteen thousand six hundred and twenty-two, besides Women and little Children— that is always understood.

Never did Maugis[3] the Hermit bear himself so valiantly with his Pilgrim's Staff against the Saracens (of whom is written in the Acts of the Four Sons of Aymon) as did this Monk in encountering the Enemy with the Staff of the Cross.

---

[1] *as a Sickle*. "Tout aussi droict qu'une *faucille*", *La resurrection de Jenin Landore*, *A.Th.F.* ii. 26. Cf. Mark Twain on the street *called Straight*, *Innocents abroad*, ii. c. 13.

[2] *Faye-la-Vineuse*, a town near Chinon, situated on so rugged a steep, that in order to get there one has to make the entire circuit of the mountain (Le Duchat). Perhaps a pun is intended on *la rue de la Foi*, which leads straight to Paradise. (Fr. ed.)

[3] *Maugis*, a cousin of the four sons of Aymon, who became a hermit, but accompanied Renaud against the Saracens and performed prodigies of valour with his pilgrim's staff (*IV fils Aymon*, cc. 27, 30, 31). (Histoire des IV fils Aymon et de leur cousin le subtil Maugis, lequel fut Pape de Rome, ensemble la chronique de Mabrian, Roi de Hierusalem: folio, Paris 1525.)

CHAPTER XXVIII

How Picrochole took by Assault La Roche-Clermaud, and the Reluctance and Difficulty which Grandgousier made in undertaking War

WHILE the Monk was skirmishing, as we have said, against those who were entered into the Close, Picrochole in great Haste passed the Ford of Vede[1] with his Men, and attacked La Roche-Clermaud, at which Place no Resistance was made to him whatever. And because it was already Night he determined to quarter himself and his People in that Town, and to cool his pungent[2] Choler.

In the Morning he stormed the Bulwarks and the Castle, which he repaired thoroughly and provided with requisite Munitions, thinking to make his Retreat there, if he should be assailed from elsewhere; for the Place was strong both by Art and Nature, by reason of its Situation and Aspect.

Now let us leave them there, and return to our good Gargantua, who is at Paris, very intent on the Study of good Learning and athletic Exercises, and to the good Old man Grandgousier his Father, who after Supper is warming his Cods by a good, clear, and great Fire, and while his Chestnuts are roasting is writing on the Hearth with a Stick burnt at one End, wherewith they poke the Fire,[3]

---

[1] The *Vede* (*G.* 4) is a small stream passing between Seuilly and La Roche-Clermaud and falling into the Vienne about a mile past Chinon. Cf. *R.E.R.* v. 81–2 and map ix. 120.

[2] Fr. *pungitive* (not *pugnative*). Cf. Ducange, s.v. *pungativus* or *pungitivus* = piquant.

[3] Cf. Mantuanus, *Ecl.* v. 81:

> "Tunc juvat hibernos noctu vigilare Decembres
> Ante focum et cineri ludos inarare bacillo,
> Torrere et tepidis tostas operire favillis
> Castaneas plenoque sitim restinguere vitro
> Fabellasque inter nentes ridere puellas".

This charming domestic idyll, evidently borrowed from Mantuanus, has naturally been anticipated by former writers: Aristoph. *Pax*, 1131; Plato, *Rep.* ii. 372 C; Theocr. ii. 60; and perhaps most nearly by Xenophanes of Colophon ap. Athen. ii. 54 E. Sterne utilises it in *Tristram Shandy*, iv. 21.

telling to his Wife and Family pleasant Stories of Times gone by.[1]

At this Time one of the Shepherds who was guarding the Vines, named Pillot,[2] presented himself before him, and related to the full the Outrages and Pillage which Picrochole, King of Lerné, was committing in his Lands and Domains, and how he had pillaged, wasted, and sacked the whole Country, except the Close of Seuillé, which Friar John of the Trencherites had saved, to his great Honour; and that at present the said King was in La Roche-Clermaud, and there with great Despatch was entrenching himself and his Men.

"Alas! alas!" said Grandgousier, "what is this, good People? Do I dream, or is it true that they tell me? Picrochole, my old Friend from all time, in every way of my own Race and Alliance, does he come to attack me? Who stirs him? Who pricks him on? Who leads him? Who hath thus counselled him? Ho, ho, ho, ho, ho, my God and my Saviour, help me, inspire me, counsel me as to what I ought to do.

"I protest, I swear before Thee,—so mayest Thou shew Favour unto me—that never did I Displeasure to him, Damage to his People, or Ravage in his Lands; but, clean contrary, I have succoured him with Men, Money, Favour and Counsel, in every case where I could discern his Advantage. That he hath then at this Point outraged me can only be through the Evil Spirit. Good God, Thou knowest my Heart,[3] for from Thee can nothing be hidden. If it chance that he have become mad, and that Thou hast sent him hither to me to restore his Senses, grant me Power and Wisdom to bring him to the Yoke of Thy holy Will by good Discipline.

"Ho, ho, ho, my good People, my Friends and my loyal Servants, must it needs be that I summon[4] you to help me? Alas! my Old age required henceforward nought but Repose, and all my

---

[1] Cf. also Burton's *Anatomy*, ii. 2. 4: "Or tell old stories by the fire-side...as old folks usually do, remembering afresh and with pleasure ancient matters... which happened in their younger years".

[2] *Pillot*, a diminutive of *Pierre*. (Fr. ed.)

[3] Fr. *Courage*, heart (cf. iv. 35 *fin.*) = Ital. *coraggio*.

[4] Fr. *empescher* (G. 47; iii. 34). Used in the old legal sense, "to claim a right as Seigneur"; not in its usual meaning, *to hinder*. Cf. Ducange, s.v. *impechiare*.

Life I have sought for nothing so much as Peace. But now (I see it well) I needs must load with Harness my poor Shoulders,[1] weary and weak as they are, and in my trembling Hand take the Lance and the Mace, to succour and safeguard my poor Subjects. Right will have it so; for by their Labour am I maintained, by their Sweat am I nourished, myself, my Children and my Family.

"This notwithstanding, I will not undertake War till I have tried all the Arts and Means of Peace.[2] On that I am resolved."

Then he caused his Council to be convoked, and set forth the Matter just as it was. And it was determined that they should send some discreet Man to Picrochole, to know wherefore he had thus suddenly fallen away from Peace and invaded those Lands to which he had no Right whatever. Further, that they should send for Gargantua and his People for the Preservation of the Country and its Defence in its present Need. All this was pleasing to Grand-gousier, and he commanded that so it should be done.

Whereupon he at once sent his Basque Lackey[3] to bring Gargantua with all Diligence. And he wrote to him as follows:

---

[1] Cf. Virg. *Aen.* ii. 509–11 (of Priam):

"Arma diu senior desueta trementibus aevo
Circumdat nequiquam umeris, et inutile ferrum
Cingitur".

[2] "Bonus princeps nunquam omnino bellum suscipiet nisi cum tentatis omnibus nulla ratione evitari poterit", Erasm. *Instit. Principis Christiani* (Delaruelle, p. 258, *Revue d'hist. litt. de la France*).

[3] *Basque Lackey.* The Basques were proverbial for their fleetness of foot. Pantagruel's messenger was named Carpalim (*P.* 23 *sqq.*), from καρπάλιμος, swift. It is implied that he was a Greek in *P.* 9. Numidian *cursores* were employed by the Romans. Cf. Mayor's *Juvenal*, v. 52.

CHAPTER XXIX

The Tenour of the Letter Grandgousier wrote to Gargantua

"The Fervency of thy Studies required that for a long time I should not recall thee from thy philosophic Repose, if the Presumption[1] of our Friends and former Allies had not at this present broken in[2] upon the Security of my Old age. But since such is my fated Destiny, that I should be disquieted by those in whom I most trusted, it is necessary for me to recall thee to the Help of the People and the Property, which by natural Right are entrusted[3] to thee.

"For even as Arms are powerless abroad unless there be good Counsel at home,[4] so is the Study vain and the Counsel unprofitable, which at a fitting Season is not carried out and put into Effect by Valour.[5]

"My Intention is not to provoke but to appease; not to assault but to defend; not to make Conquests but to guard my loyal Subjects and hereditary Dominions; into which Picrochole has entered in a hostile manner without Cause or Occasion, and from day to day pursueth his furious Enterprise with Excesses that are intolerable to free-born Men.

"I have made it my Duty to moderate his tyrannical Choler, offering him all that which I thought might give him Satisfaction;

---

[1] *Presumption.* Fr. *confiance* here = Lat. *confidentia*. Cf. Cic. *Tusc.* iii. § 14.

[2] Cf. Cic. *de Off.* i. § 154: "Quis est enim tam cupidus in perspicienda cognoscendaque rerum natura ut si ei tractanti contemplantique res cognitione dignissimas subito sit allatum periculum discrimenque patriae, cui subvenire opitularique possit, non illa omnia relinquat et abjiciat?"

[3] Fr. *affiés*, Lat. *adfidare*. Cf. Ducange, *s.v.* "That he may evermore have *affiance* in Thee" (Prayer for the King in the Litany).

[4] "Parvi enim foris sunt arma nisi sit consilium domi", quoted in Cic. *de Off.* i. § 76.

> "While that the armed hand doth fight abroad
> The advised head defends itself at home."
>
> Shakesp. *Hen. V*, i. 2. 178.

[5] "Etenim cognitio contemplatioque naturae manca quodam modo atque incohata sit si nulla actio rerum consequatur", Cic. *de Off.* i. § 153.

and several times have I sent loving Messages to him, to learn wherein, by whom, and how he felt himself wronged; but from him have I had no Answer but wilful Defiance, and that in my Lands he pretended to no Right save that of his own good Pleasure. Whereby I discerned that the eternal God hath given him over[1] to the Guidance of his free Will and his own Understanding, which cannot choose but be wicked, if it be not continually guided by Divine Grace; and that He hath sent him hither to me, to keep him in his Duty and to bring him to know himself by painful Experience.

"Therefore, my well-beloved Son, upon sight of this Letter,[2] return hither as soon as thou canst with all Diligence, to succour, not me so much (which in any case, in Duty[3] thou art naturally bound to do) as thine own People, whom by Reason thou oughtest to save and guard. The Exploit shall be carried out with as little Effusion of Blood as shall be possible; and if it may be, by Devices more expeditious, by Sleights and Stratagems of War, we shall save all the Souls, and send them merry to their Homes.

"My dearest Son, the Peace of Christ our Redeemer be with thee.

"Salute from me Ponocrates, Gymnast and Eudemon.

"This twentieth of September.[4]

"Thy Father, GRANDGOUSIER".

---

[1] *given him over*, etc. Cf. Ps. lxxx. 13: "Dimisi eos secundum desideria cordis eorum".

[2] Fr. *ces lettres veues* (*P.* 12). The regular chancery phrase. Cf. Lat. *hae litterae*.

[3] *Duty*. Fr. *pitié = piété*, Lat. *pietas*. Cf. *G.* 7; *A.P.F.* iii. 254.

[4] *This twentieth of September*. M. Lefranc (*R.E.R.* ix. 155) would fix the actual date of these occurrences a few days before this, in the year 1532, when the tension between Antoine Rabelais and Gaucher Sainte-Marthe was very acute, and during the time that Rabelais was paying a visit to his native country from Lyons and completing the last chapter and the Prologue to *Pantagruel*. He would make Rabelais witness of these events, and suggests that they are the inspiration of the *Gargantua* (from the 25th chapter to the foundation of the Abbey of Thelema) published in October 1534.

CHAPTER XXX

How Ulrich Gallet[1] was sent unto Picrochole

THE Letter being dictated and signed, Grandgousier ordered that Ulrich Gallet, his Master of Requests, a wise and discreet Man, whose Merit and good Advice he had proved in difficult and debateful Affairs, should go unto Picrochole, to set forth to him what had been resolved upon by them.

At that same Hour the good man Gallet set forth, and having passed the Ford, asked the Miller[2] of the Condition of Picrochole; who answered him that his Soldiers had left him neither Cock nor Hen, and that they had shut themselves in La Roche-Clermaud, and that he would not advise him to proceed farther for fear of the Scouts, for that their Fury was enormous. Which he readily believed, and lodged that Night with the Miller.

The next Morning he betook himself with a Trumpeter to the Gate of the Castle, and required of the Guards that they should bring him to speak to the King for his Advantage.

These Words being reported to the King, he would in no wise consent that they should open the Gate, but he went himself on to the Rampart, and said to the Ambassador: "What is the News? What do you wish to say?"

Then the Ambassador began to speak as follows:

---

[1] In his *Dictionnaire étymologique* Ménage affirms that Ulrich Gallet was of Chinon, and that Galet le Joueur, who built the *Hôtel de Sully* at Paris, claimed to be of the same family. This is confirmed in *R.E.R.* iii. 406, *Les notes de Bouchereau*. Also, Jehan Gallet, "avocat du Roi à Chinon, proche parent et collègue d'Antoine Rabelais", is the intermediary and agent of the community in the law-suit of 1532–6. Cf. "*ancienne confédération*", *G.* 47 (*R.E.R.* vii. 320).

[2] *the Miller* of the *Moulin du Pont* (cf. iii. 23) just above the Ford of Vede. The road from La Devinière to La Roche-Clermauld crosses the Vede at this point. (Fr. ed.)

CHAPTER XXXI

The Harangue made by Gallet to Picrochole

"No juster Cause of Grief can arise among Men, than when from the Source from which by right they should expect Favour and Goodwill, they receive Hurt and Damage. And not without Cause (although without Reason) many, having fallen into such Ill-fortune, have esteemed this Indignity less supportable than the Loss of their own Life; and, in case that they have not been able to correct this by Force or other Device, they have deprived themselves of this Light.

"It is, therefore, no wonder if King Grandgousier, my Master, is full of high Displeasure and perturbed in his Mind at thy furious and hostile Approach; wonderful would it be if he were not stirred by the unparalleled Excesses, which have been committed by thee and thy People upon his Lands and Subjects; towards whom has been omitted no Example of Inhumanity. This of itself is to him so grievous, from the hearty Affection wherewith he hath always cherished his Subjects, that it could not be more so to any mortal Man. Yet it is to him above human Apprehension grievous, in that it is by thee and thine that these Wrongs and Offences have been committed; by thee, who from all recorded Time and the Times of old, thou and thy Fathers, hadst formed a Friendship with him and all his Ancestors; which up to the present you had together inviolably maintained, kept and preserved as sacred; so much so, that not only he and his People, but foreign[1] Nations, Poitevins, Bretons, Manceaux[2] and those who dwell beyond the Canary Islands and Isabella,[3] have thought it as easy to pull down the

---

[1] *foreign.* Fr. *barbares,* from Gk. βάρβαρος = non-Greek.
[2] The Poitevins, Manceaux and Bretons had been defeated by Charles VIII at St Aubin du Cormier in 1488. Cf. c. 50. (Fr. ed.)
[3] *Isabella* was the first town built by Europeans in America. Columbus founded it on the north side of Hispaniola (Hayti) in 1493, at his second visit to the island, and gave it the name of the Queen of Spain.

Firmament and to set up the Depths above the Clouds as to put asunder your Alliance; and they have so much dreaded it in their Enterprises, that they have never dared to provoke, irritate or do Harm to the one, through Fear of the other.

"Nay further, this sacred Friendship hath so filled this Side of the World, that there are few People[1] at this time dwelling throughout all the Continent and the Isles of the Ocean who have not ambitiously aspired to be received[2] into it, on Covenants made on your own Conditions, esteeming a Confederation with you as highly as their own Lands and Dominions; so that in all the recorded Past there has been no Prince or League so savage or haughty, who has dared to invade, I do not say your Territories, but those of your Confederates. And if by headstrong Counsel they have attempted any new Design against them, on hearing of the Name and Title of your Alliance, they have at once desisted from their Enterprises. What Madness then stirs thee now, breaking through all Alliance, treading underfoot all Friendship, transgressing all Right, to invade his Lands as an Enemy, without having been by him or his in any way injured, irritated or provoked? Where is Faith? Where is Law? Where is Reason? Where is Humanity? Where is the Fear of God? Thinkest thou that these Wrongs are hidden from the eternal Spirits and from the Supreme God, who is the just Rewarder of all our Undertakings? If thou dost so think, thou deceivest thyself, for all Things will come before His Judgment.

"Is it the fatal Destinies or the Influence of the Stars,[3] which desire to put an end to thy Ease and Rest? Thus it is that all Things have their End and Period, and when they have come to their

---

[1] *there are few People*, etc. With this clause may be compared Suet. *Aug.* c. 21 *fin.*

[2] *aspired to be received*, etc. Cf. Virg. *Aen.* vii. 236:

> "Multi nos populi, multae...
> Et petiere sibi et voluere adjungere gentes".

[3] *Influence of the Stars.* Often in Milton and elsewhere of the astrological power. Cf. *P.L.* x. 661:

> "and taught the fixt
> Their *influence* malignant when to shower".

highest Point[1] they are utterly thrown down; for they cannot remain long in such a Condition. This is the End of those who cannot by Reason and Temperance moderate their Fortunes and Prosperities.

"But if it was so ordered by Fate,[2] and thy Happiness and Ease must now come to an End, must it needs occur in troubling my King, him by whom thou wert set up? If thy House was doomed to fall in Ruin, must it therefore in its Ruin fall on the Hearth[3] of him who had furnished it? The Matter is so far beyond the Bounds of Reason, so repugnant to Common sense, that it can hardly be conceived by human Understanding, and will remain incredible to Strangers, until its undoubted and testified Effect has made them perceive that nothing is holy or sacred to those who have emancipated themselves from God and Reason, to follow the Bent of their perverse Affections.

"If any Wrong had been wrought by us on thy Subjects and Dominions, if Countenance had been shewn by us to thy Ill-wishers, if we had not succoured thee in thy Affairs, if thy Name and Fame had by us been wounded; or (to speak more truly) if the Calumniating Spirit, attempting to bring thee to Evil, had by deceitful Appearances and mocking Fantasies put into thy Understanding the Belief that we had been guilty towards thee of anything unworthy of our ancient Friendship, thou oughtest first to have enquired into the Truth thereof, and then to admonish us of it; and we would have so satisfied thee to thy Heart's Desire that thou shouldest have had Occasion to be contented. But, O eternal God! what is thy Enterprise? Wouldest thou as a perfidious Tyrant thus pillage and lay waste the Kingdom of my Master? Hast thou found him so cowardly and blockish that he would not, or so destitute of Men and Money, of Counsel and military Skill, that he could not resist thy unjust Assaults?

---

[1] *to their highest Point,* etc. Cf. Lucan, i. 70:

> "Invida fatorum series summisque negatum
> Stare diu".

"Boni habitus ad summum progressi periculosi sunt; non enim manere possunt in eodem statu neque quiescere", Hipp. *Aph.* i. 3 (transl. Cornarius).

[2] Fr. *phée,* for *fée* (cf. *P.* 29; iv. prol.), from Lat. *fatum.*

[3] Fr. *atres,* Lat. *atria.* Cf. *G.* 2.

"Depart hence presently, and to-morrow retire for ever[1] into thine own Territory, without committing any Disorder or Violence by the way; and pay withal a thousand Besants[2] of Gold for the Damage thou hast wrought in these Lands: half thou shalt pay to-morrow, the other half on the Ides of May next coming, leaving with us meantime for Hostages the Dukes of Tournemoule, Basdefesses and Menuail, together with the Prince of Gratelles and the Viscount of Morpiaille".

---

[1] *for ever*. Fr. *pour tout le jour* = *pour toujours*. The only time Rabelais uses this form of speech. (Fr. ed.)

[2] *Besants* (G. 51). So called from Byzantium, where they were coined. *Byzantius nummus aureus ab Impp. Constantinop.* It seems to be a name commonly given to all oriental gold coins and to have had no special value assigned to it (Ducange). They were in considerable currency during the second (Carolingian) dynasty.

CHAPTER XXXII

How Grandgousier, to buy Peace, caused the Cakes to be restored

WITH that the Good man Gallet was silent; but Picrochole to all his Discourse gave no other Answer save: "Come and fetch them,[1] come and fetch them. They have a good Pestle and Mortar[2] here; they will knead some Cakes for you".

Then he returned to Grandgousier, whom he found on his Knees, bareheaded, bending low in a little Corner of his Chamber, praying God that he would vouchsafe to assuage the Choler of Picrochole and bring him to Reason, without proceeding thereto by Force.

When he saw the Good man returned, he asked him: "Ha, my Friend, my Friend, what News do you bring me?"

"All Order is orderless", said Gallet; "the Man is quite out of his Senses and forsaken of God."

"Yea, but," said Grandgousier, "my Friend, what Cause doth he put forward for this Outrage?"

"He hath set forth to me no Cause whatever," said Gallet, "save that in great Anger he said some Words to me about Cakes. I know not but that some Wrong may have been done to his Cake-bakers."

"I will thoroughly understand it," said Grandgousier, "before resolving further upon what should be done."

Then he sent to know about this Business, and found that indeed some Cakes had been taken by force from Picrochole's People, and that Marquet had received a Blow of a Cudgel on his Head; nevertheless everything had been well paid for, and the said Marquet had first wounded Forgier with his Whip over the Legs. And it

---

[1] *Come and fetch them,* μολὼν λαβέ. The answer of Leonidas at Thermopylae to Xerxes when he demanded his arms. Plut. *Apoph. Lacon.* (*Leon.* 11) 225 C; Erasm. *Apoph.* lib. i (*Leon.* 52).

[2] Fr. *ilz ont belle couille et molle. Couille* in O. Fr. was used for a mortar; *molle* was a pestle.

appeared to all his Council that he ought to defend himself with all his Might.

"This notwithstanding", said Grandgousier: "since it is only a Question of a few Cakes, I will endeavour to content him; for it is entirely against my Will to wage War."

Then he made Enquiries how many Cakes had been taken, and hearing that there were four or five Dozen, he commanded that five Cart-loads should be made that very Night, and that one of them should be of Cakes made with fresh Butter, fine Yolks of Eggs, fine Saffron and fine Spices, to be bestowed upon Marquet, and that for his Damages he ordered to be given seven hundred thousand and three Philippuses[1] to pay the Barber-surgeons who had dressed his Wound; and over and above he gave him the Farm of La Pommardière[2] in Freehold to him and his Heirs for ever.

To conduct and carry through all this, Gallet was sent, who on the way near the Osier-bed caused to be plucked a number of large Bundles of Canes and Reeds, and made them garnish the Carts around with them, and each of the Carters; he himself carried one in his Hand, wishing thereby to give them to understand that they asked only for Peace,[3] and that they were come to purchase it.

When they had come to the Gate, they asked to speak with Picrochole on the part of Grandgousier. Picrochole would not allow them Entrance on any Terms, nor go to speak with them; and he sent them word that he was busy, but that they might say what they wished to Captain Toucquedillon, who was mounting a Piece of Ordnance on the Walls.

Then said the Good man to him: "My Lord, to withdraw you from all this Dispute, and to remove every Excuse against your returning to our former Alliance, we do hereby restore unto you the Cakes which are in Controversy. Our People took five Dozen;

---

[1] *Philippus* (iii. 37), a *sol tournois* or 12 deniers, coined by Philip V (Ducange).

[2] *La Pommardière.* This was given as a salve for his *pommade* or pummelling (R.). There was a farm of this name near Chinon in the commune of Seuilly, which belonged to the Rabelais family, then to Baudelon, the Gallet family and the family Dusoul (*R.E.R.* iii. 52).

[3] *asked only for Peace.* Cf. Virg. *Aen.* vii. 153:

"Ire jubet ramis velatos Palladis omnes
Donaque ferre viro pacemque exposcere Teucris".

they were very well paid for; we love Peace so well that we restore
unto you five Cart-loads, of which this one here is for Marquet,
who has most to complain of. Furthermore, to content him entirely, here are seven hundred thousand and three Philippuses
which I deliver to him; and for the Damages he might claim, I
give up to him the Farm of La Pommardière in perpetuity to him
and his Heirs, to be held in Fee-simple.[1] See here is the Deed of
Conveyance. And for God's sake let us live hereafter in Peace, and
do you withdraw into your Lands cheerfully, giving up this Region
here, in which you have no Right whatever, as you yourselves
confess, and let us be Friends as before".

Toucquedillon related the whole of this to Picrochole, and more
and more exasperated his Courage, saying to him:

"These Clowns be rarely afraid. Perdy! Grandgousier be-
wrayeth himself, poor Toper; it is not his Art to go to War but
much rather to empty Flagons. I am of Opinion that we hold fast
to these Cakes and the Money, and for the rest that we fortify ourselves here with all Speed and follow up our Fortune. What! do
they think they have to do with a Ninny-whoop, that they feed you
with these Cakes? That is what it is; the good Treatment and great
Familiarity that you have hitherto held with them hath made you
contemptible[2] in their Eyes:

> Lick a Villain, he will kick you;
> Kick a Villain, he will lick you".[3]

"Sa, sa, sa," said Picrochole, "by St James, they shall catch it:
do as you have said."

---

[1] Fr. *franc-alloy* or *franc-alleu*, hereditary property free from all duties to a
higher lord. From Merovingian Latin *allodium* (a word of German origin, in
common with all feudal terms), it is from O.H.G. *alôd* (Brachet).

[2]   "Grant privaulté engendre vilité."   Coquillart, i. 7.
"Nimia familiaritas generat contemptum. Nam ex conversatione aequali
contemptio dignitatis nascitur" (ff. i. 18. 19), Joh. Nev. 176. 2.

[3]   "Oignez villain il vous poindra,
                   Poignez villain il vous oindra;
                   A brief parler d'un villoyn,
                   Il ne vault rien ne près ne loing."
                                    Les Motz dorés de Cathon (1533).

On the enormities of the *Villanus*, cf. Merl. Coc. *Mac.* xiii. *sub fin.*

"Of one thing", said Toucquedillon, "I wish to warn you. We are here badly enough victualled, and but meagrely provided with Arms for the Stomach. If Grandgousier were to lay Siege to us, I should go this Moment and have all my Teeth drawn, so that only three should remain, and so for your Soldiers as well as myself. Even with them, we shall only go on too fast in devouring our Provisions."

Said Picrochole: "We shall have only too much Victuals. Are we here to eat or to fight?"

"Certainly to fight", said Toucquedillon; "but

<blockquote>From the Paunch comes the Dance,[1]</blockquote>

and

<blockquote>Stomach famished, Strength is banished".[2]</blockquote>

"Too much prating!" said Picrochole. "Seize upon what they have brought."

And so they seized Money and Cakes, Oxen and Carts, and sent off the Men without saying a Word, only that they were not to come so near again, for a Reason that should be told them to-morrow.

Thus without doing anything they returned to Grandgousier, and recounted the whole Matter to him; adding that there was no Hope to bring them to Peace save by a sharp and fierce War.

---

[1]   "Car la danse vient de la panse."   Villon, *Test.* 25. Also in *La vie du Maulvais Riche*, *A.Th.F.* iii. 372; *A.P.F.* i. 258, ii. 39.

[2]   σίτου καὶ οἴνοιο· τὸ γὰρ μένος ἐστὶ καὶ ἀλκή.   Hom. *Il.* xix. 161. "*Où faim regne force exule*. Où force est raison n'a lieu", Joh. Aegid. *Ad.*

CHAPTER XXXIII

How certain Ministers of Picrochole, by headstrong Counsel,
put him in extreme Peril

AFTER the Cakes had been ransacked, there appeared before
Picrochole the Duke of Menuail, Count Spadassin and Captain
Merdaille,[1] and said to him:

"Sire,[2] this day we make you the happiest and most chivalrous
Prince that ever was since the Death of Alexander the Mace-
donian".

"Be covered, be covered", said Picrochole.

"Grammercy, Sire", said they; "we present you our humble
Duty. The Manner is as follows:[3]

"You will leave here some Captain in Garrison, with a small
Band of Men to guard the Place, which seems to us strong enough,
by Nature as well as by the Fortifications of your devising.

"You will divide your Army into two Parts, as you know well
how to do.

"The one Part will go and fall upon this Grandgousier and his
Men. By this he will at the very first Attack easily be discomfited.
There you will gain Money in Heaps; for the Clown hath enough

---

[1] *Merdaille.* Cf. Cl. Marot, *2ème Epistre du coq à l'asne*:

> "Le roy n'entend pas que Merdaille
> Tienne le rang des vieux routiers".

One of Erasmi *Colloquia* is entitled *Concio seu Merdardus.*

[2] *Cyre*, D. *Sire*, A. From κύριος, sometimes spelt *Syre.*

[3] *The Manner is as follows*, etc. In the *Chanson de Roland* (st. 202) Roland
boasts that with his sword Durandal he has conquered Anjou and Brittany,
Poitou and Maine, Normandy, Provence and Aquitaine, Lombardy and
Romagna, Bavaria and Flanders, Bulgaria and Poland, Constantinople,
Saxony, Scotland, Wales, Ireland and England. In Lucian's *Navigium seu Vota*,
c. 30. g, Samippus in a day-dream conquers Greece and Ionia, subjugates
Caria, Lycia, Pamphylia, and goes on through Mesopotamia to Babylon and
Ctesiphon (J. Plattard, *L'œuvre de Rabelais*, p. 208).

and to spare. *Clown*, say we, because a noble Prince hath never a Penny.[1] To hoard up Treasure is the Act of a Clown.[2]

"The other Part meantime will draw towards Onys, Saintonge, Angomois and Gascony; with that Perigord, Medoc and Elanes.[3] Without Resistance they will take Towns, Castles and Fortresses. At Bayonne, St John-de-Luc, and at Fontarabia you will seize all the Shipping, and coasting along towards Galicia and Portugal, you will sack all the Seaports as far as Ulisbonne,[4] where you will have a Supply of all the Equipment required by a Conqueror. 'Sbody, Spain will surrender, for they are but a set of Loggerheads.[5] You will pass by the Strait of Sibyle[6] and there will you erect two Pillars more magnificent than those of Hercules, for the perpetual Memory of your Name, and this Strait shall be called the Picrocholinic Sea.[7]

"When you have passed the Picrocholinic Sea, behold Barbarossa[8] yields himself your Slave."

"I will take him", said Picrochole, "with free Pardon."

"Nay," said they, "provided he have himself christened.

"And you will take by storm the Kingdoms of Tunis, Hippo,

---

[1]　　　　　　"Ung noble prince, ung gentil roy
　　　　　　N'a jamais ne pile ne croix."
　　　　　　　　　　　　Le Roux de Lincy, *Prov. Franç.* ii. 96.

[2] "Nihil est tam angusti animi tamque parvi quam amare divitias: nihil honestius magnificentiusque quam pecuniam contemnere", Cic. *de Off.* i. § 68.

[3] *Elanes* is for Landes. Cf. *P.* 23. *In landis Burdigalensibus* occurs in Turpini, *Chronicon*, c. 11.

[4] *Ulisbonne*, Ulysses' town = Lisbon. A letter from John, King of Portugal, to Politian (*Ep.* x. 2) is dated *ex Ulixbona*, Oct. 23, 1491. Pliny (8. 166) has Olisipo, and Strabo speaks of Olusipon on the Tagus (iii. 152) and of an Ὀδύσσεια πόλις (iii. 149). This is derived from some legendary account of Ulysses wandering in the Atlantic. Cf. Dante, *Inf.* xxvi. 100–142; Tennyson's *Ulysses*.

[5] *Loggerheads*. Fr. *madourrez*, from Gascon *madourre*, rough, clownish: cf. iii. 12, "un *modourre* Corytus de la Toscane". This is the Toulousain form = blockhead. (Fr. ed.)

[6] *Sibyle* (Lat. *Abyla*), the rock opposite Calpe (Gibraltar), now Sebta. Cf. *G.* 2; v. 15.

[7] *Picrocholinic Sea*. Cf. "Entommeric sea" (iii. 23) and "vitreo daturus Nomina ponto", Hor. *C.* iv. 2.

　　　　　　　　"and shall be
　　　　Sponsor at last to some now nameless sea."
　　　　　　　　　　　　Calverley, *Ode on Beer*.

[8] *Barbarossa*. The corsair Khair Eddyn (1476–1546). Cf. *Epp. Rom.* i. § 1.

Algiers, Bona, Corona,¹ yea all Barbary.² Going further, you will
take into your Hand Majorca, Minorca, Sardinia, Corsica and the
other Isles of the Ligurian and Balearic Sea. Coasting along by the
left, you will become Master of all Gallia Narbonensis,³ Provence
and the Allobrogians, Genoa, Florence, Lucca, and then Good-
bye to⁴ Rome. Poor My Lord the Pope⁵ is already dying with
Fear."

"By my Faith," said Picrochole, "I'll none kiss his Slipper."⁶

"Italy taken, see Naples, Calabria, Apulia and Sicily all ransacked, and Malta too. I only wish those jovial Knights, formerly
of Rhodes,⁷ would resist you, to see their Funk."

"I would willingly", said Picrochole, "go to Loretta."⁸

"Not at all, not at all", said they. "That will be on your
Return.

"From there we will take Candia, Cyprus, Rhodes and the
Cyclades Islands and fall upon the Morea. We have it at once. By
Saint Treignan,⁹ the Lord preserve Jerusalem! for the Soldan is
not comparable to you in Power."

"I will then", said he, "have Solomon's Temple rebuilt."

"No, not yet", said they; "wait a little. Never be too hasty in

---

¹ *Corona* = Cyrene, of which the modern name is Corène.

² *Barbary*, the whole region of North Africa, Tripoli, Tunis, Algeria and
Morocco.

³ *Gallia Narbonensis* is Languedoc. *Gallia Cisalpina* is mentioned in iv. 58 and
explained in the *briefve declaration*.

⁴ *à Dieu seas*. Gascon for *à Dieu soit*.

⁵ Fr. *Monsieur du Pape*. Cf. M. de L'Ours, *P.* 4; M. du Paigne, *P.* 17; M. du
Roy, *P.* 30 *fin*.

⁶ *kiss his Slipper* (iii. 48), as the Emperor Henry IV did for Gregory VII at
Canossa in 1077, and Federigo Barbarossa for Alexander III at Venice in 1177.

⁷ *Knights of Rhodes*, formerly of Jerusalem, where their first Grand Master
was Fra Gerardo (1113–20). Driven from Jerusalem, they were established in
Rhodes in 1310. On Jan. 1, 1523, the Grand Master Villiers de l'Isle Adam
(1521–34) and his followers, nearly 5000 in number, quitted Rhodes for ever,
which the Order had held for 212 years. (An account of the siege of Rhodes
from July 1522 is given in the *J.B.P.* pp. 114 *sqq.*) On Oct. 26, 1530, they
took formal possession of Malta, which had been assigned to them by Charles V.
Cf. *Epp. Rom.* i. § 5.

⁸ *N.-D. de Loretta*, whither the Virgin's house was believed to have been
transported by angels.

⁹ *Saint Treignan*, called also St Ringan (cf. Scott's *Pirate*, c. 25), the Scottish
saint (*P.P.* 6; *P.* 9; *G.* 36).

your Undertakings. Do you know what Octavian Augustus used to say? *Festina lente*.

"It is right that you should first have Asia Minor, Caria, Lycia, Pamphylia, Cicilia, Lydia, Phrygia, Mysia, Bithynia, Carrasia,[1] Satalia,[2] Samagaria, Castamena,[3] Luga, Sebasté right up to the Euphrates."

"Shall we see", said Picrochole, "Babylon and Mount Sinai?"

"There is no Need for it", said they, "at this Time. Have we not ranged far enough in having crossed the Hyrcanian[4] Sea, ridden over the two Armenias[5] and the three Arabias?"[6]

"By my Faith," he said, "we are all Dead men. Ha, poor Souls!"

"What is the Matter?" said they.

"What shall we have to drink in these Deserts? For Julian Augustus[7] and all his Host died there of Thirst, as the Story goes."

"We have already given Order for all that", said they. "In the Syriac Sea you have nine thousand and fourteen great Ships, laden with the best Wines in the World: they have come to Jaffa. There have been found twenty-two hundred thousand Camels and sixteen hundred Elephants, which you will have taken at one Hunting near Sigeilmes,[8] when you entered into Libya; and besides this, you had all the Caravan to Mecca. Did they not furnish you with a Sufficiency of Wine?"

"Yes", said he; "but we did not drink it fresh."

"By the Powers," said they, "not of a little Fish![9] A mighty

---

[1] *Carrasia*, the ancient Sardis, capital of Lydia. (Fr. ed.)

[2] *Satalia* (iv. 25), formerly Attalia (Acts Apost. xiv. 25), now Adalia in Pamphylia, on the coast of Caramania.

[3] *Castamena*, Kastamoun, from *Castra Comneni*. One of the principal places on the route of Stamboul to Samsoun. (Fr. ed.)

[4] *the Hyrcanian* (*i.e.* Caspian) sea.   [5] *two Armenias*, the great and the small.

[6] *three Arabias*, *deserta*, *felix* and *petraea*.

[7] *Julian the Apostate* thus lost his army and his life A.D. 363, owing to the treachery of the Parthians (Amm. Marcell. xxv. 3).

[8] *Sigeilmes*. Arab. *Sidjilmassa*. A considerable place in the Middle Ages, now gone to ruin. It has been identified with some town in the oasis of Tafilet in Morocco. The phrase "when you entered into Libya" shews that it is in Africa (*R.E.R.* viii. 218).

[9] Fr. *Vertus non pas d'un petit poisson*. Suggested by the drinking powers of a fish. *Vertus d'autre que d'un petit poisson* occurs in iii. 32, and *vertus d'un petit poisson* in iv. 33.

Man, a Conqueror, one who pretends and aspires to Universal Empire, cannot always have his Ease. God be praised that you have come, you and your Men, safe and sound as far as the River Tigris."

"But", said he, "all this time what is being done by that Part of our Army which discomfited the swill-pot Clown Grandgousier?"[1]

"They are not idle", said they; "we shall soon meet them. They have taken for you Brittany, Normandy, Flanders, Hainault, Brabant, Artois, Holland and Zealand. They have crossed the Rhine over the Bellies of the Switzers and Lansknechts, and part of them have subdued Luxemburg, Lorraine, Champaigne, Savoye as far as Lyons, in which Place they have found your Garrisons returning from the naval Conquests in the Mediterranean Sea; and they have reassembled in Bohemia, after having sacked Suevia, Würtemberg, Bavaria, Austria, Moravia and Styria; then they have together fiercely set upon Lübeck, Norway, Sweden, Riga, Dacia,[2] Gothia, Greenland and the Easterlings[3] as far as the Frozen Sea. This done, they have conquered the Isles of Orkney and subjugated Scotland, England and Ireland. From there sailing through the Sandy Sea[4] and by the Sarmatians, they have conquered and dominated Prussia, Poland, Lithuania, Russia, Wallachia, Trans-Silvania and Hungary, Bulgaria and Turkey, and are now at Constantinople."

"Let us go", said Picrochole, "and betake ourselves to them as soon as possible, for I wish also to be Emperor of Trebizond.[5] Shall we not kill all those Dogs of Turks and Mahometans?"

---

[1] The notion of this body of troops detached from the royal army conquering different regions is also in the *Navigium* of Lucian. (Fr. ed.)

[2] *Dacia* is the name given to Denmark by Aeneas Sylvius (Pope Pius II), *Hist. Europ.* c. 33. Turpini, *Chronicon,* c. 11 has "Ogierus, rex Daciae".

[3] *les Estrelins* (*P.P.* 5; iv. N.P.) are the Baltic merchants of the Hanseatic league. (Commynes, iii. 5. p. 246, v. 18) "*Esterlingi* ii Germaniae populi qui a Daniae confiniis habitabant". *R.E.R.* vii. 343.

[4] *The Sandy Sea* (*Pontus Sabulosus* of Ptolemy) seems to be the Kattegat, Great Belt and the straits between Scandinavia and Denmark, all of which are full of shoals.

[5] The empire of Trebizond, founded in 1204 by Alexis Comnenus, after the conquest of Constantinople by the Latins, is frequently mentioned in the chivalric romances (Fr. ed.): *La Conqueste du trèspuissant Empire de Trebizonde par Renauld du Montauban* (Paris, s.d.).

"What a' Devil else shall we do?" said they. "Yes, and you will give their Goods and Lands to those who shall have served you faithfully."

"Reason", said he, "will have it so. It is but just. I give you Carmania,[1] Syria and all Palestine."

"Ah, Sire," said they, "it is your Goodness. Grammercy; God grant that you may always prosper."

There was present there at that time an old Gentleman experienced in divers Hazards, a very old Soldier in War, named Echephron,[2] who, hearing this Discourse, said:

"I am greatly afraid that all this Enterprise will be like the Farce[3] of the Pitcher of Milk, wherewith a Cordwainer made himself rich in his Day-dreams; and afterwards when the Pitcher was broken, had not wherewith to make a Dinner. What do you propose by these fine Conquests? What will be the End of all these Travails and Travels?"

"It will be", said Picrochole, "that when we have returned we shall repose at our Ease."

Then said Echephron:[4] "And if by chance you should never return from there?—for the Voyage is long and perilous.—Is it not better that we should take our Ease now at once, without putting ourselves to these Risks?"

"O," said Spadassin, "Perdy! here is a fine Dotard; why, let us go hide in the Chimney-corner, and there spend our Life and our Time with the Ladies, stringing Pearls or spinning like Sardanapalus.[5]

---

[1] *Carmania*. The modern Kirman, a province of Persia to the west of Baluchistan, reaching down to the Straits of Ormuz.

[2] Gr. Ἐχέφρων (Hom. *Od.* iii. 413), prudent, sensible.

[3] This farce supplied Des Periers with his charming novel (xii) *La laitière et le pot au lait*, afterwards popularised by La Fontaine.

[4] The episode of the advice of Echephron, indeed the whole chapter, is an adaptation and amplification of Plutarch, *vit. Pyrrhi*, c. 14, where the minister Cineas vainly attempts to dissuade Pyrrhus from attacking the Romans. It is given in Erasm. *Apoph.* lib. v (*Pyrrhus* 24).

[5] *Sardanapalus*, the effeminate king of the Assyrians. Cf. Diod. ii. 23. 1; Athen. viii. 528 F; Juv. x. 362, with Mayor's note.

"Sardanale preux chevalier,
Qui conquist le regne de Cretes,
En voulut devenir moullier
Et filer entre pucellettes."   Villon, *Double Ballade.*

Whoso nothing ventures,[1]
Hath nor Horse nor Mule:
So saith Solomon."
"Whoso too much ventures",
quoth Echephron,   *"Loseth Horse and Mule:*
Answereth Malcon."

"Enough", said Picrochole; "let us go on. I only fear these devilish Legions of Grandgousier: while we are in Mesopotamia, if they set upon our Rear, what Remedy?"

"A very good one", said Merdaille. "A nice little Order, which you will send round to the Muscovites, will put in the Field for you in a moment four hundred and fifty thousand picked fighting Men. O only make me your Lieutenant-general, and I would kill a Comb for a Pedlar.[2] I bite, I charge, I smite, I seize, I slay, I abjure everything."

"On, on," said Picrochole, "let all be got ready. Let him that loves me, follow."[3]

Erasm. *Ad.* iii. 7. 27: "*Sardanapalus*, deliciis usque adeo effeminatus ut inter eunuchos et puellas ipse puellari cultu desidere sit solitus".

[1] *Whoso nothing ventures*, etc. Imitated from *Les contreditz de Marcoul et de Salomon*, a curious dialogue in old French verse (1509), adapted from *Salomonis et Marculphi dialogus* (Coloniae 1487). The following is a specimen verse:

"Qui saiges homme sera
Ia trop ne parlera,
Ce dist Salomon.
Qui ja mot ne dira
Grant noise ne fera,
Marcol li respond".

The Communying of Solomon and Marcolphus in English was issued by Gerard Leeu at Antwerp 1492-3. A facsimile reprint with a bibliographical account was published in 1892 by Mr E. Gordon Duff. Burton alludes to it in *Anat.* iii. 2. 5. 3: "Solomon deceased as ugly as Marculphus". Marculphus is represented as an ugly, uncouth clown who caps Solomon's proverbs with coarse, homely, mother-wit.

[2] *Comb for a Pedlar*. In his excitement the speaker reverses the order of the words; he means that he would "kill a pedlar for a comb", *i.e.* he would take a man's life for the merest trifle. For a similar bloodthirsty expression cf. *C.N.N.* 86: "Il sembloit qu'ilz voulsissent tuer quaresme".

[3] "(Germani) ubi quis ex principibus in concilio dixit se ducem fore, *qui sequi velint profiteantur*, consurgunt ii qui et causam et hominem probant", Caes. *B.G.* vi. 23. § 7.

CHAPTER XXXIV

How Gargantua left the City of Paris to succour his Country, and how Gymnast encountered the Enemy

A T this self-same Hour Gargantua, who had gone forth from Paris immediately on reading his Father's Letter, riding on his great Mare, had already passed the Nun's Bridge,[1] himself, Ponocrates, Gymnast and Eudemon; who to follow him had taken Post horses. The rest of his Train came on by even Journeys, bringing all his Books and philosophical Apparatus.

When he had arrived at Parillé he was informed by the Farmer of Gouguet,[2] how Picrochole had entrenched himself in La Roche-Clermaud, and had sent Captain Tripet with a huge Army to attack the Wood of Vede[3] and Vaugaudry,[4] and that they had utterly ravaged everything, Cocks and Hens alike, as far as the Wine-press of Billard,[5] and that it was strange and hard to be believed, what Excesses they were carrying on throughout the Country; insomuch that Gargantua was affrighted and did not well know what to say or what to do.

---

[1] *the Nun's Bridge,* near Chinon, now destroyed. It was built in 1159 by Henry II of England (*R.E.R.* i. 80). It was at the southern extremity of the faubourg St Jacques. The tolls belonged to the nuns of Fontevrault. (Fr. ed.) "Après Chinon commencent les grandes lieues, passe les pontz de la Nonnain qui sont arches de pierre le long de demy lieue", Ch. Estienne, *Guide des chemins de France,* fol. 50, v° (*R.E.R.* xi. 25).

[2] *Gouguet,* a village of the commune of Beaumont-en-Verron to the west of Chinon; but possibly a man named Goguet is intended. Rabelais had a friend in Poitou named Hilaire Goguet. There was a large family bearing this name (*R.E.R.* iii. 71).

[3] *the Wood of Vede* is a wood near the castle of Auché on the left bank of the Vienne, where the river Vede or Veude falls into the Vienne about 3½ miles east of Chinon. It was part of the property of Gaucher Sainte-Marthe, who has been identified with Picrochole (*R.E.R.* iv. 336), but it is actually on the Negron, a little stream close to Chinon. (Fr. ed. p. lxxiii.)

[4] *Vaugaudry,* a hamlet in the commune of Chinon on the Vienne, near its junction with the Vede.

[5] *le pressouer Billard.* The hamlet of St Lazare formerly bore this name (*R.E.R.* v. 73).

But Ponocrates counselled him that they should proceed to the Lord de la Vauguyon,[1] who at all times had been their Friend and Ally, and that they should be better advised by him on all Matters; which they did incontinently, and found him steadily determined to assist them. He was of Opinion that Gargantua should send some one of his Men to reconnoitre the Country, and to learn in what Condition the Enemy were, in order that they might proceed thither by Plans formed according to the present State of things. Gymnast offered himself to go; but it was determined, as the better Course, that he should take with him some one who knew the Ways and By-paths, and the Rivers thereabout.

Then they set out, he and Prelinguand,[2] an Esquire of Vauguyon, and without giving Alarm they scouted on all Sides. Meantime Gargantua refreshed himself and took some Food with his Men, and ordered to be given to his Mare a *Picotin*[3] of Oats, that is, three-score and fourteen Quarters and three Bushels.

Gymnast and his Companion rode on till they fell in with the Enemy, all scattered and in Disarray, pillaging and plundering all that they could; and from as far off as they could see him, they ran upon him in Crowds to ransack him.

Then he cried out to them: "My Masters, I am a poor Devil: I beg of you to have mercy on me. I have yet one Crown left; we will drink it, for it is *aurum potabile*,[4] and this Horse here shall be sold to pay my Welcome; that done, retain me as one of your own Men, for never was there man[5] who knew better to take, lard,

---

[1] *la Vauguyon* (G. 35, 43).

[2] *Prelinguand.* Cf. *R.E.R.* x. 273, 278–82, 427.

[3] *Picotin* is the quantity or modicum of anything allowed to a beast; also used figuratively.

[4] *aurum potabile* (v. 16). This was the form into which the chymists tried to reduce gold, so that being the most perfect of substances it might serve as a panacea for all diseases. Moses was quoted as a precedent in the use of it, when he ground the golden calf to powder and made the children of Israel drink it (Exod. xxxii. 20). Sir T. Browne is incredulous of its good effects (*Pseud. Epid.* i. 5. § 3, iii. 22). Burton speaks of it, *Anat.* ii. 4. 1. 5. It was suggested as a remedy for Pope Julius II in his last illness (Gregor. xiv. 1. § 6). It is used here in a different, though obvious sense.

[5] *never was there man*, etc. Cf. Hom. *Od.* xv. 321:

> δρηστοσύνη οὐκ ἄν μοι ἐρίσσειε βροτὸς ἄλλος
> πῦρ τ' εὖ νηῆσαι διά τε ξύλα δανὰ κεάσσαι,
> δαιτρεῦσαί τε καὶ ὀπτῆσαι καὶ οἰνοχοῆσαι.

roast, and dress, nay, perdy! to dismember and devour a Hen, than I that am here; and for my *proficiat* I drink to all good Companions".

Then he undid his Leathern Bottle, and without putting his Nose therein he took a handsome Draught. The Chuffs looked at him, opening their Mouth a full Foot wide, and putting out their Tongues like Greyhounds, in expectation to drink after him; but at this Point up came Tripet, their Captain, to see what was the matter.

To him Gymnast offered his Bottle saying: "Take it, Captain, drink boldly from it; I have made Proof of it; it is Wine of La Faye Monjau".[1]

"What!" said Tripet, "this Johnny is gibing at us. Who art thou?"

Gymnast said: "I am a poor Devil".

"Ha!" said Tripet, "since thou art a poor Devil, 'tis reason that thou shouldst go thy Way, for every poor Devil goes free everywhere without Tax or Toll. But it is not the Custom for poor Devils to be so well mounted. Therefore, Master Devil, come down, that I may have the Horse, and if he does not carry me well, Master Devil, you shall carry me, for I much like the Notion that a Devil like you should carry me off."

---

[1] *vina Faymongiana* from *la Faye-Monjau* (*Faia monachalis*), a village of Les Deux-Sèvres, 10 miles from Niort, at one time celebrated for its wine, which was sometimes given as a present to great personages (*R.E.R.* ii. 160).

CHAPTER XXXV

How Gymnast nimbly killed Captain Tripet and others of Picrochole's Men

WHEN they heard these Words, some amongst them began to be afraid, and crossed themselves with all their Hands, thinking that this was a Devil in disguise.

Then one of them named Good John, Captain of the Franc-taupins,[1] drew his Prayer-book out of his Cod-piece and cried aloud: "Ἅγιος ὁ Θεός.[2] If thou be of God,[3] speak; if thou be of the Other, get thee gone". Yet went he not away; and several of the Band heard this and departed out of the Company; all which Gymnast did remark and consider.

Wherefore he made Semblance to alight from his Horse,[4] and when he was poised on the mounting (*i.e.* left) Side he nimbly performed the Stirrup-leather Feat, with his Backsword by his Side, and passing underneath he let himself go into the Air, and placed himself with his two Feet on the Saddle and his Back turned

---

[1] *Franc-taupins* (*P.P.* 5; *P.* 7; iii. 8), a body of sappers and miners (from *taupe*, a mole) formed by Charles VII and abolished by Louis XII. They were reputed great cowards.

[2] The first words of the Greek prayer called τρισάγιον, chanted on Good Friday in the Roman Church at Mass: Ἅγιος ὁ θεός, ἅγιος ἰσχυρός, ἅγιος ἀθάνατος ἐλέησον ἡμᾶς. Cf. *P.* 14. The τρισάγιον occurs in the Gallic missal and was sung in Greek and Latin. Cf. Gibbon, c. 47 (vol. vi. p. 45).

[3] *If thou be of God*, etc. Cf. Patelin, l. 652:

> "Allez-vous-en de par les diables
> Puisque de par Dieu ne peult estre".

[4] Much of the account of the feats of Gymnast may be derived from a passage in the *Hypnerotomachia* (cf. c. 9), which forms part of the Chess tournament given in v. 25: "Immediate se vide una pugna, uno torniamento, tanto delectabile, cum tanto praesta & subitanea vehementia, cum inclinarse fina in terra, facendo poscia uno repente & torculario salto & quale Mymphurio tornatorio" (? the Vaulter of Ferrara, *G.* 23) "cum due revolutione nel aere una opposita ad laltra. Et poi sencia mora, posto il pede dextro ad terra, tre fiate rotauase. Et poi subito laltro pede al contrario intorniaua. Tutta questa actione....Cum le sue profunde inclinatione & composite vertigine & facile saltatione, cum venusti gesti...", c. 10. h. recto. Cf. also Montaigne, *Essais*, i. 48; *Voyages*, p. 531 (ed. d'Ancona).

towards the Horse's Head. Then he said: "My Case goes back-wards".

Then in the very same Posture that he was, he fetched a Gambol on one Foot, and turning to the Left, failed not to recover his proper Position without missing a Jot.

Then said Tripet: "Ha, I will not do that at this Time, and for a good Reason".

"Bah!" said Gymnast, "I failed; I am going to do this Leap backwards."

Then with great Strength and Agility he fetched the Gambol as before, turning to the Right. This done, he put the Thumb of his right Hand on the Saddle-bow and raised the whole of his Body into the Air, supporting himself entirely by the Muscle and Nerve of the said Thumb, and so turned himself round three times. At the fourth Turn reversing his whole Body without touching any-thing, he gathered himself together between his Horse's two Ears, holding stiffly[1] the whole of his Body in the Air on the Thumb of his left Hand, and in that Posture performed the Wind-mill Flourish;[2] then clapping the Flat of his right Hand on the Middle of the Saddle, he gave himself such a Swing that he seated himself on the Crupper,[3] as do our Gentlewomen.

This done, he quite easily passed his right Leg over the Saddle and put himself in Posture to ride *en croup*.

"But", said he, "it were better for me to get between the Saddle-bows."

Then, supporting himself on the Thumbs of his two Hands on the Crupper before him, he threw himself backwards Heels over Head in the Air and came down between the Saddle-bows in a good Seat: then with a Somersault he raised the whole of his Body into the Air, and so stood with his Feet together between the

---

[1] Fr. *soudant* (L. Lat. *solidando = firmando*, Ducange).

[2] Fr. *le tour du moulinet*. "*Moulinets* are a series of six cuts in fencing with the two-handed sword, the rapier and the 'great stick' (perhaps = quarter-staff), probably so called because they resemble the movements of windmills", A. Hutton, *Cold Steel*, pp. 152 *sqq.*; Scott, *Ivanhoe*, c. 11; *Quentin Durward*, c. 1.

[3] Fr. *sus la crope*. Cf. Hept. *Nov.* 42 (p. 310): "lequel avoit mené sa soeur... *en croupe* derrière lui"; Merl. Coc. Baldus, xi. 235: "*in groppam* saltare cavalli"; Dante, *Inf.* xii. 95: "E che porti costui *in su la groppa*".

Pommels, and there turned round more than a hundred times[1]
with his Arms extended like a Cross, and as he did so he cried out
with a loud Voice: "I rage, Devils, I rage, I rage: hold me, Devils,
hold me, hold me".

Whilst he was thus vaulting, the Chuffs in great Amazement said
one to the other: "By the Halidame, 'tis a Goblin or a Devil thus
disguised:

> *Ab hoste maligno*[2]
> *Libera nos, Domine*".

And so they fled headlong, looking behind them like a Dog when
he runs off with a Goose's wing.

Then Gymnast, seeing his Advantage, got down from his Horse,
drew his Sword, and laid great Blows on the highest-crested of
them, and overthrew them in great Heaps, wounded, damaged
and bruised, without any one resisting him (for they thought he
was a starved Devil, as much on account of his wonderful Feats in
vaulting as by the Talk Tripet had held with him, calling him poor
Devil), except that Tripet would traitorously have cleft his Skull
with his Lansknecht Sword;[3] but he was well armed and felt
nothing of this Stroke but the Weight of the Blow. Upon this he
suddenly turned round and let drive a feint Thrust[4] at the said
Tripet, and while he was defending himself above he sliced him
through with a single Blow, Stomach, Colon and the half of his
Liver;[5] whereby he fell to the Earth, and as he fell he gave up

---

[1] *more than a hundred times.* Sterne has reproduced the whole of this chapter
up to this point in *Tristram Shandy* (v. 29) as an illustration of the quibbles of
polemical theology.   [2] *Ab hoste maligno*, etc., from some Litany.

[3] Fr. *espée lansquenette.* "This sword was specially affected by the German
mercenary foot-soldiers" (*Lansknechts*, cf. *P.* 28); "The blade was very broad
in comparison with its length and double-edged. The hilt consisted generally
of two rings formed by the *quillons* curved as a figure 8. The grip was more or
less conical, the broad base of the cone forming the pummel", E. Castle, *Schools
and Masters of Fence,* p. 229 n.

[4] Fr. *estoc volant.* Littré explains as "bâton ferré que l'on pouvait cacher sous
ses habits", but here it must mean a feint thrust.

[5] These organs can be cut through with a single blow, if the blow be given
slightly upwards (Le Double, p. 306).

γαστέρα γάρ μιν ἔτυψε παρ' ὀμφαλόν· ἐκ δ' ἄρα πᾶσαι
χύντο χαμαὶ χολάδες· τὸν δὲ σκότος ὄσσε κάλυψεν.

Hom. *Il.* xxi. 180.

ψυχὴ δὲ καὶ οὐταμένην ὠτειλὴν
ἔσσυτ' ἐπειγομένη, τὸν δὲ σκότος ὄσσε κάλυψεν. Id. *ibid.* xiv. 518.

more than four Pottles of Potage, and his Soul mingled with the Potage.

This done, Gymnast withdrew, considering that we ought never to pursue Strokes of Luck to their Full Extent, and that it is fitting for all Cavaliers to use their Lady Fortune with Respect,[1] without harassing or distressing her. And so, mounting his Horse, he set Spurs to him, riding straight on the Road to Vauguyon, and Prelinguand[2] with him.

---

[1] "Fortunam reverenter habe", Auson. *Epig.* viii. 7, quoted in the margin of *Facetus* (cf. G. 14) in the *Autores octo morales*, and in Burton's *Anat.* i. ii. 5. 5.

[2] *Prelinguand* (*P.P.* 5; G. 36; iv. 40; *Brelinguandus*, G. 14). This word has been taken by Le Duchat as equal to *praegustator* (Lat. *prae lingere*). M. Sainéan derives it from the Provençal, giving the meaning spruce, dandified, smart.

CHAPTER XXXVI

*How Gargantua demolished the Castle at the Ford of Vede,
and how they passed the Ford*

WHEN he had come thither, he recounted the Condition in which
he had found the Enemy, and the Stratagem he had used single-
handed against all their Band; declaring that they were nothing
but Marauders, Plunderers and Brigands, ignorant of all military
Discipline, and advising them to set forward boldly, for it would
be very easy for them to strike them down like Beasts.

Then Gargantua mounted on his great Mare, accompanied as
we have before described, and finding on his way a tall and large
Alder[1]—which was commonly called St Martin's Tree, because a
Pilgrim's Staff,[2] which St Martin formerly planted there, had
grown to that Size—said: "See, here is what I wanted; this Tree
will serve me as a Staff and a Lance". With that he tore it easily
from the Earth, plucked off its Boughs and trimmed it to his liking.

Meantime his Mare staled to ease her Belly; but it was in such
Abundance that it caused a Deluge for seven Leagues round; and
all this Flood drew off to the Ford of Vede,[3] and so swelled it along
the Stream, that the whole of this Troop of the Enemy were
drowned with great Horror, except some who had taken the Road
towards the Hillsides on the Left.

When Gargantua had come to the Neighbourhood of the Wood
of Vede, he was informed by Eudemon that within the Castle[4] was

---

[1] *Alder*, reading *alne*, with A. B reads *asne* and the later editions *arbre*. The
reading *alne* undoubtedly suits the context and gives a better sense. The
miraculous growth of St Martin's staff is told in *R.E.R.* viii. 334.

[2] *Pilgrim's Staff*. Fr. *bourdon*, from M. Lat. *burdo*, which is properly a mule
bred from a she-ass. These mules were smaller than those produced by the other
cross. Thus the *bourdon* would be the pilgrim's *mule*. Cf. Ducange, *s.v.*

[3] The road from La Vauguyon to the Ford of Vede is on a direct slope from
the rising ground above. (Fr. ed.)

[4] The castle at the Ford of Vede belonged to Gaucher de Sainte-Marthe, the
original of Picrochole; it must have been with great gusto that Rabelais introduces its demolition here. Cf. *R.E.R.* iv. 337, ix. 120. Its situation has not been
exactly determined and *may* be altogether imaginary. (Fr. ed.)

some Remnant of the Enemy; in order to be sure of this, Gargantua cried out as loud as he could: "Are you there, or are you not there? If you are there, be there no more; if you are not there, I have nothing to say".

But a ruffian Gunner, who was on the Parapet,[1] let fly at him a Cannon-shot and hit him furiously on the right Temple, yet for all this did him no more Hurt than if he had thrown a Plum at him.

"What is that?" said Gargantua; "do you throw Grape-stones at us? The Vintage shall cost you dear"; thinking indeed that the Bullet had been a Grape-stone.

Those who were within the Castle playing at Bandy-ball, on hearing the Noise, ran to the Towers and Ramparts, and shot at him more than nine thousand and twenty-five Shots from Falconets and Arquebuses, aiming them all at his Head, and so thick did they shoot at him that he cried out:

"Ponocrates, my Friend, these Flies here are blinding me; give me a Branch of these Willows to drive them away"; thinking that the Bullets and Stones shot from Artillery had been Gad-flies.

Ponocrates informed him that they were no other Flies but Gunshot, which they were firing from the Castle. Then he charged with his great Tree against the Castle, and with mighty Blows threw down Towers and Ramparts and laid it all level with the Earth. By this Means those who were therein were all crushed and beaten to Pieces.

Setting out thence, they came to the Mill Bridge and found all the Ford covered with dead Bodies, in such a Crowd that they had choked up the Mill-stream; these were they who had perished in the urinal Deluge of the Mare.

At this Point they were at a stand, as to how they could get over, in view of the Obstruction of these Carcases.[2] But Gymnast said:

"If the Devils have passed over there, I shall pass well enough".

---

[1] *Parapet.* Fr. *machicoulys*, properly one of the holes in the projecting parapet of a castle, through which were poured boiling oil or lead on to the heads of the assailants.

[2] Valerius Maximus (ix. 2. E. 2) records that Hannibal made a bridge of Roman corpses for his army to cross the Vergellus, a stream which falls into the Aufidus between Cannae and Canusium.

"The Devils", said Eudemon, "have passed, to carry off the damned Souls."

"By St Treignan," said Ponocrates, "he will pass over then as a necessary Consequence." [1]

"Yea, verily," said Gymnast, "or I shall stick fast in the Way."

And setting Spurs to his Horse he passed over readily, without the Horse ever taking Fright at the dead Bodies; for he had accustomed him, according to the Teaching of Aelian,[2] to fear neither Arms* nor dead Bodies—not by killing Men as Diomedes killed the Thracians, while Ulysses placed the Carcases of his Enemies before the Feet of his Horses, as Homer relateth—but by putting a Scarecrow among his Hay, and making him regularly go over it when he gave him his Oats.

The three others followed him without fail, except Eudemon, whose Horse set his right Foot knee-deep into the Paunch[3] of a great fat Chuff, who lay there on his Back drowned, and could not draw it out; and he remained thus entangled, till Gargantua with the End of his Staff thrust down the rest of the Chuff's Tripes in the Water, while the Horse pulled out his Foot; and, what is a marvellous Thing in Hippiatry,[4] the said Horse was cured of a Ring-bone, which he had on that Foot, by the Contact with the Inwards of this great Lout.

---

* *armes*, ABC; *ames*, D: but the reference to Aelian shews that *armes* is imperative.

[1] *as a necessary Consequence, i.e.* as a "poor Devil". Cf. *G.* 34.

[2] The practice of throwing scarecrows stuffed with chaff before horses so as to accustom them to step on bodies is attributed to the Persians by Aelian (*Nat. An.* xvi. 25), who refers to the passage in the *Iliad* (x. 488–93) in which Diomedes is represented as slaying the Thracians who were in charge of the horses of Rhesus, and Ulysses as *withdrawing* the dead bodies (ἐξερύσασκεν—ὑπάγει in Aelian) from before the horses which were newly arrived and therefore unaccustomed to the sights of a battle-field. The reading *mettoyt les corps...ès pieds de ses chevaulx* is assuredly in error. This reference to Aelian is probably taken from Pierre Gilles (v. 30), whose translation runs thus: "equos ad strepitum et sonitum assuescere cogunt, armataque cadaverum simulachra sub ipsum foenum subjiciunt, ut caesorum conspectum in bello ferre consuescant....Quod quidem ipsum Homerus haud sane ignoravit cum Diomedem quidem in Iliade scripsit Thracas jugulare Ulyssem vero interfectos pedibus subtrahere" (P. Gilles, iv. 9, Lugd. Seb. Gryphius, 1533). Cf. *R.E.R.* x. 451.

[3] Cf. "les navrez, auxquels les chevaulx et gens de pieds passerent par-dessus le ventre", *Le Roman de Mabriant*, fo. 58 verso.

[4] *Hippiatry* (Gk.), farriery, veterinary surgery. Cf. *Hippiatria sive Marescalcia Laurentii Rusii* (Paris, Ch. Wechel, fol. 1531).

CHAPTER XXXVII

How Gargantua, in combing his Head, caused Cannon-balls to fall out of his Hair

Having got clear of the Bank of the Vede, a short time after they arrived at the Castle of Grandgousier,[1] who was awaiting them with great Longing. At Gargantua's coming they entertained him with all their might; never were People seen more merry; for *Supplementum Supplementi Chronicorum*[2] declares that Gargamelle died there of Joy. For my part, I know nothing of it, and care mighty little[3] either for her or any other Woman.

The Truth was that Gargantua, in changing his Clothes and combing his Head with his Comb, which was nine hundred Ells[4] long, furnished with large Elephants' Tusks, all entire, caused to fall at every Rake more than seven Balls, which had stuck in his Hair at the Razing of the Castle at Vede-wood.

Seeing this, Grandgousier his Father thought they had been Lice, and said to him: "How now, my dear Son, hast thou brought us as far as here Sparrow-hawks[5] from Montagu College?[6] I did not mean that thou shouldst keep Residence there".

---

[1] *Grandgousier's Castle.* La Devinière, Rabelais' birthplace.

[2] "*Supplementum Chronicorum,* omnes fere historias continens, etc. etc.... primum a reverendo patre Jacobo Philippo Bergomate Ord. Eremitarum professo conscriptum." (Cf. *G.* 14.) "Cui insuper addita est nostrorum temporum brevis quaedam accessio eorum annorum historias complectens quae ab anno 1500 ad annum 1535 gestae sunt" (Opera Jacobi Nyverdi, fo. Paris 1535).

[3] *care mighty little.* Rabelais evidently thinks that any account of a woman is beneath the dignity of history (cf. iv. 10), like Thucydides, who mentions only one by name (ii. 101) and makes Pericles declare that woman's greatest glory is not to be talked about for good or for evil among men (ii. 45).

[4] *nine hundred Ells long.* Cf. "Jam rigidos pectis rastris, Polypheme, capillos", Ovid, *Met.* xiii. 764. Fr. *canne* (*G.* 8). In Gascon measure = 8 pans = 1·805 metres. Bourdette, *Annales de Labédâ*, vol. i. p. xlix. Ducange makes it a Hebrew measure of 8 palms = 1·981 metres.

[5] *sparrow-hawks,* a euphemism, like Mark Twain's *chamois* in Swiss hotels (*Tramp Abroad,* c. 25). Two passages from the *Colloquia* of Erasmus furnish a sufficient commentary: "Unde prodis?—E collegio Montis Acuti—Ergo ades nobis onustus litteris.—Immo pediculis" (*Georgius—Livinus*); "*SA.* Ante annos triginta vixi Lutetiae in collegio cui nomen ab aceto. *LA.* Illic ut audio parietes ipsi mentem habent theologicam. *SA.* Sic est ut dicis; ego tamen praeter corpus pessimis infectum humoribus et pediculorum largissimam copiam nihil istinc extuli" (Ἰχθυοφαγία *sub-fin.*).

[6] *Montagu College,* founded in 1314 by Gilles Aycelin de Montaigu, Arch-

Then Ponocrates answered: "My Lord, think not that I placed him in the College of Vermin which is called Montagu; I would rather have put him among the Beggars that do haunt Saint Innocents,[1] by reason of the enormous Cruelty and Villainy that I have known there. For the Galley-slaves among the Moors and Tartars, the Murderers in criminal Dungeons, nay the very Dogs in your House are far better treated than the forlorn Creatures in the said College; and if I were King of Paris, Devil take me if I would not put Fire thereto, and cause to be burnt the Principal and Regents, who allow this Inhumanity to be practised before their Eyes".

Then taking up one of the Bullets he said: "These be Cannonshot which lately your Son Gargantua received, as he was passing before the Forest of Vede, by the Treason of your Enemies. But they have been so rewarded for it, that they have all perished in the Ruins of the Castle as the Philistines did by the Device of Samson, and those whom the Tower of Siloam overwhelmed, of whom it is written in *Luc. xiij* [4].

"I am of opinion that we should pursue them while Fortune is on our side, for Occasion hath all her Locks before.[2] When she hath passed by, you can no longer recall her; she is bald in the back Part of her Head and never again returneth."

"Verily", said Grandgousier, "it shall not be at this Time, for I wish to make you a Feast for to-night and bid you right welcome."

This said, they made ready Supper, and, in addition to the usual Fare, were roasted sixteen Oxen, three Heifers, thirty-two Calves, sixty-three Rent-kids,[3] ninety-five Sheep, three hundred sucking Pigs soused in Must, eleven score Partridges, seven hundred Wood-

---

bishop of Rouen, was crumbling in 1483. It was reinstated under Jean Standonck, himself once a "poor" scholar at Sainte-Geneviève who treated the "poor" students ("Capets") with great rigour. The "rich" students, of whom Calvin was one, almost equalled the "poor" in numbers. The successors of Standonck were Noel Beda (cf. *P.* 7) and Pierre Tempeste (iv. 21). Cf. *R.E.R.* vii. 288.

[1] The cemetery *des Innocents* (*P.* 7, 16), at the corner of the *rue des Innocents* and the *rue S. Denis*, was infested with beggars. The earth of this cemetery was credited with great powers of decomposing dead bodies. Cf. *A.P.F.* ix. 61; *J.B.P.* p. 454; Paré, iii. p. 707 b: "on trouvoit la terre toute labourée comme l'on voit le cimetière sainct Innocent durant quelque grande mortalité". For a full account of Sainct Innocent see Pierre Champion's *Villon*, i. pp. 303 *sqq.*

[2]   "Fronte capillata, post est Occasio calva."
                                                    Dion. Cato, *Dist. Mor.* ii. 26.

[3] Fr. *chevreaux moissoniers*, from *moisson*, the milk of a cow. (S. in Fr. ed.)

192 of the works

cock, four hundred Capons from Loudun[1] and Cornouaille,[2] six thousand Pullets and as many Pigeons, six hundred Guinea-fowls, fourteen hundred Leverets, three hundred and three Bustards, and seventeen hundred Cockerels.[3]

Venison they could not so suddenly get, only:

Eleven wild Boars, which the Abbot of Turpenay[4] sent, and eighteen Fallow-deer given by the Lord of Grammont; together with seven score Pheasants which were sent by the Lord of Essars,[5] and some dozens of Ring-doves, Waterhens, Teal, Bitterns, Curlews, Plovers, Heath-cock,[6] Briganders, Dunlins,[7] young Lapwings, Sheldrakes, Shovelers, Herons, Hernshaws, Coots, Criels, Storks, little Bustards, Oranges, Flamingoes (which are Phoenicopters), Land-rails, Turkey-hens, a quantity of buck-wheat Porridge,[8] and a store of Brewis.

There was Abundance of Food[9] and no mistake, and it was handsomely served by Slap-sauce, Hotchpot and Pille-verjuice, Grandgousier's Cooks.

Janot, Micquel and Clean-glass supplied them right well with Drink.

---

[1] *Loudun* (G. 48; v. 6), about 14 miles south-west of Chinon, was celebrated for its poultry.

[2] *Cornouaille,* an ancient county in Brittany, of which Quimper (now the chief town of dep. Finisterre) was capital.

[3] Fr. *hutaudeaulx* (iv. 59), cockerels trimmed to look like capons, mentioned by the great fourteenth-century cook Taillevent (p. 11, ed. 1892) as *hetoudiaux* and *estoudeaulx* = Lat. *pullaster.*

[4] *L'abbé de Turpenay* (1526–39), Philippe Hurault de Chiverny. Also *abbé* of Bourgueil, Marmoutiers, St Aubin d'Angers and Pontlevoy. He introduced a superior vine at Bourgueil, since planted throughout the country, proving a source of considerable wealth (*R.E.R.* iv. 407). The abbey of Turpenay and the lordship of Grammont were near the forest of Chinon and abounded in game.

[5] The *Seigneur des Essarts* (cant. Langeais) was probably Nicholas de Herberay, translator of the Amadis romances (Jannet). Cf. Saint-Gelais, ii. 128 (ed. Elz.).

[6] *Heath-cock.* Fr. *francolys* (*francolinus vulgaris*), the ἀτταγᾶς in Aristoph. *Aves,* 249. Cf. Rogers, p. lv; Athen. ix. 387 F.

[7] *Dunlins.* Fr. *tyransons* = *bécassine de mer.*

[8] Fr. *coscossous* (*coscotons,* iii. 17; iv. 59; v. 23; *ambergris coscoté, P.* 21). A kind of Moorish dish made by working flour with water into little balls and so composing a kind of porridge. Cf. Scott's *St Ronan's Well,* c. 16: "What the devil did he care for Burgess's sauces, he that had eat his *Kouscousou* spiced with nothing but the sand of the desert?"

[9] A banquet even more lavish than this is provided for Messer Gaster in iv. 59, in which the same waterfowl appear. The country round Chinon with its marshes and forests was full of game, especially adapted for hawking.

CHAPTER XXXVIII

How Gargantua ate six Pilgrims in a Salad[1]

THE Subject requireth that we relate what happened to six Pilgrims, who were coming from Saint Sebastian near Nantes,[2] and who to find Shelter for themselves that Night, for fear of the Enemy had hid themselves in the Garden on the Pea-straw between the Cabbages and the Lettuces.

Gargantua found himself somewhat thirsty, and asked if they could find some Lettuces to make a Salad; and hearing that there were there some of the finest and largest in the Country (for they were as large as Plum-trees or Walnut-trees[3]) was minded to go there himself, and brought off in his Hand what he thought good. Therewith he carried off the six Pilgrims, who were in so great Fear that they durst neither speak nor cough.[4]

As he was washing them first at the Fountain,[5] the Pilgrims said to one another in a low Voice: "What shall we do? We are being drowned here amongst these Lettuces. Shall we speak? But if we speak he will kill us for Spies".

And as they were thus deliberating, Gargantua put them with his Lettuces on to a Dish of the House, as large as the Tun at Cisteaux,[6] and with Oil, Vinegar and Salt ate them to refresh

---

[1] This account is another version of the story told in *P.* 32 of Rabelais travelling inside Pantagruel's mouth, borrowed from Lucian's *Vera Historia*, i. 30–9.

[2] St Sebastian's body was claimed to be at Piligny near Nantes (cf. c. 45), though the same claim is made by Rome, Soissons and Narbonne (R). St Sebastien d'Aigne, cant. Nantes, on the left bank of the Loire, was a celebrated resort for pilgrims (*R.E.R.* x. 106).

[3] Theophrastus (*H.P.* vii. 4. 5) speaks of lettuces with stalks so large that they were used to make garden doors—θύραι κηπουρικαί, which Pliny (19. 135) translated *ostiola olitoria*.

[4] *durst neither speak nor cough.* This is told of the spy who was secreted in a hollow pillar by King Hugh of Constantinople to listen to the boastings of Charlemagne and his Peers (*Galien Rethoré*, c. 8).

[5] The fountain of La Devinière still exists. It is vaulted and let into the wall and contains a basin to receive the water. (Fr. ed.)

[6] St Bernard (1091–1153), Abbot of Clairvaux, was called in to help the Cistercians, who had been founded (1098) by Robert of Moelme in Burgundy

himself before Supper, and he had already swallowed five of the Pilgrims.

The sixth was still on the Dish, hidden under a Lettuce, all except his Pilgrim's staff, which appeared above. Seeing this, Grandgousier said to Gargantua: "I think that is the Horn of a Snail there; do not eat it".

"Why not?" said Gargantua. "They are good all this Month."[1]

And drawing up the Staff, he took up the Pilgrim withal and ate him very easily; then he drank a horrible Draught of strong Wine,[2] waiting till the Supper was served.

The Pilgrims, thus devoured, kept themselves from the Grinders of his Teeth as best they could, and thought that they had been thrust in some deep Dungeon of the Prison; and when Gargantua drank the great Draught, they thought to have been drowned in his Mouth, and the Torrent of Wine nearly carried them into the Gulf of his Stomach. Nevertheless, skipping with their Staves, as do Saint Michael's Palmers,[3] they put themselves in shelter under the Bank of his Teeth.

But, by Ill-luck, one of them groping the Country with his Staff, to know if they were in safety, struck roughly against the Cleft of a hollow Tooth and rapped the Nerve of the Jaw, whereby he caused very great Pain to Gargantua, so that he began to cry out for the Rage that he felt. To ease himself therefore of the Pain, he called for his Tooth-pick, and going in the direction of the Rook Walnut-tree,[4] unnestled me our Gentlemen, the Pilgrims.

For he hooked one by the Legs, another by the Shoulders,

---

at Cîteaux, in the diocese of Châlons; thus St Bernard was looked upon as their second founder, and the Cistercians were often called Bernardins. This tun (cf. c. 39) was said to have been made by him and to have contained 914 hogsheads.

[1] all this Month (P. 30; v. 6): snails were specially in request at vintage-time. (Fr. ed.)

[2] strong Wine. Fr. vin Pineau; this was of the growth of La Devinière (c. 5).

[3] Fr. Micquelotz, or Micheletz, were pilgrims to St Michel sur mer in Normandy. They had to use their staves to leap over the sands at ebb-tide. Cf. G.C. 8; P.P. 5; v. 25; C.N.N. 65; A.P.F. x. 372.

[4] Fr. noyer grollier (cf. iii. 32 fin.). This is another allusion to La Devinière. For grolle cf. G. 22 sub fin.; iv. 52; noix groslière, iv. 63, probably = a tree that produced large walnuts which the rooks affected; or grolle may be the target set up in this tree.

another by the Wallet, another by the Pouch,[1] another by the Scarf; and the poor Wretch who had rapped his Tooth with his Staff, him he hooked by the Cod-piece; nevertheless, this was a great Piece of Luck for him, for it lanced a pocky Botch[2] for him which had martyrised him from the time when they came past Ancenis.[3] So the Pilgrims, being dislodged, ran away across the Plantation[4] at a round Trot and the Pain ceased.

At this time he was called by Eudemon to Supper, for everything was ready. "I will go off then", said he, "to p—s away my Misfortune."

Then did he p—s so copiously that the Water cut off the Road for the Pilgrims, and they were constrained to cross the large Flood.[5] Passing from there by the Bank of the Spinney on the open Road, they all fell, excepting Fournillier, into a Trap which had been made to take Wolves in a Net,[6] from which they escaped by means of the Readiness of the said Fournillier, who broke all the Snares and the Ropes.

Having escaped from there, they lay for the rest of that Night in a Lodging near le Couldray, where they were comforted for their Misfortune by the goodly Words of one of their Company named Wearyfoot,[7] who pointed out to them that this Adventure had been predicted by David in the Psalms.[8]

---

[1] *Pouch.* Fr. *foillouze* (iii. 41). G. Bouchet (iii. 131) explains it as *gibbecière*. (Fr. ed.)

[2] *Botch.* "Pheraeus Jason deploratus a medicis vomicae morbo, cum mortem in acie quaereret, volnerato pectore medicinam invenit ex hoste", Pliny, 7. 166. Cf. Cic. *de Nat. Deor.* iii. § 70; Val. Max. i. 8. E. 6; Plut. *de cap. ex. inim. util.* c. 6. 89 C.

[3] *Ancenis*, a town in Brittany between Angers and Nantes, 34 miles from Angers.

[4] Fr. *la plante* is a newly planted vineyard, cf. iii. 32, "la plante du grand Cormier". (D.)

[5] *Flood.* Fr. *boyre* = *le deluge urinal* of Gargantua. Properly a canal for irrigation. (Fr. ed.) ? Mill-dam. (D.)

[6] Fr. *trainnée* (L.L. *trana*, Ducange), anything drawn, a train (of gunpowder, in *P.* 16, 25), an intrigue, *C.N.N.* 61. Here a net. Cf. *R.R.* 11,813:

> "Et la povreté vont preschant
> Et les grans richesses peschant
> As saynes (σαγήνη) et as *trainaus*".

[7] Fr. *Lasdaller.* "Sotz *las d'aller* et sotz hastifz", *Monologue des Sots joyeulx*, *A.P.F.* iii. 16. (Fr. ed.)

[8] This adaptation of the 124th Psalm (123rd Vulg.) was intended to ridicule

Cum exsurgerent homines in nos,
Forte vivos deglutissent nos,

When we were eaten in the Salad with Grains of Salt;

Cum irasceretur furor eorum in nos,
Forsitan aqua absorbuisset nos,

When he drank the great Draught;

Torrentem pertransivit Anima nostra,

When we crossed the great Flood;

Forsitan pertransisset Anima nostra
Aquam intolerabilem

Of his Urine, wherewith he cut off our Path.

Benedictus Dominus, qui non dedit nos in captionem
dentibus eorum. Anima noster sicut passer erepta
est de laqueo venantium,

When we fell into the Trap,

Laqueus contritus est by Fournillier
Et nos liberati sumus. Adjutorium nostrum, etc.

---

the "applications" of the preachers of that time. The "moralisings" of the *Gesta Romanorum* are of the same nature. Cf. R. E. Prothero, *The Psalms in human life*, c. 7. There is intended also a burlesque of the ancient canticle of the pilgrims to St James of Compostella.

> "*Quand* nous fûmes sur le pont qui tremble...
> *Quand* nous fûmes au port de Blaye,   (cf. iv. 64)
> *Quand* nous fûmes dedans les Landes,   (*P.* 23; *G.* 33)
> *Quand* nous fûmes dedans l'Espagne,
>   Nous fûmes joyeux
> De voir sortir de ces montagnes
>   Si grand odeur,
> De voir le roman fleurier
>   Thym et lavande:
> Nous rendîm's grâce a Jesus Christ
>   Et luy chantâm's louange."

(Cited by Fleury, p. 262.)

CHAPTER XXXIX

How the Monk was feasted by Gargantua, and of the jovial Discourse he held at Supper[1]

WHEN Gargantua was at Table, and the first Part of the Messes had been despatched, Grandgousier began to recount the Origin and the Cause of the War raised between him and Picrochole, and came to the Point of narrating how Friar John of the Trencherites had triumphed at the Defence of the Abbey-close, and commended his Prowess as above that of Camillus, Scipio, Pompey, Caesar and Themistocles.

Upon this Gargantua desired that he should be sent for at once, to the end with him they might consult on what was to be done. At their Wish the Major-domo went to fetch him, and brought him along merrily with his Staff of the Cross, on Grandgousier's Mule.

When he was come, a thousand Caresses, a thousand Huggings and a thousand Good-days were given him:

"Ha, Friar John my Friend, Friar John my brave Cousin, Friar John in the Devil's name, let me clip thee round the Neck, my Friend,—let me have thee in my Arms—Cza, my Codling, I must gripe thee till thy Reins crack".

And Friar John made merry. Never was any one so courteous or gracious.

"Come, come," said Gargantua, "a Stool here near me at this End."

"With all my Heart," said the Monk, "since it is your good Pleasure.—Page, some Water. Pour it, my Boy, pour it; it will refresh my Liver. Give it me here, that I may—gargle my Throat."

"*Deposita cappa*",[2] said Gymnast; "let us take off this Frock."

---

[1] This and the next two chapters consist principally of the discursive chatter of the Monk, on the model of *G.* 5.

[2] *Deposita cappa*. These words are from the rituals which point out the places where the officiating priest should take off his cope. (M.)

"Ho, Pardy," said the Monk, "my good Sir,[1] there is a Chapter[2] *in Statutis Ordinis* which would not allow this Point."

"Pish!" said Gymnast, "a Fig for your Chapter! This Frock burdens both your Shoulders; put it off."

"My Friend," said the Monk, "leave it with me; for, I swear, I drink only the better for it. It makes all my Body right merry. If I should lay it aside, my Friends the Pages will make Garters of it, as I was once served at Coulaines.[3] Besides, I shall have no Appetite; but if in this Habit I sit at Table, then, pardy! I will drink to thee and to thy Horse. And so lustily. God save the Company. I had supped; but for all that I will eat not a whit the less, for I have a paved Stomach[4] as hollow as the Boot[5] of Saint Benêt, ever open like a Lawyer's Pouch.

Of every Fish except the Tench,[6]

take the Wing of the Partridge, or the Thigh of a Nun; is it not to die like a jolly Fellow[7] when a Man dies with stiffened Limbs? Our Prior loves exceedingly the white of a Capon."

"In that", said Gymnast, "he doth not resemble the Foxes; for of the Capons, Hens and Pullets which they carry off, they never eat the White."

"Why?" said the Monk.

---

[1] Fr. *mon gentilhomme*. This was not at this time a term of disrespect, though Brantôme records that his uncle M. de Chataigneraye greatly resented it when he was thus addressed by the Princesse de la Roche-sur-Yon. (D.)

[2] *Chapter in Statutis Ordinis*. Probably the one forbidding monks to quit their dress under penalty of excommunication (M.). Rabelais had incurred the charge of "apostasy" for a breach of this statute: cf. *supplicatio pro apostasia*.

[3] *Coulaines* (G. 47), a place near Chinon on the Vienne, south of Verron.

[4] *paved Stomach*. "Vallatam gulam, ut ait Caecilius", Macrob. *Sat.* iii. 15. 9.

[5] *Boot of Saint Benêt* (iv. 16; v. 47). The huge tun of St Benêt at Bologna. For *Boot = Butt* cf. iv. 43. L.L. *butta*, Ital. *botta*. There was also a tun of St Bernard at Clairvaux containing 800 *muids* (G. 38); Gibbon, c. 59.

[6] This proverb runs thus:

"De tous les poissons fors que la tenche
Prens le dos et laisse la penche".

Others make a difference, rejecting only amongst fresh-water fish the eel, *tench*, lamprey, crawfish. Burton, *Anat.* i. 2. 2. 1.

[7] Fr. *falotement*. An allusion to a proverbial expression:

"Arrectus moritur monacha quicumque potitur".

Glossa Metulini ad Eberardi Graecismum, c. 18. l. 24.

"Because they have no Cooks to cook them," answered Gymnast, "and if they are not sufficiently cooked they remain red and
not white. The Redness of Meats is an Indication that they are not
done enough, except Lobsters and Crayfish, which are cardinalised
in boiling."[1]

"Feste Dieu Bayard,"[2] said the Monk, "the Hospitaller[3] of our
Abbey hath not his Head well boiled, for he has his Eyes as red as
a Cup made of Alder-wood. This Leveret's Thigh[4] is good for the
Gouty.

"By the bye, my Trowel,[5] why is it that the Thighs of a Gentlewoman are always fresh?"

"This Problem", said Gargantua, "is neither in Aristotle, nor
in Alexander of Aphrodisias,[6] nor in Plutarch."[7]

"It is", said the Monk, "for three Reasons, by which a Place is
naturally refreshed:

"*Primo*, because the Water runs down its whole Length;

"*Secundo*, because it is a shady Place, obscure and dark, on which
the Sun never shines;

"And *thirdly*, because it is continually ventilated by the Breezes

---

[1] *cardinalised in boiling.* Cf. *Hudibras*, ii. 2. 29:

> "The sun had long since in the lap
> Of Thetis taken out his nap;
> And like a lobster boiled, the moon
> From black to red began to turn".

Cardinals first wore "purple" at the Council of Lyons (Innocent IV), anno
1245 (Ducange, s.v. *Rubens*).

[2] *Feste Dieu Bayard* was the favourite adjuration of Bayard (iv. 67).

[3] Fr. *enfermier*, the brother who tends the sick. Lat. *infirmarius*, Gk. νοσοκόμος.
L'enfermière occurs in *C.N.N.* 21 and *nosocome* = νοσοκομεῖον in *G.* 51.

[4] "Podagras mitigari [tradunt] pede leporis viventis absciso, si quis secum
adsidue portat", Pliny, 28. 220. Pepys makes it a cure for colic, *Diary*, Jan. 20,
1664.

[5] *à propos truelle* (*bon jour maçon*) (*P.* 12) is a proverbial expression of persons
who speak of one thing with reference to another. It occurs in other forms iii.
18 and *A.P.F.* x. 66. Another form is:

> "Où es-tu, masson, sans truelle?
> Dieu met en mal an ton aumusse".

[6] Aristotle and Alexander of Aphrodisias (cf. *G.* 10) had written προβλήματα;
translations had been published in one volume (Venice 1489).

[7] In Plutarch the *Symposiaca* or *Quaestiones conviviales* were entitled *Problems*.

of the North-wind,[1] of the Smock,[2] and of the Cod-piece to boot.

"And heartily to it. Page, to our Tippling. Gulp,[3] gulp, gulp! What a good God we have, who giveth us this good Drink.

"I call Him to witness, if I had lived in the Time of Jesus Christ I would have been well on guard against the Jews taking Him in the Garden of Olivet. And more, the Devil fail me, if I would have failed to hamstring those Gentlemen the Apostles, who fled so cowardly after they had well supped, and left their good Master in His Need. I hate worse than Poison a man who runs away when he ought to play a good Knife—and Fork. Oh, that I am not King of France for fourscore or a hundred Years! Perdy! I would make curtailed Curs of the Run-a-ways from Pavia.[4] A Quartan ague take them! Why did they not die there rather than leave their good Prince in that Strait? Is it not better and more honourable to die fighting valiantly than to live flying villainously?

"We shall not have many Goslings to eat this Year. Ha, my

---

[1] The *vent de bise* (iv. 43) is, and always has been, looked upon as cold and disagreeable: *Mais li doleureus vens de bise*, R.R. 6774.

[2] *vent de chemise* is used of the *ruses*, caprices and coquetteries of a woman. Cf. Coquillart, i. 8, ii. 284; *A.P.F.* iii. 135. Cf. also *Hudibras*, iii. 1. 689:

> "They've more punctilios and capriches
> Between the petticoat and breeches,
> More petulant extravagances
> Than poets make 'em in romances".

[3] *Gulp*. Fr. *crac, crac, crac*. Cf. Meyer, *Anthol.* 1069. 15.

> "Percutit et frangit vas, vinum deffuit, ansa
> Stricta fuit, *glut, glut* murmurat unda sonans",

quoted by Mayor, *Juvenal*, iv. 28.

[4] The Swiss mercenaries and the Duc d'Alençon, who commanded the rear-guard, fled at the battle of Pavia (Feb. 24, 1525), when Francis I was taken prisoner by the Imperialists under the Marquis of Pescara. Perhaps a reference is also intended to Bonnivet, who was killed there (*R.E.R.* vi. 374). "Aut manenti vincendum aut moriendum", Erasm. *Ad.* iii. 5. 10. Cf.

> "Plus desirans par honneur faire approche
> De mort que vivre à honteuse reproche".
>   Cretin, *L'apparition du Mareschal sans reproche*, p. 137.

> "L'escolle de ceulx de Pavie;
> Fy de l'honneur, vive la vie!"
>   Cl. Marot, *Epist.* 44 (1535).

Friend, give me some of that Hog. Diavolo! there is no more
Must:[1] *Germinavit radix Jesse.*[2]

"I renounce my Life on't, I am dying of Thirst. This Wine is
none of the worst. What Wine did you drink in Paris? I give myself
to the Devil if I did not once keep open House there to all Comers
more than six Months.[3]

"Do you know Brother Claude of the Haults Barrois?[4] O the
jolly Companion that he was! But what Fly hath stung him?[5] He
doth nothing but study since I don't know when. I do not study,
for my Part. In our Abbey we never studied, for fear of the Mumps.
Our late Abbot used to say that it was a monstrous thing to see a
learned Monk. Pardy, Sir, my Friend, *magis magnos*[6] *clericos non
sunt magis magnos sapientes.*

"You never saw so many Hares as there are this Year. I have
not been able to come by a Goshawk or a Tassel-gentle anywhere
in the World. My Lord de la Bellonière had promised me a Lanner-

---

[1] Among the dishes served in c. 37 were "300 sucking pigs soused in must";
cf. also iv. 59.

[2] *Germinavit radix Jesse* occurs in the Breviary in one of the Antiphons at
Lauds, on the festival of Circumcision, and in the vigil of Epiphany. It is
adapted from Isaiah xi. 1. *Jesse* in the then popular pronunciation = *J'ay soif*.
Hence Friar John says: "je meurs de *soif*", suggested by the word *Jesse* (M.L.).
In iv. 45 Poissy is distorted into *Pet-sec*, and Blois was pronounced and written
Blès. *A.P.F.* xii. 128.

[3] Cf. Cordier, 28. 17: *Il fait chere à tous venans.* Friar John probably means at
some Benedictine monastery, in which order hospitality was a great virtue.
Perhaps at St Denis as a Benedictine. Cf. *P.* 18 and *R.E.R.* vi. 38.

[4] The name of *Barrois* and *Hauts-Barrois* is given to the inhabitants of Bar-sur-
Seine and Bar-sur-Aube. (Joh.)

[5] *what Fly hath stung him?* Cf. Cl. Marot, *Epig.* 224, an adaptation of Martial's
"Non amo te Sabidi" (*I do not love thee, Dr Fell*):

> "Jan, je ne t'aime point, beau sire,
> Et ne sçay quell' mouche me poind,
> Ne pourquoy c'est; je ne puis dire
> Sinon que je ne t'aime point".

[6] *magis magnos*, etc. Perhaps originally from Job xxii. 9: "Non sunt longaevi
sapientes", in A.V. and R.V., "It is not the great that are wise". The moral of
a story in *Cento Novelle Antiche* 75 (or 94) is *Ogni uomo che sa lettera non è savio.*
Montaigne quotes Rabelais (i. 24). Chaucer, referring to *C.N.A.*, has:

> "The grettest clerks been noght the wysest men.
> As whylom to the wolf thus spak the mare".   *C.T.* A. 4054.

> "Non est multum magnus clericus."   Cordier, 56. § 36.

hawk, but he wrote to me not long ago that he had become pursy.[1] The Partridges will eat up our Ears this Year.[2] I take no Pleasure in fowling with a Tunnel-net,[3] for I take Cold at it. If I do not run, if I do not bustle about, I am not at my Ease. True it is that in jumping over the Hedges and Bushes my Frock leaves some Jags behind. I have got a rare Greyhound. Devil a bit a Hare escapes him. A Groom was leading him to my Lord Maulevrier,[4] and I robbed him of him. Did I do wrong?"

"No, Friar John", said Gymnast; "no, by all the Devils, no."

"So", said the Monk, "shall one deal with these Devils as long as they last.[5] By the Powers, what would that lame Fellow have done with it? 'Sbody, he takes more Pleasure when he gets a Present of a good Yoke of Oxen."[6]

"How now," said Ponocrates, "do you swear, Friar John?"

"It is only", said the Monk, "to embellish my Speech.[7] These be Colours[8] of Ciceronian Rhetoric."

---

[1] *pursy, i.e.* asthmatic. Fr. *pantays.* Hawks were sometimes subject to this. Cf. *R.E.R.* x. 370.

[2] *Partridges will eat up our Ears.* Does this refer to the game laws and the penalty of loss of ears?

[3] Fr. *la tonnelle*, into which partridges were driven.

> "C'est la perdrix qu'on veult *en la tonnelle*
> Faire tomber."
>
> Cl. Marot, *Chant* xxii, *à la Royne de Navarre* (1536).

[4] Pierre de Brézé, Comte de Maulevrier, *grand veneur de France* to Louis XI, was lame and very wealthy. Cf. iv. N.P.: "richer than Maulevrier the club-foot". His grandson Louis de Brézé, Grand Seneschal of Normandy, married in 1515 Diane de Poitiers (1499–1566), afterwards mistress of Henry II (cf. Brantôme, ix. 356). He has a magnificent tomb in Rouen cathedral (†1531). A pun is intended between *gentil levrier* and *Maulevrier*, as before between *lanier* and *Bellonière*. The castle of la Bellonière was not far from Basché and was owned by the same family, the *du Puy* (G. 23). *R.E.R.* v. 58.

[5] *I.e.* till one is rid of them (Morellet).

[6] *a... Yoke of Oxen. Chasser aux bœufs* is an old expression to signify a rich miserly fellow. Cf. Shakesp. 2 *Hen. IV*, iii. 2. 42: "Shallow: 'How, a good yoke of bullocks at Stamford fair?'"

[7] *to embellish my Speech.* "Vox quaedam libera atque effrenatior augendi causa: iracundia...*optatio atque execratio.* His fere luminibus *illustrant orationem sententiae*", Cic. *de Orat.* iii. § 205.

[8] *Colours*, etc. Cf. iii. 34 n. Cf. also Ebrardi Graecismus, c. 3: *De coloribus rhetoricis*; "Mille couleurs de rhetorique", Coquillart, *Le Blason*, ii. 161.

CHAPTER XL

*Why Monks are shunned by the World, and why some have
bigger Noses than others*

"By my Faith as a Christian," said Eudemon, "I am lost in
Contemplation, when I consider the Worthiness of this Monk, for
he maketh us all merry here. How is it then that men drive away
Monks from all good Companies, calling them Trouble-feasts, just
as Bees drive away the Drones from around their Hives? *Ignavum
fucos pecus*, says Maro, *a praesepibus arcent*."[1]

To this answered Gargantua: "There is nothing so true as that
the Frock and the Cowl draw on themselves the Opprobrium,
Insults and Maledictions of the World, just as the Wind called
Caecias attracts the Clouds.[2]

"The absolute Reason is because they eat up the Offscouring of
the World, that is to say the Sins,[3] and as Scavengers, men cast them
into their Retreats, that is their Convents and Abbeys, separated
from civil Conversation, as are the Retreats of a House.

"But if you can conceive why an Ape in a Family is always
mocked and teased, you will understand why the Monks are
shunned by all, old and young alike.

"The Ape doth not guard the House as doth a Dog; he doth not
draw the Plough like the Ox; he produceth no Milk, nor Wool as
doth the Sheep; he carrieth no Burdens as doth the Horse.[4] That

---

[1] Virg. *G.* iv. 168. "Fucus (= a pretence); a drone is so called; for he resembles a bee, but is injurious to them, because he produces nothing himself,
and consumes the produce of others", Servius, *ad loc.* Erasmus (*Ad.* ii. 8. 65)
uses the same metaphor concerning the Mendicants, calling them *fucos crabroni-
bus aculeatiores*.

[2] "Quemadmodum caecias nubes, itidem improba vita probra ad se attrahit."
Translated from Plut. *Mor.* 88ᴇ by Erasmus, *Ad.* i. 5. 62. καικίας (Arist. *Eq.*
437) is E.N.E., Lat. *Vulturnus*. Aristotle, *Meteor.* ii. 6, gives the proverb, and is
himself quoted by Aul. Gell., ii. 22 and Pliny, 2. 125.

[3] "Peccata mei populi comedetis" (Hosea, iv. 8). This is quoted by Erasmus
(*Ad.* iii. 2. 37, *Pontificalis cena*), with the remark that such hard food requires the
strongest wine to digest it.

[4]   "Pondera portat equus, bos terram sulcat aratro;
           Vellera portat ovis, servat ovile canis."   Alanus, *in Parabolis*.

which he doth is to bemire and spoil everything, which is the Reason why he gets from every one Gibings and Bastinadoes.

"In like manner a Monk—I mean one of those lazy Monks— doth not labour like the Peasant, nor guard the Land as doth the Man-at-arms, nor heal the Sick like the Physician, nor preach and instruct the World like the good Evangelical Doctor and Preceptor, nor import Commodities and Things necessary for the State like the Merchant. This is the Reason why they are hooted at and abhorred by all".

"Nay," said Grandgousier, "but they pray God for us."

"Nothing less", answered Gargantua. "True it is that they disquiet the whole Neighbourhood by jangling their Bells."

"Yea, verily", said the Monk; "a Mass, a Matins and a Vesper well rung are half said."

"They mumble through a great Store of Legends[1] and Psalms, in no ways understood by them; they count a Number of Pater- nosters interlarded with long *Ave Marias*, without thinking of or understanding them, and this I call a Mocking of God and not Prayer.

"But may God be their Aid if it is for us that they pray, and not through Fear of losing their Manchets and rich Soups. All true Christians of all Estates, in all Places, in all Times pray to God, and the Spirit prayeth and intercedeth for them, and God receiveth them into Favour.

"Now such is our good Friar John. Therefore every one wisheth for him in his Company. He is no Bigot; he is not a Tatterde- malion; he is honest, merry, resolute and a good Companion; he works, he labours, he defends the Oppressed, he comforts the Afflicted, he succours the Distressed; he guards the Abbey-close."

"I do", said the Monk, "far more than that; for whilst we are despatching our Matins and Anniversaries in the Choir, meantime I make Cross-bow Strings and polish Bolts and Quarrels;[2] I make Snares and Purse-nets to take Coneys.[3] Never am I lazy. But ho!

---

[1] *a great Store of Legends*, etc. Cf. Erasm. *Mor. Enc.* c. 54 and c. 60.

[2]   "Je fais arcs, arbalestres, frondes,
                   Fleches, viretons et *carrotz*."   *Le Varlet à louer, A.P.F.* i. 83.

[3] "Facito aliquid boni operis ut semper te diabolus inveniat occupatum… vel fiscellam texe junco…texantur et lina capiendis piscibus", *Jerome to the*

what ho! some Drink here, some Drink. Bring the Fruit; these be
Chestnuts of the Wood of Estrocs.[1] With good new Wine it will
make you a Composer of Bum-sonnets; you are not yet well
seasoned with Liquor here. Perdy, I drink at every Ford, like a
Proctor's horse."[2]

Gymnast said to him: "Friar John, take away the Dew-drop[3]
that hangs at your Nose".

"Ha, ha," said the Monk, "am I not in Danger of drowning,
seeing that I am in Water up to my Nose? No, no. *Quare? Quia*[4]

> As Water it goeth not in, though as Water it may come out,
> For it hath received full Measure of the Vine-bunch Antidote.

"O my Friend, he that hath winter Boots of such Leather as
this[5] may boldly fish for Oysters; they would never let Water."

"Why is it", said Gargantua, "that Friar John hath such a fine
Nose?"

"Because", replied Grandgousier,[6] "God hath so willed it, who

---

monk Rusticus, pt. iii. *Epist.* 39. A large portion of this letter is given in 3 D. v.
(*de consec.*) c. 33, perhaps suggested to Jerome by Virg. *Ecl.* ii. 71:
> "Quin tu aliquid saltem potius quorum indiget usus
> Viminibus mollique paras detexere junco".

[1] *Estrocs* in Bas-Poitou, very fertile in fruit, and renowned for chestnuts
(*R.E.R.* ii. 148, vi. 404).

[2] *Proctor's horse.* The *promoteur* or proctor was a commissary or fiscal procurator in ecclesiastical jurisdictions. As he was generally a poor horseman his
horse would drink where he liked in spite of him. Proctors possessed in
ecclesiastical jurisdiction powers of administration and thus were the frequent
recipients of small presents. (Fr. ed.)

[3]   "Mouchez-la, s'elle a *la roupie*."   *A.P.F.* i. 166.
> "Et au bout du nez *la rouppie*."
>   Coquillart, *Mon. des Perr.* ii. 274.
>   "madidique infantia nasi."   Juv. x. 199.
>   "nil spissius illa
> Dum bibitur, nil clarius est dum mingitur, unde
> Constat quod multas faeces in corpore linquat."
>   Henricus Abrincensis, quoted by Burton, *Anat.* I. ii. 2. 1.
>   "Aquam foras vinum intro."   Petronius, c. 52.

[4] *Quare? Quia.* "Every why hath a wherefore" (Shakesp. *Com. Err.* ii. 2. 45);
"For every why he had a wherefore", *Hudibras*, i. 1. 132.

[5] *Such Leather as this, i.e.* as my skin, which never takes in water. Cf. iv. 24,
where Panurge's skin is similarly watertight.

[6] Sterne gives Grandgousier's reason, *Tristram Shandy*, iii. 41.

creates us in such Form and to such End, according to His divine Pleasure, even as a Potter fashioneth his Vessels."

"Because", said Ponocrates, "he was one of the first at the Fair of Noses. He chose one of the finest and largest."[1]

"Marry, come up", said the Monk. "According to the true monastic Philosophy it is because my Nurse had soft Breasts; and in suckling, my Nose buried itself as though in Butter, and there swelled and grew like Dough within the Kneading-trough. Hard Breasts in Nurses make Children snub-nosed.[2] But hey day:

Ad formam nasi[3] *cognoscitur ad te levavi.*

I never eat Sweetmeats.[4] Page, some Tipple. Also some Toasts."

---

[1] Cf. *Tristram Shandy*, iv. 1.

[2] Cf. *Tristram Shandy*, iii. 38. Sterne puts this down to Paré. I have found the following on the subject: "Puis soy faite ligature propre, en sorte qu'elle ne presse sur le nez, de peur de rendre le patient camus", *Des Playes du Nez*, viii. 27. Cf. Aelian, *Nat. An.* xvi. 23: Σκιρᾶται...εἰσὶ σιμοὶ τὰς ῥῖνας, εἴτε οὕτως ἐκ βρεφῶν ἁπαλῶν ἐνθλάσει τῇ τῆς ῥινὸς διαμείναντες, εἴτε κ.τ.λ.

[3] *Ad formam nasi*, etc. (cf. iv. 54). "Codrus adscribit: 'Ad formam nasi', *et quae sequuntur*", Tiraqueau, *de legg. conn.* ix. 99, ed. 3a (p. 102, 2. ed. 2a); "Licet illa meretrix dixerit 'Nase, me decepisti'", Joh. Nev. *Sylv. Nupt.* ii. fo. 79, 1–2.

[4] Obviously because they spoil the taste of the wine.

CHAPTER XLI

How the Monk made Gargantua sleep, and of his Hours
and Breviary

SUPPER being finished, they consulted of the Business in hand, and it was determined that about Midnight they should set out in skirmishing Order, to learn what Watch and Ward their Enemies kept; and in the mean Season they should take some little Repose, so as to be more fresh. But Gargantua was unable to sleep, whichever Side he turned himself.[1]

Then said the Monk to him: "I never sleep well at my Ease except when I am at Sermon or at Prayers. I entreat you, let us begin, you and I, the seven Psalms, to see if you will not soon be asleep".

The Notion pleased Gargantua well, and beginning at the first Psalm,[2] when they came to the *Beati quorum* they both fell asleep.

But the Monk never failed to wake before Midnight, so much accustomed was he to the Hour of Claustral Matins. Being awaked himself, he woke up all the others singing with a full Voice the Song:

What ho! Regnault, awake thee, wake!
What ho! Regnault, awake![3]

When they were all aroused he said: "My Masters, it is said that Matins begin with coughing, and Supper with drinking. Let us act

---

[1] Cf. v. 15; Hom. *Il.* xxiv. 3, 10 *sqq.* and Gringore, *la Coqueluche*, i. 193:

"Ils se couchent de costé, de travers,
Sur l'estomach, puis tous platz à l'envers,
Et si les metz tous les jours en esmoy".

[2] *the first Psalm* is the first penitential Psalm (the 6th), the second being the 32nd (or 31st in the Vulgate) beginning *Beati quorum*. The seven in the Vulgate are 6, 31, 37, 50, 101, 129, 142.

[3] *What ho! Regnault*, etc. Le Duchat records that this is an old song which in his time was often in the mouth of workmen. It is still sung in several provinces, but Thomas replaces Regnault. (Fr. ed.)

contrariwise; let us now begin our Matins with drinking; and in the Evening when the Supper comes in, we will cough it with the best".

Upon this said Gargantua: "Drink so soon after sleeping?[1] That is not to live after the Rules of Medicine. We should first clear the Stomach of all its Superfluities and Excrements".

"'Tis rarely prescribed!" said the Monk. "May a hundred Devils leap on my Body if there are not more old Drunkards than old Physicians.[2] I have made Terms with my Appetite with a Covenant of this sort, that it always goeth to Bed with me, and for that I always see well to it during the Day; also it riseth with me. You look after your Castings[3] as much as you like, I am going after my Tiring."[4]

"What Tiring do you mean?" said Gargantua.

"My Breviary",[5] said the Monk; "for, just as Falconers, before they feed their Hawks, do make them tire[6] upon a Hen's Leg to purge their Brains of Rheums and to sharpen their Appetite, so taking this merry little Breviary in the Morning, I scour my Lungs throughout, and there am I, ready to—drink."

---

[1] *Drink so soon after Sleeping?* Cf. cc. 21, 22.

[2] *more old Drunkards*, etc. "With Rabelais, that French Lucian, drunkenness is better for the body than physic, because there be more old drunkards than old physicians", Burton, *Anat.* I. ii. 2. 2. The *proverbia communia* of Joh. Aegidius Nuceriensis (1519) give "On voit plus de vieulx gourmands (hyurognes, Rab.) que de vieulx medecins".

[3] *Castings* (Fr. *cures* (*G.* 56 *fin.*)), a term in falconry, used with reference to Gargantua's remark. Cf. *R.E.R.* x. 367.

[4] *Tiring* (Fr. *tyrouer*), also = Drawer.

[5] *Breviary*, a flask made in the shape of a breviary. Cf. *G.* 5; iv. A.P., 20, 21; v. 46. With reference to this, *tiroir* has the meaning of small chains or book-marks to a book, and especially a service-book (*R.E.R.* x. 429).

[6] *tire* (Fr. *tirer*), a term in falconry, signifying to seize ravenously and prey upon. The meaning can be seen from the following lines:

"as an empty eagle, sharp by fast,
Tires with her beak on feathers, flesh and bone".

Shakesp. *Ven. and Adon.* 56.

Cf. 3 *Hen. VI*, i. 1. 269; *Cymb.* iii. 4. 97. Cf. also Bud. *in Pand.* i. p. 586: "rursusque ad praedam instituunt inediaque perdomitant, inditis in os stupeis turundis caruncula praeditis aut involutis, ingluviem eorum ludificantes: simul enim sic evocatis pituitis et excrementis volaciores reddi perhibent, simul famem irritari atque ita in obsequium redigi".

"After what Use",[1] said Gargantua, "do you say these fine 'Hours' of yours?"

"After the Use of Fécamp," said the Monk, "with three Psalms and three Lessons,[2] or Nothing at all for him that will none. I never subject myself to Hours; the Hours are made for Man, not Man for the Hours.[3] Wherefore I make mine in the fashion of Stirrup-leathers;[4] I shorten or lengthen them when it seemeth good to me.

> *Brevis oratio penetrat Caelos,*
> *Longa potatio evacuat Scyphos.*[5]

Where is that written?"

"By my Faith," said Ponocrates, "I know not, my Pillicock, but thou art worth Gold."

"In that", said the Monk, "I resemble you. But *venite apotemus*."[6]

Then they made ready Carbonadoes in abundance, and fine Brewis of Prime,[7] and the Monk drank as he would. Some kept him company, others let it alone.

After that, each one began to arm and equip himself. And they armed the Monk against his Will; for he wished for no other Arms than his Frock before his Stomach and the Staff of the Cross in his

---

[1] *Use*, *i.e.* the custom of a particular church. Cf. *the Sarum use*. The Benedictine Abbey of Fécamp in Normandy was proverbial for the laxity of its discipline (Le Duchat: de Marsy).

[2] Cf. Patelin, ll. 772–3:

> "Et cest avocat *portatif*   (cf. P. 7)
> A trois leçons et a trois pseaumes!"

The shortest service was of three lessons and three psalms, the longest of nine lessons and nine psalms. Cf. iii. 15.

[3] *the Hours*, etc. Adapted from St Mark ii. 27. Cf. also *G.* 52, iv. 64 and

> "Et mihi res non me rebus subjungere conor".
>
> Hor. *Epp.* i. 1. 19

[4] *Stirrup-leathers.* Cf. Coquillart, *Mon. Coq.* ii. 215: "Il ne me sert que d'estrivier".

[5] *Brevis oratio*, etc. Perhaps adapted from Ecclus. xxxv. 21: "Oratio humiliantis se nubes penetrabit". Quoted Erasm. *Colloq.* (*Epicureus, fin.*) and *Piers Plowman*, C. xii. 297 (= A. xi. 304). Joh. Aegid. gives in his *prov. comm.*:

> "Briefve oraison tantost monte au ciel
> Et longuement boire faict les verres vuyder".

[6] *venite apotemus*, a parody of the *invitatorium* of the Breviary in the Matins service of the festival of Circumcision.

[7] *Brewis of Prime.* Cf. *G.* 21.

Fist. However, to please them, he was armed from Head to Foot and mounted on a fine Neapolitan[1] Charger, with a huge Sabre by his Side. With him went Gargantua, Ponocrates, Gymnast, Eudemon, and five-and-twenty of the most adventurous of Grandgousier's House, all armed at proof, with Lances in their Hands, mounted like St George,[2] each having an Arquebusier behind him.

---

[1] *Neapolitan.* Fr. *du royaume* (*Epp. Rom.* iii. § 10; Shakesp. *Merch. of V.* i. 2. 39) from Ital. *cavallo di regno* [di Napoli]. These horses were highly prized. Cf. "in Salerno più che in niun' altra parte del *reame*" (Masuccio, *Nov.* 40) and "(equus) natus de prole *Reammi*", Merl. Coc. ix. l. 54 from end.

[2] Cf.   "Le dict vallet monté comme un Sainct Georges."

Cl. Marot, *Epist.* xxix. 38.

CHAPTER XLII

How the Monk encouraged his Companions, and how he hanged upon a Tree

So go forth the noble Champions on their Adventure, well resolved to know what Enterprise they should follow up, and what they would have to guard against, when the Day of the great and horrible Battle should come.[1]

And the Monk encouraged them, saying: "My Children, have neither Fear nor Doubt; I will conduct you safely. God and St Benêt be with us! If I had Strength to match my Courage, 'Sdeath! I would pluck them all for you like a Duck. I fear nothing but the Artillery.

"Yet I do know a Prayer taught me by the Sub-sacristan[2] of our Abbey, which guardeth a Man safe from all Mouths of Fire; but it will profit me nothing because I put no Faith in it. Nevertheless, my Staff of the Cross will play the Devil.

"Perdy! whosoever of you shall play the Duck,[3] I give myself to the Devil if I do not make a Monk of him in my Stead and huddle him into my Frock.[4] It bringeth a Cure to men's Cowardice.

---

[1] "Antequam veniat dies Domini magnus et horribilis", Joel ii. 31.

[2] One of the duties of the Sub-sacristan or *Matricularius* was to see to the trimming and extinguishing of the lights in the church (Clark's *Augustinian Customs*, p. 73). St Barbara was invoked to save persons from gunshot wounds and lightning, her father, who beheaded her, having been burnt up by lightning (*Legenda Aurea*, c. 202). "The pentagon of Apollo, the pentacle of Solomon, was looked upon as a sure defence from lightning and fire, now the sign of a German pothouse", King's *Gnostics*, p. 427 (2nd ed.).

[3] *play the Duck* (iii. 6), *i.e.* the coward, like ducks which dive to escape danger. Cf. Cretin, p. 137:

"Aller plonger dedans l'eaue comme canes".

Hudibras, i. 1. 513:

"To dive like wild-fowl for salvation".

[4] Perhaps this huddling into a frock is aimed at the Franciscans who put dying men into a Franciscan habit to guard them against demons. Cf. Erasm. *Colloq.* (*Exequiae Seraphicae*).

211

14-2

"Have you never heard speak of the Greyhound of my Lord of Meurles,[1] which was worth nothing in the Field? He put a Frock about his Neck, and, Copsbody,[2] neither Hare nor Fox ever escaped from him; and what is more, he lined all the Bitches in the Country, although before he had been broken-reined and *de frigidis et maleficiatis*".[3]

The Monk, as he said these Words in a Heat, passed under a Walnut-tree on the Way towards the Osier-bed, and spitted the Visor of his Helmet on the Stump of a great Branch of the Tree. This notwithstanding, he put Spurs fiercely to his Horse, which was skittish under the Spur, so that he bounded forwards; while the Monk, trying to unfasten his Visor from its Hook, let go the Bridle and with his Hand hung on to the Branches, while his Horse stole away from beneath him.

By this means the Monk remained hanging from the Walnut-tree, and crying "Help" and "Murder"; swearing also that there was Treason.

Eudemon first perceived him, and calling Gargantua said: "Sire, come and see Absalom hanging".

When Gargantua had come, he considered the Countenance of the Monk, and the Posture in which he was hanging, and said to Eudemon: "You have shot beside the Mark in comparing him to Absalom, for Absalom was hung up by his Hair; but the Monk being a Shaven-pate is hanging by his Ears".

"Help me," cried the Monk, "in the Devil's name. 'Tis a fine Time to be prating, is it not? You seem to me to be like the Decretalist Preachers,[4] who say that whosoever shall see his Neighbour

---

[1] N. de Montlaur, lord of *Meurles*, of an ancient family of Montpellier, existing still in the time of Le Duchat.

[2] Fr. *par le Corps Dieu!* "C'estoit son sermant ordinaire, ainsin que ces vieux et anciens grands capitaines ont sceu choisir et avoir aucuns particuliers à eux: comme Monsr de Bayard juroit: 'Teste Dieu, Bayard!'...le bon homme M. de la Roche du Maine juroit: 'Teste Dieu pleine de reliques!'" (cf. iv. 20), Brantôme, i. 2. 5 (*M. de la Trimouille*).

[3] *de frigidis*, etc. (iii. 14). Δ, iv. 15. 1. For the efficacy of a frock cf. *G*. 39; iii. 27.

[4] *Decretalist Preachers.* "Augustini sententiam salutarem esse puto qui scribit quemque nostrum potius debere studere qua ratione ab hac labe et noxa originali eximatur quam ut velit curiose inquirere quomodo in eam inciderit. Et narrat quemdam semel in puteum cecidisse, qui cum ejularet et conquere-

in danger of Death, is bound, under penalty of three-forked[1] Excommunication, rather to admonish him to make Confession and
to put him in a State of Grace than to help him. When then I shall
see them fallen into a River and ready to be drowned, instead of
going after them and giving them a Hand, I shall make them a fine
long Sermon *de contemptu Mundi et fuga Saeculi*,[2] and when they are
stark dead I will go and fish for them."

"Do not stir, my Bullyrook", said Gymnast; "I am coming to
help thee, for thou art a pretty little *Monachus*:

> *Monachus in claustro*
> *Non valet ova duo;*[3]
> *Sed quando est extra*[4]
> *Bene valet triginta.*

"I have seen above five hundred hanged Men, but I never saw
one who had better Grace in hanging; if I had as good a Grace I
would willingly hang thus all my Life."

"Shall you soon have done preaching?" said the Monk. "Help
me in God's name, since you will not in the name of the Other.[5]
By the Habit that I wear, you shall repent of it *tempore et loco
praelibatis*."[6]

---

retur supervenienti cuidam et sollicite inquerenti quomodo illuc esset prae-
cipitatus, respondit: 'Quomodo huc ceciderim quaerere desinas, illud vero
sedulo cures ut me hinc extrahas'", Melander, *Joco-seria*, i. 520 (D). The latter
part refers evidently to "The boy bathing" of the *Fabulae Aesopicae* (Babrius,
165), which is adapted by La Fontaine, i. 19. Cf. Erasm. *Apoph*. lib. vi (*varie
mixta*, 64).

[1] *three-forked*. Fr. *trisulce* (P. 32). "Cui dextra *trisulcis* Ignibus armata est",
Ovid, *Met*. ii. 848; "*trisulco* telo", Seneca, *Thyest*. 1089.

[2] *de contemptu Mundi*, etc. was a treatise of Pope Innocent III, alluded to by
Panurge in iv. 8, where he is given a preachment similar to this.

[3] *Non valet ova duo, i.e.* he is no good for "questing" or foraging purposes.

[4] *Sed quando est extra*. On this subject Ioh. Nevizanus says in his *Sylva Nuptialis*,
fo. 29. 3: "Nulli sunt deteriores religiosis qui claustra exiverunt". Monks are
forbidden to leave the cloister in 2 D. 16. 1. 8.

[5] *the Other* (G. 35), *i.e.* the Devil, in whose name he had asked for help before,
reversing Juno's "Flectere si nequeo superos Acheronta movebo", Virg. *Aen*.
vii. 312.

> "Allez-vous-en de par les dyables,
> Puisque par Dieu ne peult estre!"   Patelin, l. 652.

[6] *praelibatis*, an old forensic term = *praedictis*, aforesaid. In the *Cortegiano*, ii.
52, an ignorant Sienese takes the word as a proper name, *Prelibato*. *His praelibatis* occurs in Macrob. *S.S.* i. 3. 1.

Then Gymnast got off his Horse, and, climbing up into the Walnut-tree, lifted up the Monk by the Gussets with one Hand, and with the other undid his Visor from the Stump of the Tree, and so let him fall to the Ground and himself after him.

When the Monk had come down, he rid himself of all his Armour[1] and threw one Piece after another about the Field, and taking up again his Staff of the Cross he remounted his Horse, which Eudemon had stopped from running away.

So they went on merrily, keeping the Road to the Osier-bed.

---

[1] "And David put them off him. And he took his staff in his hand", 1 Sam. xvii. 39.

"Like little David in Saul's doublet."   *Hudibras*, i. 3. 1346.

CHAPTER XLIII

How the Scouts of Picrochole were met by Gargantua, and how the Monk slew Captain Rushforth, and then was made Prisoner by the Enemy

A T the Report of those who had escaped from the Rout, when Tripet was untriped, Picrochole was seized with great Wrath, hearing that the Devils had set upon his Men; and all that Night held a Council, at which Rashcalf[1] and Toucquedillon resolved that his Powers were such that he could defeat all the Devils in Hell, if they should come. This Picrochole did not fully believe; also he did not distrust it.

Wherefore he sent, under the conduct of Count Rushforth, to reconnoitre the Country, sixteen hundred Knights, all mounted on light Horses in skirmishing Order, all well sprinkled with Holy Water, and every one having for his Cognisance a Stole as a Scarf, against all Hazards, if they should meet the Devils; so that by the Virtue of this Gregorian[2] Water, as well as of the Stoles, they should make the Devils disappear and vanish.

They went on then to near Vauguyon[3] and the Hospital, but never found any one to whom to speak; whereupon they returned by the upper Road, and in the Abode and Hut[4] of a Shepherd near le Coudray they found the five Pilgrims. Having bound and blindfolded them, as though they were Spies, they carried them off, notwithstanding the Exclamations, Adjurations and Requests that they made.

---

[1] *Rashcalf.* Fr. *Hastiveau.* This in French is an early ripe pear, which was much esteemed. (Lacroix, quoted by Skeat; Chaucer, *C.T.* A. 3248, *The Miller's Tale.*)

[2] It was Pope Gregory who brought holy water into credit. The sanctification of water with salt in it, is maintained D. iii. 20 (*de consecr.*) with references to Heb. iii. 13 and 4 Reg. ii. 20.

[3] *la Vauguyon* (*G.* 34). The Hospital (Fr. *la Maladerie*), now St Lazare, is at the south extremity of the Nun's bridge (*R.E.R.* vii. 380).

[4] *Hut.* Fr. *tugure,* from Virg. *Ecl.* i. 69: "Pauperis et tuguri congestum caespite culmen".

When they had come down from there towards Seuillé they were heard by Gargantua, who said to his People:

"Comrades, there is here an Encounter for us, and they are in number more than ten times as many as we are. Shall we charge them?"

"What a Devil else shall we do?" said the Monk. "Do you value Men by their Number[1] and not by their Valour and Courage?" Then he cried out: "Charge! Devils, charge!"

Hearing this, the Enemy thought indeed that they had been very Devils, whereupon they began to fly headlong, except Rushforth, who laid his Lance in rest and struck the Monk with his utmost Force in the middle of the Chest; but encountering the horrific Frock it bent back[2] in the Steel-point, just as though you should strike against an Anvil with a small Wax-candle.

Then the Monk with his Staff of the Cross gave him so sturdy a Blow between the Neck and Shoulders on the acromion Bone[3] that he stunned[4] him and made him lose all Sense and Motion; and he fell at the Feet of his Horse.

And seeing the Stole which he wore as his Scarf he said to Gargantua: "These Men here are but Priests; that is only the Beginning of a Monk. By Saint John, I am a complete Monk; I will kill them for you like Flies".

Then he followed after them at full Gallop, so that he caught up the hindermost and beat them down like Rye, striking right and left at random.

---

[1] *by their Number.* Cf. Erasm. *Ad.* ii. 4. 99: *Non curat numerum lupus,* from Virg. *Ecl.* vii. 52.

[2] Fr. *reboucha.* Cf. Cordier, 24. § 4: "rebouche ce clou avec le marteau"; "le dard rebourcea", *A.P.F.* vi. 284. Cf. also Ovid, *Met.* xii. 480:

"Non secus haec resilit quam tecti a culmine grando
Aut si quis parvo feriat cava tympana saxo";

and 490: "Tela *retusa* cadunt".

ἀνεγνάμφθη δέ οἱ αἰχμή.   Hom. *Il.* iii. 348.

[3] *acromion* (ἄκρος ὦμος) *Bone.* The acromion *process* (*apophyse*) must be meant, which joins the shoulder-blade to the collar-bone. Cf. *omoplate,* iv. 31; Hippoc. *de Artic.* § 13; Paré, xiii. 9 (cf. Le Double, p. 309); Scott, *Guy Mannering,* c. 41.

[4] Fr. *estonna* (iv. 62). So Shakespeare uses *astonish* in the sense of *stun* (*Hen. V,* v. 1. 40).

Gymnast immediately asked Gargantua whether they should pursue them.

To which Gargantua answered: "On no account; for according to true military Discipline, you must never drive your Enemy into the pass of Despair, because such a Necessity doth multiply his Strength and increases his Courage, which was already cast down and broken, and there is no better Help to Safety for men who are dismayed[1] and recreant[2] than to hope for no Safety whatever.[3] How many Victories have been wrested from the Hands of the Victors by the Vanquished, when they have not been satisfied with Reason, but have attempted to put all to utter Slaughter and totally to destroy their Enemies, without leaving a single one to bear the News! Always open to your Enemies all the Gates and Roads, and rather make for them a Bridge of Silver[4] in order to send them away".

"Yea, but", said Gymnast, "they have the Monk."

"Have they the Monk?" said Gargantua. "Then upon my Honour it will be to their Hurt. But, to provide against all Chances, let us not retreat yet; let us wait here in Silence, for I think that by this time I understand well enough the Tactics of our Enemies. They are guided by Luck[5] and not by Counsel."

---

[1] Fr. *estommis* (*G.* 2, st. 2) = O.F. *estormis*. "Fu li poples toz *estormis*", R. de Rou. iii. 9972. LL. *stormus*, Germ. *Sturm* (Ducange and Diez).

[2] Fr. *recreus*. "Recrediti vel recreanti appellati qui in duello victos se profitebantur" (Ducange).

[3]   "Una salus victis nullam sperare salutem." Virg. *Aen.* ii. 354. "Plerumque enim desperatione robur augetur" (Servius, *ad loc.*); "Nullus perniciosior hostis est quam quem audacem angustiae faciunt, longeque violentius semper ex necessitate quam ex virtute corruitur", Seneca, *N.Q.* ii. 59. §5.

"Have time to rally and prepare
Our best and last defence, despair;
Despair, by which the galant'st feats
Have been achieved in greatest straits." *Hudibras*, iii. 2. 585.

[4] *Bridge of Silver.* It is recorded by Erasmus, *Apoph.* lib. viii (*Alphonso*, 14), that this saying was the admiration of Alphonso, but that he did not know the author. It is Aristides in Plutarch's *Themistocles*, c. 16, who advises that not only should the bridge of boats, which allowed the escape of the Persians, *not* be broken up, but rather another bridge be built to facilitate their escape. Paré has (vol. iii. p. 707a) "ains au contraire dist qu'on devoit leur faire des ponts d'or et d'argent pour les laisser passer".

[5] *guided by Luck.* "Qui secundos optat eventus dimicat arte non casu", Joh. Salisb. *Polic.* vi. 19.

As they were thus waiting under the Walnut-trees, the Monk in the meantime went on in Pursuit, charging all those whom he met, without giving Quarter to any, until he met with a Horseman who was carrying behind him one of the poor Pilgrims. And there, as he was about to rifle him, the Pilgrim cried out:

"Ha, my Lord Prior, my good Friend, my Lord Prior, save me, I beseech you".

On hearing these Words, the Enemy faced about, and seeing that there was nobody there but the Monk who was making this Havock, loaded him with Blows as men do an Ass with Wood;[1] but of all this he felt nothing, especially when they struck him on his Frock, so hard was his Skin.

Then they handed him over to two Archers to guard, and turning round they saw no one against them, whereby they thought that Gargantua had fled with his Troop. Then they rode towards the Walnut-trees as hard as they could, to find them, and left the Monk there alone with two Archers in guard.

Gargantua heard the Noise and the Neighing of the Horses, and said to his Men:

"Comrades, I hear the Rumble[2] of our Enemies and I perceive some of them who are coming against us in a Crowd. Let us close up here and hold the Road in good order. By this means we shall be able to withstand them to their Loss and our Honour".

---

[1] loaded...an Ass with Wood, i.e. all over, so that nothing can be seen of him.

$$ἤδε δ' ὥστ' ὄνου ῥάχις$$
$$ἔστηκεν ὕλης ἀγρίας ἐπιστεφής,$$

says Archilochus of the island of Thasos, quoted by Plut. de Exil. c. 12. 604c.

[2] I hear the Rumble. Cf. Virg. Aen. ix. 394:

"Audit equos audit strepitus et signa sequentum".

CHAPTER XLIV

*How the Monk rid himself of his Guards, and how Picrochole's
Scouts were defeated*

THE Monk, seeing them go off thus in Disarray, conjectured that
they were going to attack Gargantua and his Men, and he grew
wondrous sad that he could not succour them. Then he did consider the Countenance of his two Archers in guard over him, who
would willingly have ridden after the Troop to plunder something
there, and who were all the time looking towards the Valley in
which the others were going down.

Furthermore he reasoned saying: "These Men here are right
badly skilled in Practice of War, for they have not required my
Parole, and have not taken my Sword from me".

Immediately afterwards he drew his said Sword, and with it
smote the Archer who held him on the Right, cutting clean through
his jugular Veins and the sphagitid Arteries[1] of his Neck, together
with the Uvula[2] as far as the two Glands,[3] and withdrawing his
Weapon, laid open the Spinal Marrow between the second and
third Vertebrae. Upon this the Archer fell quite dead.

And the Monk, turning his Horse to the Left, ran upon the other,
who seeing his Companion dead, and the Monk at an advantage
over him, cried with a loud Voice: "Ha, my Lord Prior,[4] I yield
myself; my Lord Prior, my good Friend, my Lord Prior".

---

[1] *The sphagitid Arteries* are the main arteries of the neck (now *carotid*), as the
jugular are the principal veins. αἱ δὲ δεύτεραι φλέβες ἐκ τῆς κεφαλῆς παρὰ
τὰ ὦτα διὰ τοῦ αὐχένος σφαγιτίδες καλεόμεναι, Hippoc. *de Oss. nat.* § 9. Cf. also
Galen, *de usu part.* xvi. 14. An erroneous notion of Galen's giving the origin of
the two carotids from a single stem is pointed out by Vesalius (J. F. Payne,
Harv. Orat. (1906)).

[2] *Uvula.* Fr. *gargareon.* Cf. Paré, iv. 14: *De l'uvule, ou luette, ou gargareon.*

[3] *two Glands* (Fr. *adenes*, Gk. ἀδένες) are the glands of the neck generally; but
here the *amygdali*, or tonsils, are intended. Cf. iv. 30; τὰ παρίσθμια, Galen,
de usu part. xi. 5.

[4] The title "My Lord Prior" gives some support to the identification of
Brother John with Buinard, Prior of Sermaise near Chinon. Cf. c. 27.

And the Monk cried out likewise: "My Lord Posterior,[1] my Friend, my Lord Posterior, you shall have it on your Posterior".

"Ha!" said the Archer, "my Lord Prior, my dear Lord Prior, may God make you an Abbot."

"By the Habit that I wear", said the Monk, "I will make you a Cardinal on the spot. Do you put Churchmen to Ransom? You shall have a red Hat from my Hand this instant."

And the Archer cried out: "My Lord Prior, my Lord Prior, my Lord Abbot that is to be, my Lord Cardinal, my Lord Everything. Ha, ha, hês, no, my Lord Prior, my good little Lord Prior, I yield myself to you".

"And I yield thee to all the Devils",[2] said the Monk.

Then at one Blow he sliced his Head, cutting his Scalp over the *ossa petrosa*[3] and taking off the two *ossa bregmatis*[4] and the *sagittal Commissure*[5] with a great Part of the *coronal*[6] Bone, and in doing this he cut through the two *Meninges*,[7] and made a deep Gash in the two posterior Ventricles of the Brain; so the *cranium* remained hanging on his Shoulders by the Skin of the *pericranium*[8] behind, in the Form

---

[1] *Lord Posterior.* Cf. Erasm. *Coll.* (*Pereg. Rel. ergo*): "*ME. ὕστερον πρότερον* novi in tropis. *OG.* Tenes. Hic qui priori proximus est Prior est posterior. *ME.* Subpriorem dicis".

[2] Some Genoese ambassadors having addressed Louis XI thus: "Sire, nous nous donnons à vous", the King replied: "Et moi je vous donne à tous les diables". Cf. also Cretin, p. 202:

"Ou je vous donne et livre à tous les diables".

[3] *ossa petrosa* (τὰ λιθοειδῆ τῶν ὀστῶν, Galen, *de usu part.* ix. 10), the lower part of the temporal bone of the skull, in which the internal organs of hearing are situated.

[4] *ossa bregmatis* (βρεχμός, Hom. *Il.* v. 587, from βρέχω, because they are the last to harden) are the bones containing the Fontanel or cavity at the top of the head (Hippoc. *Coac. praen.* § 168; Galen, *de usu part.* xi. 20). They are now called the *parietal* bones.

[5] The *sagittal Commissure* is the *parietal* suture which goes lengthwise over the skull uniting the *parietal* bones.

[6] The *coronal* is the anterior bone of the skull, in modern anatomy the *frontal* bone.

[7] The two *Meninges* (αἱ διτταὶ μήνιγγες, Galen, *de usu part.* viii. 3), called *les membranes* in iv. 30, are the membranes that envelop the brain, the *pia mater*, the *dura mater*, and the *arachnoid membrane*, which last is a discovery of more modern anatomy. Cf. Le Double, pp. 274 and 307.

[8] "The membrane called the *pericranium*, which connects the dura mater with the skull", Galen, *de usu part.* viii. 9.

of a Doctor's Bonnet, black without and red within. So he fell to
the Ground stark dead.

This done, the Monk set Spurs to his Horse, and followed on the
Way held by the Enemy, who had encountered Gargantua and his
Companions on the high Road, and were so diminished in Number
by the enormous Slaughter wrought upon them by Gargantua with
his great Tree, by Gymnast, Ponocrates, Eudemon and the others,
that they began to retreat in all Haste, altogether affrighted and
troubled in Sense and Understanding, as if they had seen Death's
proper Form and Semblance before their Eyes.

And—as when you see an Ass[1] with a Junonian *oestrus* under his
Tail, or a Fly that stings him, running hither and thither without
keeping to Path or Road, throwing his Load on to the Ground and
breaking his Bridle and Reins, without at all taking Breath or
Rest, and no man can tell what stirs him, for they see not aught that
touches him—so fled these Folk bereft of their Senses, without
knowing the Cause of their Flight; so much are they pursued by
nothing but a Panic Terror[2] which they had conceived in their
Souls.

The Monk, seeing that they had no Thought of anything save to
take to their Heels, gets off his Horse and clambers on to a huge
Rock which was over the Road, and with his mighty Sabre struck
on to these Runaways with a great Turn of Strength, without

---

[1] This is a ludicrous piece of mock-heroic describing an ass driven wild by
a gad-fly, with a reminiscence of Io persecuted by Juno (*Oestro percitus*, Erasm.
Ad. ii. 8. 54). The word *oestrus* seems derived from Servius, *in Georg.* iii. 148:
"*oestrus* autem Graecus est, latine *asilus*, vulgo *tabanus* vocatur". Cf. Fr. *tahons*
in iv. 58. Butler is perhaps inspired by this in *Hudibras*, i. 2. 839–55. Cf. also
Ovid, *Met.* xi. 334:

> "Concita membra fugae mandat similisque juvenco
> Spicula crabronum pressa cervice gerenti
> *Qua via nulla ruit*".

[2] *Panic Terror* (*Panicus casus*, Erasm. *Ad.* iii. 7. 3). In the earlier Greek writers
sudden and causeless terrors are spoken of, but not attributed to Pan. Cf. however, Herod. vi. 105. Pausanias (x. 23. 7) attributes them to Pan. Plutarch, *Is.
et Osir.* c. 14. 356 D, says that when the Panes and Satyrs near Chemmis in
Egypt discovered and published the treacherous death of Osiris, the sudden
confusion and alarms that arose among the multitude got the name of "panics".
Cicero speaks of them three times in his letters. Politian, *Misc.* No. 28. Cf. also
2 Kings vii. 6–7; Montaigne, i. 17 *fin.*

stinting or sparing any. So many of them did he slay and over-throw, that his Sword broke in two Pieces. Then he bethought himself that enough Massacre and Slaughter had been wrought, and that the Rest should escape to bear the News.

Therefore he seized in his Fist the Battle-axe of one of those who lay dead there, and got upon the Rock again, passing his Time in seeing the Enemy flying and stumbling over the dead Bodies; except that he made all lay down their Pikes, Swords, Lances and Arquebuses; and those who carried the Pilgrims bound he made dismount, and gave over their Horses to the said Pilgrims, keeping them with him under the Shelter of the Hedge; and also Toucque-dillon, whom he kept as his Prisoner.

CHAPTER XLV

How the Monk brought in the Pilgrims, and the good Words which Gargantua gave them

THIS Skirmish over, Gargantua retreated with his Men, except the Monk, and at Daybreak they came to Grandgousier, who in his Bed was praying to God for their Safety and Victory. And, seeing them all safe and sound, he embraced them lovingly and asked for Tidings of the Monk. But Gargantua answered him that without doubt their Enemies had the Monk.

"Then", said Grandgousier, "they will have Ill-luck"; which had indeed been true. Whence the Proverb is still in Use, "to give a man the Monk".

Then he commanded a good Breakfast to be provided for their Refreshment. When all was ready, they summoned Gargantua, but he was so much concerned that the Monk was nowhere to be found, that he would neither drink nor eat.

All of a sudden the Monk arrives,[1] and from the Gate of the Outer Court he bawls out: "Fresh Wine, fresh Wine, Gymnast, my Friend".

Gymnast went out and saw that it was Friar John, who was bringing in five Pilgrims[2] and Toucquedillon Prisoner. Whereupon Gargantua went out to meet him, and they made him the best Welcome they could, and brought him before Grandgousier, who questioned him about all his Adventure.

The Monk told him everything; how he had been taken, how he had rid himself of the Archers, of the Butchery he had wrought on the Road, and how he had recovered the Pilgrims and brought

---

[1] Scott is indebted to this passage for the idea of the Clerk of Copmanhurst bringing Isaac of York out of the dungeon of Torquilstone in *Ivanhoe* (c. 32). The notion is perhaps derived from Ovid (*Met.* xi. 90–99): "At Silenus abest, etc." Silenus had been carousing with King Midas, who brought him back after ten days. Friar John behaves in a similar manner in iv. 10.

[2] *five Pilgrims*. One of the six had been carried off by the enemy at the end of c. 43.

in Captain Toucquedillon. Then they fell to banqueting merrily all together.

Meantime Grandgousier enquired of the Pilgrims from what Country they were, whence they came and whither they were going.

Wearyfoot answered for them all: "My Lord, I am from St Genou in Berry, this one is from Palluau, this one from Onzay, this one from Argy and this one from Villebrenin.[1] We come from Saint Sebastian near Nantes,[2] and we are returning from there by our short Stages".

"Yea," said Grandgousier, "but what went you to do at Saint Sebastian?"

"We went", said Wearyfoot, "to offer up our Vows to him against the Plague."

"Oh, poor Creatures," said Grandgousier, "do you think that the Plague comes from Saint Sebastian?"

"Yea, verily", replied Wearyfoot; "our Preachers do affirm it unto us."

"Is it so?" said Grandgousier. "False Prophets! do they proclaim to you such Deceits? Do they in this fashion blaspheme the Just and Holy men of God, that they make them like unto Devils, who work nought but Mischief among men? just as Homer writeth that the Plague was sent into the Grecian Host by Apollo, and as the Poets feign a great Rabble of Vejoves and maleficent Deities.[3]

"Just so at Sinays did a certain Hypocrite[4] preach that Saint

---

[1] *St Genou*, etc. These places are all in Berry; *St Genou* 6 miles north-west of Buzançais on the Indre, *Palluau* a marquisate 3 miles farther on, *Onzay* between Amboise and Blois, *Argy* about 4 miles from Buzançais, and *Villebrenin* not far from Châteauroux.

[2] St Sebastian's body was supposed to be at Piligny near Nantes (cf. c. 37). He is the patron saint of the *Misericordia*.

[3] Rabelais is referring to the 1st book of the *Iliad*, where Apollo sends the plague on the Greeks (48–52), and to a passage in Gellius (v. 12), who discusses the derivation of *Jovis* from *juvo*, and indicates a number of *Vejoves* who were maleficent, pointing out that Apollo as bearing arrows is looked upon as one of them (§§ 11, 12). The *Vejoves* (cf. v. 6) are spoken of in Ovid (*Fast.* iii. 445) as minor Jupiters. Macrobius (*Sat.* vi. 8, 18) makes the *ve* to be either intensive or the reverse. Cf. *Vedjovis* in Warde Fowler's *Roman festivals*, p. 121.

[4] Fr. *caphart*. This word gets its form from the monkish frock (*cappa*), but it bears much the same meaning as *quêteur*, a mumping friar who by means of false relics, etc. swindled the common people. Cf. *G.* 54; iii. 6; Erasm. *Ad.* iv. 8. 55.

Antony sent Fire into men's Legs, Saint Eutropius made men Dropsical, Saint Gildas Lunatics, Saint Genou made them Gouty.[1] But I punished him in so exemplary a Fashion—although he called me a Heretic—that since that time no such Hypocrite whatever has dared to set Foot in my Territory. And I wonder that your King allows them to preach such scandalous Doctrine throughout his Kingdom. For they are more deserving of Punishment than those, who by Art magical[2] or other Device have brought the Plague into the Country. The Plague killeth only the Body, but Impostors* like this poison the Souls."

As he was saying these Words the Monk came in quite hearty, and asked them: "Whence come you, you poor Wretches?"

"From Saint Genou", said they.

"And how", said the Monk, "doth the Abbot Tranchelion,[3] the good Toper? and the Monks, what Cheer do they keep? 'Sbody, they have a Fling at your Wives while you are thus roaming Romewards."

"Hin hen!" said Wearyfoot, "I have no Fear for mine; for whoso shall see her by Day shall never break his Neck on a Visit to her in the Night."

"You have drawn the wrong Colour again",[4] said the Monk. "She may be as ugly as Proserpine, but I swear she will be turned

---

* AB, *mais ces predications diaboliques infectionnent les âmes des pauvres et simples gens.*

[1] *St Antony's fire* is erysipelas. *St Eutropius facit hydropicos. St Gildas,* from Gilles, the common name for a half-witted fellow. *St Genou,* the patron saint of the gouty, in allusion to the knee. Corn. Agrippa (*de van. scient.* c. 57) and H. Estienne (*Apol. pour Hérod.* c. 58) inveigh against this ascription of names and powers to the various saints, from the diseases which they are supposed to heal or inflict. Cf. iv. 50. Hippocrates (*de morbo sacro,* c. 1, epilepsy) similarly protests against the gods being made responsible for diseases (i. 592). Cf. *Progn.* c. 1.

[2] *by Art magical.* Certain persons called *boute-pestes* were found guilty at Geneva in 1530 of endeavouring to propagate the plague by anointing the locks of houses, etc. with some sort of maleficent grease (*R.E.R.* ix. 453).

[3] Antoine de la Garde de Tranchelion, Abbot of St Genou in 1512, vicar-general of the Cardinal of Prié (Lacroix). He was a member of the family of Tranchelion, who were seigneurs of Palluau-sur-Indre (*R.E.R.* vii. 327).

[4] Fr. *bien rentre de picques.* A metaphor from cards, when a player has exchanged his own hand for "miss", much for the worse. So in iii. 34 we find *b. r. de treufles noires,* iv. 33 and 52 *de picques noires.* Good luck is expressed by *rentré de cœurs:* Noel du Fail, *Propos Rustiques,* c. 14.

over, since there be Monks around, for a good Workman puts all Pieces of Timber to use equally.[1] May I be peppered, if you do not find them enlarged on your Return, for the very Shadow of an Abbey-steeple is prolific."[2]

"It is", said Gargantua, "like the Water of the Nile in Egypt,[3] if you believe Strabo and Pliny, *lib. vij., chap. iij.*; Think only what Virtue is in Loaves, in Clothes, and in Bodies!"[4]

Then said Grandgousier: "Go your ways, poor Men, in the name of God the Creator; and may He be as a Guide to you perpetually; and henceforward be not so ready to undertake these idle and unprofitable Journeys. Maintain your Families, labour each one in his Vocation, instruct your Children and live as the good Apostle Saint Paul directeth you. If you do this, you will have the Protection of God, of the Angels and of the Saints ever with you, and there shall be neither Plague nor Evil that shall bring you Hurt".

After this Gargantua led them into the Hall, to take their Refection; but the Pilgrims did nothing but sigh, and they said to Gargantua:

"O how happy is the Land that hath such a Man for its Lord! We are more edified and instructed by this Discourse which he hath held with us, than by all the Sermons that ever were preached to us in our Town".

"That is", said Gargantua, "what Plato saith, *lib. v. de Republ.* that States would then be happy, when their Kings should philosophise, or Philosophers rule."[5]

---

[1] "A good wit will make use of anything", Shakesp. 2 *Hen. IV*, i. 2. 227; Arist. *de part. an.* iv. 10. 687 b; "Good workmen never quarrel with their tools", Byron, *Don Juan*, i. 201.

[2] "*TH.* Ego sic affectus sum ut ubicunque videro illam sacrosanctissimam vestem putem adesse angelos Dei: eamque domum esse felicem cujus limen crebro teritur illorum pedibus. *PH.* Et ego arbitror pauciores esse steriles feminas ubi illi agunt familiariter", Erasm. *Colloq.* (*Exseq. Seraph.*). A similar polemic against these pilgrimages may be found in Erasm. *Colloq.* (*Peregrinatio religionis ergo*).

[3] "In Aegypto, ubi fetifer potu Nilus amnis", Pliny, 7. 33, quoted Bud. *in Pand.* i. p. 394. Cf. also Aelian, *Nat. An.* iii. 34; Athen. ii. 41 F.

[4] "Amores inducuntur quibusdam rebus manibus vel vestibus inunctis", Agrippa, *de occulta philos.* i. 45. The texts read *Pline avise*, etc., which yields no sense. It seems necessary to make the sentence begin with *Avise* as an imperative.

[5] Plato's "ubi reges philosophantur aut philosophi regnant" has become a

Then he caused their Wallets to be filled with Victuals, their Bottles with Wine, and to each of them he gave a Horse to ease him for the rest of his Journey, and some Caroluses[1] to live upon.

---

commonplace. Cf. Plut. *Numa*, c. 20. 73 D; Val. Max. vii. 2. E. 4; Capitol. *vit. M. Antonini*, c. 27. § 7; Erasm. *Mor. Enc.* c. 24; More's *Utopia*, d. ii fo.; Bacon, *Adv. Learning*, i. 7. § 3. Appian, *Hist. Rom.* (*de bello Mithr.* c. 27), does not share Plato's opinion.

[1] *Carolus* (*Albi cum K coronato*) (iii. 17; iv. 50), a silver piece coined under Charles VIII, bearing a K crowned, worth 10 deniers of Tours (Ducange). Le Double (p. 204) makes them worth only 4 deniers of Tours. Cf. Montaigne, *Voyages*, p. 559 (*Thiers*).

CHAPTER XLVI

How Grandgousier humanely entreated Toucquedillon his Prisoner

TOUCQUEDILLON was presented to Grandgousier and questioned by him on the Enterprise and Conduct of Picrochole, as to what Object he proposed by this tumultuary Hubbub. To this he answered that his End and Purpose was to conquer the whole Country, if he could, in return for the Injury done to his Cakebakers.

Grandgousier said: "It is undertaking too much; He that grips too much holds fast but little. It is no longer the Time thus to conquer Kingdoms, to the Hurt of our near Christian Brother. This Imitation of the ancient Herculeses, Alexanders, Hannibals, Scipios, Caesars, and other such, is contrary to the Profession of the Gospel, by which we are enjoined to guard, save, rule and administer, each one his own Country and Territory, and not in hostile guise to invade others; and that which the Saracens and Barbarians formerly called Prowess, we now call Robbery and Wickedness.[1] He had done better to keep himself in his own Domain, governing it like a King, than to bluster in mine, pillaging it like an Enemy; for by a wise Government he would have augmented it; by plundering me he will be destroyed.

"Go your ways in the Name of God; follow after right Undertaking; point out to your King the Errors that you shall discover, and never give him Counsel with a View to your own particular Profit;[2] for together with the Public good, Private advantage is also lost. As for your Ransom I give it up to you in full, and desire that your Arms and Horse be restored to you.

---

[1] "Ex historiographis multi...probant haudquaquam probanda, plerique pessima exempla imitanda proponunt. Nam qui Herculem....Alexandrum, Hannibalem, Scipionem, Caesarem miris laudibus depingunt, quid nisi magnos et furiosos latrones descripserunt?" Agrippa, *de van. scient.* c. 5.

[2] *particular Profit.* "illa quae bonum publicum semper evertunt studia privata", Sid. Apoll. iv. 25. 1.

"Such should be the Conduct between Neighbours and ancient Friends, seeing that our Difference is not properly War; as Plato *lib. v. de Rep.* would not have it called War, but Sedition,[1] when the Greeks took up Arms one against another; and if by evil Fortune such should arise, he directs that every Moderation should be used. If you still call it War, it is yet but skin-deep, it entereth not into the deep Recesses of our Hearts; for neither of us is wronged in his Honour, and in its whole Amount it is only a Question of redressing some Fault committed by our People, I mean both yours and ours; and although you did take Cognisance of it, you should have let it pass; for the disputing Parties were such as to merit Contempt rather than Notice;[2] especially seeing that I offered them Satisfaction according to the Wrong.

"God will be the just Assessor of our Differences; and Him I beseech rather by Death to remove me from this Life, and to suffer my Goods to perish before my Eyes, than that in anything He should be offended by me or mine".

When he had finished these Words, he summoned the Monk, and before all of them asked him: "Friar John, my good Friend, is it you who took Prisoner the Captain Toucquedillon here present?"

"Sire," said the Monk, "he is present; he is of Age and Discretion; I would rather you should know by his Confession than by my Words."[3]

Then said Toucquedillon: "My Lord, it is he indeed who took me, and I freely yield myself his Prisoner".

"Have you put him to Ransom?" said Grandgousier to the Monk.

"No", said the Monk; "for that I care nothing."

"How much", said Grandgousier, "would you take for his Capture?"

---

[1] *not...War, but Sedition.* This maxim of Plato (*Rep.* v. 470 B) is insisted on in Erasm. *Instit. Principis Christiani* (*de bello suscipiendo*): "Plato seditionem vocat, non bellum, quoties Graeci cum Graecis belligerantur, idque si quando incidisset, modestissime jubet geri".

[2] *such as to merit Contempt,* etc. "Nam si hujusmodi homunculum nomines... majore honore quam contumelia afficias", Q. Metellus Numidicus apud Gell. vii. 11. 3.

[3] For a boastful claim of capture cf. Shakesp. 2 *Hen. IV*, iv. 3. 37–70, where Falstaff makes much of his prowess in taking Sir John Colville.

"Nothing, nothing", said the Monk; "that doth not sway me."

Then Grandgousier commanded that in the presence of Toucquedillon should be counted out to the Monk sixty-two thousand Salutation-pieces[1] for this Prize; which was done whilst they made a Collation for the said Toucquedillon; of whom Grandgousier asked whether he would stay with him or choose rather to return to his King.

Toucquedillon replied that he would take whichever Course he should advise him.

"Then", said Grandgousier, "return to your King, and God be with you."

Then he gave him a fine Sword of Vienne[2] with a golden Scabbard made with beautiful Scrolls of Goldsmith's work, and a golden Collar weighing seven hundred and two thousand Marks,[3] garnished with precious Stones, to the value of a hundred and sixty thousand Ducats,[4] and ten thousand Crowns[5] besides, as an honourable Present.

After these Proceedings Toucquedillon mounted his Horse, and for a Safe-conduct Gargantua gave him thirty Men-at-arms and six score Archers under the command of Gymnast, to escort him as far as the Gates of La Roche-Clermaud, if need were.

When he had set out, the Monk restored to Grandgousier the sixty-two thousand Angels that he had received, saying: "Sire, it is not at this Time that you should make such Presents. Wait till the End of this War, for none can tell what Accidents may arise,

---

[1] *Salutation-pieces*, Fr. *salutz* (iv. prol., 54; *Epp. Rom.* iii. § 10), were gold pieces dating from Charles VI of France (Feb. 6, 1422), minted in great numbers in the reigns of Henry V and Henry VI of England. On the obverse the arms of England and France, and the Virgin and Angel Gabriel each behind a shield, and on a scroll the word AVE between their hands. The superscription was *Henricus Dei gratia Francorum et Angliae rex*. On the reverse a flat cross between a lily and a leopard. Value 25 solidi (Ducange).

[2] *Vienne* in Dauphiné was long celebrated for its sword cutlery.

[3] The weight of the mark was about 250 gr. (Fr. ed.)

[4] *Ducat* (*P.P.* 6; *P.* 21; iv. 53), a Venetian coin in considerable currency throughout Europe, worth intrinsically 11 f. 85 c. The name is derived from the legend on it: "Sit tibi, Christe, datus quem tu regis ipse *Ducatus*", or from the *Ducatus Appuliae*; they were first coined by Roger King of Sicily, A.D. 1240 (Cartier).

[5] Fr. *escus d'or* were worth a little less than the *salutz* (10s.).

and War made without good Provision of Money hath only a quick Burst of[1] Strength. Money is the Sinews of War".[2]

"Well then," said Grandgousier, "at the End I will content you by some honourable Recompense, and also all those who shall have done me good Service."

---

[1] Fr. *souspirail*. ὀλίγη δέ τ᾽ ἀνάπνευσις πολέμοιο, *Il*. xi. 801 and xvi. 43, quoted by Erasm. *Ad*. iii. 1. 31.

[2] "*Nervos belli* pecuniam infinitam", Cic. *Phil*. v. § 5; "Pecuniae belli civilis nervi sunt", Tac. *Hist*. ii. 24; Erasm. *Apoph*. vii (*Bion*. 8). Machiavelli disputes this, *Discorsi*, ii. 10. The sinews of war, as a learned author calls the *caisse militaire* (Scott, *Waverley*, c. 42).

CHAPTER XLVII

How Grandgousier sent for his Legions, and how Toucquedillon
slew Rashcalf and was afterwards slain by Order of Picrochole

IN those same Days the Men of Bessé, Old Market, St James
Burgh, le Trainneau, Parillé, Rivière, Roches Saint Paul, Vau-
breton, Pautillé, le Brehemont, Clainbridge, Cravant, Grandmont,
les Bourdes, la Villaumère, Huymes, Segré, Hussé, Sainct-Louant,
Panzoust, les Coldreaux, Verron, Coulaines, Chosé, Varennes,
Bourgueil, Isle Bouchard, le Croullay, Narsay, Candé, Montsoreau[1]
and other neighbouring Places, sent Embassies unto Grandgousier,
to tell him that they were advised of the Wrongs which Picrochole
was doing him, and for the sake of their ancient Confederation
they offered him all their Power, in Men as well as Money, and
other Munitions of War.

The Money from all these, raised by the Conventions which
they sent to him, amounted to six score and fourteen millions
and two and a half Crowns of Gold. The Forces were fifteen
thousand Men-at-arms, thirty-two thousand light Horse, eighty-
nine thousand Arquebusiers, a hundred and forty thousand
Volunteers, eleven thousand two hundred Cannons, double
Cannons, Basilisks and Spiroles.[2] There were forty-seven thousand
Pioneers; the whole Force being victualled and paid for six Months
and four Days.

This Offer Gargantua did not refuse,[3] nor accept altogether;
but thanking them heartily, he said that he would arrange this

---

[1] Of the thirty-one places mentioned here, nine, viz. Varennes, Montsoreau,
Candes, Chousé-sur-Loire, Bourgueil, Brehemond, Huismes, la Villaumaire,
Ussé, are on or near the Loire, the others are all on or near the Vienne. These
riparian towns and villages had formed themselves into a confederation under
the direction of Antoine Rabelais, father of the author of *Pantagruel*, the senior
avocat of the district and lord of Chavigny-en-Vallée and of la Devinière, to
contest the encroachments of Gaucher de Sainte-Marthe. Cf. *G.* 26.

[2] For the various pieces of artillery see *G.* 26.

[3] *Gargantua did not refuse.* This should be *Grandgousier*.

War by such Policy that there should be no need to call out[1] so many honest Folk.

He was content to despatch an Officer to bring along in order the Legions[2] which he maintained ordinarily in his Places of la Devinière,[3] Chaviny, Gravot and Quinquenais, amounting in Number to two thousand five hundred Men-at-arms, sixty-six thousand Foot-soldiers, twenty-six thousand Arquebusiers, two hundred great Pieces of Artillery, twenty-two thousand Pioneers and six thousand light Horse, all in Companies so well fitted and furnished with their Paymasters, Sutlers, Farriers, Armourers and other Men necessary for a military Train, all so well instructed in the military Art, so well armed, so perfectly knowing and following their Colours, so ready to hear and obey their Captains, so expeditious to run, so strong in Charging, so cautious in Adventure that they rather resembled a Concert of Organ-pipes and a perfect Arrangement of Clock-work than an Army or Squadron of Horse.

On his Return, Toucquedillon presented himself before Picrochole, and related to him at length what he had both done and seen. At the End he counselled him by powerful Arguments to come to an Agreement with Grandgousier, whom he had found to be the honestest Man in the World; adding that it was neither Right nor Reason thus to molest his Neighbours, from whom they had never received aught but Good; and with regard to the main Point, that they would never come out of this Enterprise save to their great Damage and Mischief, for the Power of Picrochole was not so great but that Grandgousier could easily overthrow them.

He had not well finished speaking thus, when Rashcalf said out aloud: "Most unhappy is the Prince who is served by such Men as are so easily corrupted, as I perceive Toucquedillon to be; for I see that his Heart is so changed that he would willingly have allied

---

[1] *call out.* Fr. *empescher.* Cf. *G.* 28.

[2] *Legions.* This name was given to the contingents furnished by the *communes*, which Francis I incorporated in his infantry in 1523. (Fr. ed.) Rabelais would gladly use the word as reminiscent of the Roman army.

[3] *la Devinière* (*G.* 5) was a vineyard and a hamlet between Chinon and Lerné. It was most probably the birthplace of Rabelais. *Gravot* (*P.P.* prol.; *G.* 51; iv. N.P.) was about 15 miles north-west of Chinon on the other side of the Loire, near Bourgueil. *Chavigny* was just beyond Lerné. *Quinquenais* (*G.* 51; iv. 14, 44, 55) was a vineyard close to Chinon, the wine of which is vaunted by Rabelais. These were properties of the Rabelais family.

himself with our Enemies to fight against us and betray us, if they had wished to retain him; but just as Virtue is praised and esteemed by all, Friends and Foes alike, so is Wickedness soon known and suspected; and although our Enemies use it to their Advantage, still they always hold the Wicked and Traitors in Abomination".[1]

At these Words Toucquedillon, flying out, drew his Sword and with it ran Rashcalf through the Body a little above the left Breast, of which he died incontinently. And drawing his Sword from the Body he said boldly: "So perish he who Vassals true shall blame".[2]

Picrochole straightway grew furious, and, seeing the Sword and Scabbard so richly chased and diapered,[3] called out:

"Did they give thee this Weapon to slay feloniously in my Presence my right good Friend Rashcalf?"

Then he commanded his Archers to hew him in Pieces, which was done instantly, and so cruelly that the Chamber was all covered with Blood; afterwards he had the Body of Rashcalf honourably buried and that of Toucquedillon thrown over the Walls into the Ditch.

The News of these Outrages was known by the whole Army, whereat several began to murmur against Picrochole, insomuch that Grippeminault[4] said to him: "My Lord, I know not what will be the Issue of this Enterprise. I see your Men but little staunch in their Hearts. They consider that we are here ill provided with Victuals, and already much diminished in Numbers by two or three Sallies. Furthermore, great Reinforcements of Men come in to your Enemies. If we are once besieged, I see not how it can end otherwise than in our total Overthrow".

"Muck, muck", said Picrochole; "you are like the Eels of Melun;[5] you cry out before they skin you. Only let them come."

---

[1] hold... Traitors in Abomination. "Quippe proditores etiam iis quos anteponunt invisi sunt", Tac. Ann. i. 58. The Castilian proverb: "Though we love the treason we hate the traitor", Don Quixote, i. c. 32.

[2]   ὡς ἀπόλοιτο καὶ ἄλλος ὅτις τοιαῦτά γε ῥέζοι. Hom. Od. i. 47.

[3] Fr. diapré, stained with blood. (Fr. ed.)

[4] Grippeminault is the Archduke of the Furred Law Cats in v. 11–15; the text actually has Grippepinault, but AB and the editors (Jannet, de Montaiglon and Marty-Laveaux) read Grippeminault.

[5] the Eels of Melun, etc. A proverb derived probably from a market cry Anguilles de Melun avant qu'on les ecorche (i.e. quite fresh); thus the proverb arose: "Anguilles de Melun qu'on crie avant qu'on ne les ecorche" (H. Clouzot).

CHAPTER XLVIII

*How Gargantua attacked Picrochole within La Roche-Clermaud
and defeated the Army of the said Picrochole*

GARGANTUA had the entire Charge of the Army: his Father remained in his Castle.[1] And inspiring them with Courage by kind
Words, he promised great Rewards to those who should perform
any Deeds of Valour.[2]

After this they came on to the Ford of Vede,[3] and by Boats and
Bridges lightly constructed they passed over without a Break. Then
considering the Situation of the Town, that it was in a high and
advantageous Place, he deliberated over-night on what was to be
done.

But Gymnast said to him: "My Lord, such is the Nature and
Complexion of the French, that they are worth nothing but at the
first Rush.[4] *Then* they are worse than Devils, but if they delay they
are fainter than Women. My Advice therefore is that now, presently, after your men have a little taken Breath and Food, you
give Order for the Assault".

This Advice was found good. Therefore he drew out all his Army
into the open Field, putting his Reserves on the side of the Rising
ground. The Monk took with him six Companies of Foot and two
hundred Men-at-arms, and with great Diligence crossed the Marsh
and occupied the Ground above the Well,[5] right up to the Highway
from Loudun.

---

[1] *in his Castle*, *i.e.* La Devinière.

[2] There is a paper in *R.E.R.* v. 7–21 pointing out the knowledge of military
preparations and evolutions displayed by Rabelais in these chapters.

[3] *the Ford of Vede* on the Negron. Cf. *R.E.R.* v. 205 and the plan in ix. 120.
Boats and bridges were not at all necessary, but Rabelais' great campaign
required all the usual appliances of war.

[4] *The French...are worth nothing but at the first Rush*, etc. From Livy, x. 28. 4:
"prima [Gallorum] proelia plus quam virorum, postrema minus quam
feminarum esse". This is given in Erasm. *Apoph.* lib. vi. 103 (*varie mixta*).
Machiavelli devotes a chapter in *Discorsi sopra Livio* (iii. 36) to the consideration of this trait. Cf. also Caes. *B.G.* iii. 19. § 6; Strabo, iv. 197.

[5] *the Well.* Fr. *le Puy Girard*, now Peux Girard, a farm at the south of La Roche-
Clermault (*R.E.R.* v. 18, ix. 122).

Meantime the Assault went on. Picrochole's Men did not know whether it was best to sally forth and receive them, or rather to keep within the Town without stirring. But he set out madly with a Troop of Men-at-arms of his Guard, and thereupon was received and treated with great Cannon-shot which hailed on the Hill-sides; whereupon the Gargantuists retired to the Valley, so as better to give way to the Artillery.

Those of the Town defended themselves the best they could, but their Shots passed over and beyond, without striking any one.

Some of his Company that had escaped the Artillery set fiercely upon our Men, but got little by it; for they were all received betwixt the Files and dashed to the Ground. Seeing this, they would have retreated, but in the meanwhile the Monk had seized upon the Pass; whereupon they took to flight without Order or Discipline.

Some would have given them Chase, but the Monk held them back, through fear lest, as they followed the Fugitives, they might lose their Ranks, and at this Pass those from the Town should set upon them. Then after waiting some Space and none appearing to encounter him, he sent Duke Phrontistês to advise Gargantua to advance, so as to gain the Hill on the Left, to cut off the Retreat of Picrochole by the Gate on that Side.

This Gargantua did with all Diligence, and sent thither four Legions of the Company of Sebastus;[1] but they could not reach the Height so soon but that they must needs meet face to face Picrochole and those who were dispersed with him.

Then they charged them stoutly; notwithstanding, they were much damaged by those who were on the Walls by their Archery and Artillery. Seeing this, Gargantua went with a strong Party to their Relief; and his Artillery began to play upon the Walls in this Quarter so strongly that the whole Force of the Town was withdrawn thither.

The Monk, seeing the Side which he was besieging denuded of Men and Guards, courageously led on to the Fort, and succeeded so well that he gained a Footing on it, himself and some of his Men,

---

[1] *the Company of Sebastus.* Cf. Acts xxvii. 1, σπείρης Σεβαστῆς: in the Vulgate, *cohortis Augustae. Sebastus* recurs *G. 51 fin.*

believing that more Fear and Terror is wrought by those who come
up fresh in a Conflict than by those who are already engaged in it
with all their Might.[1] Anyhow, he gave no Alarm whatever, till
all his Men had gained the Wall, excepting the two hundred Men-
at-arms whom he left outside as a Provision against Accidents.

Then he raised an horrible Shout,[2] he and his Men together, and
without Resistance they put to the Sword the Guards of that Gate
and opened it to their Men-at-arms, and in all Confidence ran together towards the East Gate,[3] where the Havock was going on,
and coming up in the Rear overthrew all the Enemy's Force.

The Besieged, seeing that the Gargantuists had won the Town
at all Points, surrendered to the Monk at Discretion. He made
them give up their Weapons and Arms, and retreat all of them, and
shut themselves up in the Churches; seizing all the Staves of the
Crosses,[4] and stationing men at the Gates to keep them from going
forth. Then opening the Eastern Gate, he sallied forth to the Help
of Gargantua.

But Picrochole believed that Succour was come to him from the
Town, and in Presumption ventured forward more than before,
until Gargantua cried out: "Friar John, my Friend, Friar John,
Welcome in good time". Upon this Picrochole and his Men, per-
ceiving that all was lost, took to Flight on every side.

Gargantua pursued them till near Vaugaudry,[5] killing and slaying, and then sounded the Retreat.

---

[1] *those who come up fresh*, etc. Cf. Thuc. v. 9: τὸ γὰρ ἐπιὸν ὕστερον δεινότερον
τοῖς πολεμίοις τοῦ παρόντος καὶ μαχομένου (Motteux); Livy, xxvii. 45. 6:
"semper quod postremum adjectum sit, id rem totam videri traxisse".

[2] *Then he raised an horrible Shout*, etc. This seems imitated from Herodotus
(iii. 158), whose first book Rabelais translated, according to Tiraqueau (*de
leg. conn.* ed. 2 fol. 74 verso): "Darius now, keeping to the plan agreed
upon, attacked the walls on every side, whereupon Zopyrus (cf. *P.* 24) played
out the remainder of his stratagem. While the Babylonians, crowding to the
walls, did their best to resist the Persian assault, he threw open the Cissian and
the Belian gates and admitted the enemy. Such of the Babylonians as witnessed
the treachery took refuge in the temple of Jupiter Belus".

[3] *East Gate* should be *West*, as it was from the right to the left.

[4] Remembering his own exploits therewith. Cf. *G.* 27.

[5] *Vaugaudry* is hardly 5 miles from La Roche-Clermaud.

CHAPTER XLIX

*How Picrochole in his Flight was overtaken by Ill-fortune,
and what Gargantua did after the Battle*

PICROCHOLE thus in Despair fled away toward the Isle Bouchart.[1]
On the Road to Rivière[2] his Horse stumbled and fell, upon which
he was so much enraged that in his Choler he slew him with his
Sword. Then finding no one to remount him, he was going to take
an Ass from the Mill that was near there; but the Millers belaboured
him all over with Blows and stripped him of his Habiliments, and
gave him a scurvy canvas Jacket to cover himself withal.

And so departed this poor choleric Wretch; afterwards, as he
was crossing the Water at Port Huaux,[3] and recounting his Ill-
fortune, it was foretold him by an old club-foot[4] Hag that his
Kingdom should be restored to him at the Coming of the Cockicranes.[5] From that time forth no one knows what has become of
him. Nevertheless, I have been told that he is at present a wretched
Porter[6] at Lyons, choleric as ever, and always pestering all Strangers
concerning the Coming of the Cockicranes, in certain Hope, according to the Prophecy of the old Hag, that at their Coming he
shall be restored to his Kingdom.

---

[1] *l'Isle Bouchart* (G. 47; iii. 25; iv. 12–15; v. 4) is a village on an island about
10 miles higher up the Vienne from Chinon.

[2] *Rivière* is about 2 miles from Chinon on the Vienne.

[3] *le Port Huaux* is a village on the Indre about midway between Azay le
Rideau and the junction of the Indre and the Loire. It was here that travellers
used to cross the Indre (*R.E.R.* xi. 25).

[4] Fr. *lourpidon*, Lat. *loripes*.

[5] The *Cockicranes* may also be ortolans, which are migratory birds. Cf. Pliny,
10. 63: "*Cychramus* perseverantior festinat pervenire ad expetitas sibi terras";
"Est etiam historia non adeo notissima, nationem quandam hominum fuisse
propter Heracleam ab Hercule constitutam, Cylicranorum composito nomine
ἀπὸ τῆς κύλικος", Macrob. *Sat.* v. 21. § 8. Athenaeus, xi. 462A, records
that Hercules destroyed the Cylicranes who committed acts of piracy, and
founded on that site the town of Heraclea which was called Trachinia.

[6] It seems as though Rabelais wished to satirise some pet aversion of his own
at Lyons, as well as Gaucher Sainte-Marthe.

After their Return, Gargantua first called a Muster-roll of his Men, and found that but few of them had been lost in the Battle, to wit, some few Foot-soldiers of the Company of Captain Tolmère, and Ponocrates, who had an Arquebus-ball in his Doublet. Then he caused them to take Refreshment, each in his Company, and commanded his Paymasters that this Repast should be defrayed and paid for in their Behalf, and that there should be no Outrage whatever committed in the Town, seeing it was his own. After their Repast, they were to appear in the Square before the Castle, and there receive six Months' Pay; which was all carried out.

Then he caused to be assembled before him in the said Square all those that remained of the Party of Picrochole, to whom in the presence of all his Princes and Captains he spoke as follows:

CHAPTER L

The Harangue which Gargantua made to the Vanquished

"OUR Fathers, Grandfathers and Ancestors in all recorded Time have had this Feeling and this Disposition, that of the Battles won by them they have chosen rather to raise, as a Sign and Memorial of their Triumphs and Victories, Trophies and Monuments in the Hearts of the Vanquished by Clemency, than in the Lands conquered by them by Architecture; for they more esteemed the lively Recollection of men gained by Liberality, than the mute Inscriptions on Arches, Columns and Pyramids, subject to the Injuries of the Climate and the Envy of every one.[1]

"You may very well remember the Clemency which they showed towards the Bretons on the Day of St Aubin du Cormier,[2] and at the demolishing of Parthenay.[3] You have heard, and hearing admired, the gentle Treatment they showed towards the Barbarians of Spagnola,[4] who had pillaged, depopulated and ransacked the maritime Borders of Olonne and Thalmondais.

---

[1] "Arcus enim et statuas, aras etiam templaque demolitur et obscurat oblivio, neglegit carpitque posteritas.... Non ergo perpetua principi fama...sed bona concupiscenda est; ea porro non imaginibus et statuis, sed virtute et meritis prorogatur", Pliny, *Panegyr.* c. 55; Erasm. *Apoph.* lib. vii. (*Antisth.* 17).

[2] *St Aubin du Cormier* (iv. *A.P.*), about 20 miles north-east of Rennes in Brittany, *la lande de la Rencontre*, was the scene of a battle (July 28, 1488) between the armies of Charles VIII of France and Francis II, Duke of Brittany, supported by the Duke of Orleans, afterwards Louis XII, and English, German and Gascon allies. The Bretons were completely defeated and the Duke taken prisoner. He was released in 1491 by Charles VIII.

[3] The fortifications of Parthenay (iv. 38; cf. *R.E.R.* ii. 231) were destroyed by the troops of Charles VIII in 1487 fighting against Dunois. The upshot was that Charles married Anne of Brittany, and the duchy thus became attached to the French crown. The historical facts mentioned make it certain that, here at least, Grandgousier represents Louis XII among whose ancestors Charles VIII would be deemed to count. Princess Anne (1476–1514) was daughter of Francis II and married (1) Charles VIII Dec. 1491, (2) Louis XII Jan. 1499, although she had been in the first instance betrothed to Maximilian of Austria, whose daughter Marguerite had been betrothed to Charles VIII.

[4] *Barbarians of Spagnola.* No trace has been discovered of any attack by Spaniards on the coast at Olonne (*R.E.R.* ii. p. 248), but cf. Froissart, cc. 297–9.

"All this Hemisphere has been filled with the Praises and Congratulations which you yourselves and your Fathers bestowed, when Alpharbal,[1] King of Canaria, not satisfied with his own Fortunes, did furiously invade the Land of Onyx,[2] practising Piracy throughout all the Armorican Islands[3] and the neighbouring Regions. He was taken and overcome in a set naval Fight by my Father, whom may God preserve and protect.

"But what did we see? In a Case in which other Kings and Emperors, yea those who have themselves styled *Catholic*,[4] would have miserably ill-treated him, roughly imprisoned him and put him to an exorbitant Ransom, he treated him with Courtesy and Loving-kindness, lodged him with himself in his Palace, and out of his incredible Graciousness sent him back under Safe-conduct, loaded with Gifts, loaded with Favours, loaded with all Offices of Friendship.

"And what came of it? The King, being returned to his Country, called an Assembly of all the Princes and Estates of his Kingdom, set forth to them the Humanity he had found in us, and desired them to deliberate on this in such a way that the World should therein have an Example in them of gracious Honour, as it already had in us of an honourable Graciousness. Thereupon it was decreed by unanimous Consent that an Offer should be made to us

---

[1] Conjecture is not safe as to the identity of Alpharbal, though the Canary Islands are mentioned in *P.* 11, 23; *G.* 13, 31.

[2] *The Land of Onyx* (*G.* 33) is the Pais d'Aunix (*Pagus Alanensis*), a small seaside tract containing La Rochelle.

[3] *The Armorican Islands* are the islands off the West Coast: Belle-Ile, Noirmoutiers, Yeu, etc. (Fr. ed.) Reference may possibly be intended to the attacks made on that coast by the English under Sir Edward Howard in 1512–13. Cf. *A.P.F.* vi. 98; *Camb. Mod. Hist.* i. 480.

[4] *Catholic.* This is certainly an allusion to the treatment of Francis I, after his capture at Pavia in 1525 by Charles V (who was styled the *Catholic* King by the Pope). Francis was imprisoned first in the Certosa at Pavia, afterwards in uncomfortable quarters in Madrid, and humiliating terms were exacted of him by the treaty of Madrid, viz. the cession of Burgundy, Flanders and Artois, the renunciation of all claims to Milan and Naples, and the restoration to the Constable Bourbon of his forfeited domains. The two elder sons of Francis were given as hostages for the performance of the treaty in 1526. The treaty of Cambrai—the "Paix des Dames" in 1529—ratified this, with the modification that two million crowns should be paid in lieu of the cession of Burgundy.

of their entire Lands, Domains and Kingdom, to be disposed of according to our Discretion.

"Alpharbal in his own person immediately returned with nine thousand and thirty-eight great Ships of burden, bringing not only the Treasures of his House and Royal Family, but of nearly all the Country; for as he was embarking to set sail with a west-north-east[1] Wind, every one in crowds threw on board the Ships Gold, Silver, Rings, Jewels, Spices, Drugs and aromatic Perfumes, Parrots, Pelicans, Apes, Civet-cats, spotted Weasels and Porcupines.[2] He was accounted no good Mother's Son, who did not cast in whatever he had that was rare.

"When he had arrived, he wished to kiss the Feet of my Father aforesaid; this Act was deemed unworthy, and was not allowed, so he was embraced as a Companion: he then offered his Presents; they were not received, as being far too excessive. He gave himself up as a Bondsman and Servant voluntarily, himself and his Posterity; this was not accepted because it did not seem equitable. He surrendered, according to the Decree of his States-General, his Lands and Kingdom, proffering the Deed and Conveyance, signed, sealed and ratified by all those who were concerned to do it; this was altogether refused and the Contracts thrown in the Fire.

"The End of it was that my Father began to lament with Compassion and to weep copiously, when he considered the free Goodwill and Simplicity of the Canarians; and by choice Words and fitting Sentences[3] he made light of the good Turn he had done them, declaring that he had not done them any Service that was to be valued in the Estimation of a Button,[4] and if he had shewn them anything in the way of Courtesy, he was only bound to do it. But so much the more did Alpharbal augment it.

---

[1] *west-north-east* should probably be east-north-east.
[2] *Parrots, Pelicans*, etc. Perhaps enlarged from 1 Kings x. 22 and 25: "ivory and apes and peacocks, etc."
[3] "potest id quidem fuse et copiose et omnibus electissimis verbis gravissimisque sententiis et augeri et ornari", Cic. *de Fin.* iii. § 26.
[4] Cf. iii. 22, *Je ne m'en soucie d'un bouton,* and

"Certes ge ne vail un bouton".   *R.R.* 9239.

"Sans faille des vilains gloutons
Ne donnas-ge deus boutons".   Id. 10,413.

"What was the Issue? Whereas for his Ransom, taken at an extreme Rate, we should have been able tyrannically to exact twenty times a hundred thousand Crowns and to keep as Hostages his eldest Children, they voluntarily made themselves perpetual Tributaries, and bound themselves to deliver to us every Year two millions of Gold four-and-twenty Carats[1] fine. These were paid to us here the first Year; the second Year of their own Free will they paid twenty-three hundred thousand Crowns; the third Year twenty-six hundred thousand; the fourth Year three Millions; and so much do they always raise it of their own good Will that we shall be constrained to prevent them from bringing us any more.

"This is the Nature of Gratitude. For Time, which gnaws away and diminishes all Things, only augments and increases Benefits, because one noble Act freely done to a Man of Reason grows continually by his generous Thoughts and Remembrance.[2]

"Being unwilling, therefore, in any way to degenerate from the hereditary Graciousness of my Parents, I do now forgive you and set you at Liberty and make you frank and free as you were before.

"Moreover, at your Going out at the Gates, you shall have every one of you three Months' Pay, to enable you to reach your Houses and Families; and you shall be conducted in Safety by six hundred Men-at-arms and eight thousand Foot under the Command of my Esquire Alexander, to the end that you may not be injured by the Peasants.[3]—God be with you!

"I regret with all my Heart that Picrochole is not here, for I would have given him to understand that it was without my Will and without any Hope of increasing either my Estate or my Name, that this War was undertaken. But seeing that he is lost, and no one knows where or how he has disappeared, it is my Wish that his Kingdom should remain undiminished with his Son; and because

---

[1] *four-and-twenty-carats* (Gk. κεράτια, Bud. *de Asse*, ii. p. 219), *i.e.* pure gold. The carat was the 24th part of a denier. (Fr. ed.)

[2] *one noble Act*, etc. Cf. Milton, *P.L.* v. 71:

"Since good, the more
Communicated, more abundant grows".

[3] *injured by the Peasants.* In return for the ill-usage they endured from the mercenaries the peasants used to retaliate savagely whenever they got a chance. (Fr. ed.)

he is too young—for he is not yet full five Years old—he shall be governed and instructed by the ancient Princes and the learned Men of the Kingdom.

"And inasmuch as a Kingdom thus left desolate would readily be ruined, if the Covetousness and the Avarice of its Administrators were not curbed,[1] I ordain and will that Ponocrates be Intendant over all his Governors, with Authority thereunto requisite, and that he be constantly with the Child, until he shall find him fit and able to rule and govern by himself.[2]

"I hold that a too nerveless and weak Readiness to pardon Evil-doers is the Occasion to them of more lightly doing wrong again, through such pernicious Trust and Favour.

"I bear in mind that Moses, the meekest Man[3] that was in his time on the Earth, did sharply punish the Mutinous and Seditious among the Children of Israel.

"I bear in mind that Julius Caesar, who was so gracious a Commander that Cicero said of him, 'that his Fortune had nothing higher than that he could, and his Temper nothing better than that he would, save and pardon every one'.[4] Notwithstanding this, he did in certain Instances rigorously punish the Authors of Rebellion.

"Following these Examples, I desire before you depart that you deliver up to me:

---

[1] "Vae tibi, terra, cujus rex puer est, et cujus principes mane comedunt", Eccles. x. 16. Special reference is probably intended to the miseries entailed by the minority of Charles VI, who succeeded in 1380 at the age of thirteen under the guardianship of three uncles, the dukes of Anjou, Berry and Burgundy, and perhaps to the long minority of Henry VI of England.

[2] "Rectorem quoque solitus (Augustus) apponere aetate parvis aut menti lapsis, donec adolescerent aut resipiscerent", Suet. ii. 48. Cf. also Val. Max. vi. 6. § 1; Tac. *Ann.* ii. 67. The Archduke Philip of Castile died in 1505 and left his son Charles under the protection of Louis XII; the latter appointed as his tutor Antoine de Crouy, Seigneur de Chievres, who fulfilled his trust admirably; cf. *G.* 15.

[3] "Erat enim Moyses vir mitissimus super omnes homines qui morabantur in terra" (Num. xii. 3). For his punishments cf. Exod. xxxii. 27; Num. xi. 31-3; xii. 9, 10; xvi.

[4] "Nihil habet, Caesar, nec fortuna tua majus quam ut possis, nec natura tua melius quam ut velis servare quam plurimos" (Cic. *pro Ligario*, § 38, cited by Quintilian, viii. 5. 7). He severely punished the authors of rebellion; cf. Caes. *B.G.* iii. 16.

"Firstly, that fine Fellow Marquet, who has been the Origin and First cause of this War by his vain Presumption;

"Secondly, his Companions the Cake-bakers, who neglected to correct his headstrong Folly on the spot;

"And lastly, all the Advisers, Captains, Officers and Servants of Picrochole, who have incited, applauded or counselled him to go out of his Borders, in order thus to trouble us."

CHAPTER LI

How the victorious Gargantuists were recompensed after the Battle

WHEN this Harangue had been made by Gargantua, the Seditious men required by him were delivered up, excepting Spadassin, Merdaille and Menuail, who had fled six Hours before the Battle, one as far as the Neck of Laignel[1] at a stretch, the other as far as the Valley of Vire,[2] the other right to Logroine,[3] without looking behind them or taking Breath on the Road; and two Cake-bakers who were slain in the Fight. Gargantua did them no other Hurt save that he ordered them to pull at the Presses of his Printing-house,[4] which he had newly set up.

Then those who had died there he caused to be honourably buried in the Valley of the Walnut-trees and the Field of Burn-witch. The wounded he had dressed and treated in his great Hospital.[5] Afterwards he took thought for the Damages done to the Town and its Inhabitants, and had them reimbursed for all their Losses, on their sworn Declaration. And he caused a strong Fort to be built there, appointing thereto a Garrison and Guard, to defend themselves better for the future against sudden Risings.

At his Departure he graciously thanked all the Soldiers of his

---

[1] *Laignel*. Col d'Agnello in the *Alpes maritimes* by which Francis led his army in 1515. (Fr. ed.)

[2] *Val de Vire*, a valley in Normandy formed by the Vire, which flows past Vire and St Lo, and falls into the *Baie de la Seine*. It gives its name to the *Vaux de Vire* of Olivier Basselin. Longfellow has written a charming lyric on Basselin and the Valley of the Vire.

[3] *Logroine*. Logroño in Spain, just beyond Pampeluna, one of the cities taken by Charlemagne. (*Prise de Pampelune*, saec. xiv (*init.*).)

[4] The Printing-house in the Louvre had been supplemented by Francis I. (Fr. ed.)

[5] *Hospital* (Fr. *nosocome*, cf. *G*. 39). For the hospital near Seuilly cf. iv. 50 (Le Double, pp. 320–1). "Nosocomiis proprio aere fundatis", *Breviar. Rom.* Aug. 7, *lect.* iv. The care for the wounded is an anticipation of modern practice (cf. *R.E.R.* v. 21).

Legions who had been present at this Defeat, and sent them back
to winter in their Quarters and Garrisons, except some of the
decumane[1] Legion, whom he had witnessed performing some Exploits in the Field; and the Captains of the Bands, whom he took
with him to Grandgousier.

At the Sight and Coming of them the Good man was so joyous
that it would be impossible to describe it. He then made them a
Festival, the most magnificent, the most sumptuous and the most
delicious that had been seen since the time of King Ahasuerus.

As they came from Table he distributed to each of them[2] the
Ornamentation of his Sideboard, which was in Weight eighteen
hundred thousand and fourteen Besants of Gold, in great antique
Vessels, huge Pots, large Basons, big Tasses, Cups, Goblets, Can-
delabra, Baskets, Sauceboats, Flower-pots, Comfit-boxes and other
such Plate, all of massive Gold, besides the precious Stones, Enamel-
ling, and Workmanship, which by all men's Estimation exceeded
the Worth of the Material.

Besides, he had counted out from his Coffers, to each of them
twelve hundred thousand Crowns in ready Money; and over and
above to each of them he gave in perpetuity (unless they died without Heirs) his Castles and Lands adjoining, according as they were
most convenient to them. To Ponocrates he gave La Roche-
Clermaud; to Gymnast le Couldray; to Eudemon Montpensier;
Le Rivau to Tolmère; to Ithybolle Montsoreau; to Acamas Candé;
Varennes to Chironacte; Gravot to Sebastus; Quinquenais to
Alexander; Ligré to Sophrôn; and so of his other Places.[3]

---

[1] *decumane*, an allusion to Caesar's favourite *tenth* legion, cf. *B.G.* i. 42. For
decumane in another sense (*huge, portentous*) cf. iii. 38; iv. 23, 32; v. 22 and Erasm.
Ad. iv. 9. 54.

[2] *distributed to each of them*, etc. Presents of this kind are often made by the
heroes in the Romances of Chivalry.

[3] The places here mentioned are, as usual in this book, in the vicinity of
Chinon, and are properties belonging to Antoine Rabelais. The Greek names
of the warriors are in keeping with the "Hellenistic" tendency found in Rabelais. It may be observed that La Devinière is not assigned to anyone. It was
Grandgousier's (= Ant. Rabelais) own residence (*R.E.R.* iii. 57–60).

CHAPTER LII

How Gargantua caused to be built for the Monk the Abbey of Thelema[1]

THERE remained only the Monk to provide for, whom Gargantua wished to make Abbot of Seuillé, but he refused it. He wished to give him the Abbey of Bourgueil or Saint-Florent,[2] which ever would suit him better, or both if it pleased him; but the Monk gave him a decided Answer that over Monks he would have no Charge or Government.

"For how", said he, "should I be able to govern others, when I cannot govern myself?[3] If you think that I have done you acceptable Service, or that in the future I can do so, give me leave to found an Abbey after my own Device."

The Request pleased Gargantua, and he offered him all the Country of Thelema[4] by the River Loire to within two Leagues of the great Forest of Port-Huault. The Monk then requested Gargantua to institute his religious Order in a Manner exactly opposite to that of all others.

"In the first place then," said Gargantua, "you must not build Walls all round it, for all other Abbeys are proudly walled (*murées*)."

"Exactly," said the Monk, "and not without Reason; where

---

[1] *Thelema*. The main idea in the word is the Greek θέλημα, will, pleasure. The LXX, translating the first verse of Eccles. xii, gives οὐκ ἔστι μοι ἐν αὐτοῖς θέλημα, "I have no pleasure in them". The actual name may well have been taken from *Thelemia*, one of the two nymphs sent by Queen Eleutherillida to conduct Poliphilus to the palace of Queen Telosia (τέλος), possibly the prototype of Queen Entelecheia in the *Fifth Book*. These are personages in the *Hypnerotomachia Poliphili*, cf. G. 9 n.

[2] These were two rich Benedictine abbeys: Bourgueil (c. 47) four leagues from Saumur, St Florent quite close to it. The accumulation of benefices and church offices was specially scandalous under Leo X. Cf. *P.P.* 5; Gregor. xiv. 3. § 4.

[3] κάκιστον ἔλεγεν ἄρχοντα εἶναι τὸν ἄρχειν ἑαυτοῦ μὴ δυνάμενον, Plut. *Apoph.* (*Catonis*, 8) 198E, quoted in Erasm. *Apoph.* lib. v (*Cato*, 8). A number of passages to the same purport are got together in Erasm. *Ad.* i. 1. 3 ("Non bene imperat nisi qui paruerit imperio").

[4] The abbey of Thelema, if we follow the text, must be placed at the confluence of the Cher and the Loire near Rupuanne, north-west of Chinon.

there is *Mur* before and *Mur* behind, there is plenty of Murmur, Envy and mutual Conspiracy."

Moreover, seeing that in certain Convents in this World it is the Practice that if any Woman or Women (I speak of chaste and honest Women) enter in, they immediately cleanse the Place over which they have passed,[1] it was ordered that if any Man or Woman of any religious Order should enter into this Abbey by Chance or Accident, all the Places over which they had passed should be scrupulously cleansed.

And because in the Religions of this World everything is compassed about, limited and regulated by Hours, it was decreed that in this Abbey there should not be Clock or Dial of any kind whatever,[2] but that all their Business should be arranged according to Occasions and Opportunities; "for", said Gargantua, "the most real Loss of Time that he knew, was that of counting the Hours[3]—what Good comes of it?—and the greatest Dotage in the World was to regulate one's self by the Sound of a Bell, and not by the Dictates of Good sense and Understanding".

Item, because at that time they placed in religious Houses no Women save those who were one-eyed, lame, hunch-backed, ugly, ill-made, lunatic, senseless, bewitched or blemished, nor Men save those who were sickly, ill-born, silly and a Burden to their Family...[4]

"Apropos," said the Monk, "a Woman who is neither fair nor good, to what Purpose serves such?"[5]

---

[1] This is practised by the Carthusians. By particularising "honest Women" Rabelais implies that this strictness is relaxed in other cases.

[2] The same principle is insisted on by Rabelais in iv. 64 and enforced by several amusing reasons.

[3] Angelo Poliziano (*G.* prol.), also a canon, being asked whether he had ever read the *canonical* "*Hours*", replied: "Once; and it was the greatest waste of time I ever made" (Melanchthon, *Loci communes*; cf. *P.* 7).

[4] "Qui defectuosiores inter filios nobilium apparent, clericali statui adjiciuntur, quasi mundo inutiles, licet Deo execrabiles: siquidem contra Dei praeceptum ecclesiis et monasteriis offeruntur, aut claudi aut caeci aut in aliqua parte deformes et debiles" (cf. v. 4) John, Bishop of Chiemsee, suffragan of Salzburg, *Onus Ecclesiae*, xxii. 8.

[5] Fr. *à quoi vault toile?* The pronunciation of *telle* (Lat. *talis*) and *toile* (Lat. *tela*) was the same in Rabelais' time.

> "S'abiller à mode nouvelle,
> Porter moitié drap moitié toille."   Coquillart, i. 83.
> "Vers en terre, araigne en sa *telle*."   *A.P.F.* vii. 277.

"To make a Nun of", said Gargantua.

"Yea," said the Monk, "and to make Shirts"...
it was ordered that here should be admitted no Women that were
not fair, well-featured and of a good Disposition, nor Men that
were not handsome, well-made and well-conditioned.

Item, because in the Convents of Women Men never entered
but at unawares and clandestinely, it was decreed that here there
should be no Women in case there were no Men, nor Men in case
there were no Women.

Item, because Men and Women alike, once received into religious Orders, after their Year of Probation, were forced and
bound to remain there for ever, so long as their Life should last,
it was established that Men and Women alike, received into this
House, might go out thence whenever it seemed good to them,
without Let or Hindrance.

Item, because ordinarily the Religious Orders made three Vows,
to wit, of Chastity, Poverty and Obedience, it was appointed that
those who took these Orders might be honourably married, that
every one might be rich, and live at Liberty.

With regard to the lawful Age, the Women were to be received
there from ten to fifteen Years, and the Men from twelve to eighteen.

CHAPTER LIII

How the Abbey of the Thelemites was built[1] and endowed

FOR the Building and Furnishing of the Abbey, Gargantua caused to be given out in ready Money twenty-seven hundred thousand eight hundred and thirty-one long-woolled Sheep; and every Year, till the whole should be completed, he charged on the Income of the River Dive[2] sixteen hundred and sixty-nine thousand Sun-crowns[3] and as many Crowns of the Pleiades.[4]

For the Foundation and Maintenance thereof, he gave in perpetuity twenty-three hundred and sixty-nine thousand five hundred and fourteen Rose Nobles[5] as a fee-farm Rent, free of all Burdens and Service, and payable every Year at the Gate of the Abbey. And of this he gave a Grant to them in fair Letters-Patent.

The Building was hexagonal in Shape, in such fashion that at each Angle was built a large round Tower of sixty Paces in diameter; and they were all alike in Size and Design.

The River Loire ran on the North or *Septentrionic* side. On the Bank of it was situated one of the Towers called *Arctic*. Facing towards the East was another called *Caläer*; the next following was called *Anatole*, the next after *Mesembrine*, the next after that *Hesperian*, and the last *Cryerine*.

---

[1] For plans and a careful account of the Abbey and its architecture the reader may be referred to *Rabelais en Italie et à Metz* by M. Arthur Heulhard.

[2] Fr. *sus la recepte de la Dive*. The Dive is a little marshy river rising in Poitou and, with the Thouet, falling into the Loire just beyond Saumur. The modern French expression would be *sur les brouillards de la Seine* (Lacroix). Perhaps a pun on Lat. *dives* is intended.

[3] Fr. *escus au soleil* (*P.P.* 6; iii. prol.; iv. N.P.), gold pieces of Louis XI (1475). Over a crown in the device was the sun with eight rays.

[4] *Crowns of the Pleiades* (Fr. *à l'estoille poussiniere*, probably = windy money, cf. iv. 43) is, of course, money of Rabelais' own coinage. *L'estoille pouciniere* occurs in Villon, *Ballade au nom de la fortune*, p. 133.

[5] *Rose Nobles* (*P.P.* 6; iii. 25; Cretin, p. 246), gold pieces first struck by Edward III of England (1344) and current till Elizabeth's time. The rose finds place as the emblem of England. "1 *Grossus Angliae valeat in Britannia* 4 *denarios Angl.*, 20 *grossi valeant* 1 *Nobile vocatum Angelot*" (Ducange).

251

Between each Tower was a Space of three hundred and twelve Paces.

The whole was built in six Stages, counting the Cellars underground as one. The second Stage was vaulted in the form of a Basket-handle. The rest was ceiled[1] with Plaster of Flanders[2] in the form of pendent Tail-pieces. The Top was covered with fine Slate with a backing of Lead, with Figures of little Dwarfs and Animals well arranged and gilded; together with the Gutters which came out of the Wall between the Casements, painted in diagonal Shape in gold and azure down to the Ground, where they ended in great Conduit-pipes which all led into the River below the Building.

The said Building was a hundred times more magnificent than is Bonnivet,[3] Chambourg or Chantilly;[4] for in it were nine thousand three hundred and thirty-two Chambers,[5] each one furnished with an inner Chamber, a Cabinet, a Wardrobe, a Chapel[6] and an Opening into a great Hall.

Between each Tower, in the Middle of the said Main-building, was a winding Staircase within this same Building; its Steps were, some of Porphyry, some of Numidian Stone,[7] and some of serpentine[8] Marble, twenty-two Feet in Length and three Fingers thick, laid twelve in Number between each Landing-place. In every Landing there were two fine antique Arches, by which the Light was admitted; and through them there was an Entrance into a

---

[1] Fr. *embrunché*, from Lat. *imbricare*, to cover with tiles or to ceil. "Imbricata appellat Vitruvius inter se haerentia imbricum modo; sunt autem imbrices tegulae convolutae quales Lugduni visuntur", Bud. *in Pand.* i. p. 536.

[2] Fr. *guy de Flandres* (= Lat. *gypsum*). This plaster was in great repute for making key-stones in the vaulted ceilings of churches, etc. "Usus gypsi in albariis, sigillis aedificiorum et coronis gratissimus", Pliny, 36. 183.

[3] *Bonnivet*, a castle near Châtelleraut in Poitou, built by Admiral Bonnivet, 1513 to 1525, in which year he was killed at Pavia. Cf. *G.* 9 n.; *R.E.R.* ii. 148.

[4] *Chambourg* (or *Chambord*) and Chantilly were not begun till 1536 and therefore do not appear in ABC.

[5] *nine thousand three hundred and thirty-two Chambers.* The space of the building would allow only of about 300. (Fr. ed.)

[6] *Chapel.* These private chapels or oratories would be instead of the great seignorial chapel, which is not provided here.

[7] *Numidian Stone* is *giallo antico.* Great quantities of this marble were used in ancient Roman buildings, principally for pillars. Pliny finds the first trace of its use in 78 B.C. (36. 49).

[8] *serpentine*, Gk. ὀφίτης (v. 37); "serpentium maculis similis", Pliny, 36. 55.

Cabinet, made with Lattice-windows, and of the Breadth of the said Staircase; and the Ascent went up to the Roof and there ended in a Pavilion. By that Staircase there was an Entrance on each Side into a great Hall, and from the Halls into the Chambers.

From the *Arctic* Tower to the *Cryerine* were the fine great Libraries of Books in Greek, Latin, Hebrew, French, Italian and Spanish, arranged in the different Stages[1] according to these Languages.

In the midst was a marvellous winding Staircase,[2] the Entry to which was outside the Building in an Arch six Fathoms broad. It was built in such Symmetry and Breadth that six Men-at-arms with Lance in rest could ride abreast right to the Top of the whole Building.

From the *Anatole* to the *Mesembrine* Tower were fine spacious Galleries[3] all painted with ancient Feats of Arms, Histories, and Descriptions of the Earth.[4] In the midst thereof was a like Ascent and a Gate, as we have said there was on the River-side.

Upon that Gate was written in large antique Letters the Inscription which followeth:

---

[1] Fr. *estages*. Hebrew and Greek would probably occupy the ground-floor, thus leaving a storey each for the other languages.

[2] *winding Staircase*, perhaps suggested by the staircase in the palace at Blois.

[3] *Galleries*, probably *loggias* commanding a view of the environs. (Fr. ed.)

[4] *Descriptions of the Earth* (Lat. *mappa mundi*). Such maps were illuminated with gold and colours; the seas illustrated by fishes and sea-gods, monsters, etc.; the *fauna* and *flora* of each country depicted with the accounts of travellers, etc. In the Vatican there is a gallery of such geographical charts. Cf. iii. 28 on *mappe monde*.

CHAPTER LIV

Inscription put over the Great Gate of Thelema[1]

Enter not here, ye Hypocrites and Bigots,
Ugly old Apes and pursy Whimperers,
With Necks awry,[2] worse Boobies than the Goths,
Or Ostrogoths, precursors of Magoths;[3]
Woe-begone Vermin,[4] Cowl[5]-and-Sandal Wearers,

---

[1] M. Plattard, in a careful paper (*R.E.R.* x. 291–304) on the subject of Rabelais' reputation as a poet among his contemporaries, reduces his title to that credit to this poem, which he points out is a not very successful attempt to imitate the arrangement of verses and rimes then in vogue among the rhétoriqueurs. As members of this school he instances Molinet, Gringore, Cretin, Lemaire, J. Bouchet and even Marot. The great features in this style are the *rimes équivoques* and the *rimes batelées*. The first is when the same rimes on the two, three or even four last syllables are repeated in subsequent words: cf. st. I, *boursouflés*, *empantouflés*, *escorniflés*, and st. II, *populaire, capulaire, patibulaire*. The second is when the rime of the first line is repeated in the hemistich of the next line, *e.g.*

> "Cy n'entrez pas, hypocrites, *bigots*,
> Vieux *matagots*, marmiteux boursouflés,
> Torcoux, badauts, plus que n'estoient les *Gotz*,
> Ny *Ostrogotz*, precurseurs des *magotz*...".

[2] Fr. *torcoulx* (Ital. *torti colli*). Cf. Pers. iii. 80: "Obstipo capite et figentes lumine terram". The wry-necked, sanctimonious Franciscans are probably intended. Cf. *P.* 7, 30.

[3] *Goth and Magoth*, probably with some slight reference to Gog and Magog, but in *Les grandes Cronicques*, c. 10, they are the enemies of King Arthur, and were defeated by Gargantua. From the sack of Rome by Alaric and the Visigoths, the word Goths came to designate "humani generis hostes" in all forms. Ronsard, in his poem *Les Misères du Temps*, ad fin., has

> "Je n'aime point ces mots qui sont finis en *ots*,
> Gots, Cagots, Austregots, Visgots et Huguenots".

[4] *Cagots* (*canes Gothi*) were the remnant of the Visigoth Arians, who were allowed to live as *pariahs* in certain places in Lavedan, but with special places of worship (Bourdette, *Annales de Labédâ*, vol. i. pp. 37–9). Cf. *R.E.R.* viii. 154. In *R.E.R.* viii. 180, M. Sainéan insists that they are the white lepers (*ladres blancs*) of Brittany, who have merely a white smooth skin with no spots, as opposed to the *ladres verts*. He cites Paré, vol. iii. p. 350, ed. Malgaigne.

[5] Fr. *caphard*. From *cappa* comes *caphardum*, a kind of hood; hence = hypocrite (Ducange).

Cadgers bemittened, flagellating[1] Spungers,
Hooted Gorbellies, Stirrers-up of Heats;
Begone elsewhere to sell your wicked Cheats.
    Your wicked Frauds and Cheats
    Would fill my Fields and Streets
    With utter Villainy;
    So with false Harmony
    Would jangle Music's sweets
    Your wicked Frauds and Cheats.

Enter not here, Attorneys gorging Fees,
Scribes, Lawyers' Clerks,[2] the People that devour,
Ye Office-holders, Scribes and Pharisees,
Old Judges, who, like very Curs to seize,
Bring the good Citizens to their last Hour.[3]
The Gallows on the Fees you earn do lower:

---

[1] Fr. *frappart* (*P.* 7; iv. 15). Cf. Saint-Gelais, ii. 298:

> "Il vint l'autre jour un cafard
> Pour prescher en nostre paroisse,
> Et je luy dis: 'Frere *Frapard*,
> Qui vous faict ici venir? Est-ce
> Pour dresser l'âme pescheresse,
> Ou pour chercher la brebis errante?'
> 'Non', dit-il, 'la brebis je laisse,
> Pour avoir la laine de rente'".

[2] Fr. *Basauchiens*. *La Basoche* (Lat. *basilica*) was the old guild (founded in 1302) of the writers in the *Palais de Justice* in Paris. They are mentioned again in iii. 21 and iv. 32, but only as the producers of feeble Morality-plays. They were a kind of juristic Sorbonne. They had a King, a Chancellor, a Master of Requests, and Ushers. They held meetings on Wednesdays and Saturdays in the great Hall of the *Parlement*. After the death of Francis I, at the insurrection of Guienne, the King of La Basoche supplied the King of France with a contingent of 6000 of his subjects. Their arms were three gold inkstands on an azure field and the legend *Sigillum magnum regum Basochiae*. They were the first comic actors and authors in Paris, introducing *Farces*, *Soties* and *Moralités* as a relief from the Mysteries and Passion-plays of the monks. Several orders were directed against them by the *Parlement* from 1476 to 1582 to curb their mischievous spirit. They were heard of as late as 1789 (R). Finally they were broken up at the storming of the Bastille in 1790 and incorporated in the National Guard.

[3] *Bring...to their last Hour.* Fr. *mettez au capulaire*, from *capulum*, a bier. "Jam instat capulo, Il est sur le bort de la fosse", Cordier, 16. § 23; "Ait Plautus (*M.G.* iii. 1. 33) capularis senex", Serv. *in Aen.* xi. 64 *cap. sen.*; Apuleius, *Apol.* p. 511; "ire ad capulum", Lucr. ii. 1174.

Thither go bray:[1] *here* be no spendthrift Fruits,
For which in your Courts men stir up Lawsuits.
    Lawsuits and wordy Strife
    Have here but little Life
    For men to spend their Time.
    For *you* to growl and whine,
    I pray may e'er be rife
    Lawsuits and wordy Strife.

Enter not here, close-fisted Usurers,
Lickerish Renders, who add Pile to Pile,
Griping Graymalkins, greedy Pettifoggers,
Snub-nosed and bent, who fill your iron Lockers
With Thousand-marks,[2] insatiate the while.
You ne'er are cloyed, when ye pack Lucre vile
And heap it high, pinch-bellied Poltroons base;[3]
May cruel Death for this your Face deface!
    Deface Face not of Man
    Of folk, from here to ban
    To bray elsewhere; for it
    In here would not be fit.
    Void this our free Domain,
    Deface Face not of Man.

Enter not here, ye doting Mastiff curs,
Evening nor Morning, churlish jealous Drones;

---

[1] *Thither go bray.* "Il viendra braire", Patelin, l. 462.

[2] The mark (*marca*) was a weight and money of different values in various provinces in France, England and Germany. "A thousand marks" was also used to signify a large *sum* of money. Cf. *R.R.* 14,052: "Por mils mars de fin or molu", and in the 34th sermon of *Dormi secure* (*G.* 14) occurs: "Multi petunt pro *mille marcis*". "Regia libra Parisina 16 unciarum est; ejus semissem monetarii et aurifices libram sibi fecerunt *marcam* eam vocantes. *marca* = 64 grossi (= drachmae). 1 drachma = 2½ sterlinos", Bud. *de Asse*, ii. p. 162.

[3] *pinch-bellied Poltroons base.* Fr. *poltrons à chicheface*. *Chicheface* is a monster who devours all patient wives and therefore is very lean from scarcity of food. *Bigorne* (or Bicorne), who lives on patient husbands, is fat. There is a piece by John Lydgate published by Mr Halliwell for the Percy Society, vol. ii. p. 129, entitled *Bycorne and Chichevache*, to be found also in Dodsley, vol. xii. p. 302. *Chichevache* occurs in Chaucer's *Clerkes Tale*, E. 1188. Cf. note in Skeat's ed. vol. v. pp. 351–2. In *A.P.F.* ii. 187–203 is a poem of *Bygorne* and an account of him, and in xi. 277–92 a similar account of *Chicheface*.

Nor you again, seditious Mutineers,
Spirits, Hobgoblins, "Danger's"[1] Servitors,
Or Greeks or Latins, harsher than Wolves' Tones:
No! Mangy Knaves, infected to the Bones,
Avaunt! elsewhere your eating Sores defer,
All tetter-barked and full of Dishonour.
> But Honour, Praise, Delight
> With us are ever plight
> In joyous Tunes around.
> In Body all are sound;
> This Blessing fills them quite
> With Honour, Praise, Delight.

Here enter in, and welcome be ye here,[2]
And coming dwell, all noble Cavaliers.
Here is the Place where Incomes through the Year
Do come in largely, so that we make Cheer
To great and small by thousands, Fortune's Heirs.
You shall be my familiar loving Peers,
Merry and sprightly, dainty of Speech and Pen,
And in a Word, all worthy Gentlemen.
> All worthy Gentlemen,
> Sober in Wit and keen,
> Without Vulgarity,
> Filled with all Courtesy.
> Here shall your Hosts[3] be seen,
> All worthy Gentlemen.

Here enter, who the Holy Gospel's Dower
With nimble Wit expound, though Mocks abound;

---

[1] *Dangier*, in the *Roman de la Rose* and in the amatory poets of the fifteenth century, *e.g.* Charles d'Orléans, is the person who comes in the way of lovers, generally the father or husband.

[2] A liberal-minded Prior had inscribed over the gate of his priory: "Porta patens esto; nulli claudaris honesto". His churlish successor altered the stops thus:
"Porta patens esto nulli; claudaris honesto". *Mensa philosophica*, iv. 35.

[3] *Hosts*. Fr. *houstils—houstilier*, *hostiliarius* for *hospitalarius* (Ducange). The French word *hoste* is used of the soul as the *guest* of the body in iii. 4, and of the body as the *host* of the spirit in iii. 13. It bears both meanings, like the Latin *hospes*, which also = stranger, like the old Latin *hostis*.

Here shall you find a Refuge and a Tower
'Gainst Foemen's Error, who with Gloss's[1] Power
And their false Style would poison all around:
Come in, that here we found our Faith profound,
And then confound by Speech and Writing stirr'd
The Enemies of our Holy Word.

     Our Holy Writ and Word
     Shall evermore be heard
     Here holily averr'd;
     Each Knight it on shall gird,
     Each Lady with it stirr'd,
     Our Holy Writ and Word.

Here enter in, Ladies of high Degree,
Here frank and fearless. Come without Retard,
Flowers of Beauty, Faces heavenly,
With Bearing upright, wise, discreet to see;
In this Abode is Honour's Rest and Guard.
The lordly Lord, who did this Place award,
And shall reward, for you hath made this Haven,
And for its Maintenance hath much Gold given.

     Gold given by free Gift
     Obtains a full free Shrift
     For him that it awards;
     And shall with rich Rewards
     All honest men uplift,
     Gold given by free Gift.

---

[1] Fr. *Postille*, from *post illa verba*, a phrase to introduce an explanation (Ducange). An epitaph on Nicolas de Lyra contains the words *Hic jacet qui Biblia postillavit.*

CHAPTER LV

How the Habitation of the Thelemites was ordered[1]

IN the midst of the Base Court was a magnificent Fountain[2] of fine Alabaster; on the Top thereof were the three Graces with Horns of Abundance,[3] and they did spout Water from their Breasts, Mouth, Ears, Eyes and other open Passages of their Body.

The Inside of the Building over the said Base Court stood upon great Pillars of Chalcedony and Porphyry with goodly Arches[4] of ancient Fashion, within which were fine, long and spacious Galleries, adorned with Paintings and Horns of Stags, Unicorns, Rhinoceroses, Hippopotami, Elephants' Teeth, and other things worth seeing.

The Lodging of the Ladies took up the Part from the *Arctic* Tower to the *Mesembrine* Gate; the Men occupied the rest. Before the said Ladies' Lodgings, to the end that they might have their Recreation, withoutside between the two first Towers were the Tilt-yard, the Hippodrome, the Theatre and Swimming-baths, with admirable Baths in three Stages,[5] well furnished with all Accommodations and abundance of Myrrh-water.

---

[1] Several details of this chapter are borrowed from the *Hypnerotomachia Poliphili*, mentioned in *G*. 9 and in iv. 25 (*briefve declaration*), and of which so liberal use is made in the *Fifth Book*.

[2] "In the middest of this great base court, I did behold a goodly Fountaine of cleare water spinning from the verie toppe as it were to the foundation", *Hyp*. c. 8. e. viii verso; E.T. p. 104.

[3] "Vppon the which Challice was made an artificious foote set vnder the three Graces naked, of fine Gold.... From the teetes of their breastes the ascending water did spinne out like sylver twist. And everie one of them in their right hand did holde a *Copie* full of all kinds of fruites, which did extend in length vp aboue their heades", *Hyp*. c. 8. f. recto; E.T. p. 105.

[4] *with goodly Arches*, etc. "Et erano cento Archi, concludeuano uno Pomerio floridante. Per singulo dumque degli Archi era situata una Ara di rubente *Porphyro* optimamente liniata.... In questo medio centrico mysteriosamente era fundata una basi di diaphano Chalcedoni [Fr. Cassidoine] in forma cubica", *Hyp*. c. 8. f. recto.

[5] *three Stages, i.e.* Caldarium, Tepidarium and Frigidarium. Rabelais must have intended them to be over one another, though the Roman *thermae* do not seem to have been so arranged.

By the side of the River was the fair Pleasure-garden; in the midst of it the pretty Labyrinth. Between the two other Towers were the Courts for Tennis and Ballon. On the side of the *Cryerine* Tower was the Orchard, full of all manner of Fruit-trees, all arranged in quincuncial[1] Order. At the End was the great Park, abounding in all kinds of Wild game.

Between the third Pair of Towers were the Butts for the Arquebus, the Bow and the Cross-bow. The Offices were outside the Hesperian Tower one Storey high; the Stables beyond the Offices, and in front of them the Falconry, managed by Falconers[2] very expert in the Art. And it was yearly furnished[3] by Candiotes, Venetians and Sarmatians with all sorts of model Birds, Eagles, Gerfalcons, Goss-hawks, Sacres, Laniers, Falcons, Sparrow-hawks, Merlins and others, so well manned and tamed, that flying of themselves from the Castle to disport themselves in the Plains, they would take whatever they encountered.[4] The Kennels were a little farther off on the way towards the Park.

All the Halls, Chambers and Closets were hung with Tapestry in divers sorts, according to the Season of the Year. All the Pavement was covered with green Cloth. The Beds were all embroidered. In each Withdrawing-room was a Mirror of Crystal set in a Frame of fine Gold and garnished all round with Pearls, and it was of a Size such that it could truly and fully represent the whole Figure.

---

[1] *quincuncial, i.e.* like the Roman Quincunx. (Cf. Cic. *de Sen.* § 59; Pliny, 17. 78; Bud. *de Asse,* i. pp. 49 *sq.*) "Il quale rotondo era levato dal aequato paccimento *Quincuncio* cum il circumdato Porphyro", *Hyp.* c. 8. f. recto.

[2] *Falconers.* Fr. *asturcier (P.P. 5),* from "asturco, accipiter major, qui *Astur* Julio Firmico dicitur. *Astor* Italis, *Autour* Gallis" (Ducange). In Shakesp. *All's Well,* v. 1. 7, the first folio gives a stage direction "Enter a gentle *Astringer*", which was in later editions given as "Enter a gentleman". *Astringer* probably represents *Asturcier,* a falconer (Madden). A distinction was made assigning the word "falconer" to the long-winged falcons and "astringer" to the custodian of the *estridges* or goshawks.

[3] *And it was yearly furnished,* etc. Cf. Bud. *in Pand.* p. 586: "Adventitii hodie pinnarii anniversaria negotiatione ex Creta importantur, *sacros sacellosque* appellant, quasi ἱέρακας et ἱερακίσκους". Cf. also Serv. *in Aen.* xi. 721. The Venetians, with their trade in the Levant, imported falcons from Armenia, Persia, etc. while the Sarmatians (*i.e.* Danes, Norwegians, Prussians, etc.) imported *gerfalcons (R.E.R.* x. 364).

[4] *they would take whatever,* etc. Cf. Shakesp. *Ham.* ii. 2. 450: "We'll e'en to it like the French falconers, fly at anything we see".

At the Going-out of the Halls of the Ladies' Lodgings were the Perfumers and Trimmers, through whose Hands the Men passed when they went to visit the Ladies. These also furnished every Morning the Chambers of the Ladies with Rose-water, Orange-flower-water, and Angel-water,[1] and gave to each a precious Casket that breathed forth all manner of aromatic Scents.

---

[1] "And as I suspected, each potte (*cassolette* Popelin) had seuerall waters, as it were, one with Rose-water, another with water of Orange flowers, another of myrtle....And these boyling together they did yield a most pleasant and fragrant smell", *Hyp.* c. 9. g. verso; E.T. p. 126; Popelin i. p. 169. *Eau d'ange* is mostly made from the common myrtle (H. Correvon).

CHAPTER LVI

How the Brethren and Sisters of Thelema were apparelled

THE Ladies at the first Foundation of the Order dressed themselves[1] according to their Pleasure and Judgment. Afterwards of their own free Will they reformed themselves in the Fashion which here followeth:

They wore Stockings of Scarlet or Purple,[2] and they drew on the said Stockings above the Knee exactly three Fingers-breadth, and the List was ornamented with fine Embroidery and Incision.

The Garters were of the Colour of their Bracelets, and took in the Knees above and below.

Their Shoes, Pumps and Slippers were of red, crimson or violet Velvet, pinked and jagged like Lobsters' Beards.

Over their Smock they put on a pretty Kirtle[3] of some fair silk Camblet. Above this they did on their Vardingale of Taffeta, white, red, tawny, grey, etc. Over this the Petticoat of silver Taffeta made with Embroideries of fine Gold intertissued with Needle-work, or according as they thought good, and corresponding to the Temperature of the Weather, of Satin, Damask or Velvet; orange, tawny, green, ash-coloured, blue, bright yellow, red, crimson, white, Cloth of Gold, Cloth of Silver, and of Purl, embroidered according to the Festivals.

Their Gowns, according to the Season, were of Cloth of Gold with silver Fringe, of red Satin trimmed with gold Purl, of white, blue, black, dun Taffeta, silken Serge, silk Camblet, Velvet, Cloth

---

[1] The dress of the sisters of Thelema seems to be a development of the dress of the nymphs in the *Hypnerotomachia*, c. 7. e. ii recto; E.T. p. 84.

[2] Fr. *migraine* = demi-graine; scarlet being produced by cochineal, *migraine* by a smaller infusion of it; M. d'Héricault in his edition of Coquillart makes out the dye to be *alkermes* (iii. 18), and to be derived from the juice of the *yeuse* (Ital. *elce*, Lat. *ilex*, holm-oak). The *kokkos*, as it is called by Dioscorides, iv. 48, is the berry of the *prinos* or holly-oak, but the dye is rather got from the insect which is on the shrub. Cf. iii. 18 and Paus. x. 36. 1, with a most interesting note by Sir J. Frazer.

[3] *Kirtle.* Fr. *vasquine*, Span. *basquina*.

of Silver, Gold Tissue, Silver Brocade, Velvet or Satin purfled with Gold in divers Imagery.

In Summer, some days instead of Gowns they wore fair flowing Robes[1] with the aforesaid Bravery, or Moorish Bernouse[2] of violet Velvet with gold Fringe on silver Purl, or with gold Cords studded at the Crossings with little Indian Pearls.[3] And they always carried a fair Panache, of the Colour of their Cuffs, well tricked out with Spangles[4] of Gold.

In Winter their Gowns[5] were of Taffeta, of Colours as above-named, trimmed with the Fur of spotted Lynxes, black Weasels, Calabrian Martens, Sables,[6] and other costly Furs.

Their Beads, Rings, Neck-chains, Carcanets were of precious Stones, Carbuncles, Rubies, Balai-rubies, Diamonds, Sapphires, Emeralds, Turquoises, Garnets, Agates, Beryls, Pearls and magnificent Margarites.[7]

Their Head-dresses were according to the Season; in Winter of the French fashion, in Spring of the Spanish, in Summer of the Tuscan, excepting on the Holy days and Sundays, on which Days they wore the French Head-dress, because it is more honourable and better befitting matronly Modesty.

The Men were apparelled after their Fashion:

Stockings for their nether Limbs, of Tamine,[8] or of cloth Serge scarlet, purple, white or black;

Their Trunk hose, of Velvet of the same Colour, or very near

---

[1] Fr. *marlottes* (*marlota*), a sort of Spanish cloak that was worn in Béarn (Ducange, who quotes the present passage).

[2] Fr. *bernes*, a kind of cloak with a hood, called in Leo Africanus, book ii, *Ilbernus*. Span. *Albornoz*, Arab. *al-bornos*.

[3] *little Indian Pearls.* The Indian pearls were most esteemed. "Clarior (candor) in Rubro mari repertis, Indicos specularium lapidum squama adsimulat alias magnitudine praecellentes", Pliny, 9. 113.

[4] Fr. *papillettes* (*pampillettes*, iv. 13).

[5] *Gowns.* Fr. *robes*, reaching to the knees.

[6] Fr. *zibellines*, Ital. *zibellino*. Cf. *soubeline* (iii. 16); *R.E.R.* x. 475.

[7] *Margarites.* Fr. *unions.* Cf. *G.* 8.

[8] Fr. *estamet* (*G.* 8), Lat. *stamen*, mod. "tammy", a cloth-rash (Cotgrave), a coarse sort of canvas. *Tamis* and vb. *tamiser* are used for boulting flour, *C.N.N.* 17. Cf. Skeat's *Chaucer, Leg. F.W.* ll. 2352–68 (Philomela).

"De Sarrasin qui d'*estamines*
Cuevret les vis as Sarrasines."   *R.R.* 21,945.

approaching thereto, embroidered and jagged according to their Fancy.

Their Doublet, of Cloth of Gold or Silver, of Velvet, Satin, Damask, or Taffeta, of the same Colours, cut, embroidered and trimmed to perfection.

The Points, of Silk of the same Colours; the Tags were of Gold beautifully enamelled.

Their Mantles and Cloaks[1] were of Cloth of Gold or Silver Tissue, Cloth of Silver or Velvet, purfled as they thought fit.

Their Gowns, as costly as those of the Ladies.

Their Girdles, of Silk, of the Colours of the Doublet.

Each one had a gallant Sword by his Side, with the Handle gilt, the Scabbard of Velvet of the Colour of his Hose, the Tip of Gold and Goldsmith's work; the Dagger was of the same.

Their Cap was of black Velvet, adorned with many Jewels and Buttons of Gold; the white Plume above it was daintily parted by Rows of gold Spangles, at the End of which hung in Sparkles fair Rubies, Emeralds, etc.

But such was the Sympathy between the Men and the Women, that each Day they were arrayed in like Apparel; and that they should not fail in this, there were certain Gentlemen appointed to tell the Men each Morning what Livery the Ladies wished to wear on that Day, for all was done according to the Decision of the Ladies.

In these Clothes so fitting, and Habiliments so rich, do not suppose that either one or the other lost any Time whatever; for the Masters of the Wardrobes had all the Vestments so ready every Morning, and the Ladies of the Bedchamber were so well skilled, that in a trice they were ready and dressed from Head to Foot.

And that they might have these Accoutrements with the better Conveniency, around the Wood of Thelema was a great Block of Houses half a League long, very neat and well arranged; wherein dwelt Goldsmiths, Lapidaries, Embroiderers, Tailors, Gold-drawers, Velvet-weavers, Tapestry-makers, Upholders, and

---

[1] Fr. *chamarre*, a long, loose, thin, flowing garment. Scott, *Ivanhoe*, c. 7, has the word *simarre* as Rebecca's thin upper wrap of silk.

wrought there, each one at his own Trade, and all for the aforesaid Brethren and Sisters.

They were furnished with Matter and Stuff from the Hands of the Lord Nausiclete,[1] who every Year brought to them seven Ships from the Perlas and Cannibal Islands,[2] laden with gold Ingots, raw Silk, Pearls and precious Stones.

If any fine Pearls began to grow old and changed from their native Whiteness, these by their Art they did renew, by giving them to be eaten to some fine Cocks,[3] as men use to give Castings[4] to Hawks.

---

[1] Ναυσίκλειτος or Ναυσίκλυτος is the title of the Phaeacians in the *Odyssey*, lib. vi. *sqq.*

[2] *Perlas.* The Pearl Islands, five or six in number, lie at the entrance of the Gulf of Panama. The Cannibal or Caribee Islands are the Antilles. Cf. iv. *Ep. Ded.* "Aliqui ab Anthropophagis, qui Canibales appellantur, capti comesique foedam miserabilis audaciae memoriam reliquerunt", Paul. Jovius, *Hist.* lib. 34.

[3] *to be eaten by Cocks.* In the *Fabulae Aesopi* of the *Autores octo morales* (cf. G. 14), the Cock, finding a jewel on a dung-hill, remarks as follows:

"Si tibi nunc esset qui debuit esse repertor,
Quem limus sepelit viveret arte nitor".

[4] *Castings.* Fr. *cures.* Cf. G. 41; *R.E.R.* x. 368–9. Averroes is reported to have prescribed that pearls losing their whiteness should be given to pigeons to swallow; but the pigeons must be killed immediately so that the digestive power of the birds should not damage the pearls in weight or value. In *Ceylon Asiat. Journal*, 1825, p. 51, the same direction is given with regard to fowls.

CHAPTER LVII

How the Thelemites were governed in their Manner of Living

ALL their Life was laid out, not by Laws, Statutes, or Rules, but according to their Will and free Pleasure. They rose from their Bed when it seemed good to them, they drank, ate, worked, slept, when the Desire came upon them. None did awake them, none did constrain them either to drink or to eat, or to do anything else whatsoever; for so had Gargantua established it.

In their Rule there was but this Clause:

DO WHAT THOU WILT,[1]

because that Men who are free, well-born, well-bred, conversant in honest Company, have by nature an Instinct and Spur, which always prompteth them to virtuous Actions and withdraweth them from Vice;[2] and this they style Honour. These same Men, when by vile Subjection and Constraint they are brought down and enslaved, do turn aside the noble Affection by which they freely were inclined unto Virtue, in order to lay aside and shake off this Yoke of Slavery;[3] for we do always strive after Things forbidden and covet that which is denied unto us.[4]

---

[1] In *Les Grandes Cronicques*, c. 10, King Arthur says to Gargantua, *Faictes ce que vous vouldrez.*

[2] "Erat enim ratio profecta a rerum natura et ad recte faciendum impellens et a delicto avocans", Cic. *Legg.* ii. § 10. Cf. Diog. Laert. vii. § 87; Serv. *in Aen.* ix. 182.

[3]
> ἥμισυ γάρ τ' ἀρετῆς ἀποαίνυται εὐρύοπα Ζεὺς
> ἀνέρος, εὖτ' ἄν μιν κατὰ δούλιον ἦμαρ ἕλησιν.

Hom. Od. xvii. 322.

Cf. Seneca, *de Benef.* vi. 30. § 4: "Non vides quemadmodum illos in praeceps agat extincta libertas et fides in obsequium servile submissa?"

> "Qu'ils ont lor naturel franchise
> A vil servitude soumise."   *R.R.* 5881.

[4]
> "Nitimur in vetitum semper cupimusque negata."

Ovid. Am. iii. 4. 17, quoted by Ioh. Nev. iv. fo. 130. 2.

By means of this Liberty they entered into a laudable Emulation
to do all of them what they saw did please one. If any one of the
Men or Ladies said "Let us drink", they all drank. If any said
"Let us play", they all played. If one said "Let us go disport
ourselves in the Fields", they all went thither.[1]

If it were to go a-hawking or hunting, the Ladies mounted on
fine Mares, with their prancing Palfrey, each carried on her Fist,
daintily begloved, either a Sparrow-hawk or a Lanneret or a
Merlin. The Men carried the other kinds of Hawks.[2]

So nobly were they taught that there was neither He nor She
amongst them but could read, write, sing, play on musical Instruments, speak five or six Languages, and compose therein in Verse
as well as in Prose.[3]

Never were seen Knights so worthy, so valiant, so dexterous both
on Foot and on Horseback, more vigorous, more nimble, better at
handling all kinds of Weapons, than were there.

Never were seen Ladies so handsome,[4] so dainty, less froward,
better taught with their Hands, with their Needle, in every
womanly Action that is honest and gentle, than were there.

For this Reason, when the Time was come that any Man wished
to go forth from the said Abbey, either at the Request of his Parents
or for some other Cause, he carried with him one of the Ladies,
her who should have taken him for her faithful Servant, and they
were married together. And if they had formerly lived in Thelema
in Devotion and Friendship, still more did they so continue in

---

[1] "If one of us be merrie and delightsome, the other sheweth her selfe the
more glad and pleasaunt, and our delectable and perticipated friendship is
with an attentive consideration perpetually vnyted and knitte together", *Hyp.*
c. 7 (*fin.*), e. iii. verso; E.T. p. 88.

[2] *other kinds of Hawks*: the "long-winged" hawks, gerfalcons, peregrines and
goshawks. The countryside about Chinon with the confluence of the Vienne and
the Loire would enable the youthful Rabelais to learn much about river-fowl
and falconry. At the end of his notes on the Pandects Budé devotes some pages
to the details of this sport, to which he was addicted as a young man. Cf. *R.E.R.*
x. 366–71.

[3] Fr. *carme...oraison solue* = Lat. *carmen* and *oratio soluta*. Cf. v. prol.

[4] Fr. *propres*. Cf. Heb. xi. 23: "Because they saw that he [Moses] was a
proper child".

Wedlock; insomuch that they loved one another to the End of their Days as on the first Day of their Marriage.[1]

I would not forget to write down for you a Riddle[2] which was found on digging the Foundation of the Abbey, engraved on a great Plate of Bronze.

It was thus, as followeth:

---

[1] "In his picture of an ideal society the author of *Gargantua* glorifies the ladies simply because it is necessary to his conception of antimonasticism, but he does not praise them for their own sake" (*R.E.R.* ii. 85). For his real opinion cf. *G.* 37; iv. 10.

[2] *Riddle.* Fr. *enigme.* Cf. *R.E.R.* ix. 95.

CHAPTER LVIII

A Prophecy in Riddles[1]

POOR Mortals, who good Fortune do desire,
Lift up your Hearts and to my Words give Ear.
If it be granted firmly to believe
That by the Bodies in the Firmament
The Human Spirit can itself attain
To say before the Things that are to come,
Or if we can by Help of Power Divine
Obtain the Knowledge of our future Lot,
So as to judge in well-assured Discourse
Of Years remote the Destiny and Course,
I do to wit to whoso will attend
That this next Winter, without more Delay—
Nay, sooner—in the Place where now we are,
There will go forth a certain Sort of Men,
Wearied of Rest and chafing under Ease,
Proceed unchecked, in open Light of Day,
Suborning Men of all Conditions
To Difference and Factions, Party-strife;
And whoso will believe them and give Ear,
Whatever be the Cost and Consequence,
They will bring open and apparent Strife—
Friends and near Kinsmen 'gainst their Friends and Kin.

---

[1] This poem, with the exception of the first two and the last ten lines, is borrowed from Mellin de Saint-Gelais. It is intended as a protest against the persecution of the Protestants proceeding at that time, under pretence of describing a game of tennis, the more so because of the great pains taken both by Saint-Gelais and Rabelais to shew that the allusion throughout is to tennis. No edition of Saint-Gelais' poems was published before 1547 (Lyon, Pierre de Tours), but many pieces of his were circulated in MS. among friends and in court circles. This poem then and the *Antidoted Conundrums* of c. 2 must have been communicated to Rabelais orally or in MS. M. Plattard has given good reasons for believing that friendly relations subsisted between the two men in 1533–8; the present *Énigme* was not *published* till 1574 (*R.E.R.* ix. 90–108).

The forward Son will hazard the Reproach[1]
To range himself against his proper Sire;
Even the Great ones, come of noble Line,
By their own Vassals see themselves assailed,
And Honour's Due, Respect and Reverence[2]
Shall for that time lose Order and Degree.
For men shall say that each one in his Turn
Should go above and then return below.
And on this Point shall be so many Broils,
So many Discords, Comings, Goings-forth,
That History, wherein are Marvels told,
Hath no Record of like Disturbances.
Then shall be seen a many Man of Worth,
Sent forward by the Spur of Youth's hot Blood
And too great Credence in this strong Desire,
Dead in Life's Flower or brought to low Degree.
And none shall ever lay aside the Task,
If once he shew his Mettle in the Fray,
Till he have filled, by Quarrels and Debates,
The Heavens with Noise, the Earth with pacing Steps.
Men without Faith, that time shall wield no less
Authority than Truth's own Champions;
For all shall follow the Desire and Creed
Of the ignorant and foolish Multitude,
Of whom the basest shall be held as Judge.
Oh, Deluge baneful and most damnable!
Deluge, I say, and say it rightly too;
For this same Travail shall be for all Time;
Nor shall the Earth be ever freed from it,
Until there issue, spreading widely forth,
Outbursting Waters; whereby Combatants,
E'en the most moderate, shall be caught and drenched;

---

[1] *Reproach*. Fr. *impropere*. The *Improperia* or Reproaches are sung in the Roman Church on Good Friday. "My people, what have I done to thee? Or in what have I wronged thee? Answer me" (Micah vi. 3); "*Improperium* ejus portantes", Heb. xiii. 13. Sir T. Browne has (*Rel. Med.* 1. § 3) "Improperations and terms of scurrility".

[2] *Respect and Reverence*, etc. "The child shall behave himself proudly against the ancient, and the base against the honourable", Isaiah iii. 5.

And with good Right, for that their stubborn Heart,
Addicted to this Combat, shall not spare
Even the Flocks of the most innocent Beasts,
But of their Sinews and uncleanly Entrails
They make a sacrifice—not to the Gods,
But to the common Service of Mankind.
So now I leave to your Reflexion,
How duly can the Universe be ordered,
And what Repose in Turmoil so profound
The Body of the round Machine[1] shall find.
The happiest those who most shall hold to it,
And most abstain from Loss or Spoil thereof,
Who most endeavour, every Way they can,
To hold it safe and make it Prisoner,
In such a Place that the poor lost Ball
From Him alone who made her shall find Help.
And what is worst in this sad Accident,
The clear bright Sun, before he sinks i' the West,
Shall let thick Darkness spread all over her,
Beyond Eclipse's Gloom or natural Night:
Whence at one Stroke she'll lose her Liberty
And all the Favour and Brightness of high Heaven,
Or, at the least, in Desolation bide.
  But she, before this Ruin and this Loss,
Shall long have shewn to outward Senses clear
A Quaking vaster and more violent
Than Etna[2] erst was so much shaken withal,
When on a Son of Titan she was hurled:
And not more sudden may we think was caused

---

[1] *The round Machine* has a double reference: (1) to the tennis-ball, (2) to he
Earth. Cf. Cl. Marot, *Epist.* 27 *fin.*:

> "Dieu tout-puissant te doint, pour t'estrener,
> Les quatre coings du monde gouverner,
> Tant pour le bien de *la ronde machine*,
> Que pour autant que surtous en es digne".

Hugues Salel, p. 63:
> "Le createur de *la ronde machine*".

[2] *Etna.* Cf. Virg. *Aen.* iii. 571–82; Ovid, *Met.* v. 346–58.

The Movement that Inarime[1] gave Birth,
Whenas Typhöeus, horribly enraged,
Sent Rocks and Mountains hurtling in the Sea.
  Thus in a little Time shall be appeased
This sad Condition, and so often changed,
That even those who shall have held it so
Shall leave it, that New-comers take their Place.
Then shall the Days be fair and prosperous
To put an End to this long Exercise.
For the deep Waters, whereof ye hear speak,
Shall cause that each bethink him to retire.
And ever, ere the Separation come,
There shall be clear appearing in the Air
The Heat absorbing of a mighty Flame
To bring to an End the Waters and the Emprize.
  And when these Things are fully finished,[2]
'Tis seen the Elect are joyously refreshed
With heavenly Manna and all Kinds of Joys,
And furthermore, in honest Recompense
Are full endowed. The others at the End
Are stripped of all. And this the Reason is,
That when the Toils are ended at this Point,
Each one may gain his Lot predestinate.

---

[1] *Inarime . . . Typhöeus.* Cf. Hom. *Il.* ii. 783 and Virg. *Aen.* ix. 716:

> "durumque cubile
> Inarime Jovis imperiis imposta Typhoeo".

"Amore tropo me molesta, più che la grave Inarime Typhone" (*Hyp.* c. 16. m. verso). Inarime was called Pithecusa, now Ischia, in the Tyrrhenian sea, off Cumae (Strabo, v. 244–8).

[2] In the earlier editions the last ten lines are as follows:

> "Then there results that those too much enthralled,
> Pained, wearied, overwrought and sore distressed,
> By the holy Will of the eternal Lord
> Shall from their Toils be happily refreshed.
> Then will be seen by Knowledge absolute
> The Fruit and Blessing gained by Patience:
> For he that shall have suffered more Distress
> Before, shall now by Destiny's Decree
> Be more rewarded. O how blest is he
> Whoso can persevere unto the End!"

Such was the Bargain. O how blessed is he
Whoso shall persevere unto the End![1]

The Reading of this Document[2] finished, Gargantua sighed deeply and said to the Company:

"It is not then at this Time only that people who are called to the Faith of the Gospel are persecuted; but happy is he who shall not be offended, and who shall always aim at the Mark, at the White, which God, by His dear Son, hath set up before us, without being distracted or turned aside by his carnal Affections".

The Monk said: "What think you in your Understanding is meant and signified by this Riddle?"

"How?" said Gargantua. "The Continuance and Upholding of Divine Truth."

"By Saint Goderan,"[3] said the Monk, "that is not my Explanation; the Style is that of Merlin the Prophet.[4] Put upon it all the Allegories and grave Expositions that you will, and dote about it, you and the Rest of the World, as much as you like.

"For my Part, I believe there is no other Meaning enveloped in

---

[1] In the *Énigme* of Saint-Gelais explanations are placed in the margin. Thus:

l. 13 *Le jeu de Paume* opposite "the Place where now we are".
l. 14 *Les faiseurs de partis* opposite "a certain Sort of Men".
l. 22 *Les joueurs* opposite "Friends and near Kinsmen".
l. 30 *Le changement de lieu* opposite "Should go above".
l. 43 *Les arbitres* opposite "Men without Faith".
l. 47 *Le nacquet* (marker) opposite "the basest".
l. 53 *Les sueurs* opposite "Outbursting Waters".
l. 58 *Les raquettes* opposite "of their Sinews".
l. 64 *L'esteuf* (tennis ball) opposite "the round Machine".
l. 69 *Les fosses des jeux* opposite "In such a Place".
l. 97 *Le feu qu'on fait* opposite "of a mighty Flame".

[2] *Document*. Fr. *monument*, Lat. *monumentum*.

[3] *St Goderan*, Bishop of Saintes and Abbot of Maillezais, 1060–73. He is mentioned in Trithemius, *De viris illustribus Ord. S.B.* iii. 329. His ring, his crozier and epitaph on a leaden plate were discovered at Maillezais in 1883. He is not to be confounded with *Saint Godegran*, who is mentioned in *G.* 17.

[4] *Merlin the Prophet*. A grotesque attribution of this poem of Mellin de Saint-Gelais to Merlin, the necromancer and prophet of the Arthurian legend and a considerable figure in the *Grandes Cronicques*. Saint-Gelais (1491–1558), almost an exact contemporary of Rabelais, was a natural son of Octovien Saint-Gelais, Abbot of Reclus, almoner and librarian to Francis I and Henry II. He was a lyric poet of some merit, contesting the palm with Clément Marot.

it than a Description of a Game at Tennis hidden under obscure Words.

"The Suborners of Men are the Makers of Matches, who are commonly Friends, and after the two Chases are made, he that was in the Service-end of the Court goeth out and the other cometh in. They believe the first who saith whether the Ball was above or below the Line.[1] The Waters are the Sweat. The Strings of the Racquets are made of the Guts of Sheep or of Goats. The round Machine is the Pellet or Tennis-ball. After the Game they refresh themselves before a clear Fire and change their Shirts; and with Goodwill they banquet, but more merrily those who have gained. And good Cheer withal."[2]

---

[1] *above or below the Line.* In tennis at that time instead of the net between the players a cord was often used and the players would appeal to the spectators as to whether the ball had passed above or below. Cf. Cordier, 59. § 16: "Ad vos refero, spectatores. Attigitne?" and § 46: "Non transivit super funem. Est sub fune". (Cf. iii. 11.)

[2] In the earlier editions the end is given in a much shorter form: "I think it is the Description of the Game of Tennis and that the round Machine is the Tennis-ball, and these Sinews and Entrails of innocent Beasts are the Racquets, and these Men who are heated and contending are the Players. The End is that after having well toiled they go to banquet and great Good Cheer".

APPENDIX

ALMANACK OF 1533

ALMANACK for the Year 1533, calculated on the Meridian of the noble City of Lyons and on the Parallels of Latitude of the Kingdom of France.

Composed by me, Francis Rabelais, Doctor in Medicine
and Professor in Astrology, etc.

The Disposition of this present Year 1533.

Because that I see among all Learned folk the prognostic and judicial Part of Astrology is in disrepute, as much on account of the Vanity of those who have treated of it as of the yearly Falsification of their Promises, I will confine myself for the present to recount to you what I found thereof by the Calculations of Cl. Ptolemy and others, etc. I venture to say that, considering the frequent Conjunctions of the Moon with Mars and Saturn, etc., in the said Year in the Month of May, there cannot help being notable Mutation of Kingdoms as well as Religions, which is contrived by Agreement of Mercury with Saturn, etc....

But these be Secrets of the close Council of the Eternal King, who disposes everything that is and that is done, according to His free Purpose and good Pleasure. These it is better to say nothing of, and to adore them in Silence, as is said *Tob. xij.* [7]. "It is well done to conceal the Secret of the King." David the Prophet saith, *Psalm lxiiij* according to the Chaldaic Letter[1]: "Lord God, Silence belongeth to Thee in Sion"; and the Reason he gives *Psalm xvij*: "For He hath made Darkness His secret Place". Wherefore in all Cases we sought to humble ourselves and entreat Him, even as

---

[1] The Chaldaic version (cf. *P.* 8) or *Targum* represents the Jewish interpretation of the first centuries of the Christian era. (Lowe and Jennings, *On the Psalms*, vol. II. p. vii.) A partial quotation from this is here given. In the Authorised and Revised Versions it runs thus: "Praise waiteth for thee, O God, in Zion" (Ps. lxv. 1). σοὶ πρέπει ὕμνος (LXX). Politian (*Misc.* 83) gives both versions: *Tibi silentium laus, Deus in Sion* and *Te decet hymnus, Deus in Sion.* Lowe and Jennings translate: "To Thee silent resignation is praise".

Jesus Christ our Lord hath taught us, that not what we wish and ask for should be done, but that which pleases Him and which He hath determined before the Heavens were formed, only that in everything and everywhere His glorious Name should be hallowed. Let us draw the Veil on what is written in the eternal Registers, which it is not lawful for mortal Man to handle or to know, as is testified *Acts i.* [7]. "It is not for you to know the Times and Moments which the Father hath put in His own Power." And this Rashness is threatened by His Penalty by the wise Solomon, *Prov. xxv.* "Whoso prieth out His Majesty, shall be crushed thereby, etc."[1]. . . .

---

[1] "Qui scrutator est majestatis opprimetur a gloria" (Prov. xxv. 27); quoted in Innoc. III, *de contemptu mundi*, i. 18 and in Piers Plowman, C. xvii. 218.

WAGES OF RABELAIS AT THE HOSPITAL AT LYONS[1]

Wages of the new physician in the place of M. Pierre Roland, who is called M. Françoys Rabellet.

SATURDAY the xvth day of the month of february, the year one thousand five hundred and thirty-two.[2]

. . . .

. . . . Further, paid to the physician of the present hospital for his wages for three months, to wit november december and january last past, at the rate of forty livres a year, ten livres.

Saturday the seventeenth of the month of january, the year one thousand five hundred and thirty-three.[3]

...Further, paid to M. Françoys Rabellais, physician of the present hospital, in deduction from his wages due to him since the end of the month of january MVᶜXXXII the sum of twenty-seven tournois livres.

Saturday, last day of the month of february, the year one thousand five hundred and thirty-three.[4]

...Further, paid to physician of the present hospital for his wages five crowns, worth eleven livres, five sols.

Saturday, first day of the month of august, the year one thousand five hundred and thirty-four.

It appears that the wages of the physician are only xl livres.

...Further, paid to the physician of the present hospital for his wages or in deduction from them the sum of twenty-five tournois livres.

Saturday, xiiith day of february, the year one thousand five hundred and thirty-four.[5]

...Further, paid to M. Françoys Rebellese physician of the present hospital the sum of fifteen tournois livres in deduction from his wages granted to him by my Lords the Councillors aforesaid.

---

[1] Translated from the extracts in the edition of M. Marty-Laveaux, vol. iii. p. 324.

[2] *thirty-two.* According to our reckoning this would be 1533, because the French year did not begin till Easter.

[3] = 1534.   [4] = 1534.   [5] = 1535.

ELECTION OF PIERRE DU CASTEL AS PHYSICIAN OF THE GREAT HOSPITAL OF THE RHONE-BRIDGE IN THE PLACE OF RABELAIS[1]

Sonday xiiiith february MV^c thirty-four,[2] in the hospital after dinner Master Charles[3]   physician, made request to have the office of physician of the said hospital in the place of M. Rabellaise, who has absented himself. M. Pierre du Castel has made a like request for himself.

Tuesday xxiiird february MV^cXXXIIII in the common room after dinner...The aforesaid councillors have taken steps to provide a physician for the hospital of the Rhone-bridge in the place of master Rabelays who has absented himself and abandoned the said hospital without giving notice or taking leave, also to consider the requests made on the part of master Charles   , master Canape and master du Castel, for some were of opinion that they should provide therefor and proceed to elect one or the other, the rest that they ought to wait till after Easter to see if the said Rabellays would come or not.

The said Sieur Humbert Gimbre, councillor, came in and was asked his opinion on what has been said above and he said and opined as follows:

The said Gimbre opined and said that they ought to provide for the election, and that there has been time enough to have thought of it. With regard to the requests that had been made to him, his intention was to elect and nominate the said master Charles, nevertheless because that since then M. de Montrotier who gives every year to the said hospital III^c tournois livres and more, makes great and urgent request for the said master du Castel, seeing also that the least of the two is sufficiently good, he gives his voice and elects the said master du Castel.

Sieur Jacques Fenoil, for like reasons and in order not to divert

---

[1] Translated from the extracts given by M. Marty-Laveaux, vol. iii. p. 326.
[2] = 1535.
[3] The surname is on every occasion omitted, but Lacroix identifies Master Charles with Charles Marais, mentioned in the Fifth Book as a distinguished physician at Lyons. Cf. v. 30, n. 10.

the said sieur de Montrotier from the good he does to the said hospital, also monsieur Vauzelles his brother, for the love he bears him and the good he does to the said hospital, has given and gives his voice to the said master du Castel, as being right fit and sufficient.

The said Pierre Durand said that they ought to put off providing for this till after Easter, for he has heard that the said Rabellays is at Grenoble and can return.

The said De la Porte says that it is not requisite to proceed so promptly without due consideration therein.

Monsieur Jehan Guillaud says that they ought to take due consideration.

The said Rochefort is strongly of opinion that they should wait, and that he should like to know the opinion of monsieur de Montrotier.

The said Camus said that he knows well the intention of the said sieur de Montrotier, who makes great and urgent request on behalf of the said master du Castel, and that he has learned from the physicians and apothecaries that the said du Castel is very sufficient to have the said office, and he gives him his voice.

The said Guillen leaves it to the majority of voices.

The said Manissier is of opinion not to provide therein for the present.

The said Doulhon in conclusion, by reason of the diversity of the opinions adjourned the matter till thursday next, for the consulate and meantime every one will think it over.

Friday vth march MV^c thirty-four in the common room... The said Councillors proceeded to elect a physician for the service of the great hospital of the Rhone-bridge in the place of master François Rabellayse, physician, who hath absented himself from the town and from the said hospital, without taking leave, for the second time, and they all with one voice elected master Pierre du Castel, doctor, physician, at the stipend nevertheless of thirty tournois livres to which sum of xxx livres they have lowered the former stipend, which was forty tournois livres, and for this they had him summoned, and after having declared to him the said election he accepted it at the said stipend of thirty livres as long as it shall please the consulate; who hath promised and sworn to well serve the aforesaid to diligently and loyally perform his duty.

EPISTLE OF DEDICATION
TO
THE TOPOGRAPHY OF ANCIENT ROME
BY
JOHN BARTHOLOMEW MARLIANI[1]

FRANCIS RABELAIS, PHYSICIAN,
TO THE MOST ILLUSTRIOUS AND LEARNED
LORD JOHN DU BELLAY,[2]
BISHOP OF PARIS AND MEMBER OF THE PRIVY COUNCIL,
SENDS HEARTY GREETING

MOST ILLUSTRIOUS PRELATE,

The immense Store of Kindness, by which you lately thought me worthy to be advanced and distinguished, hath sunk so deep in my Memory, that I feel certain it can by no means be erased or brought to Oblivion by Length of Time. And I only

---

[1] The title-page of the book runs as follows: TOPOGRA|PHIA ANTIQUAE | ROMAE | IOANNE Bartholemae Marliano | Patritio Mediolanensi | autore | APUD SEB. GRYPHIUM | LVGDVNI | 1534.

[2] Jean du Bellay, the second brother (1492–1560), Bishop of Bayonne (1532), then of Paris (Nov. 25, 1532), Limoges and Le Mans, afterwards Arch-bishop of Bordeaux, minister of Francis I in England and then in Rome; Cardinal 1535, and lieutenant-general to the King during the invasion of Provence by the Imperialists (cf. *P.* 7, "The Entry of Antony de Leive into the Lands of Bresil"). After the death of Francis I, Feb. 1547, he returned to Rome with Rabelais from Metz about the middle of 1547. He resigned the bishopric of Paris March 15, 1551 (O.S.) and was succeeded by his nephew Eustache March 18, the same year. On the death of Marcellus II in 1555 he was one of the *papabili*, but Paul IV Caraffa was elected. He died in Rome Feb. 16, 1560 and was buried in the Minims' church of Trinità dei Monti. At the restoration of this church in 1774 and again in 1816 many memorials perished, and pro-bably his amongst them. (Forcella, *Iscrizioni*, vol. III. p. 107.) He was also Prior of Saint Maur-des-Fossés, near Paris, of which Rabelais was perhaps canon for a short time (cf. 2nd Petition to Pope Paul III). He was in Rome in 1534 (after an embassy to England Nov.-Dec. 1533), 1535–6, 1547–9, 1550, and afterwards. This letter refers to his first visit, when his purpose was to induce Clement VII to withdraw the sentence of excommunication against Henry VIII, which had been pronounced the previous July 11, or at least to defer its fulmination. He was also intent on gaining a cardinal's hat for himself. His efforts failed in both cases. The sentence against Henry was pronounced at the consistory of March 23, 1534, and Clement VII died Sept. 25.

wish it were as easy for me to pay due Homage to the Immortality
of your Praises, as it is my Purpose ever to pay to you the Thanks
that you deserve, and to recompense you, if not with equal kind
Offices (for how could I?), still with Honour justly your Due, and
with grateful Thoughts. For by your marvellous Kindness you
have conferred upon me that which has been the dearest Wish of
my Heart from the Time when I first felt any Interest in Letters,
viz. that I might be able to traverse Italy and pay a Visit to Rome,
the World's Capital; and you have enabled me not only to visit
Italy—in itself a rapturous Notion—but also to visit it in your Company, you who of all men under Heaven are distinguished for
Learning and Courtesy—the Value to be set on which I have not
yet fully realised. To me indeed it was more to see you at Rome than
to have seen Rome itself. To have been at Rome may fall to any
one's Lot, and lies before all, except those who are maimed and
disabled in all their Limbs; but to have seen you at Rome successful, with incredible Congratulations of every one, was a Source
of Pleasure; to have taken part in Affairs at the time when you
were conducting that illustrious Embassy, on which you had been
sent to Rome by our most triumphant King Francis, was a matter
for Boasting; to have been by your Side when you pronounced
your Speech on the Affairs of the King of England, in the most
sacred and dignified Conclave in the World, was a point of high
Felicity. What Pleasure came over us then, with what Joy were we
elated, what Delight we felt, when we witnessed you speaking, to
the Wonderment of the Chief Pontiff Clement himself, the Admiration of the purple-robed Judges of that most distinguished Order
of Cardinals, and the Applause of every one! What Stings[1] accompanied by Pleasure did you leave in the Minds of all your
Hearers! How conspicuous was the Intelligence in your Sentiments, your Subtlety in arguing, Dignity in answering, Sharpness
in Confutation, Freedom in Speaking! Again, your Diction was so
pure, that you seemed almost the only one who spoke Latin in
Latium; but again so weighty, that perfect Courtesy and Refinement

---

[1] "Quid Pericles?...cujus in labris veteres comici [Eupolis Δῆμοι] leporem
habitasse dixerunt, tantamque in eo vim fuisse ut in eorum mentibus qui
audissent quasi *aculeos* quosdam relinqueret", Cic. *de Orat*. iii. § 138. Cf. also
Val. Max. viii. 9. E. 2.

attended on your unparalleled Dignity.[1]   Indeed I often heard
men, who were the most fastidious Critics in Rome, calling you the
culled Flower[2] of all France (in the Phrase of Ennius), and declaring that within the Memory of man the Bishop of Paris was the
only true Frank-speaker,[3] and that King Francis' Affairs were admirably managed, when he had the du Bellays on his Council;
for that France could not easily produce men of more conspicuous
Distinction, of weightier Authority, or of more polished Culture.

But, long before we were in Rome, I had firmly fixed in my
Mind and Thoughts of a Notion of the things, a Longing for which
had attracted me thither. For I had determined first to visit the
men of Learning, who had attained Celebrity in those Parts
through which our Journey lay, to confer with them in a friendly
manner, and to hear their Opinion on some doubtful Problems
which had long held me in Perplexity[4]. Next, to examine, in
pursuance of my Profession, Plants, Animals and some Drugs,
which were said to be wanting in France and abundant in Italy.
And lastly, to pourtray the Appearance of the City with my Pen, as
though with a Pencil, so that there might be nothing which, on my
Return from abroad, I could not readily furnish to my Countrymen from my Books. On that Subject I had brought with me a
miscellaneous Collection of Notes from various Authors, Greek
and Latin. And at first indeed I succeeded fairly well, though not
at all points as I could have wished. For Italy possesses no Plants
and also no Animals which I had not seen and known before. The
unique Plane-tree I saw at the "Mirror" of Diana of Aricia.[5] The

---

[1] "Quid jucundius auribus nostris umquam accidit hujus oratione Catuli?
quae est pura sic ut Latine loqui paene solus videatur, sic autem gravis ut in
singulari dignitate omnis tamen adsit humanitas ac lepos", Cic. *de Orat.* iii.
§ 29. (Lugd. Seb. Gryph. 1533.)
[2] "Flos delibatus populi Suadaeque medulla", quoted in Cic. *Brutus*, § 58;
de Sen. § 50; Enn. *Annales*, 353. Cf. Gellius, xii. 2. § 3; Quint. ii. 15. 4. The points
about *Periclis aculei* and *Suadae medulla* are carefully elaborated in Politian's
Miscellanea, c. 91.
[3] *Frank-speaker.* Erasm. *Apoph.* lib. iv. (Philip. 35) "Demochares dictus
Parrhesiastes", from Seneca, *de Ira*, iii. 23. § 2. The pun on Paris and παρρησιάζειν
occurs also in *G.* 17. Lucian gives himself the name παρρησιάδης in *Piscator*, § 19.
[4] With this compare Thaumast's declaration in *P.* 18.
[5] *Mirror of Diana, Speculum Dianae*, now Lago di Nemi, near La Riccia
(*Aricia*). Cf. Servius, *ad Aen.* vii. 515. τόδ' Ἀρτεμίσιον ὃ καλοῦσι νέμος:
Strabo, v. p. 239. "The worship of Artemis was peculiarly associated with low-
lying land and reed-covered marshes": W. M. Ramsay, *Journ. Hell. Stud.* iv.

last of my Intentions I carried out so diligently that I believe that no one's House is better known to its Master[1] than Rome and all its Streets and Lanes are to me. Nor were you unwilling to bestow what Leisure you had from your important and laborious Embassy, in visiting the Places of Interest in the City; and, not satisfied with seeing what was open to View, you even caused Excavations to be made, purchasing a Vineyard[2] of some Value for that Purpose. Consequently, when we had to remain longer than you expected, and when, in order to gain some permanent Result from my Studies, I set about an Account of the Topography of the City, with the help of Nicolas Le Roy[3] and Claude Chappuis,[4] two Youths in your Following of great Merit and Interest in Antiquities, I found to my Surprise Marliani's Book just begun printing. Its Completion was as great Relief to me as the Assistance of Juno Lucina is to Women in hard Labour. For I was labouring with the same Burden, and indeed I was troubled in my Mind and inmost Thoughts about bringing it out. For although the Subject itself was not difficult to think out, it did not appear easy to arrange with Perspicuity, Aptness and Neatness my ill-digested and cumbrous

---

p. 36. "Lucus et ara Dianae" make a *purpureus pannus* in Hor. *A.P.* 16. "In quo ruta facit nemus Dianae": Mart. xi. 18. 4. Cf. Burn's *Rome and the Campagna*, p. 353; Lanciani, *Pagan and Christian Rome*, p. 60; Frazer's *Golden Bough* (2nd ed.), vol. i. p. 4.

[1] "Nota magis nulli domus est sua quam mihi lucus Martis", etc., Juv. i. 7. Cf. *P.* 16: "he knew all the Streets and Alleys of Paris like his *Deus det*".

[2] *purchasing a vineyard.* These were the *thermae Diocletiani* built by D. and Maximian in A.D. 306. The Bishop purchased the greater portion of the baths and laid out gardens among the picturesque ruins, known under the name of *horti Belleiani*; at his death, however, creditors seized the estate (Lanciani, *Ruins and Excavations of Ancient Rome*, p. 435). He is accused by Lanciani (p. 266) of having destroyed the marble incrustations of the hall of the Curia in 1550.

[3] *Nicolas le Roy* taught jurisprudence at Bourges about 1534. He was probably a native of Touraine or Orléanais, and known to Calvin. Perhaps Antoine le Roy, who was at one time curé of Meudon, and who composed the *elogia Rabelaisiana*, was of the same family.

[4] *Cl. Chappuis*, probably related to the "Captain (Michel) Chappuis" in *G.* 8, was chamberlain and librarian to Francis I and afterwards Dean of Rouen: author of a panegyric on the King. A poem of his dedicated to Francis I, 1543, entitled *L'Aigle qui fait la Poule devant le Coq*, is given in *A.P.F.* iv. 47 sqq.

"Je ne voy point qu'un Sainct Gelais,
Un Heroet, un Rabelais,
Un Brodeau, un Seve, un Chappuy,
Voysent escrivant contre luy."
Cl. Marot, *Epist.* (51) *de Fripelipes à Sagon* (1537).

Heap of Matter. I put up a Quadrant[1] of the Invention of Thales of Miletus, and set out a Circle in the East and West, and South and North directions, and divided it across, marking out Points with my Eyes; Marliani adopted the Plan of beginning his Delineation[2] from the Mountains. I am so far from disapproving this System of Description, that I congratulate him highly for having anticipated me in my Attempt at this very Thing. For he alone has carried out more than one could have expected from any of our times, however erudite. So well has he finished his Task, and handled his Matter so thoroughly to my Satisfaction, that I would not hesitate to allow that I myself singly owe as much to him, as all the Students of refined Learning themselves.

It certainly was annoying that you had to leave the City at the express Summons[3] of your Prince and your Country, before the Book was completed. Nevertheless I used Care and Diligence that as soon as it was given to the Public it should be sent to Lyons, where is the Home and Abode of my Studies. That was due to the Efforts and Diligence of John Sevinus,[4] one who may truly be called "versatile"; but for some Reason or other it was sent out without a Dedication. Therefore, that it might not see the Light shapeless as it was and without a Head,[5] so to speak, it was determined to send it forth under the Auspices of your most illustrious Name. With your conspicuous Courtesy I feel sure that you will take all this in good part and continue your Regard for me. Farewell.

Lyons, August 31, 1534.

---

[1] Lat. *sublato Sciothero*. This word and notion are taken from Pliny, 2. 187: "Umbrarum hanc rationem et quam vocant *gnomonicen* invenit Anaximenes Milesius, Anaximandri [*et Thaletis* some MSS] discipulus, primusque horologium quod appellant *sciothericon* Lacedaemone ostendit". Cf. also Vitruvius, i. 6. § 6: "Gnomon indagator umbrae qui graece σκιαθήρας dicitur"; Bud. *Pand.* p. 581 on ff. xix. l. 11. § 18; Strabo, ii. 126: διὰ τῶν σκιαθηρικῶν γνωμόνων ἀνευρεῖν.

[2] Lat. *graphice*. "Effectum est Sicyone...ut pueri ingenui ante omnia *graphicen*, hoc est picturam in buxo, docerentur", Pliny, 35. 77. Cf. Arist. *Pol.* viii. 3. 1337b. 24, 1338a. 18; Plut. *de fac. in orbe lunae*, c. 2. 920E.

[3] *at the express Summons*. Cf. Cic. *Off.* iii. § 121: "nisi me e medio cursu clara voce patria revocasset".

[4] *Jean Sevin*, probably a secretary at the French embassy. (V.-L. Bourrilly.)

[5] *without a Head*. "Sine capite fabula", Erasm. *Ad.* i. 1. 14; ἴδοις ἄν...ἄλλους ἀκέφαλα σωματα εἰσάγοντας, ἀπροοιμίαστα, Lucian *de hist. conscr.* c. 23; "*Jo. Dytebrodii De terribiliditate Excommunicationum libellus acephalos*", P. 7.

CAMBRIDGE: PRINTED BY WALTER LEWIS, M.A., AT THE UNIVERSITY PRESS